Biology 111 & 112 Laboratories

University of North Alabama, Biology Department

Custom Edition

Perry | Morton | Perry

CENGAGE
Learning·

Australia • Brazil • Japan • Korea • Mexico • Singapore • Spain • United Kingdom • United States

Biology 111 & 112 Laboratories, University of North Alabama, Biology Department, Custom Edition

Senior Manager, Student Engagement:

Linda deStefano

Janey Moeller

Manager, Student Engagement:

Julie Dierig

Marketing Manager:

Rachael Kloos

Manager, Production Editorial:

Kim Fry

Manager, Intellectual Property Project Manager:

Brian Methe

Senior Manager, Production and Manufacturing:

Donna M. Brown

Manager, Production:

Terri Daley

Laboratory Manual for Non-Majors Biology, 6th Edition
James W. Perry, David Morton, Joy B. Perry

© 2013 Cengage Learning. All rights reserved.

Laboratory Manual for General Biology, 5th Edition
James W. Perry, David Morton, Joy B. Perry

© 2007 Cengage Learning. All rights reserved.

For product information and technology assistance, contact us at
Cengage Learning Customer & Sales Support, 1-800-354-9706

For permission to use material from this text or product,
submit all requests online at **cengage.com/permissions**
Further permissions questions can be emailed to
permissionrequest@cengage.com

This book contains select works from existing Cengage Learning resources and was produced by Cengage Learning Custom Solutions for collegiate use. As such, those adopting and/or contributing to this work are responsible for editorial content accuracy, continuity and completeness.

Compilation © 2014 Cengage Learning

ISBN-13: 978-1-305-01224-0

ISBN-10: 1-305-01224-0

WCN: 01-100-101

Cengage Learning

5191 Natorp Boulevard
Mason, Ohio 45040
USA

Cengage Learning is a leading provider of customized learning solutions with office locations around the globe, including Singapore, the United Kingdom, Australia, Mexico, Brazil, and Japan. Locate your local office at:
international.cengage.com/region.

Cengage Learning products are represented in Canada by Nelson Education, Ltd. For your lifelong learning solutions, visit **www.cengage.com/custom.**
Visit our corporate website at **www.cengage.com.**

Printed in the United States of America

Brief Contents

The Scientific Method

OBJECTIVES

After completing this exercise, you will be able to

1. define *scientific method, mechanist, vitalist, cause and effect, induction, deduction, experimental group, control group, independent variable, dependent variable, controlled variables, correlation, theory, principle, bioassay;*
2. explain the nature of scientific knowledge;
3. describe the basic steps of the scientific method;
4. state the purpose of an experiment;
5. explain the difference between cause and effect and correlation;
6. describe the design of a typical research article in biology;
7. describe the use of bioassays.

INTRODUCTION

To appreciate biology or, for that matter, any body of scientific knowledge, you need to understand how the **scientific method** is used to gather that knowledge. We use the scientific method to test the predictions of possible answers to questions about nature in ways that we can duplicate or verify. Answers supported by test results are added to the body of scientific knowledge and contribute to the concepts presented in your textbook and other science books. Although these concepts are as up-to-date as possible, they are always open to further questions and modifications.

One of the roots of the scientific method can be found in ancient Greek philosophy. The natural philosophy of Aristotle and his colleagues was mechanistic rather than vitalistic. A **mechanist** believes that only natural forces govern living things, along with the rest of the universe, while a **vitalist** believes that the universe is at least partially governed by supernatural powers. Mechanists look for interrelationships between the structures and functions of living things, and the processes that shape them. Their explanations of nature deal in **cause and effect**—the idea that one thing is the result of another thing (for example, Fertilization of an egg initiates the developmental process that forms an adult.). In contrast, vitalists often use purposeful explanations of natural events (The fertilized egg strives to develop into an adult.). Although statements that ascribe purpose to things often feel comfortable to the writer, try to avoid them when writing lab reports and scientific papers.

Aristotle and his colleagues developed three rules to examine the laws of nature: Carefully observe some aspect of nature; examine these observations as to their similarities and differences; and produce a principle or generalization about the aspect of nature being studied (for example, All mammals nourish their young with milk.).

The major defect of natural philosophy was that it accepted the idea of *absolute truth.* This belief suppressed the testing of principles once they had been formulated. Thus, Aristotle's belief in spontaneous generation, the principle that some life can arise from nonliving things (say maggots from spoiled meat), survived over 2000 years of controversy before being discredited by Louis Pasteur in 1860. Rejection of the idea of absolute truth coupled with the testing of principles either by experimentation or by further pertinent observation is the essence of the modern scientific method.

1.1 Modern Scientific Method *(About 70 min.)*

Although there is not one universal scientific method, Figure 1-1 illustrates the general process.

MATERIALS

Per lab room:

- blindfold
- plastic beakers with an inside diameter of about 8 cm stuffed with cotton wool
- four or five liquid crystal thermometers

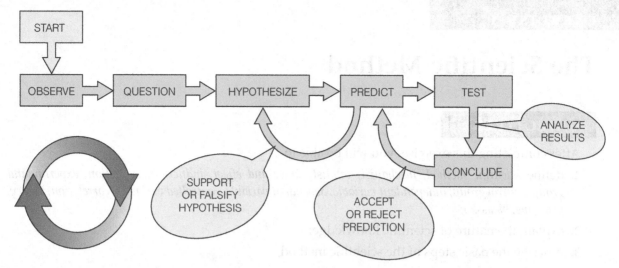

Figure 1-1 The scientific method. Support or falsification of the hypothesis usually necessitates further observations, adjustment to the question, and modification of the hypothesis. Once started, the scientific method cycles over and over again, each turn further refining the hypothesis.

PROCEDURE

Step 1. Observation. As with natural philosophy, the scientific method starts with careful observation. An investigator may make observations from nature or from the written words of other investigators, which are published in books or research articles in scientific journals and are available in the storehouse of human knowledge, the library. One subject we all have some knowledge of is the human body. The first four rows of Table 1-1 list some observations about the human body. The fifth row is blank so that you can fill in the steps of the scientific method for either the bioassay described at the end of the exercise, another observation about the human body, or anything else you and your instructor wish to investigate.

Step 2. Question. In the second step of the scientific method, *we ask a question* about these observations. The quality of this question will depend on how carefully the observations were made and analyzed. Table 1-1 includes questions raised by the listed observations.

Step 3. Hypothesis. Now we *construct a hypothesis*—that is, we derive by inductive reasoning a possible answer to the question. **Induction** is a logical process by which all known observations are combined and considered before producing a possible answer. Table 1-1 includes examples of hypotheses.

Step 4. Prediction. In this step we *formulate a prediction*—we assume the hypothesis is correct and predict the result of a test that reveals some aspect of it. This is deductive or "if-then" reasoning. **Deduction** is a logical process by which a prediction is produced from a possible answer to the question asked. Table 1-1 lists a prediction for each hypothesis.

Step 5. Experiment or Pertinent Observations. In this step we *perform an experiment or make pertinent observations* to test the prediction.

(a) Choose, along with the other members of your lab group, one prediction from Table 1-1. Coordinate your choice with the other lab groups so that each group tests a different prediction.

(b) In an experiment of classical design, the individuals or items under study are divided into two groups: an **experimental group** that is treated with (or possesses) the independent variable and a **control group** that is not (or does not). Sometimes there is more than one experimental group. Sometimes subjects participate in both groups, experimental and control, and are tested both with and without the treatment.

In any test there are three kinds of variables. The **independent variable** is the treatment or condition under study. The **dependent variable** is the event or condition that is measured or observed when the results are gathered. The **controlled variables** are all other factors, which the investigator attempts to keep the same for all groups under study.

(Photo by D. Morton.)

vein segment

valves

Figure 1-2 Veins under the skin.

TABLE 1-1 Some Observations About the Human Body

Observation	Question	Hypothesis	Prediction
I. Veins containing blood are seen under the skin. Swellings present along the vein are often located where veins join together.[a]	What is the function of the swellings?	Swellings contain one-way valves that allow blood to flow only toward the heart.	If these valves are present, then blood flows only from vein segments farther from the heart to the next segments nearer the heart and never in the opposite direction.
II. People have two ears.	What is the advantage of having two ears?	Two ears allow us to locate the sources of sounds.	If the hypothesis is correct, then blocking hearing in one ear will impair our ability to determine a sound's source.[b]
III. People can hold their breath for only a short period of time.	What factor forces a person to take a breath?	The buildup of carbon dioxide derived from the body's metabolic activity stimulates us to take a breath.	If the hypothesis is correct, then people will hold their breath a shorter time just after exercise compared to when they are at rest.
IV. Normal body temperature is 98.6°F.	Is all of the body at the same 98.6°F temperature?	The skin, or at least some portion of it, is not 98.6°F.	If the hypothesis is correct, then a liquid crystal thermometer will record different temperatures on the forehead, back of neck, and forearm.
V. _____	_____	_____	_____

[a] The portion of the vein between swellings is called a segment and is illustrated in Figure 1-2.

[b] This is especially the case for high-pitched sounds because higher frequencies travel less easily directly through tissues and bones.

Note: The italicized statements show how the scientific method is applied to the predictions in Table 1-1 or give examples of the scientific method in practice.

To test the prediction that blocking hearing in one ear impairs our ability to point out a sound's source (row II in Table 1-1), a group of subjects is tested first with no ears blocked (control group) and then with one ear blocked (experimental group). The independent variable is the blocking of one ear; the dependent variable is the ability to point out a sound's source; and the controlled variables are the standard conditions used for each trial—same test sound, same background noise, same procedure for each subject (same blocked ear, same instructions, same sequence of trials, same time between trials), and recruitment of appropriate subjects.

Sometimes the best tests of the predictions of a hypothesis are not actual experiments but further pertinent observations. One of the most important principles in biology, Darwin's theory of natural selection, was developed by this nonexperimental approach. Although they are a little more difficult to form, the nonexperimental approach also has variables.

To test the prediction that a liquid crystal thermometer will record different temperatures on the forehead, back of neck, and forearm (row IV of Table 1-1), the independent variable is location; the dependent variable is temperature; and the controlled variables are using the same thermometer to measure skin temperature at the three locations and measuring all of the subjects at rest.

INSTRUCTIONS. Members of groups testing predictions in rows I, II, and IV of Table 1-1 read items 1, 2, or 3, respectively. Then all groups describe in item 4 an experiment or a pertinent observation to test their prediction.

1. To test the prediction in row I of Table 1-1, determine the direction of blood flow between vein segments as follows:
   (a) With arms dangling at their sides, identify in as many group members as possible a vein segment either on the back of the hands or on the forearms.
   (b) Demonstrate that blood flows in vein segments: Note their collapse due to gravity speeding up blood flow when each subject's arm is raised above the level of the heart.
   (c) Lower the arm to a position below the heart and stop blood flow through the vein segment by permanently pressing a finger on the swelling farthest from the heart.
   (d) Use a second finger to squeeze the blood out of the vein segment past the next swelling toward the heart.
   (e) Remove the second finger and note whether blood flows back into the vein segment.
   (f) Remove the first finger and note whether blood flows back into the vein segment.
   (g) Repeat c–e, only reverse the order of the swellings—first stop blood flow through the swelling nearest the heart, then squeeze the blood out of the vein segment in a direction away from the heart past the next swelling.
2. To test the prediction in row II of Table 1-1, you will need a blindfold and a beaker stuffed with cotton wool to block hearing in one ear. Quantify how well a blindfolded group member can point out the source of a high-pitched sound by estimating the angle (0–180°) between the line from source to subject and the line along which the subject points to identify the source.
3. To test the prediction in row IV, you will need liquid crystal thermometers to measure skin temperature.
4. Describe your experiment or pertinent observation:

   _____

   _____

   _____

   _____

   _____

   _____

   _____

   _____

   _____

5. Describe the variables involved with testing the prediction your group chose from Table 1-1.
   - Independent variable—

     _____

     _____

   - Dependent variable—

     _____

     _____

   - Controlled variables—

     _____

     _____

6. After your instructor's approval, perform the procedure you outlined in item 4 and record your results in Table 1-2. You may not need all of the rows and columns to accommodate your data.
7. Describe or present your results in one of the bar charts shown on the next page.

Step 6. Conclusion. *To make a conclusion*—the last step in one cycle of the scientific method—you use the results of the experiment or pertinent observations to evaluate your hypothesis. If your prediction does not occur, it is rejected and your hypothesis or some aspect of it is falsified. If your prediction does occur, you may conditionally accept your prediction and your hypothesis is supported. However, you can never completely accept or reject any hypothesis; all you can do is state a probability that one is correct or incorrect. To quantify this probability, scientists use a branch of mathematics called *statistical analysis*.

Even if the prediction is rejected, this does not necessarily mean that the treatment caused the result. A coincidence or the effect of some unforeseen and thus uncontrolled variable could be causing the result. For this reason, the results of experiments and observations must be *repeatable* by the original investigator and others.

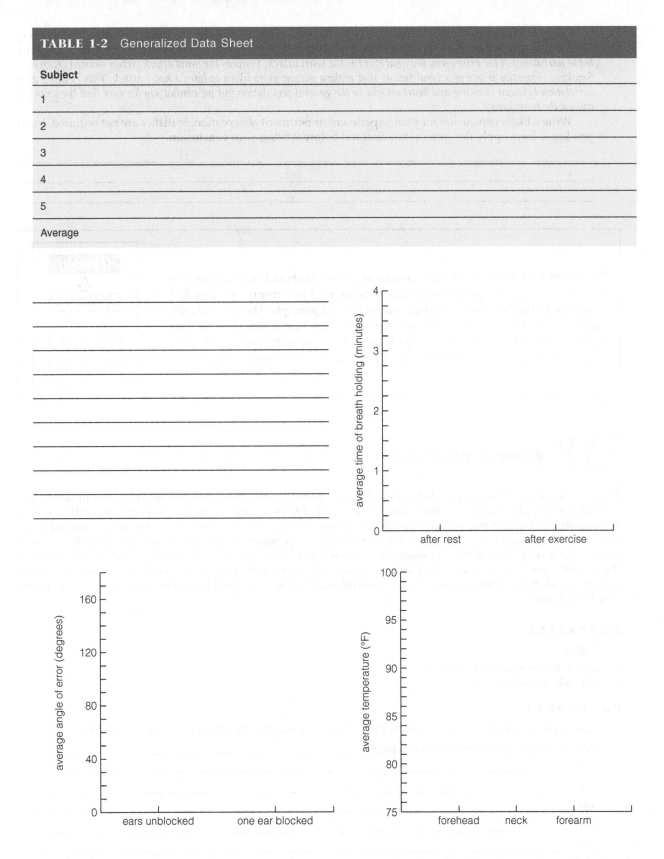

TABLE 1-2	Generalized Data Sheet
Subject	
1	
2	
3	
4	
5	
Average	

Even if the results are repeatable, this does not necessarily mean that the treatment caused the result. *Cause and effect*, especially in biology, is rarely proven in experiments. We can, however, say that the treatment and result are correlated. A **correlation** is a relationship between the independent and the dependent variables.

Severe narrowing of a coronary artery branch reduces blood flow to the heart muscle downstream. This region of heart muscle gets insufficient oxygen and cannot contract and may die, resulting in a heart attack. The initial cause is the narrowing of the artery and the final effect is the heart attack. Perhaps the heart attack victim smoked cigarettes. Smoking cigarettes is one of several factors that make a person more likely to have a heart attack. This is based on a correlation between smoking and heart attacks in the general population but we cannot say for sure that the smoking caused the heart attack.

Write a likely conclusion for your experiment or pertinent observation. Statistics are not required, but if you know how, apply the correct statistical test before writing your conclusion.

_____

_____

_____

THEORIES and PRINCIPLES: When exhaustive experiments and observations consistently support an important hypothesis, it is accepted as a **theory**. A theory that stands the test of time may be elevated to the status of a **principle**. Theories and principles are always considered when new hypotheses are formulated. However, like hypotheses, theories and principles can be modified or even discarded in the light of new knowledge. Biology, like life itself, is not static but is constantly changing.

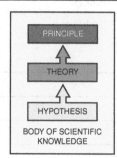

| 1.2 | **Research Article** *(About 20 min.)* |

The account of one or several related cycles of the scientific method is usually initially reported in depth in a research article published in a scientific journal. The goal of the scientific community is to be cooperative as well as competitive. Writing research articles allows scientists to share knowledge. They provide enough information so that other scientists can repeat the experiments or pertinent observations they describe. The journal *Science* along with several others presents its research articles in narrative form, and many of the details of the scientific method are understood and not stated. However, adherence to the modern scientific method is expected, and the scientific community understands that it is as important to expose mistakes as it is to praise new knowledge.

MATERIALS

Per student:
- a typical research article in biology
- a research article from *Science*

PROCEDURE

1. Check the design of a typical research article in biology and list the titles of its various sections.

    (a) Example: Abstract-summary of paper _____

    (b) _____

    (c) _____

    (d) _____

    (e) _____

    (f) _____

2. Read the article, then fill in the blanks in the following statements or answer the question.

    (a) Any changes in the dependent variable are described in the _____ section.

    (b) Which section contains the details necessary to repeat this experiment or observation?

    _____

(c) Which section contains the questions being asked, the predictions, or the hypotheses?

_____

(d) The _____ section contains the conclusions.

3. Look at an article from the journal *Science*. What steps of the scientific method are included in the narrative?

_____

_____

_____

1.3 Bioassay *(Portions of two days)*

You no doubt know through various media sources of the myriad chemicals that pervade modern life. These substances can be beneficial or toxic to plants or animals. It's obvious that drinking gasoline is bad for you, but this is an extreme example. The broad questions are, What effects do new chemicals have on living organisms, and at what exposure level do they exert these effects? To answer these questions, we perform experiments known as bioassays. Bioassays are used by the pharmaceutical industry to test new drugs. Agricultural firms determine the effectiveness of new fertilizers and herbicides with bioassays. Some industries measure the effects their waste discharges on aquatic organisms with bioassays. A **bioassay** establishes the quantity of a substance that results in a defined *effective dose* (ED)—that is, the dose that produces a particular effect. In the case of toxic substances, the standard measurement of toxicity is known as an LD_{50} (the lethal dose causing the death of 50% of the organisms exposed to the substance).

In this experiment you will test the hypothesis that many everyday substances affect germination of the seeds of Wisconsin Fast Plants™, members of the mustard family. Predictions are that if this is so then the timing of seed germination will change, and if germination occurs, the extent of germination as measured by the length of roots and stems will change. If possible, you will use your results to estimate ED or LD_{50} for the substance tested.

MATERIALS

Per student:

- fine-pointed, water-resistant marker ("Sharpie" or similar)
- 35-mm film canister with lid prepunched with four holes
- 4 microcentrifuge tubes with caps
- 4 paper-towel wicks
- disposable pipet and bulb
- forceps
- 8 RCBR seeds (Wisconsin Fast Plants™)
- 15-cm plastic ruler

Per student group (6):

- solution of test substance (paint thinner, household cleaner, perfume, coffee, vinegar, and so on)
- distilled water (dH_2O) in dropping bottle

PROCEDURE

1. Using a fine-pointed, water-resistant marker, label the caps and sides of the four microcentrifuge tubes 1.0, 0.1, 0.01, and C (for "Control").
2. Place 10 drops of the test solution into the tube labeled 1.0. This tube now contains the full concentration (100%) of the test solution. A test solution can be anything you and your instructor decide to test. Write the name of your test substance. _____
3. Make *serial dilutions* of the solution, producing concentrations of 10% and 1% of the test substance (Figure 1-3). Start by adding nine drops of distilled water (dH_2O) to the tubes labeled 0.1 and 0.01.
4. Remove a small quantity of the solution from tube 1.0 with the disposable pipet and place *one* drop into tube 0.1. Mix the contents thoroughly by "thipping" the side of the microcentrifuge tube (flicking the sides of the bottom of the tube with the index finger of your dominant hand while holding the sides of the top of the tube between the index finger and thumb of your other hand). Return any solution remaining in the pipet to tube 1.0. Tube 0.1 now contains a concentration 10% of that in tube 1.0.

5. Now, from tube 0.1, remove a small quantity of the solution with the disposable pipet and place *one* drop in tube 0.01. Mix the contents thoroughly and return any solution left in the pipet to tube 0.1. Tube 0.01 now contains a 1% concentration of the original.
6. From the dropping bottle, place 10 drops of dH_2O into tube C. This is the control for the experiment; it contains none of the test solution.
7. Insert a paper towel wick into each microcentrifuge tube (Figure 1-4). With your forceps, place two RCBR seeds near the top of each wick. Close the caps of the tubes. Do not allow any of the wick to protrude outside the cap.
8. Carefully insert the microcentrifuge assay tubes through the holes in the film canister lid (Figure 1-5). Set the experiment aside in the location indicated by your instructor.

Figure 1-3 Serial dilution of test substance.

(Photo by J. W. Perry.)

Figure 1-4 One of the four assay tubes.

(Photo by J. W. Perry.)

Figure 1-5 Experimental apparatus.

(Photo by J. W. Perry.)

9. At this point, write a prediction for your experiment in Table 1-2.
10. State your experimental variables.
    - Independent variable—

      _____

      _____

    - Dependent variable—

      _____

      _____

    - Controlled variables—

      _____

      _____

11. After 24 hours or more, examine your experiment to see how many and which seeds germinated. Record your results in Table 1-3. Record seeds as "germinated" (G) or "did not germinate" (DNG), and for germinated seeds indicate the extent of germination by measuring and recording the length in millimeters (mm) of the roots and shoots of seed 1 (S1) and seed 2 (S2) for each tube.
12. You have studied the effect of your substance on only a small number of seeds. To make your analysis more reliable, you should analyze a larger number of seeds. In an effort to increase reliability, pool your data with those students who tested the same substance. Calculate the averages and record them in Table 1-3.
13. If germination occurred in more than one group, graph the results in Figure 1-6, plotting the growth of roots and shoots at each concentration.

response (length in mm)

0 or "C"   0.01   0.1   1.0
fraction of test substance

Figure 1-6 Effect of _____ on germination of RCBR seeds (O = roots and ● = shoots).

TABLE 1-3	Effect of					on Germination of RCBR Seeds	

Prediction: _____

		My Experiment				Class Averages	
		Roots		Shoots (mm)			
Tube	Germination	S1	S2	S1	S2	Roots	Shoots
C (dH$_2$O)							
1.0							
0.1							
0.01							

14. If germination occurred in the lower concentrations but not the higher ones, what effective dose prevents germination? Alternatively, could you have defined any other effective doses?

_____

_____

_____

15. Considering your germination results, estimate or make a statement about the LD$_{50}$ for your test substance. If negative effects on germination were observed, describe how you could modify the procedure to better determine the LD$_{50}$.

_____

_____

16. Make a conclusion regarding the effect of the test substance on germination of RCBR seeds.

_____

_____

17. Does your conclusion allow you to accept or reject your prediction? Is the hypothesis supported or falsified? Explain your answer.

_____

_____

_____ 1. The natural philosophy of Aristotle and his colleagues was
(a) mechanistic
(b) vitalistic
(c) a belief in absolute truth
(d) a and c

_____ 2. A person who believes that the universe is at least partially controlled by supernatural powers can best be described as a(n)
(a) teleologist
(b) vitalist
(c) empiricist
(d) mechanist

_____ 3. The first step of the scientific method is to
(a) ask a question
(b) construct a hypothesis
(c) observe carefully
(d) formulate a prediction

_____ 4. Which series of letters lists the first four steps of the scientific method (see question 3) in the correct order?
(a) a, b, c, d
(b) a, b, d, c
(c) c, a, b, d
(d) d, c, a, b

_____ 5. In an experiment the subjects or items being investigated are divided into the experimental group and
(a) the nonexperimental group
(b) the control group
(c) the statistics group
(d) none of these choices

_____ 6. The variables that investigators try to keep the same for both the experimental and the control groups are
(a) independent
(b) controlled
(c) dependent
(d) a and c

_____ 7. Variables that are *always* different between the experimental and the control groups are
(a) independent
(b) controlled
(c) dependent
(d) a and c

_____ 8. The results of an experiment
(a) don't have to be repeatable
(b) should be repeatable by the investigator
(c) should be repeatable by other investigators
(d) must be both b and c

_____ 9. The detailed report of an experiment is usually published in a
(a) newspaper
(b) book
(c) scientific journal
(d) magazine

_____ 10. Bioassays can be used to
(a) test new drugs
(b) determine the effectiveness of new fertilizers and herbicides
(c) measure the effects their waste discharges have on aquatic organisms
(d) do all of these choices

EXERCISE 1

The Scientific Method

POST-LAB QUESTIONS

Introduction

1. How does the modern scientific method differ from the natural philosophy of the ancient Greeks?

1.1 Modern Scientific Method

2. List the six steps of one full cycle of the scientific method.

   a. _____

   b. _____

   c. _____

   d. _____

   e. _____

   f. _____

3. What is tested by an experiment?

4. Within the framework of an experiment, describe the

   a. independent variable— _____

   b. dependent variable— _____

   c. controlled variables— _____

5. Is the statement, "In most biology experiments, the relationship between the independent and the dependent variable can best be described as cause and effect," true or false? Explain your answer.

6. Is a scientific principle taken as absolutely true? Explain your answer.

1.2 Research Article

7. What is the function of research articles in scientific journals?

1.3 Bioassay

8. Define the design and structure of a bioassay.

Food for Thought

9. Describe how you have applied or could apply the scientific method to an everyday problem.

10. Do you think the differences between religious and scientific knowledge make it difficult to debate points of perceived conflict between them? Explain your answer.

Measurement

OBJECTIVES

After completing this exercise, you will be able to

1. define *length, volume, meniscus, mass, density, temperature, thermometer*;
2. recognize graduated cylinders, beakers, Erlenmeyer flasks, different types of pipets, and a triple beam balance;
3. measure and estimate length, volume, and mass in metric units;
4. explain the concept of temperature;
5. measure and estimate temperature in degrees Celsius;
6. explain the advantages of the metric system of measurement.

INTRODUCTION

One requirement of the scientific method is that results be repeatable. As numerical results are more precise than purely written descriptions, scientific observations are usually made as measurements. Of course, sometimes a written description without numbers is the most appropriate way to describe a result.

2.1   Metric System *(About 60 min.)*

Logically, units in the ideal system of measurement should be easy to convert from one to another (for example, inches to feet or centimeters to meters) and from one related measurement to another (length to area, and area to volume). The metric system meets these requirements and is used by the majority of citizens and countries in the world. Universally, science educators and researchers prefer it. In most nonmetric countries, governments have launched programs to hasten the conversion to metrics. Any country that fails to do so could be at a serious economic and scientific disadvantage. In fact, the U.S. Department of Defense adopted the metric system in 1957, and all cars made in the United States have metric components.

    The metric reference units are the **meter** for length, the **liter** for volume, the **gram** for mass, and the **degree Celsius** for temperature. Regardless of the type of measurement, the same prefixes are used to designate the relationship of a unit to the reference unit. Table 2-1 lists the prefixes we will use in this and subsequent exercises.

    As you can see, the metric system is a decimal system of measurement. Metric units are 10, 100, 1000, and sometimes 1,000,000 or more times larger or smaller than the reference unit. Thus, it's relatively easy to convert from one measurement to another either by multiplying or dividing by 10 or a multiple of 10:

$$\text{nano} \begin{cases}\text{meter}\\\text{liter}\\\text{gram}\end{cases} \xleftarrow[\div 1000]{\times 1000} \text{micro} \begin{cases}\text{meter}\\\text{liter}\\\text{gram}\end{cases} \xleftarrow[\div 1000]{\times 1000} \text{milli} \begin{cases}\text{meter}\\\text{liter}\\\text{gram}\end{cases} \xleftarrow[\div 10]{\times 10} \text{centi} \begin{cases}\text{meter}\\\text{liter}\\\text{gram}\end{cases} \xleftarrow[\div 100]{\times 100} \begin{cases}\text{meter}\\\text{liter}\\\text{gram}\end{cases}$$

TABLE 2-1   Prefixes for Metric System Units

Prefix of Unit (Symbol)	Part of Reference Unit
nano (n)	$1/1,000,000,000 = 0.000000001 = 10^{-9}$
micro (μ)	$1/1,000,000 = 0.000001 = 10^{-6}$
milli (m)	$1/1000 = 0.001 = 10^{-3}$
centi (c)	$1/100 = 0.01 = 10^{-2}$
kilo (k)	$1000 = 10^{3}$

In this section, we examine the metric system and compare it to the American Standard system of measurement (feet, quarts, pounds, and so on).

MATERIALS

Per student pair:

- 30-cm ruler with metric and American (English) Standard units on opposite edges
- 250-mL beaker made of heat-proof glass
- 250-mL Erlenmeyer flask
- 3 graduated cylinders: 10-mL, 25-mL, 100-mL
- 1-quart jar or bottle marked with a fill line
- one-piece plastic dropping pipet (not graduated) or Pasteur pipet and bulb
- graduated pipet and safety bulb or filling device
- 1-pound brick of coffee
- ceramic coffee mug
- 1-gallon milk bottle
- metric tape measure
- 1-L measuring cup

- nonmercury thermometer(s) with Celsius (°C) and Fahrenheit (°F) scales (about 220–110°C)
- hot plate
- 3 boiling chips
- thermometer holder

Per student group:

- a triple beam balance

Per lab room:

- source of distilled water (dH_2O)
- metric bathroom scale
- source of ice

PROCEDURE

A. Length (15 min.)

Length is the measurement of a real or imaginary line extending from one point to another. The standard unit is the meter, and the most commonly used related units of length are

1000 millimeters (mm) = 1 meter (m)
100 centimeters (cm) = 1 m
1000 m = 1 kilometer (km)

For orientation purposes, the yolk of a chicken egg is about 3 cm in diameter. Since the differences between these metric units are based on 10 or multiples of 10, it's fairly easy to convert a measurement in one unit to another.

1. For example, if you want to convert 1.7 km to centimeters, your first step is to determine how many centimeters there are in 1 km. Remember, like units may be cancelled.

$$\frac{100 \text{ cm}}{1 \text{ km}} \times \frac{1000 \text{ m}}{1 \text{ km}} = \frac{100,000 \text{ cm}}{1 \text{ km}}$$

The second step is to multiply the number by this fraction.

$$\frac{1.7 \text{ km}}{1} \times \frac{100,000 \text{ cm}}{1 \text{ km}} = 170,000 \text{ cm}$$

The last calculation can also be done quickly by shifting the decimal point five places to the right.

1.700000 km = 170,000.0 cm

Alternatively, to convert 1.7 km to centimeters, we add exponents.

$$\frac{1.7 \text{ km}}{1} \times \frac{10^2 \text{ cm}}{\text{m}} \times \frac{10^3 \text{ m}}{\text{km}} = 1.7 \times 10^5 \text{ cm} = 170,000 \text{ cm}$$

Using the method most comfortable for you, calculate how many millimeters there are in 4.8 m.

_____ mm

Now let's convert 17 mm to meters.

step 1 $\quad \dfrac{1 \text{ m}}{100 \text{ cm}} \times \dfrac{1 \text{ cm}}{10 \text{ mm}} = \dfrac{1 \text{ m}}{1000 \text{ mm}}$

step 2 $\quad \dfrac{17 \text{ mm}}{1} \times \dfrac{1 \text{ m}}{1000 \text{ mm}} = 0.017 \text{ m}$

Alternatively, you can shift the decimal point three places to the left,

0017.0 mm = 0.017 m

or add exponents:

$$\frac{1.7 \text{ mm}}{1} \times \frac{10^{-2} \text{ m}}{\text{cm}} \times \frac{10^{-1} \text{ cm}}{\text{mm}} = 17 \times 10^{-3} \text{ m} = 0.017 \text{ m}$$

Calculate how many kilometers there are in 16 cm. _____ km

2. Precisely measure the length of this page in centimeters to the nearest tenth of a centimeter with the metric edge of a ruler. Note that nine lines divide the space between each centimeter into 10 millimeters.

The page is _____ cm long.

Calculate the length of this page in millimeters, meters, and kilometers.

_____ mm   _____ m   _____ km

   Now repeat the above measurement using the American Standard edge of the ruler. Measure the length of this page in inches to the nearest eighth of an inch.

_____ in

Convert your answer to feet and yards.

_____ ft   _____ yd

Explain why it is much easier to convert units of length in the metric system than in the American Standard system.

_____

_____

_____

B. Volume (20 min.)

Volume is the space an object occupies. The standard unit of volume is the liter (L), and the most commonly used subunit, the milliliter (mL). There are 1000 mL in 1 liter. A chicken egg has a volume of about 60 mL.

   The volume of a box is the height multiplied by the width multiplied by the depth. The amount of water contained in a cube with sides 1 cm long is 1 cubic centimeter (cc), which for all practical purposes equals 1 mL (Figure 2-1).

1. How many milliliters are there in 1.7 L?

_____ mL

   How many liters are there in 1.7 mL?

_____ L

2. Use Figure 2-2 to recognize **graduated cylinders, beakers, Erlenmeyer flasks,** and the different types of **pipets.** Some of these objects are made of glass; some are plastic. Some will be calibrated in milliliters and liters; others will not be.

3. Pour some water into a 100-mL graduated cylinder and observe the boundary between fluid and air, the **meniscus.** Surface tension makes the meniscus curved, not flat. The high surface tension of water is due to its cohesive and adhesive or "sticky" properties.

Figure 2-1 Relationship among the units of length, volume, and mass in the metric system.

Figure 2-2 Apparatuses commonly used to measure volume: (**a**) pipet filling device, (**b**) pipet safety bulb, (**c**) Pasteur pipet and bulb, (**d**) Erlenmeyer flask, (**e**) glass graduated cylinder, (**f**) plastic graduated cylinder, (**g**) plastic dropping pipet, (**h**) beaker, (**i–k**) graduated pipets.

(Photo by D. Morton and J. W. Perry.)

Draw the meniscus in the plain cylinder outlined in Figure 2-3. The correct reading of the volume is at the *lowest* point of the meniscus.

4. Using the 100-mL graduated cylinder, pour water into a 1-quart jar or bottle. About how many milliliters of water are needed to fill the vessel up to the line?

   _____ mL

5. Pipets are used to transfer small volumes from one vessel to another. Some pipets are not graduated (for example, Pasteur pipets and most one-piece plastic dropping pipets); others are graduated.
   (a) Fill a 250-mL Erlenmeyer flask with distilled water.
   (b) Use a plastic dropping pipet or Pasteur pipet with a bulb to withdraw some water.
   (c) Count the number of drops needed to fill a 10-mL graduated cylinder to the 1-mL mark. Record this number in Table 2-2.
   (d) Repeat steps b and c two more times and calculate the average for your results in Table 2-2.
   (e) Explain why the average of three trials is more accurate than if you only do the procedure once.

   _____

   _____

   _____

Figure 2-3
Draw a meniscus in this plain cylinder.

TABLE 2-2	Estimate of the Number of Drops in 1 mL
Trial	**Drops/mL**
1	
2	
3	
Total	
Average	

C. Mass (25 min.)

Mass is the quantity of matter in a given object. The standard unit is the **kilogram** (kg), and other commonly used units are the milligram (mg) and gram (g). There are 1,000,000 mg in 1 kg and 1000 g in 1 kg. A chicken egg has a mass of about 60 g. Note that the following discussion avoids the term *weight*. This is because weight depends on the gravitational field in which the matter is located. For example, you weigh less on the moon but your mass remains the same as it is on earth. Although it is technically incorrect, mass and weight are often used interchangeably.

1. How many milligrams are there in 1 g?

   _____ mg

   Convert 1.7 g to milligrams and kilograms.

   _____ mg _____ kg

2. A 1-cc cube, if filled with 1 mL of water, has a mass of 1 g (Figure 2-1). The mass of other materials depends on their **density** (water is defined as having a density of 1). The density of any substance is its mass divided by its volume.

   Approximately how many liters are present in 1 cubic meter (m^3) of water? As each of the sides of 1 m^3 are 100 cm in length, it's easy to calculate the number of cubic centimeters (that is, 100 cm $\times$ 100 cm $\times$ 100 cm = 1,000,000 cc). Now just change cubic centimeters to milliliters and convert 1,000,000 mL to liters.

   _____ L

   What is its mass in kilograms?

   _____ kg

In your "mind's eye," contemplate calculating how many pounds there are in a cubic yard of water. It's easier to convert between different units of the metric system than between those of the American Standard system.

3. Determine the mass of an unknown volume of water.* Mass may be measured with a **triple beam balance,** which gets its name from its three beams (Figure 2-4). A movable mass hangs from each beam.

(a) Slide all of the movable masses to zero. Note that the middle and back masses each click into the leftmost notch.

(b) Clear the pan of all objects and make sure it is clean.

(c) The balance marks should line up, indicating that the beam is level and that the pan is empty. If the balance marks don't line up, rotate the zero adjust knob until they do.

(d) Place a 250-mL beaker on the pan. The right side of the beam should rise. Slide the mass on the middle beam until it clicks into the notch at the 100-g mark. If the right end of the beam tilts down below the stationary balance mark, you have added too much mass. Move the mass back a notch. If the right end remains tilted up, additional mass is needed. Keep adding 100-g increments until the beam tilts down; then move the mass back one notch. Repeat this procedure on the back beam, adding 10 g at a time until the beam tilts down, and then backing up one notch. Next, slide the front movable mass until the balance marks line up.

Figure 2-4 Triple beam balance.

(e) The sum of the masses indicated on the three beams gives the mass of the beaker. Nine unnumbered lines divide the space between the numbered gram markings on the front beam into 10 sections, each representing 0.1 g. Record the mass of the beaker to the nearest tenth of a gram in Table 2-3.

(f) Add an unknown amount of water and repeat the above procedure. Record the mass of the beaker and water in Table 2-3.

(g) Calculate the mass of the water alone by subtracting the mass of the beaker from that of the combined beaker and water. Record it in Table 2-3. Do not dispose of the water yet.

(h) Now measure the volume of the water in milliliters with a graduated cylinder.
What is the volume? _____ mL

TABLE 2-3 Weighing an Unknown Quantity of Water with a Triple Beam Balance

Objects	Masses (g)
Beaker and water	
Beaker	
Water	

4. Using the triple beam balance, determine the mass of (that is, weigh) a pound of coffee in grams.
_____ g

---

*Modified from C. M. Wynn and G. A. Joppich, *Laboratory Experiments for Chemistry: A Basic Introduction*, 3rd ed. Wadsworth, 1984.

D. Estimating Length, Volume, and Mass (10 min.)

Now that you have experience using metric units, let's try estimating the measurements of some everyday items. Also, you may consult the metric/American Standard conversion table in Appendix 1 at the end of the lab manual.

1. Estimate the length of your index finger in centimeters. _____ cm
2. Estimate your lab partner's height in meters. _____ m
3. How many milliliters will it take to fill a ceramic coffee mug? _____ mL
4. How many liters will it take to fill a 1-gallon milk bottle? _____ L
5. Estimate the weight of some small personal item (for example, loose change) in grams. _____ g
6. Estimate your or your lab partner's weight in kilograms. _____ kg
7. Transfer your estimates to Table 2-4.
8. Then check your results using either a ruler, metric tape measure, 100-mL graduated cylinder, 1-L measuring cup, triple beam balance, or metric bathroom scale, recording your measurements in Table 2-4. Complete Table 2-4 by calculating the difference between each estimate and measurement.

TABLE 2-4   Differences Between Estimates and Measurements

Number	Estimate	Measurement	Estimate − Measurement
1	cm	cm	cm
2	m	m	m
3	mL	mL	mL
4	L	L	L
5	g	g	g
6	kg	kg	kg

E. Temperature (About 20 min.)

The degree of hot or cold of an object is termed **temperature.** More specifically, it is the average kinetic energy of molecules. Heat always flows from high to low temperatures. This is why hot objects left at room temperature always cool to the surrounding or ambient temperature, while cold objects warm up. Consequently, to keep a heater hot and the inside of a refrigerator cold requires energy. **Thermometers** are instruments used to measure temperature.

1. Using a thermometer with both *Celsius* (°C) and *Fahrenheit* (°F) scales, measure room temperature and the temperature of cold and hot running tap water. Record these temperatures in Table 2-5.
2. Fill a 250-mL beaker with ice about three-fourths full and add cold tap water to just below the ice. Wait for 3 minutes, measure the temperature, and record it in Table 2-5. Remove the thermometer and discard the ice water into the sink.
3. Fill the beaker with warm tap water to about three-fourths full and add three boiling chips. Use a thermometer holder to clip the thermometer onto the rim of the beaker so that the bulb of the thermometer is halfway into the water. Boil the water in the beaker by placing it on a hot plate. After the water boils, record its temperature in Table 2-5. Turn off the hot plate and let the water and beaker cool to below 50°C before pouring the water into the sink.

> **Caution**
>
> *Your instructor will give you specific instructions on how to set up the equipment in your lab for boiling water.*

4. To convert Celsius degrees to Fahrenheit degrees, multiply by $9/5$ and add 32. Is 4°C the temperature of a hot or cool day? _____ What temperature is this in degrees Fahrenheit? _____ °F
5. To convert Fahrenheit degrees to Celsius degrees, subtract 32 and multiply by $5/9$. What is body temperature, 98.6°F, in degrees Celsius? _____ °C

TABLE 2-5 Comparison of Celsius and Fahrenheit Temperatures

Location	°C	°F
Room		
Cold running tap water		
Hot running tap water		
Ice water		
Boiling water		

6. In summary, the formulas for these temperature conversions are:

$$°F = \tfrac{9}{5}\,°C + 32$$
$$°C = \tfrac{5}{9}\,(°F - 32)$$

2.2 Micromeasurement *(About 30 min.)*

More and more procedures used in molecular biology and related areas require the measurement of very small masses and volumes. The following procedure introduces you to use of the electronic balance and micropipets or micropipetters. We'll do this as an experiment in part by answering the question, In the hands of students, how exact are instruments that deliver small volumes in doing what they say they do? Our hypothesis is that under these conditions these instruments perform within the manufacturer's stated specifications for the volumes they deliver.

MATERIALS

Per student group (table):
- standardized electronic balance capable of weighing 0.001 g and with at least a readability of 0.001 g, a repeatability (standard deviation) of ± 0.001 g, and a linearity of 0.002 g
- micropipets or micropipetters with matching tips (capable of delivering 10-μL, 50-μL, and 100-μL volumes)
- nonabsorbent weighing dish
- small test tube in a beaker or rack
- scientific calculator with instructions

Per lab room:
- source of distilled water (dH₂O)

PROCEDURE

1. Remember that in Section 2.1 we established a relationship between the volume and mass of water. If the mass of 1 μL of water is 1 g (Figure 2-1), how much does 1 μL weigh?

   _____ g or _____ mg

   The electronic balances have been standardized prior to lab. If the micropipets or micropipetters in the hands of students perform within manufacturer's specifications, then we can predict what 100 μL, 50 μL, and 10 μL delivered from one of these instruments will weigh. In Table 2-6, write a prediction for this experiment.

2. Fill your test tube with distilled water.
3. Turn on the electronic balance and wait a moment (usually about 5 seconds) until it is stable.
4. Place a weighing dish on the pan.
5. Press the zero or tare key of the balance. Note that the digital display reads all zeros.

Cautions on the Use of Micropipetters

- *Never adjust the micropipetter above or below the stated range or volume limit of measurement.*
- *Never use the micropipetter without a tip in place, as this will damage the internal piston mechanism.*
- *Never invert the micropipetter with a filled tip, as fluid could run up into its chamber.*
- *Never allow the plunger to snap back from the depressed position, as this could damage the piston. After drawing up or dispensing the fluid, release the plunger slowly.*
- *Never immerse the barrel of the micropipetter in fluid.*

6. Use a 100-μL micropipet or a micropipetter adjusted to 100 μL and deliver this volume into the weighing dish. Wait a second for the balance to stabilize, then read and record the mass in grams or milligrams in the correct column of Table 2-6. If you are using a toploading balance, the last digit may continue to change. In this case, use the middle number of the range of numbers displayed.
7. Tare or zero your balance and repeat step 6 for a total of 10 trials.
8. Tare or zero your balance and repeat steps 6 and 7 for the 50- and 10-μL volumes.
9. Use a scientific calculator to determine the average or mean and standard deviation for each column.
10. Plot your points on the graph and the means ± standard deviations on the bar chart:

(a)

(b)

11. Write your conclusion in Table 2-6.

TABLE 2-6 Comparison of Volumes of Water with Their Masses

Prediction:

Trial	100 μL	50 μL	10 μL
1			
2			
3			
4			
5			
6			
7			
8			
9			
10			
Mean			
Standard deviation			

Conclusion:

_____ 1. The metric system is the measurement system of choice for
   (a) science educators
   (b) science researchers
   (c) the citizens of most countries in the world
   (d) all of the above

_____ 2. A kilowatt, a unit of electrical power, is
   (a) ten watts
   (b) a hundred watts
   (c) a thousand watts
   (d) a million watts

_____ 3. A millicurie, a unit of radioactivity, is
   (a) a tenth of a curie
   (b) a hundredth of a curie
   (c) a thousandth of a curie
   (d) a millionth of a curie

_____ 4. Length is the measurement of
   (a) a line, extending from one point to another
   (b) the space an object occupies
   (c) the quantity of matter present in an object
   (d) the degree of hot or cold of an object

_____ 5. Volume is the measurement of
   (a) a line, extending from one point to another
   (b) the space an object occupies
   (c) the quantity of matter present in an object
   (d) the degree of hot or cold of an object

_____ 6. Mass is the measurement of
   (a) a line, extending from one point to another
   (b) the space an object occupies
   (c) the quantity of matter present in an object
   (d) the degree of hot or cold of an object

_____ 7. If 1 cc of a substance has a mass of 1.5 g, its density is
   (a) 0.67
   (b) 1.0
   (c) 1.5
   (d) 2.5

_____ 8. If your mass is 70 kg on the earth, how much is your mass on the moon?
   (a) less than 70 kg
   (b) more than 70 kg
   (c) 70 kg
   (d) none of the above

_____ 9. Above zero degrees, the actual number of degrees Celsius for any given temperature is _____ the degrees Fahrenheit.
   (a) higher than
   (b) lower than
   (c) the same as
   (d) a or b

_____ 10. A thermometer measures
   (a) the degree of hot or cold
   (b) temperature
   (c) a and b
   (d) none of the above

EXERCISE 2

Measurement

POST-LAB QUESTIONS

Introduction

1. What is the importance of measurement to science?

2.1 Metric System

2. Convert 1.24 m to millimeters, centimeters, and kilometers.

   _____ mm

   _____ cm

   _____ km

3. Observe the following carefully and read the volume.

   _____ mL

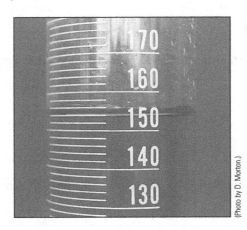

(Photo by D. Morton.)

4. Construct a conversion table for mass. Construct it so that if you wish to convert a measurement from one unit to another, you multiply it by the number at the intersection of the original unit and the new unit.

	New Unit		
Original Unit	mg	g	kg
mg	1		
g		1	
kg			1

5. How is it possible for objects of the same volume to have different masses?

6. Today, many packaged items have the volume or weight listed in both American Standard and metric units. Before your next lab period, find and list 10 such items.

Item	American Standard	Metric

7. Each °F is _____ (larger, smaller) than each °C.

2.2 Micromeasurement

8. Describe what it means to tare or zero an electronic balance. What purpose does this function serve?

Food for Thought

9. How are length, area, and volume related in terms of the three dimensions of space?

10. If you were to choose between the metric and American Standard systems of measurement for future generations, which one would you choose? Set aside your familiarity with the American Standard system and consider their ease of use and degree of standardization with the rest of the world.

Microscopy

OBJECTIVES

After completing this exercise, you will be able to

1. define *magnification, resolving power, contrast, field of view, parfocal, parcentral, depth of field, working distance;*

2. describe how to care for a compound light microscope;

3. recognize and give the function of the parts of a compound light microscope;

4. accurately align a compound light microscope;

5. correctly use a compound light microscope;

6. make a wet mount;

7. correctly use a dissecting microscope;

8. describe the usefulness of the phase-contrast, transmission electron, and scanning electron microscopes;

9. use your skills to enjoy a fascinating world unavailable to the unaided eye.

INTRODUCTION

A microscope contains lenses (for example, transparent glass), which focus radiation (such as light rays) emanating from a specimen to produce an image of that specimen and on a surface sensitive to the radiation (like the retina, the light-sensitive layer of the eye). Table 3-1 presents the three most important properties of lenses and their images.

TABLE 3-1 Important Lens and Image Properties

Property	Definition
Magnification	The amount that the image of an object is enlarged—for example, 100×.
Resolving power	The extent to which object detail in an image is preserved during the magnifying process.
Contrast	The degree to which image details stand out against their background.

3.1 Compound Light Microscope *(About 80 min.)*

The lens of a normal unaided eye can project onto the retina a focused image of an object held no closer than about 10 cm. At this distance, details separated by 0.1 mm are visible. Most cells and related structures are smaller than this, and a light microscope is needed to see them. A microscope placed between the eye and a specimen (usually a section or thin object(s) mounted on a glass slide) acts to bring the specimen very close to the eye so that you can see its details. Ultimately, the greater the proportion of the retina covered by the final image of the specimen, the greater its magnification. It does this by producing a series of magnified images.

Magnification without enough resolving power is referred to as empty, and with a light microscope, the maximum useful magnification is about 1000 times the diameter of the specimen (1000×). Above this value, additional details are missing. Furthermore, adequate contrast is needed to see the details preserved in an image. Dyes are usually added to sections of biological specimens to increase contrast.

Like automobiles, models of compound light microscopes abound, and these instruments have numerous accessories. Typical examples are shown in Figure 3-1, and one is diagrammed in Figure 3-2. If your microscope differs significantly from Figure 3-2, your instructor will give you an unlabeled diagram. If the instructor assigns you a specific microscope for your lab work, record its identification code in the second column of the first row in Table 3-2.

ocular

arm

stage clips

focus knobs

base

nosepiece

objective

stage

lever for
iris diaphragm
of condenser

illuminator

ocular

arm

nosepiece

stage

lever for iris
diaphragm
of condenser

illuminator

base

objective

mechanical
stage

fine adjustment
knob

coarse
adjustment knob

condenser
adjustment knob

condenser

oculars

nosepiece

objective

stage

lever for iris diaphragm
of condenser

illuminator

arm

mechanical stage

control knobs for
mechanical stage

fine adjustment knob

coarse
adjustment knob

base

on/off switch

rheostat

Figure 3-1 Compound light microscopes. (Photos by D. Morton and J. W. Perry.)

Figure 3-2 Compound light microscope.
Labels: ocular, objective, arm, base, illuminator, condenser, lever for iris diaphragm of condenser, stage, stage clip, coarse adjustment knob, fine adjustment knob, nosepiece

TABLE 3-2 Characteristics of My Microscope

Characteristic	Description	Function
Code		identification of my microscope
Light source		
Condenser		
Stage		
Focusing knobs		
Objectives		
Ocular(s)		

MATERIALS

Per student:

- compound light microscope
- lens paper
- lint-free cloth (optional)
- unlabeled diagram of the compound light microscope model used in your course (optional)
- prepared slides with
  a whole mount of stained diatoms
  Wright-stained smear of mammalian blood
  mounted letter *e*
- index card

- prepared slides with
  crossed colored threads coded for thread order
  unstained fibers

Per student group (4):

- bottle of lens-cleaning solution (optional)
- dropper bottle of immersion oil (optional)

Per lab room:

- labeled chart of a compound light microscope

PROCEDURE

A. Care of a Compound Light Microscope

1. To carry a microscope to and from your lab bench, grasp the **arm** (Figure 3-1) with your dominant hand and support the **base** (Figure 3-1) with the other hand, always keeping the microscope upright. *Do not try to carry anything else at the same time.* Label the arm and the base on Figure 3-2 or on the diagram given to you by your instructor.

Caution
Never wipe a glass lens with anything other than lens paper.

2. Remove the dust cover and clean the exposed parts of the optical system. First, blow off any loose dust that may be on the ocular and then gently brush off any remaining dust with a piece of lens paper.

   If the part is still dirty, breathe on the lens and gently polish it with a rotary motion, using a fresh piece of lens paper. If the part is still dirty, and *with your instructor's approval*, clean the lens with a piece of lens paper moistened with lens-cleaning solution.

3. Always remember that your microscope is a precision instrument. Never force any of its moving parts.
4. It is just as difficult to see clearly through a dirty slide as through a dirty microscope. Clean dirty slides with a lint-free cloth or with lens paper before using.
5. At the end of an exercise, make sure the last slide has been removed from the stage and *rotate the nosepiece so that the low-power objective is in the light path.* If your instrument focuses by moving the body tube, turn the coarse adjustment so that it is racked all the way down. If your microscope has an electric cord, neatly fold it up on itself and tie it with a plastic strap or rubber band. Otherwise, wind the cord around the base of the arm of the microscope.
6. Replace the dust cover before returning your microscope to the cabinet.

Now that you know how to care for your microscope, remove the instrument assigned to you from the cabinet and place it on your lab bench. Use Figure 3-1 and the chart on the wall of your lab room to identify the various parts of your microscope. Read each step below and manipulate the parts *only where indicated.* Before you start, make sure the shortest objective is in the light path.

1. *Light source.* The compound microscope uses transmitted light to illuminate a transparent specimen usually mounted on a glass slide. Newer microscopes have a built-in illuminator (Figure 3-1). Locate the **illuminator**, the *off/on switch*, and perhaps also a *rheostat*, which is used to vary the intensity of the light. On some models, the switch and the rheostat are combined. Turn on the light source and look through the ocular. If the illuminator has a rheostat, adjust the intensity so that the light is not too bright.

   (a) Label the illuminator on Figure 3-2 or on your instructor's diagram.

   (b) Describe the light source in Table 3-2, then state its function.

2. *Condenser.* For maximum resolving power, a **condenser**—with a *condenser lens* and *iris diaphragm*—focuses the light source on the specimen so that each of its points is evenly illuminated. The **lever for the iris diaphragm** of the condenser is used to open and close the condenser. Establish whether there is a condenser adjustment knob (Figure 3-1) to set the height of the condenser. *Do not turn the knob; you will learn how to use it later.*

   There may be a *filter holder* under the condenser with a blue or frosted glass disk. Many microscope manufacturers believe that blue light is more pleasing to the eye because, when used with an incandescent bulb, it produces a color balance similar to daylight conditions. Also, theoretically at least, blue light gives better resolving power because of its shorter wavelength. The frosted glass disk scatters light and can be useful in producing even illumination at low magnifications.

   (a) Label the condenser and lever for the iris diaphragm of the condenser on Figure 3-2 or on your instructor's diagram.

   (b) Describe the condenser and its related parts in Table 3-2, then state its function.

3. *Stage.* Either a pair of *stage clips* or a *mechanical stage* holds a specimen mounted on a glass slide in place suspended over a central hole (Figure 3-1).

   (a) If your microscope has a mechanical stage, skip to part b. If your microscope has stage clips, place a prepared slide of stained diatoms under their free ends. Never remove the stage clips, because they make it easier to move a slide in small increments. Skip b and do part c next.

   (b) Position a prepared slide of stained diatoms on the stage by releasing the tension on the spring-loaded movable arm of the mechanical stage (Figure 3-3a). There are two knobs to the right or left of the stage: one to move the specimen forward and backward, the other to move it laterally (Figure 3-1). Label the stage and stage clips (or mechanical stage) on Figure 3-2 or on your instructor's diagram.

vernier scale for *y*-axis

spring-loaded movable arm

direction to microscopist's body

vernier scale for *x*-axis

mechanical stage mechanism

prepared slide label

prepared slide

specimen

a

index portion of vernier scale

movable portion of vernier scale

mechanical stage mechanism

(Photos by J. W. Perry.)

b

Figure 3-3 (a) Mechanical stage. (b) Vernier scale on mechanical stage of compound light microscope. The correct reading is 19.6 mm.

(c) On most mechanical stages, each direction has a vernier scale so that you can easily locate interesting fields again and again. A vernier scale consists of two scales running side by side, a long one in millimeters and a short one, 9 mm in length and divided into 10 equal subdivisions. To take a reading, note the whole number on the long scale coinciding with or just below the zero line of the short scale. If the whole number of the long scale and the zero of the short scale coincide, the first place after the decimal point is zero. Otherwise, the first place after the decimal point is the value of the line on the short scale that coincides (or nearly coincides) with one of the next nine lines after the whole number on the long scale. For example, the correct reading of the vernier scale in Figure 3-3b is 19.6 mm.

(d) Describe the stage and its related parts in Table 3-2, then state its function.

4. *Focusing knobs* (Figure 3-1). The **coarse focus adjustment knob** is for use with the lower-power objectives, whereas the **fine focus adjustment knob** is for critical focusing, especially with the higher-power objectives. On most modern microscopes, you move the stage of the instrument up and down to focus the specimen. Modern microscopes usually have a *preset focus lock*, which stops the stage at a particular height. After setting this lock, you can lower the stage with the coarse focus knob, to facilitate changing of the specimen, and then raise it to focusing height without fear of colliding the specimen against the objective. There may also be a *focus tension adjustment knob*, usually located inside of the left-hand coarse focus knob.

   (a) Turn the coarse focus knob. Do you turn the knob toward you or away from you to bring the slide and objective closer together?

   _____

   (b) Label the coarse- and fine focus adjustment knobs on Figure 3-2 or on your instructor's diagram.

   (c) Describe the focusing knobs in Table 3-2, then state their function. Note if a preset focus lock or focus adjustment knob is present.

5. *Objectives.* The compound light microscope has at least two magnifying lenses, the objective and the ocular (Figure 3-1). The objective scans the specimen. Most microscopes have several objectives mounted on a revolving **nosepiece**. The magnifying power of each objective is labeled on its side. Usually included are these objectives: a 4× *low-power* or scanning, a 10× *medium-power* (Figure 3-4b), an about 40× *high-dry*, and perhaps an about 100× *oil-immersion objective* (Figure 3-4c). The other number often labeled on the side of nosepiece objectives is the **numerical aperture** (NA). The larger the numerical aperture, the greater the resolving power and useful magnification.

Figure 3-4 (a) 10× objective removed from microscope. (b) 100× oil immersion objective removed from microscope. (c) Ocular removed from microscope.

   Objectives are **parfocal.** That is, once an objective has been focused, you can rotate to another one and the image will remain in coarse focus, requiring only slight movement of the fine focus knob. Objectives are also **parcentral,** meaning that the center of the field of view remains about the same for each objective. The **field of view** is the circle of light you see when looking into the microscope.

   Objectives have different lengths; the lower-power objectives are shorter than the higher-power ones. That is, the working distance of objectives decreases with magnification. **Working distance** is the space between the objective lens and the slide. Therefore, the higher the power of the objective in use, the closer the objective is to the slide—and the more careful you must be.

   (a) Record the magnifying power and NA of the objectives on your microscope in Table 3-3. If your instrument does not have a particular objective, indicate that it is not present (NP).

TABLE 3-3 Objectives Present on My Compound Light Microscope

Objective	Objective Magnifying Power (ObMP)	Total Magnifying Power (ObMP × OcMP = _____×)	Numerical Aperture (NA)
Low-power			
Medium-power			
High-dry			
Oil-immersion			

    (b) Label the nosepiece and objective on Figure 3-2 or on your instructor's diagram.
    (c) Describe the objectives in Table 3-2, then state their function.
  6. *Ocular.* The magnifying lens you look into is called an **ocular** (Figure 3-4a). Oculars are generally 10×.
    (a) Since each objective has a different magnifying power, the total magnification is calculated by multiplying the magnifying power of the ocular by that of the objective in use. What is the ocular magnification power (OcMP) of the ocular(s) on your microscope?

        _____×

    Calculate the total magnification for each of your microscope's ocular/objective combinations, then record them in Table 3-3.
    (b) Label the ocular on Figure 3-2 or on your instructor's diagram.
    (c) Describe the ocular in Table 3-2, then state its function.
    (d) Your microscope will have one or two oculars mounted on a *monocular* or *binocular head*, respectively. There may be a pointer mounted in an ocular so that you can easily show a specimen detail to your instructor or another student. For a monocular microscope, it's best to use your dominant eye to look down the ocular, keeping your other eye open. Is your microscope monocular or binocular?

    _____

    (e) If your microscope is monocular, determine your dominant eye:
- Look at a small object on the far wall of your room with both eyes open.
- Form the thumb and index finger of one hand into a circle and place this circle in your line of sight, at arm's length, so that it surrounds the object.
- Close your right eye. If the object shifts out of the circle to your left, your right eye is probably dominant. If the object remains in the circle, your left eye is probably dominant.
- This time close your left eye and go through the process again. If the object shifts to the right, your left eye is dominant. If the object remains within the circle, your right eye is dominant. The more pronounced the shift, the greater the dominance. If there is no shift, neither eye is dominant.

C. Aligning a Compound Light Microscope with In-Base Illumination and a Condenser with an Iris Diaphragm

Aligning your microscope properly will not only help you see specimen detail clearly but will also protect your eyes from strain.

  1. Rotate the nosepiece until the medium-power objective is in the light path. Open the iris diaphragm.
  2. If it is not already there, place the prepared slide of stained diatoms on the stage; center and carefully focus on it. *Skip steps 3 and 4 if your microscope is monocular. Skip step 5 if your microscope does not have a control to adjust the height of the condenser.*
  3. If your microscope is binocular, adjust the interpupillary distance. Hold a different ocular tube with each hand and, while looking at the specimen, pull the tubes apart or push them together until you see one field of view. After making this adjustment, read and record the number off the scale.
    My interpupillary distance is _____.
    From now on, you can set the interpupillary distance at this number.
  4. Now compensate for any difference in diopter between the lenses of each eye:
    (a) *If there is one diopter adjustment ring around the left ocular tube,* cover your left eye with an index card and focus your microscope using the fine focus knob. Now uncover the left eye and cover your right one. Use the diopter adjustment ring to bring the specimen into focus.

(b) *If both ocular tubes have a diopter adjustment ring,* set the left one to the same number as the interpupillary distance, cover your right eye with an index card, and focus on the specimen. Then uncover the right eye and cover your left one. Use the diopter adjustment ring on the right ocular tube to bring the specimen into focus.

5. Place a sharp point (pencil, dissecting needle, or some similar object) on top of the illuminator and bring the silhouette into sharp focus by adjusting the height of the condenser.

   (a) *If the ocular on your microscope is removable (and with the permission of your instructor),* carefully slide it out and put the ocular open end down on a piece of lens paper in a safe place. Then, while looking down the ocular tube, adjust the iris diaphragm until the edge of the aperture lies just inside the margin of the back lens element of the objective (Figure 3-5). Replace the ocular.

   (b) *If the ocular cannot be removed,* close the condenser diaphragm and then open it until there is no further increase in brightness. Now close it again, stopping when you see the brightness begin to diminish.

6. If your microscope has a rheostat, adjust the illumination to a level that lets you see specimen detail and that is comfortable for your eyes. To maintain the same illumination at higher magnifications, you will have to increase its intensity.

7. For best results, repeat steps 5 and 6 each time you use a different objective.

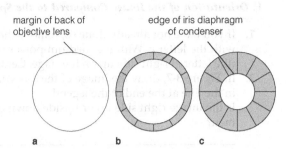

Figure 3-5 Correct setting for condenser iris diaphragm: Drawing **b** is correct. In **a,** you cannot see the edge of the iris diaphragm. In **c,** the diaphragm has been closed too much.

D. Using Different Magnifications

It's safest to observe a specimen on a slide first with low power and then, step by step, with higher-power objectives. This way you avoid colliding the objective against the slide or vice versa. Also, it's easier to use a lower-power objective to locate a specific specimen detail. This is why the low-power objective is sometimes called the scanning objective. Since the magnification is in diameters, the area of the field of view decreases dramatically with increasing magnification (Figure 3-6). It is just as easy to lose a specimen detail at higher magnifications, but once a specimen detail is lost, it's always easier to find it again if you switch to a lower-power objective.

Now follow these steps to use each objective.

1. Rotate the low-power objective into the light path.

2. If it is not already there, place a prepared slide of stained diatoms on the stage, securing it with either the stage clips or the movable arm of the mechanical stage.

3. Look through the ocular. Bring the diatoms into focus using the *coarse focus knob.* Adjust the illumination as described in steps 5 and 6 of Section C. At this magnification, the diatoms appear small. Center a diatom by moving the slide.

4. Rotate the nosepiece so that the medium-power objective is in the light path. Adjust the illumination. Focus the diatom.

5. Rotate the nosepiece so that the high-dry objective is in the light path. Adjust the illumination. Focus the diatom using the *fine focus-adjustment knob.*

6. If your microscope has an oil-immersion objective (and with the permission of your instructor), replace the prepared slide of diatoms with one with a smear of mammalian blood and repeat steps 1–5. Center and focus on a white blood cell. (See Figure 40-4 on page 644.) Most of the cells are red blood cells stained a light pink. A few cells are white blood cells with prominent blue-stained nuclei. Immersion oil, because it has optical properties similar to glass, increases resolving power and useful magnification. To use an oil-immersion objective:

   (a) Rotate the nosepiece so that the light path is midway between the high-dry and oil-immersion objectives.

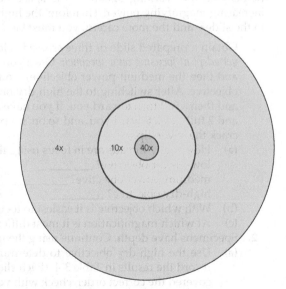

Figure 3-6 Illustration of the decreasing area of the field of view when a 4×, 10×, and 40× objective is used with a 10× ocular. The actual area of each circle has been enlarged 7.5×.

(b) Place a small drop of immersion oil onto the coverslip, using the circle of light above the specimen as a reference point.

(c) Rotate the nosepiece so that the oil-immersion objective is in the oil.

(d) Adjust the illumination and focus the white blood cell with the fine focus knob.

(e) After examining the white blood cell, rotate the oil-immersion objective out of the light path. Carefully wipe the oil from the oil-immersion objective with lens paper.

(f) Remove the slide from the stage and wipe the oil from the coverslip with lens paper.

E. Orientation of the Image Compared to the Specimen

1. If you have not already done so, remove the prepared slide of diatoms and replace it with a prepared slide with the letter *e*. With the medium-power objective in the light path, position the slide with the specimen (the letter *e*) right side up on the stage. Center the *e* in the field of view, and carefully bring it into focus.

2. In Figure 3-7, draw the image of the *e* as you see it through the ocular. Record the total magnification used in the line at the end of the legend.
   Is the image right side up or upside down compared to the specimen?

   _____

   Compared to the specimen, is the image backward as well as upside down?
   (yes or no) _____
   In summary, the image is *inverted* with respect to the specimen.

3. Move the specimen to the right while watching it through the microscope. In which direction does the image move?

   _____

4. Move the specimen away from you. In which direction does the image move?

   _____

5. Remove the slide and put it away.

Figure 3-7 Drawing of the letter *e* as seen through the ocular (_____×).

F. Depth of Field

The **depth of field** is the distance through which you can move the specimen and still have it remain in focus. Remember, the working distance—the space between the objective lens and the coverslip—decreases with increasing magnifying power. Therefore, the higher the power of the objective in use, the closer the objective is to the slide—and the more careful you must be.

1. Obtain a prepared slide of three crossed colored threads. *This exercise requires care, since you are probably not yet adept at focusing on a specimen.* Once you have the threads in focus (using first the low-power objective and then the medium-power objective), you need only use the fine focus knob to focus with the high-dry objective. After switching to the high-dry objective, try rotating the fine focus knob ½ turn away from you and then a full turn toward you. If you have not found the plane of focus, next try 1 ½ turns away from you and 2 full turns toward you, and so on. If you work deliberately, you will find the plane of focus and won't crack the coverslip.
   (a) How many threads are in focus using the
   low-power objective? _____
   medium-power objective? _____
   high-dry objective? _____
   (b) With which objective is it easiest to focus a specimen? _____
   (c) At which magnification is it most difficult to focus a specimen? _____

2. Specimens have depth. Continue using the prepared slide of three crossed colored threads.
   (a) Use the high-dry objective to determine the order of the three threads mounted on the slide and record the results in Table 3-4. (Each slide label has a code on it. When you believe that you have discovered the correct order, check with your instructor to find out if you are correct.)
   (b) Focusing carefully with the fine focus knob, move from the bottom to the upper thread.
   Did you move the knob away from or toward you? _____

3. Remove and put away the slide.

4. Viewing sections of three-dimensional structures makes interpretation of the original shape quite difficult (Figure 3-8).

TABLE 3-4 Order of Threads

Location	Color
Closest to slide	
Middle	
Closest to coverslip	

Figure 3-8 Difficulties encountered in interpreting the three-dimensional shape of objects from sections. Compare the transverse (cross) section of the cylinder with the distorted oblique section (**a**) and the longitudinal section (**b**). A similar shape to the transverse section of a cylinder results when a hollow ball is sectioned (**c**). Sectioning the hollow ball through the wall results in a solid shape.

(a) Examine a slide of the cortex of the mammalian kidney with your compound microscope (Figure 33-4 on page 523). Complete the hypotheses as to the three-dimensional shape of the structures labeled renal corpuscles and nephron tubules.
The shape of renal corpuscles is _____.
The shape of nephron tubules is _____.
(b) Check the illustration in Figure 36-3 on page 588 to see if your hypotheses are acceptable.

G. Using the Iris Diaphragm to Improve Contrast

1. Place a specimen of unstained fibers on the stage. Locate and focus on these fibers using the medium-power objective. Make sure the condenser and iris diaphragm are correctly set.
2. Close the iris diaphragm.
Does this procedure increase or decrease contrast? _____.
Although this procedure is useful when viewing specimens with low contrast, it should be used only as a last resort because resolving power is also decreased.
3. Remove and put away the slide.

H. Units of Measurement

The basic metric unit of length at the light-microscopic level is the micrometer (μm). An even smaller unit, the nanometer (nm) is often used at the electron-microscopic level.

1000 μm = 1 mm
1000 nm = 1 μm

How many nanometers are there in 1 mm? _____ nm
How many millimeters are there in 1 nm? _____ mm

1. Rotate the low-power objective into the light path.
   What is the total magnification? _____×
2. Place a transparent 15-cm ruler on the stage.
3. What is the diameter of the field of view? _____mm
4. Repeat step 3 with the medium-power objective in the light path.
   The total magnification is _____×.
   The diameter of the field of view is _____mm.
5. Use the following formula to estimate the diameter of the field of view when the high-dry objective is in the light path.

$$\frac{\text{total magnification using low-power objective} \times \text{mm counted with that objective}}{\text{total magnification of high-dry objective}} = \underline{\hspace{2cm}} \text{ mm}$$

   Once you've calculated this value, convert it to micrometers: _____μm

6. Complete Table 3-5.

TABLE 3-5 Diameter of Field of View		
Objective	**Magnifying Power**	**Diameter of Field of View**
Low-power		
Medium-power		
High-dry		
Oil-immersion		

7. You will use this information to estimate size by observing the percentage of the diameter of the field of view taken up by the specimen or part of the specimen. Using the medium-power objective, estimate the percentage of the diameter of the field of view covered by the letter *e*. The approximate diameter of the letter *e* is

$$\frac{\text{percent} \times \text{diameter of field of view (mm)}}{100\%} = \underline{\hspace{2cm}} \text{ mm}$$

8. If your microscope is equipped with an ocular micrometer, your instructor may provide directions on how to accurately measure specimen details.

3.2 How to Make a Wet Mount *(About 10 min.)*

In the mid-seventeenth century, Robert Hooke used a microscope to discover tiny, empty compartments in thin shavings of cork. He named them cells. Repeating this historic observation is a good way to learn how to prepare a wet mount.

MATERIALS

Per student:

- compound microscope, lens paper, a bottle of lens-cleaning solution (optional), a lint-free cloth (optional)
- cork

- razor blade
- glass microscope slide
- glass coverslip
- dissecting needle

Per student group (4):

■ dropper bottle of distilled water (dH$_2$O)

PROCEDURE

1. Carefully use a razor blade to cut a number of *very thin shavings* from a cork stopper. Place them on a glass microscope slide.
2. Gently add a drop of distilled water.
3. Place one end of a glass coverslip to the right or left of the specimen so that the rest of the slip is held at a 45° angle over the specimen (Figure 3-9a).

Figure 3-9 How to make a wet mount.

4. Slowly lower the coverslip with a dissecting needle so as not to trap air bubbles (Figure 3-9b).
5. Observe the wet mount, first at low magnification and then with higher power. Air may be trapped either in the cork or as free bubbles (Figure 3-10). Trapped air will appear dark and refractive around its edges. This effect is due to sharply bending rays of light. Draw what you see in Figure 3-11. Note the total magnification used to make the drawing.
6. Clean and replace the slide and coverslip as indicated by your instructor.

Figure 3-10 Free air bubble (250×).

(Photo by J. W. Perry.)

| 3.3 | Microscopic Observations *(About 20 min.)* |

Examining the microscopic world is both challenging and fun. Most of the macroscopic world has been explored, but the microscopic world is barely touched. Yet the microbes in it are essential to our very existence. So be an explorer and see what you can discover!

MATERIALS

Per student:

■ compound microscope, lens paper, a bottle of lens-cleaning solution (optional), a lint-free cloth (optional)
■ glass microscope slide
■ glass coverslip

Per student group (4):

■ pond water or some other mixed culture in a dropper bottle
■ dropper bottle of Protoslo®

Per lab room:

■ reference books for the identification of micro-organisms

PROCEDURE

1. Obtain a drop of pond water or other mixed culture from the bottom of the bottle.
2. Add a drop of Protoslo®. This methyl cellulose solution slows down any swimming microorganisms.
3. Make a wet mount (Figure 3-9).

4. Observe the wet mount with your compound microscope. Start at the upper-left corner of the coverslip and scan the wet mount with the low-power objective. When you find something interesting, focus on it and switch to the medium-power objective and then, if necessary, the high-dry objective.
5. Draw what you find on Figure 3-12 and note the total magnification.
6. Attempt to identify it using the resource books provided you by your instructor. If successful, write its name under your drawing.
7. Clean and replace the slide and coverslip as indicated by your instructor.
8. Put away your compound microscope as described on page 27.

Figure 3-11 Drawing of the microscopic structure in a cork shaving (_____×).

Figure 3-12 Drawing of microorganisms (_____×).

3.4   Dissecting Microscope *(About 10 min.)*

Dissecting microscopes (Figure 3-13) have a large working distance between the specimen and the objective lens. They are especially useful in viewing larger specimens (including thicker slide-mounted specimens) and in manipulating the specimen (when dissection of a small structure or organism is required, for example).

The large working distance also allows for illumination of the specimen from above (reflected light) as well as from below (transmitted light). Reflected light shows up surface features on the specimen better than transmitted light does.

Figure 3-13 Dissecting microscope (**a**) reflected light, (**b**) transmitted light.

a   b

(Photos by D. Morton and J. W. Perry.)

MATERIALS

Per student group:

- dissecting microscope
- specimens appropriate for viewing with the dissecting microscope (for example, a prepared slide with a whole mount of a small organism, bread mold, an insect mounted on a pin stuck in a cork, a small flower)

PROCEDURE

1. Under a dissecting microscope, view one or more of the specimens provided by your instructor. What is the magnification range of this microscope?

    _____× to _____×

2. Is the image of the specimen inverted as in the compound light microscope? (yes or no) _____
3. Describe the type of illumination used by your dissecting microscope. Is there a choice?

    _____

    _____

| 3.5 | **Other Microscopes** *(About 10 min.)* |

In future exercises you will examine pictures taken with other types of microscopes (Figure 3-14). Some will be of living cells taken with a phase-contrast microscope or similar instrument, including those using the Nomarski process. Others will be of very thin-sectioned, heavy metal–stained specimens taken with a transmission electron microscope or TEM (Figure 3-15c and d). Still others will be of precious metal–coated surfaces produced by signals from the scanning electron microscope or SEM (Figure 3-16). Table 3-6 summarizes the technology and use of these microscopes.

a phase contrast **b** Nomarski process **c** transmission electron **d** scanning electron

(Photos courtesy J. Pickett-Heaps.)

Figure 3-14 How different types of microscopes reveal detail in cells of the green alga *Scenedesmus*.

TABLE 3-6 Other Microscopes

Microscope	Technology	Use
Phase-contrast and Nomarski process	Converts phase differences in light to differences in contrast.	Observation of low contrast specimens (often living).
Transmission electron	Increases resolving power by using electrons in a vacuum and magnetic lenses instead of light and glass lenses, respectively.	Preservation of greater specimen detail allows for magnifications up to 1,000,000× or more (usually dead materials).
Scanning electron	Forms TV-like picture from a secondary electron signal, which is emitted from surface points excited by a thin beam of electrons drawn across the surface in a raster pattern.	Investigation of the fine structure of surfaces (usually dead specimens).

a

c

path of light rays (bottom to top) to eye

Ocular lens enlarges
primary image formed
by objective lenses.

prism that
directs rays to
ocular lens

Objective lenses (those closest
to specimen) form the primary
image. Most compound light
microscopes have several.

stage (holds
microscope
slide in position)

Condenser lenses focus
light rays onto specimen.

illuminator

microscope base housing
source of illumination

b

accelerated
electron flow
(top to bottom)

condenser lens
to focus beam
of electrons
onto specimen

specimen

objective
lens

intermediate
lens

projector lens

viewing
screen (or
photographic
film)

d

Figure 3-15 External view (**c**) and diagram (**d**) of a transmission electron microscope. Similar illustrations of a compound light microscope (**a, b**) are provided for comparing the similarities and differences of these microscopes. (After Starr and Taggart, 2001; (**a**) Leica Microsystems, Inc., Deerfield, IL; (**b**) George Musil/Visuals Unlimited.)

(Photo by D. Morton [a] and after Starr and Taggart, 1998 [b].)

Figure 3-16 External view (**a**) and diagram (**b**) of a scanning electron microscope.

MATERIALS

Per student group:

- photographs of TEM micrographs (negatives) or digital images
- photographs of SEM negatives or digital images

PROCEDURE

1. Examine some photographs of TEM micrographs (negatives) or digital images. The darker areas are more electron-dense in the specimen than the lighter areas.
2. Now look at some photographs of SEM negatives or digital images. The lighter areas correspond to the emission of greater numbers of secondary electrons from that part of the specimen; the darker areas emit less.
3. What type of microscope (compound light, dissecting, phase-contrast, TEM, or SEM) would you use to examine the specimens listed in Table 3-7?

TABLE 3-7 Microscope Use	
Specimen	**Microscope**
Living surface of the finger	
Dye-stained slide of a section of the finger	
Gold-coated bacteria on a single cell of the finger	
Unstained section of a biopsy from the finger	
Heavy metal–stained, very thin section of the finger	

_____ 1. Magnification
   (a) is the amount that an object's image is enlarged
   (b) is the extent to which detail in an image is preserved during the magnifying process
   (c) is the degree to which image details stand out against their background
   (d) focuses radiation emanating from an object to produce an image

_____ 2. Resolving power
   (a) is the amount that an object's image is enlarged
   (b) is the extent to which detail in an image is preserved during the magnifying process
   (c) is the degree to which image details stand out against their background
   (d) focuses radiation emanating from an object to produce an image

_____ 3. A lens
   (a) is the amount that an object's image is enlarged
   (b) is the extent to which detail in an image is preserved during the magnifying process
   (c) is the degree to which image details stand out against their background
   (d) focuses radiation emanating from an object to produce an image

_____ 4. Contrast
   (a) is the amount that an object's image of a object is enlarged
   (b) is the extent to which detail in an image is preserved during the magnifying process
   (c) is the degree to which image details stand out against their background
   (d) focuses radiation emanating from an object to produce an image

_____ 5. The maximum useful magnification for a light microscope is about
   (a) 100×
   (b) 1000×
   (c) 10,000×
   (d) 100,000×

_____ 6. The two image-forming lenses of a compound light microscope are
   (a) the condenser and objective
   (b) the condenser and ocular
   (c) the objective and ocular
   (d) none of these choices

_____ 7. Dyes are usually added to sections of biological specimens to increase
   (a) resolving power
   (b) magnification
   (c) contrast
   (d) all of the above

_____ 8. If the magnification of the two image-forming lenses are both 10×, the total magnification of the image will be
   (a) 1×
   (b) 10×
   (c) 100×
   (d) 1000×

_____ 9. The distance through which a microscopic specimen can be moved and still have it remain in focus is called the
   (a) field of view
   (b) working distance
   (c) depth of field
   (d) magnification

_____ 10. Electron microscopes differ from light microscopes in that
   (a) electrons are used instead of light
   (b) magnetic lenses replace glass lenses
   (c) the electron path has to be maintained in a high vacuum
   (d) a, b, and c are all true

EXERCISE 3

Microscopy

POST-LAB QUESTIONS

3.1 Compound Light Microscope

1. What is the function of the following parts of a compound light microscope?

   a. condenser lens

   b. iris diaphragm

   c. objective

   d. ocular

2. In order, list the lenses in the light path between a specimen viewed with the compound light microscope and its image on the retina of the eye.

3. What happens to contrast and resolving power when the aperture of the condenser (that is, the size of the hole through which light passes before it reaches the specimen) of a compound light microscope is decreased?

4. What happens to the field of view in a compound light microscope when the total magnification is increased?

5. Describe the importance of the following concepts to microscopy.
   a. magnification

   b. resolving power

   c. contrast

6. Which photomicrograph of unstained cotton fibers was taken with the iris diaphragm closed? _____

a   (Photo by J. W. Perry.)   b   (Photo by J. W. Perry.)

7. Describe how you would care for and put away your compound light microscope at the end of lab.

3.2 How to Make a Wet Mount

8. Describe how to make a wet mount.

3.4 Dissecting Microscope, 3.5 Other Microscopes

9. A camera mounted on a _____ microscope took this photo of a cut piece of cork.

(Photo by D. Morton.)

(516×).

Food for Thought

10. Why were humans unaware of microorganisms for most of their history?

Macromolecules and You: Food and Diet Analysis

OBJECTIVES

After completing this exercise, you will be able to

1. define *macromolecule, vitamin, mineral, carbohydrate, monosaccharide, disaccharide, polysaccharide, lipid, protein, amino acid, calorie;*

2. describe the basic structures of carbohydrates, lipids, glycerides, and proteins;

3. recognize positive and negative tests for carbohydrates, lipids, and proteins;

4. identify the roles that carbohydrates, lipids, proteins, minerals, and vitamins play in the body's construction and metabolism;

5. test food substances to determine the presence of biologically important macromolecules;

6. identify common dietary sources of nutrients;

7. identify the components and relative proportions of a healthy diet with respect to nutrients and calories.

INTRODUCTION

Humans are omnivores, animals who consume a wide variety of food items from several trophic levels. As with all consumers, our food items provide us with the energy stored in the chemical bonds of the food molecules, plus the raw carbon-based materials from which cellular components are built.

Food nutrients include minerals and vitamins, plus the larger molecules known as carbohydrates (which include sugars, starches, and cellulose), lipids (fats and oils), and proteins. As it happens, these last nutrients are three of the four major groups of biological **macromolecules,** large organic molecules of which all cells are made. (The fourth group is the nucleic acids that store and control the genetic instructions within a cell. These crucial macromolecules are not usually utilized by the body as nutrients, and so will not be considered in this exercise.)

Carbohydrates, lipids, and proteins supply the materials from which our cells and tissues are constructed and the energy (measured in kilocalories) to run our metabolic processes. **Vitamins** are necessary organic molecules that our bodies do not construct from other molecules; we require vitamins in our diets in only small amounts. **Minerals** are required inorganic (noncarbon-containing) nutrients such as calcium and potassium. Good health, then, depends upon ingesting the proper balance and quantities of these major nutrients.

In this exercise, you will test for the presence of carbohydrates, lipids, and proteins, and then use your knowledge to determine the macromolecular composition of various common food products. You will also analyze your own diet and compare it to a diet recommended for maintaining good health.

5.1   Identification of Macromolecules

You will use some simple tests for carbohydrates, lipids, and proteins in a variety of substances, including food products. Most of the reagents used are not harmful; however, observe all precautions listed and perform the experiments only in the proper location as identified by your instructor.

A. Carbohydrates

A **carbohydrate** is a simple sugar or a larger molecule composed of multiple sugar units. Carbohydrates are composed of carbon, hydrogen, and oxygen. Those composed of a single sugar molecule are called **monosaccharides.** Examples include ribose and deoxyribose (components of our genetic material), fructose (sometimes called fruit sugar), and glucose (a sugar that commonly serves as the most immediate source of cellular energy needs; see Figure 5-1). Monosaccharides are easily used within cells as energy sources.

Monosaccharides can be bonded together. If two monosaccharides are joined, they form a **disaccharide.** Examples of disaccharides are sucrose (common table sugar), maltose (found in many seeds), and lactose (milk sugar). If more than two monosaccharides are bonded together, the resulting large carbohydrate molecule is called a **polysaccharide.**

Animals, including humans, store glucose in the form of glycogen (Figure 5-2), a highly branched polysaccharide chain of glucose molecules. Starch (Figure 5-2), a key glucose-storing polysaccharide in plants, is an important food molecule for humans. Plant cells are surrounded by a tough cell wall made of another chain formed of glucose molecules, cellulose (Figure 5-2). Our digestive system does not break cellulose apart very well. Fibrous plant materials thus provide bulky cellulose fiber, which is necessary for good intestinal health.

Carbohydrate digestion occurs in humans as digestive enzymes produced in the salivary glands, pancreas, and lining of the small intestine break polysaccharides and disaccharides into monosaccharides such as glucose. The simple sugars are small enough to be absorbed into intestinal cells and then carried throughout the bloodstream.

Many small carbohydrate molecules react upon heating with a copper-containing compound called Benedict's reagent, changing the reagent color from blue to orange or red. A disaccharide may or may not react with Benedict's solution, depending upon how the bonding of the component monosaccharides took place.

Other tests are available for some polysaccharides, the most common of which is Lugol's test for starch. In this test, a dilute solution of potassium iodide reacts with the starch molecule to form a deep blue (nearly black) color product.

Figure 5-1 Structural diagrams of glucose.

(After Starr, 2000.)

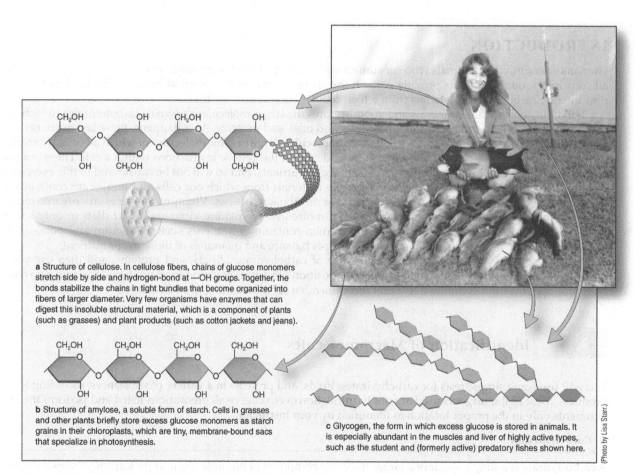

a Structure of cellulose. In cellulose fibers, chains of glucose monomers stretch side by side and hydrogen-bond at —OH groups. Together, the bonds stabilize the chains in tight bundles that become organized into fibers of larger diameter. Very few organisms have enzymes that can digest this insoluble structural material, which is a component of plants (such as grasses) and plant products (such as cotton jackets and jeans).

b Structure of amylose, a soluble form of starch. Cells in grasses and other plants briefly store excess glucose monomers as starch grains in their chloroplasts, which are tiny, membrane-bound sacs that specialize in photosynthesis.

c Glycogen, the form in which excess glucose is stored in animals. It is especially abundant in the muscles and liver of highly active types, such as the student and (formerly active) predatory fishes shown here.

(Photo by Lisa Starr.)

Figure 5-2 Molecular structure of starch, cellulose, and glycogen, and their typical locations in a few organisms.

A.1. Test for Sugars Using Benedict's Solution (About 20 min.)

MATERIALS

Per student group (4):

- china marker
- 11 test tubes in test tube rack
- test tube clamp
- hot plate *or* ring stand with wire gauze support and Bunsen burner
- 250- or 400-mL beaker with boiling beads or stones
- stock bottles* of
    Benedict's solution
    distilled water (dH$_2$O)
    glucose solution

- maltose solution
- lactose solution
- sucrose solution
- fructose solution
- starch solution
- lemon juice
- unsweetened orange juice
- colorless nondiet soda
- colorless diet soda
- vortex mixer (optional)

PROCEDURE

1. Half-fill the beaker with tap water and apply heat with a hot plate or burner to bring the water to a gentle boil.
2. Using the china marker, number the test tubes 1–11.
3. Pipet 2 mL of the correct stock solutions into the test tubes as described in Table 5-1. (If you don't know how to use the Pi-pump, check with your instructor before proceeding.)
4. Add 2 mL of Benedict's solution to each test tube, agitate the mixture by shaking the tubes from side to side or with a vortex mixer, if available, and record the color of the mixture in Table 5-1 in the column "Initial Color."
5. Heat the tubes in the boiling water bath for 3 minutes. Remove the tubes with the test tube clamp, and record any color changes that have taken place in the column "Color After Heating." Also record your conclusions regarding the presence or absence of simple carbohydrates.

TABLE 5-1 Benedict's Test for Sugars

Tube	Contents	Initial Color	Color After Heating	Conclusion
1	Distilled water			
2	Glucose			
3	Maltose			
4	Lactose			
5	Sucrose			
6	Starch			
7	Fructose			
8	Lemon juice			
9	Orange juice			
10	Nondiet soda			
11	Diet soda			

---

*Each stock bottle should have its own 2- or 5-mL pipet fitted with a Pi-pump.

A.2. Test for Starch Using Lugol's Solution (About 15 min.)

MATERIALS

Per student group (4):

- china marker
- 7 test tubes in test tube rack
- dropper bottle containing Lugol's solution
- stock bottles* of
  distilled water (dH$_2$0)
  glucose solution

maltose solution
lactose solution
sucrose solution
starch solution
cream
- vortex mixer (optional)

PROCEDURE

1. Using the china marker, number the test tubes 1–7.
2. Pipet 3 mL of the correct stock solutions into the test tubes as described in Table 5-2.
3. Record the color of each solution in the column "Initial Color" in Table 5-2.
4. Add 9 drops of Lugol's solution to each test tube, agitate the mixture by shaking the tubes from side to side or with a vortex mixer, if available, and record the color of the mixture in the column "Color After Adding Lugol's Solution." Also record your conclusions regarding the presence or absence of starch in each test solution.

TABLE 5-2	Lugol's Test for Starch			
Tube	Contents	Initial Color	Color After Adding Lugol's Solution	Conclusion
1	Distilled water			
2	Glucose			
3	Maltose			
4	Lactose			
5	Sucrose			
6	Starch			
7	Cream			

5. Hypothesize about why you got the result you did with the Lugol's test for each substance:

dH$_2$O _____

glucose _____

maltose _____

lactose _____

sucrose _____

starch _____

Does cream contain starch? _____

B. Lipids

Lipids are oily or greasy compounds insoluble in water, but dissolvable in nonpolar solvents such as ether or chloroform. Those lipids having fatty acids—hydrocarbon chains with a carboxyl (—COOH) group at one end—combine with glycerol to form glycerides, a rich source of stored energy. Lipids with three fatty acid chains attached to a glycerol backbone are called triglycerides (Figure 5-3).

---

*Each stock bottle should have its own 5-mL pipet fitted with a Pi-pump.

Lipids provide long-term energy storage in cells and are very diverse. Lipid digestion occurs primarily in the small intestine where bile produced by the liver breaks lipid globules into smaller droplets, and then pancreatic enzymes break large lipid molecules into smaller components for absorption. The lipid components are then transported throughout the body in lymph, the fluid that bathes the tissues.

Substances we think of as fats and oils are examples of lipids. One of the most simple tests for lipids is to determine whether they leave a grease spot on a piece of uncoated paper, such as a grocery sack. A test commonly used to identify fats and oils in microscopic preparations—Sudan IV—can also be used to indicate their presence in a test tube.

Figure 5-3 A triglyceride.

B.1. Uncoated Paper Test (*About 20 min.*)

MATERIALS

Per student group (4):

- china marker
- dropper bottles of
    distilled water (dH$_2$O)
    vegetable oil
- stock bottles* of
    hamburger juice
    onion juice

- colorless nondiet soft drink
    cream
- dropper bottle of Sudan IV
- vortex mixer (optional)
- piece of uncoated paper (grocery bag)

PROCEDURE

1. Place a drop of distilled water and a drop of vegetable oil on a piece of grocery bag. Set aside to dry for 10 minutes.
2. After 10 minutes, describe the appearance of each spot on the paper.

    distilled water _____

    vegetable oil _____

3. Place a drop of each test substance on a labeled spot on the grocery bag piece. Set aside to dry for 10 minutes.
4. After 10 minutes, describe the appearance of each spot on the paper.

    hamburger juice _____

    onion juice _____

    colorless
    nondiet soft drink _____

    cream _____

5. What can you infer about the lipid content of each substance?

    _____

    _____

    _____

B.2. Sudan IV Test (*About 20 min.*)

MATERIALS

Per student group (4):

- china marker
- dropper bottles of
    distilled water (dH$_2$O)
    vegetable oil
- 6 test tubes in test tube rack
- stock bottles* of
    hamburger juice
    onion juice

- colorless nondiet soft drink
    cream
- dropper bottle of Sudan IV
- vortex mixer (optional)

_____

*Each stock bottle should have its own 5-mL pipet fitted with a Pi-pump.

PROCEDURE

1. With a china marker, number the test tubes 1–6.
2. Add 3 mL of dH₂O to each test tube and then 3 mL of each substance indicated in Table 5-3 to the appropriate test tube.
3. Add 9 drops of Sudan IV to each tube, agitate by shaking the tube side, to side and then add 2 mL of dH₂O to each tube.
4. Record your results in Table 5-3.

TABLE 5-3	Test for Lipids with Sudan IV		
Tube	Contents	Observations After Addition of Sudan IV	Conclusion
1	Distilled water		
2	Vegetable oil		
3	Hamburger juice		
4	Onion juice		
5	Soft drink		
6	Cream		

Which test, the uncoated paper test or the Sudan IV test, do you think is most sensitive to small quantities of lipids?

_____

What are the limitations of these tests?

_____

_____

C. Proteins

Proteins are a diverse group of macromolecules with a wide range of functions in the human body. Many are structural components of muscle, bone, hair, fingernails, and toenails, among other tissues. Others are enzymes that speed up cellular reactions that would otherwise take years to occur. Movement of structures within cells (such as occurs during cell division) and of sperm cells is also associated with proteins.

All proteins are chains of **amino acids,** whose general structure is illustrated in Figure 5-4.

Though there are only about 20 amino acids, innumerable kinds of proteins result from different amino acid sequences. A protein begins to form when two or more amino acids are linked together by peptide bonds (bonding between the amino group of one amino acid and the acid group of another), forming a polypeptide chain (Figure 5-5). Subsequently, the chain folds and twists, with links formed between adjacent parts of the chain. Humans cannot synthesize about half of the amino acids; these essential amino acids must be obtained through our foods.

Figure 5-4 General structure of an amino acid. The R group consists of one or more atoms that make each kind of amino acid unique. (After Starr, 2000.)

Protein digestion begins in the stomach lining and continues in the small intestine, where various enzymes break protein molecules first into protein fragments, and then into amino acids, which are absorbed across the small intestine wall. The amino acids are then transported throughout the body in the blood.

Several tests are used for proteins, including Biuret reagent, which indicates the presence of peptide bonds. The greater the number of peptide bonds, the more intense the color reaction with Biuret.

(a) The first two amino acids shown are glycine (gly) and isoleucine (ile). They are at the start of the sequence for one of two polypeptide chains that make up the protein insulin in cattle.

(b) Through a condensation reaction, the isoleucine becomes joined to the glycine by a peptide bond. A water molecule forms as a by-product of the reaction.

(c) A peptide bond forms between the isoleucine and valine (val), another amino acid, and water again forms.

(d) Remember, DNA specifies the order in which the different kinds of amino acids follow one another in a growing polypeptide chain. In this case, glutamate (glu) is the fourth amino acid specified.

(After Starr, 2000.)

Figure 5-5 Peptide bond formation during protein synthesis.

C.1. Biuret Test for Proteins with Biuret Reagent (About 15 min.)

MATERIALS

Per student group (4):

- china marker
- 5 test tubes in test tube rack
- stock bottles* of
  Biuret reagent
  distilled water (dH₂O)

- starch solution
- egg albumin
- glucose solution
- colorless soft drink
- vortex mixer (optional)

PROCEDURE

1. Using the china marker, number the test tubes 1 through 5.
2. Pipet 1 mL of the correct stock solutions into the test tubes as described in Table 5-4.
3. Add 10 drops of Biuret reagent to each test tube and agitate the mixture by shaking the tubes from side to side or with a vortex mixer, if available.
4. Wait 2 minutes and then record the color of the mixture in Table 5-4, in the column "Color Reaction." Also enter your conclusion about the presence of protein in the substance.

D. Testing Unknown Food Substances (About 30 min.)

Your instructor will provide you with several samples of unidentified food substances.

PROCEDURE

1. Following the previous procedures, perform tests for carbohydrates (Benedict's test and Lugol's solution test), lipids (uncoated paper and Sudan IV tests), and proteins (Biuret reagent) on each item.
2. Record your test results (+ or – for each test) in Table 5-5.

---

*Each stock bottle should have its own 2- or 5-mL pipet fitted with a Pi-pump.

TABLE 5-4 Test for Protein with Biuret Reagent

Tube	Contents	Color Reaction	Conclusion
1	Distilled water		
2	Starch		
3	Egg albumin		
4	Glucose		
5	Soft drink		

TABLE 5-5 Tests for Unknown Food Substances

Unknown Sample Designation	Tests for Carbohydrates		Tests for Lipids		Test for Proteins
	Benedict's Test	Lugol's Test	Uncoated Paper Test	Sudan IV	Biuret Test

Note: After completing all experiments, take your dirty glassware to the sink and wash it following the directions given in *"Instructions for Washing Laboratory Glassware,"* page x. Invert the test tubes in the test tube rack so they drain. Tidy up your work area, making certain all equipment used in this exercise is there for the next class.

5.2 The Food Pyramid and Diet Analysis

The foods we eat are usually complex mixtures of various macromolecules, vitamins, and minerals that supply energy and raw materials to the body. However, food must be digested before most nutrients are available within cells. Within the digestive system, macromolecules are hydrolyzed to smaller components (proteins broken down to amino acids, for example). These smaller molecules are absorbed across the intestinal wall, transported throughout the body, and used to build and power cells. We truly *are* what we eat.

The U.S. Department of Agriculture issued its "MyPyramid" food guide in 2005 to provide daily dietary guidelines for average people of good health. Several nutrition recommendations underlie MyPyramid: moderation in portion sizes (many American portions are 2 to 3 times larger than recommended); balance among food groups to ensure that all key nutrients are included; and emphasis on daily exercise for a multitude of health benefits.

The major food groups are the grains, vegetables, fruits, dairy and soy, meat and beans, and vegetable oils. There is also an allotment of "discretionary calories" for each person. Why is it important to include each of these in our diets? What do we gain from each type of food?

Grains are high in the complex carbohydrates (starches and cellulose) that provide ready energy sources. The USDA recommends that you "make half your grains whole," meaning that *at least* half your grain intake should be whole grains, which supply important vitamins and minerals, plus the fiber needed for a healthy digestive system. Whole grains include oatmeal, brown rice, and foods whose first ingredients include the words *whole grain* or *whole wheat*.

Vegetables and **fruits** are especially important sources of the vitamins and minerals needed for a healthy diet, as well as complex carbohydrates and **phytochemicals**, a catchall term for a diverse group of molecules whose benefits we are just beginning to understand. Diets that include plenty of vegetables and fruits help prevent a variety of illnesses, including heart disease, stroke, and certain types of cancer. To meet your requirements for these important foods, mix it up. Eat more vegetables and fruits of every color and variety, especially the vegetables that provide high volume and high nutritional value with low calorie impact (unless they're deep-fried).

Low-fat **dairy** and **soy** products are important sources of calcium and provide significant amounts of proteins. Protein-rich, vitamin-D-fortified dairy and soy foods, along with weight-bearing exercise, build and maintain strong bones.

Smaller quantities are recommended of the "meat and bean" group, which includes poultry, fish, and nuts. These protein-rich foods supply essential amino acids, vitamins, and minerals, and also help maintain the "full" feeling between meals. Choose beans, fish, and lean meats and poultry, along with lower quantities of calorie-rich nuts, rather than fatty or deep-fried choices with unhealthy lipid levels.

Vegetable oils have been promoted to their own food group in MyPyramid, and include monounsaturated vegetable oils (olive oil and canola oil, for example) and polyunsaturated oils (corn oil, soybean oil). These oils are considered healthy in moderation, unlike the solid saturated fats (sour cream, butter, palm oil) and especially the harmful trans fats (partially hydrogenated vegetable oils) that are found in many processed and restaurant foods. Aim for zero trans fats in your diet.

Discretionary calories can be used to eat more foods from any food group or to eat higher-calorie forms of a food or beverage with added sugars or fats. Such foods are high in calorie-dense lipids and the simple sugars that are the "lighter fluid" (quickly used energy source) of metabolism. While some lipids are essential nutrients, other food groups on the pyramid provide those lipids in abundance. Foods that provide abundant fats and simple sugars usually contain few other nutrients and so are not recommended dietary components.

The dietary guidelines of MyPyramid vary depending upon your gender and activity level, with more calories of food energy needed to power your cells as your activity level increases. Use Table 5-6 to determine your recommended average daily calorie allowance.

TABLE 5-6 Approximate Daily Calorie Requirements

FEMALES	Sedentary (less than 30 min. moderate activity daily)	Moderate (30 to 60 min. moderate activity daily)	Active (more than 60 min. moderate activity daily)
Ages 16 to 18	1800	2000	2400
Ages 19 to 30	2000	2200	2400
Ages 31 to 50	1800	2000	2200
MALES			
Ages 16 to 18	2400	2800	3200
Ages 19 to 30	2400	2800	3000
Ages 31 to 50	2200	2600	3000

Use Table 5-7 to find out recommendations for consumption of each food group for your calorie level.

Follow the MyPyramid guidelines and eat a variety of foods to enjoy a healthy diet that provides balanced nutrients without excess calories.

A. Food Diary

In this activity you will analyze *your* diet, so that you can see in which areas you maintain good nutrition, and which areas need improvement.

PROCEDURE (to be completed before class, about 15 minutes per day)

For 2 days during the week preceding this activity, keep a complete diary of *every* food and drink item you consume other than water, unsweetened coffee or tea, or other zero-calorie beverages. In Table 5-8, record what you eat and drink, and how much (the portion size: ounces, cups, teaspoons, and so on). Enter this data in the first two columns. Be as honest, specific, and descriptive as you can. Also keep track separately of which items of processed foods contain trans fats (this information will be found on the food label). Do this for *each* meal and snack.

TABLE 5-7 Recommended Daily Food Group Intakes

Calorie level	1800	2000	2200	2400	2600	2800	3000	3200
Grains	6 oz	6 oz	7 oz	8 oz	9 oz	10 oz	10 oz	10 oz
Vegetables	2 cups (c)	2½ c	3 c	3 c	3½ c	3½ c	4 c	4 c
Fruits	1½ c	2 c	2 c	2 c	2 c	2½ c	2½ c	2½ c
Dairy & Soy	3 c	3 c	3 c	3 c	3 c	3 c	3 c	3 c
Meat & Beans	5 oz	5½ oz	6 oz	6½ oz	6½ oz	7 oz	7 oz	7 oz
Vegetable Oils	5 tsp	6 tsp	6 tsp	7 tsp	8 tsp	8 tsp	10 tsp	11 tsp
Discretionary calories*	195	267	290	362	410	426	512	650

*Discretionary calories are those "extra" calories, usually from fats and sugars, that remain when all the other food group portions and nutrients are consumed.

Eat your usual diet. Don't change your eating habits for this exercise.

It's often difficult to determine portion sizes. To do this accurately, record the information on food product labels regarding serving size and calorie content of each item whenever possible. You also may want to use a measuring cup for this activity. For nonlabeled foods, use the following guidelines:

Portion	Approximate Size of Item
1 ounce	one slice processed cheese; two dice
3 ounces meat	one deck of playing cards or computer mouse
½ cup	one tennis ball or one ice cream scoop
1 serving fruit	one baseball (*not* the larger softball)
1 cup	volume of a woman's fist
1 teaspoon	top half of thumb
1 ounce grains	½ cup oatmeal or rice or 1 cup cereal flakes or ½ English muffin or 1 slice commercial bread

TABLE 5-8 Food Diary

Food or Beverage Item	Total Portion Size	Food Group Servings in Each Food Item						
		Grains (ounces)	Vegetables (cups)	Fruits (cups)	Dairy & Soy (cups)	Meat & Beans (ounces)	Oils (teaspoons)	Calories
2-day total:								
2-day average:								

MATERIALS

Per student group (4):

- food diary data
- diet analysis books and/or computers with diet analysis software
- colored paper squares
- glue or tape

PROCEDURE

1. Complete the food diary table (Table 5-8) in class if necessary, listing everything you've ingested, including both the food group and the number of servings. Then determine how each food item is allocated as servings of the various MyPyramid food groups: grains, vegetables, fruits, dairy and soy, meat and bean, and vegetable oils. You can find portion information for common foods in online sources and/or the books provided in your classroom.
2. Determine and record the calorie content of each item using the resources provided in class.
3. Average the food group servings and calorie content over the 2 days of data collection, and use the averaged data for the rest of this activity.
4. Construct a food pyramid to visualize the MyPyramid recommendations for your gender and activity level. Use the colored paper blocks, with each block corresponding to one serving unit (ounce, cup, or teaspoon, depending on the food group involved). Glue or tape the pyramid to the bottom of page 67 in the following order, from bottom up: orange = grain group servings (ounces); blue = vegetable group servings (cups); green = fruit group servings (cups); yellow = dairy and soy group servings (cups); brown = meat and bean group servings (ounces); red = vegetable oil servings (teaspoons); and purple = discretionary calories (100 calories per block).
5. Now construct your **personal food pyramid** in the same way on the next page, using 2-day average data from your food diary.
6. Answer the following questions AFTER you have completed your 2-day food diary and pyramids:
   (a) What is your typical level of physical activity (sedentary, moderate, active)? _____
   (b) What is your approximate daily calorie requirement? _____
   (c) How does your caloric intake compare with the recommendations for your gender and activity level?

   _____

   _____

   _____

   _____

   (d) What food groups are you eating too much of? What specific kinds of nutrient molecules are you thus overconsuming? What are the potential consequences of this excess for your health?

   _____

   _____

   _____

   _____

   (e) What food groups are you not eating enough of? What kinds of specific nutrient molecules are thus underrepresented in your diet? What are the potential consequences of this deficiency for your health?

   _____

   _____

   _____

   _____

   (f) What proportion of your grain servings included whole grains? _____
   How many different *kinds* of vegetables and fruits did you consume? _____
   How many food items contained saturated or trans fats? _____
   (g) Given all the above information, describe two *reasonable* changes you could make to improve your diet and your health.

   _____

   _____

   _____

   _____

_____ 1. A carbohydrate consists of
(a) amino acid units
(b) one or more sugar units
(c) lipid droplets
(d) glycerol

_____ 2. A protein is made up of
(a) amino acid units
(b) one or more sugar units
(c) lipid droplets
(d) Biuret solution

_____ 3. Benedict's solution is commonly used
to test for
(a) proteins
(b) certain carbohydrates
(c) nucleic acids
(d) lipids

_____ 4. Glycogen is
(a) a polysaccharide
(b) a storage carbohydrate
(c) found in human tissues
(d) all of the above

_____ 5. To test for starch, one would use
(a) Benedict's solution
(b) uncoated paper
(c) Sudan IV
(d) Lugol's solution

_____ 6. Rich sources of stored energy that are
dissolvable in organic solvents are
(a) carbohydrates
(b) proteins
(c) glucose
(d) lipids

_____ 7. Rubbing a substance on uncoated paper
should reveal if it is a
(a) lipid
(b) carbohydrate
(c) protein
(d) sugar

_____ 8. Proteins consist of
(a) monosaccharides linked in chains
(b) amino acid units
(c) polysaccharide units
(d) condensed fatty acids

_____ 9. Biuret reagent will indicate the presence of
(a) peptide bonds
(b) proteins
(c) amino acids units linked together
(d) all of the above

_____ 10. The largest number of food servings in
your daily diet should be from
(a) meats and beans
(b) dairy products
(c) vegetables and fruits
(d) vegetable oils

EXERCISE 5

Macromolecules and You: Food and Diet Analysis

POST-LAB QUESTIONS

A.1. Test for Sugars Using Benedict's Solution

1. Let's suppose you are teaching science in a part of the world without ready access to a doctor and you're worried that you may have developed diabetes. (Diabetics are unable to regulate blood glucose levels, and glucose accumulates in blood and urine.) What could you do to gain an indication of whether or not you have diabetes?

2. The test tubes in the photograph contain Benedict's solution and two unknown substances that have been heated. What do the results indicate?

(Photo by J. W. Perry.)

3. How could you verify that a soft-drink can contains diet soda rather than soda sweetened with fructose?

A.2. Test for Starch Using Lugol's Solution

4. Observe the photomicrograph accompanying this question. This section of a potato tuber has been stained with Lugol's iodine solution. When you eat french fries, the potato material is broken down in your small intestine into what small subunits?

(Photo by J. W. Perry.)

B.2. Sudan IV Test

5. The test tube in the photograph contains water at the bottom and another substance that has been stained with Sudan IV at the top. What is the macromolecular composition of this stained substance?

(Photo by J. W. Perry)

6. You are given a sample of an unknown food. Describe how you would test it for the presence of lipids.

7. You wish to test the same unknown food for the presence of sugars. Describe how you would do so.

Food for Thought

8. What is the purpose of the distilled water sample in each of the chemical tests in this exercise?

9. Many health food stores carry enzyme preparations that are intended to be ingested orally (by mouth) to supplement existing enzymes in various organs like the liver, heart, and muscle. Explain why these preparations are unlikely to be effective as advertised.

10. A young child grows rapidly, with high levels of cell division and high energy requirements. If you were planning the child's diet, which food groups would you emphasize, and why? Which food groups would you deemphasize, and why?

Structure and Function of Living Cells

OBJECTIVES

After completing this exercise, you will be able to

1. define *cell, cell theory, prokaryotic, eukaryotic, nucleus, cytomembrane system, organelle, multinucleate, cytoplasmic streaming, sol, gel, envelope;*

2. list the structural features shared by all cells;

3. describe the similarities and differences between prokaryotic and eukaryotic cells;

4. identify the cell parts described in this exercise;

5. state the function for each cell part;

6. distinguish between plant and animal cells;

7. recognize the structures presented in **boldface** in the procedure sections.

INTRODUCTION

Structurally and functionally, all life has one common feature: All living organisms are composed of **cells.** The development of this concept began with Robert Hooke's seventeenth-century observation that slices of cork were made up of small units. He called these units "cells" because their structure reminded him of the small cubicles that monks lived in. Over the next 100 years, the **cell theory** emerged. This theory has three principles: (1) All organisms are composed of one or more cells; (2) the cell is the basic *living* unit of organization; and (3) all cells arise from preexisting cells.

Although cells vary in organization, size, and function, all share three structural features: (1) All possess a **plasma membrane** defining the boundary of the living material; (2) all contain a region of **DNA** (deoxyribonucleic acid), which stores genetic information; and (3) all contain **cytoplasm,** everything inside the plasma membrane that is not part of the DNA region.

With respect to internal organization, there are two basic types of cells, **prokaryotic** and **eukaryotic.** Study Table 6-1, comparing the more important differences between prokaryotic and eukaryotic cells. The Greek word *karyon* means "kernel," referring to the nucleus. Thus, *prokaryotic* means "before a nucleus," while *eukaryotic* indicates the presence of a "true nucleus." Prokaryotic cells typical of bacteria, cyanobacteria, and archaea are believed to be similar to the first cells, which arose on Earth 3.5 billion years ago. Eukaryotic cells, such as those that comprise the bodies of protists, fungi, plants, and animals, probably evolved from prokaryotes.

This exercise will familiarize you with the basics of cell structure and the function of prokaryotes (prokaryotic cells) and eukaryotes (eukaryotic cells).

6.1 Prokaryotic Cells *(About 20 min.)*

MATERIALS

Per student:

- dissecting needle
- compound microscope
- microscope slide
- coverslip

Per student pair:

- distilled water (dH$_2$O) in dropping bottle

Per student group (table):

- culture of a cyanobacterium (either *Anabaena* or *Oscillatoria*)

Per lab room:

- 3 bacterium-containing nutrient agar plates (demonstration)
- 3 demonstration slides of bacteria (coccus, bacillus, spirillum)

TABLE 6-1 Comparison of Prokaryotic and Eukaryotic Cells

Characteristic	Cell Type	
	Prokaryotic	**Eukaryotic**
Genetic material	Located within cytoplasm, not bounded by a special membrane Consists of a single molecule of DNA	Located in **nucleus,** a double membrane-bounded compartment within the cytoplasm Numerous molecules of DNA combined with protien Organized into chromosomes
Cytoplasmic structures	Small ribosomes Photosynthetic membranes arising from the plasma membrane (in some representatives only)	Large ribosomes **Cytomembrane system,** a system of connected membrane structures **Organelles,** membrane-bounded compartments specialized to perform specific functions
Kingdoms represented	Bacteria Archaea	Protista Fungi Plantae Animalia

PROCEDURE

1. Observe the culture plate with bacteria growing on the surface of a nutrient medium. Can you see the individual cells with your naked eye?

   _____

2. Observe the microscopic preparations of bacteria on *demonstration* next to the culture plate. The three slides represent the three different shapes of bacteria. Which objective lenses are being used to view the bacteria?

   _____

Can you discern any detail within the cytoplasm?

_____

   In the space provided in Figure 6-1, sketch what you see through the microscope. Record the magnification you are using in the blank provided in the figure caption. Then record the approximate size of the bacterial cells. (Return to page 34 of Exercise 3 if you've forgotten how to estimate the size of an object being viewed through a microscope.)

3. Study Figure 6-2, a three-dimensional representation of a bacterial cell. Now examine the electron micrograph of the bacterium *Escherichia coli* (Figure 6-3). Locate the **cell wall,** a structure chemically distinct from the wall of plant cells but serving the same primary function to contain and protect the cell's contents.

4. Find the **plasma membrane,** which is lying flat against the internal surface of the cell wall and is difficult to distinguish.

5. Look for two components of the **cytoplasm: ribosomes,** electron-dense particles (they appear black) that give the cytoplasm its granular appearance, and a relatively electron-transparent region (appears light) containing fine threads of DNA called the **nucleoid.**

coccus   bacillus   spirillum

Figure 6-1 Drawing of several bacterial cells (_____×). Approximate size = _____ μm.

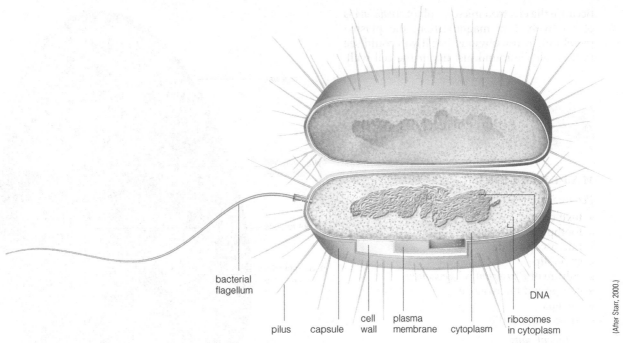

(After Starr, 2000.)

Figure 6-2 Three-dimensional representation of a bacterial cell as seen with the electron microscope.

bacterial flagellum

pilus   capsule   cell wall   plasma membrane   cytoplasm   ribosomes in cytoplasm   DNA

Another type of prokaryotic cell is exemplified by cyanobacteria, such as *Oscillatoria* and *Anabaena*. Cyanobacteria (sometimes called blue-green algae) are commonly found in water and damp soils. They obtain their nutrition by converting the sun's energy through photosynthesis.

(Photo courtesy of G. Cohen-Bazire.)

cell wall

cytoplasm with ribosomes

DNA region

plasma membrane

Figure 6-3 Electron micrograph of the bacterium *Escherichia coli* (28,300×).

6. With a dissecting needle, remove a few filaments from the cyanobacterial culture, placing them in a drop of water on a clean microscope slide.

7. Place a coverslip over the material and examine it first with the low-power objective and then using the high-dry objective (or oil-immersion objective, if your microscope is so equipped).

8. In the space provided in Figure 6-4, sketch the cells you see at high power. Estimate the size of a *single* cyanobacterial cell and record the magnification you used to make your drawing.

9. Now examine the electron micrograph of *Anabaena* (Figure 6-5), which identifies the **cell wall, cytoplasm,** and **ribosomes.** The cyanobacteria also possess membranes that function in photosynthesis. Identify these **photosynthetic membranes,** which look like tiny threads within the cytoplasm.

10. Look at the captions for Figures 6-3 and 6-5. Judging by the magnification of each electron micrograph, which cell is larger, the bacterium *E. coli* or the cyanobacterium *Anabaena*?

_____

_____

_____

Figure 6-4 Drawing of several prokaryotic cells of a cyanobacterium (_____×). Approximate size = _____ μm.

Because the electron micrograph of *Anabaena* is of relatively low magnification, the plasma membrane is not obvious, but if you could see it, it would be found just under the cell wall.

Eukaryotic Cells
(About 75 min.)

MATERIALS

Per student:

- textbook
- toothpick
- microscope slide
- coverslip
- culture of *Physarum polycephalum*
- compound microscope
- forceps
- dissecting needle

Per student pair:

- methylene blue in dropping bottle
- distilled water (dH$_2$O) in dropping bottle

Per student group (table):

- *Elodea* in water-containing culture dish
- onion bulb
- tissue paper

Per lab room:

- model of animal cell
- model of plant cell

(Photo courtesy R. D. Warmbrodt.)

Figure 6-5 Electron micrograph of *Anabaena* (11,600×).

Labels: cell wall; cytoplasm with ribosomes; DNA regions; photosynthetic membrane

A. Protist Cells as Observed with the Light Microscope

The slime mold *Physarum polycephalum* is in the Kingdom Protista. *Physarum* is a unicellular organism, so it contains all the metabolic machinery for independent existence.

PROCEDURE

1. Place a plain microscope slide on the stage of your compound microscope. This will serve as a platform on which you can place a culture dish.
2. Now obtain a petri dish culture of *Physarum,* remove the lid, and place it on the platform. Observe initially with the low-power objective and then with the medium-power objective. Place a coverslip over part of the organism before rotating the high-dry objective into place. (This prevents the agar from getting on the lens.)

Physarum is **multinucleate,** meaning that more than one nucleus occurs within the cytoplasm. Unfortunately, the nuclei are tiny; you won't be able to distinguish them from other granules in the cytoplasm.

3. Locate the **plasma membrane,** which is the outer boundary of the cytoplasm. Once again, the resolving power of your microscope is not sufficient to allow you to actually view the membrane.
4. Watch the cytoplasm of the organism move. This intracellular motion is known as **cytoplasmic streaming.** Although not visible with the light microscope without using special techniques, contractile proteins called **microfilaments** are believed responsible for cytoplasmic streaming.
5. Note that the outer portion of the cytoplasm appears solid; this is the **gel** state of the cytoplasm. Notice that the granules closer to the interior are in motion within a fluid; this portion of the cytoplasm is in the **sol** state. Movement of the organism occurs as the sol-state cytoplasm at the advancing tip pushes against the plasma membrane, causing the region to swell outward. The sol-state cytoplasm flows into the region, converting to the gel state along the margins.
6. In Figure 6-6, sketch the portion of *Physarum* that you have been observing and label it.

B. Experiment: Cytoplasmic Streaming (About 25 min.)

As you might predict, temperature affects many cellular processes. You may have observed that snakes and insects, being ectotherms (animals that gain heat from the environment and unlike humans, not primarily from metabolic activities), in nature are relatively sluggish during cold weather. Is the same true for other organisms, like the slime mold?

This simple experiment addresses the hypothesis that *cold slows cytoplasmic streaming in Physarum polycephalum*. Before starting this experiment, you may wish to review the discussion in Exercise 1, "The Scientific Method."

MATERIALS

Per experimental group:

- culture of *Physarum polycephalum*
- compound microscope
- container with ice *or* refrigerator
- timer *or* watch with second hand
- Celsius thermometer

Figure 6-6 Drawing of a portion of *Physarum* (_____×).

PROCEDURE

1. Place the *Physarum* culture on the stage of your compound microscope as described in Section A.
2. Time the duration of cytoplasmic streaming in one direction and then in the other direction. Do this for five cycles of back-and-forth motion. Calculate the average duration of flow in either direction. Record the temperature and your observations in Table 6-2.
3. Remove your culture from the microscope's stage, replace the cover, and place it and the thermometer in a refrigerator or atop ice for 15 minutes.
4. While you are waiting, in Table 6-2 write a prediction for the effect on the duration of cytoplasmic streaming by reducing the temperature of the culture of *Physarum polycephalum*.
5. After 15 minutes have elapsed, remove the culture from the cold treatment, record the temperature of the experimental treatment, and repeat the observations in step 2.
6. Record your observations and make a conclusion in Table 6-2, accepting or rejecting the hypothesis.

TABLE 6-2 Effect of Temperature on Cytoplasmic Streaming

Prediction:		
Temperature (°C)	**Time**	**Observations and Duration of Directional Flow (sec.)**

A logical question to ask at this time is *why* temperature has the effect you observed. If you perform Exercise 8, "Enzymes: Catalysts of Life," you may be able to make an educated guess (another hypothesis).

C. Animal Cells Observed with the Light Microscope

PROCEDURE

1. *Human cheek cells.* Using the broad end of a clean toothpick, gently scrape the inside of your cheek. Stir the scrapings into a drop of distilled water on a clean microscope slide and add a coverslip. Dispose of used toothpicks in the jar containing alcohol.
2. Because the cells are almost transparent, decrease the amount of light entering the objective lens to increase the contrast. (See Exercise 3, page 33.) Find the cells using the low-power objective of your microscope; then switch to the high-dry objective for detailed study.

3. Find the **nucleus,** a centrally located spherical body within the **cytoplasm** of each cell.
4. Now stain your cheek cells with a dilute solution of methylene blue, a dye that stains the nucleus darker than the surrounding cytoplasm. To stain your slide, follow the directions illustrated in Figure 6-7.

Without removing the coverslip, add a drop of the stain to one edge of the coverslip. Then draw the stain under the coverslip by touching a piece of tissue paper to the *opposite* side of the coverslip.

5. In Figure 6-8, sketch the cheek cells, labeling the **cytoplasm, nucleus,** and the location of the **plasma membrane.** (A light microscope cannot resolve the plasma membrane, but the boundary between the cytoplasm and the external medium indicates its location.) Many of the cells will be folded or wrinkled due to their thin, flexible nature. Estimate and record in your sketch the size of the cells. (The method for estimating the size is found in Part I page 34.)

Figure 6-7 Method for staining specimen under coverslips of microscope slide.

Figure 6-8 Drawing of human cheek cells (_____×).
Approximate size = _____μm.
Labels: cytoplasm, nucleus, plasma membrane

D. Animal Cells as Observed with the Electron Microscope

Studies with the electron microscope have yielded a wealth of information on the structure of eukaryotic cells. Structures too small to be seen with the light microscope have been identified. These include many **organelles,** structures in the cytoplasm that have been separated ("compartmentalized") by enclosure in membranes. Examples of organelles are the nucleus, mitochondria, endoplasmic reticulum, and Golgi bodies. Although the cells in each of the six kingdoms have some peculiarities unique to that kingdom, electron microscopy has revealed that all cells are fundamentally similar.

PROCEDURE

1. Study Figure 6-9, a three-dimensional representation of an animal cell.
2. With the aid of Figure 6-9, identify the parts on the model of the animal cell that is on *demonstration.*
3. Figure 6-10 is an electron micrograph (EM) of an animal cell (kingdom Animalia). Study the electron micrograph and, with the aid of Figure 6-9 and any electron micrographs in your textbook, label each structure listed.
4. Pay particular attention to the membranes surrounding the nucleus and mitochondria. Note that these two are each bounded by *two* membranes, which are commonly referred to collectively as an **envelope.**
5. Using your textbook as a reference, list the function for the following cellular components:

   (a) plasma membrane _____

   _____

   (b) cytoplasm _____

   _____

   (c) nucleus (the plural is *nuclei*) _____

   _____

   (d) nuclear envelope _____

   _____

Figure 6-9 Three-dimensional representation of an animal cell as seen with the electron microscope.

In the illustration, the following labels appear:

- nuclear envelope
- nucleolus } NUCLEUS
- DNA + nucleoplasm
- vesicle
- lysosome
- rough ER
- ribosomes (attached to rough ER and free cytoplasm)
- smooth ER
- vesicle
- Golgi body
- pair of centrioles
- components of cytoskeleton { microfilaments, microtubules
- plasma membrane
- mitochondrion

(From Starr, 2000.)

Figure 6-10 Electron micrograph of an animal cell (1600×).
Labels: plasma membrane, cytoplasm, nuclear envelope, nuclear pore, chromatin, rough ER, smooth ER, Golgi body, mitochondrion

nuclear pore within membrane

nucleus

(Photo courtesy W. R. Hargreaves.)

(e) nuclear pores _____

_____

(f) chromatin _____

_____

(g) nucleolus (the plural is *nucleoli*) _____

_____

(h) rough endoplasmic reticulum (RER) _____

_____

(i) smooth endoplasmic reticulum (SER) _____

_____

(j) Golgi body _____

_____

(k) mitochondrion (the plural is *mitochondria*)

_____

E. Plant Cells Seen with the Light Microscope

E.1. Elodea leaf cells

Young leaves at the growing tip of *Elodea* are particularly well suited for studying cell structure because these leaves are only a few cell layers thick.

PROCEDURE

1. With a forceps, remove a single young leaf, mount it on a slide in a drop of distilled water, and cover with a coverslip.
2. Examine the leaf first with the low-power objective. Then concentrate your study on several cells using the high-dry objective. Refer to Figure 6-11.
3. Observe the abundance of green bodies in the cytoplasm. These are the **chloroplasts,** organelles that function in photosynthesis and that are typical of green plants.
4. Locate the numerous dark lines running parallel to the long axis of the leaf. These are the air-containing **intercellular spaces.**
5. Find the **cell wall,** a structure distinguishing plant from animal cells, visible as a clear area surrounding the cytoplasm.
6. After the cells have warmed a bit, notice the **cytoplasmic streaming** taking place. Movement of the chloroplasts along the cell wall is the most obvious visual evidence of cytoplasmic streaming. Microfilaments (much too small to be seen with your light microscope) are responsible for this intracellular motion.
7. Remember that you are looking at a three-dimensional object. In the middle portion of the cell is the large, clear **central vacuole,** which can take up from 50% to 90% of the cell interior. Because the vacuole in *Elodea* is transparent, it cannot be seen with the light microscope.
8. The chloroplasts occur in the cytoplasm surrounding the vacuole, so they will appear to be in different locations, depending on where you focus in the cell. Focus in the upper or lower surface and observe that the chloroplasts appear to be scattered throughout the cell.

chloroplasts (surrounding a nucleus)

cell wall   nucleus   central vacuole

(Photo by J. W. Perry.)

Figure 6-11   *Elodea* cells (400×).

9. Now focus in the center of the cell (by raising or lowering the objective with the fine focus knob), and note that the chloroplasts lie in a thin layer of cytoplasm along the wall.

10. Locate the **nucleus** within the cytoplasm. It will appear as a clear or slightly amber body that is slightly larger than the chloroplasts. (You may need to examine several cells to find a clearly defined nucleus.)

11. Describe the three-dimensional shape of the *Elodea* leaf cell.

_____

_____

12. What are the shapes of the chloroplasts and nucleus? _____

_____

13. Now add a drop of methylene blue stain to make the cell wall more obvious. Add the stain as shown in Figure 6-7.

14. Look for the very, very tiny **mitochondria.** (If you have an oil-immersion lens on your microscope, you should use that lens.)

15. Compare the size of the mitochondria to chloroplasts:

_____

_____

E.2. Onion scale cells

1. Make a wet mount of a colorless scale of an onion bulb, using the technique described in Figure 6-12. The *inner* face of the scale is easiest to remove, as shown in Figure 6-12d.

2. Observe your preparation with your microscope, focusing first with the low-power objective. Continue your study, switching to the medium-power and finally the high-dry objective. Refer to Figure 6-13.

3. Identify the **cell wall** and **cytoplasm.**

4. Find the **nucleus,** a prominent sphere within the cytoplasm.

5. Examine the nucleus more carefully at high magnification. Within it, find one or more nucleoli (the singular is *nucleolus*). Nucleoli are rich in a nucleic acid known as RNA (ribonucleic acid), while the nucleus as a whole is largely DNA (deoxyribonucleic acid), the genetic material.

6. You may see numerous **oil droplets** within the cytoplasm, visible in the form of granulelike bodies. These oil droplets are a form of stored food material. You may be surprised to learn that onion scales are actually leaves! Which cellular components present in *Elodea* leaf cells are absent in onion leaf cells?

_____

7. If you are using the pigmented tissue from a red onion, you should see a purple pigment located in the vacuole. In this case, the cell wall appears as a bright line.

8. In Figure 6-14, sketch and label several cells from onion scale leaves.

a Cut an onion bulb into quarters.

b Remove one of the fleshy "scale" leaves.

c Snapping the "leaf" backward usually produces a ragged piece of epidermis.

d Remove a small piece of epidermis and spread it evenly in a drop of water on a slide.

d Gently lower a coverslip to prevent trapping air bubbles. Examine with your microscope. Add more water to the edge of the coverslip with an eye dropper if the slide begins to dry.

(From Peter Abramoff and Robert G. Thomson, Laboratory Outlines in Biology III. Copyright © 1962, 1963 Peter Abramoff and Robert G. Thomson. Copyright © 1964, 1966, 1972, 1982 W. H. Freeman and Company. Used by permission.)

Figure 6-12 Method for obtaining onion scale cells.

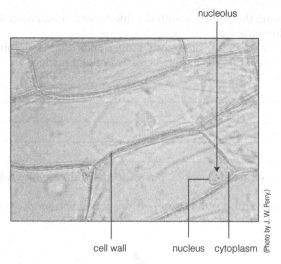

Figure 6-13 Onion bulb leaf cells (67×).
Labels: cell wall, cytoplasm, nucleus, nucleolus, oil droplets

Figure 6-14 Drawing of onion scale cells (_____×).
Labels: cell wall, cytoplasm, nucleus

F. Plant Cells as Seen with the Electron Microscope

The electron microscope has made obvious some of the unique features of plant cells.

PROCEDURE

1. Study Figure 6-15, a three-dimensional representation of a typical plant cell.
2. With the aid of Figure 6-15, identify the structures present on the model of a plant cell that is on *demonstration*.
3. Now examine Figure 6-16, a transmission electron micrograph from a corn leaf. Label all of the structures listed. *Caution: Many plant cells do not have a large central vacuole. This is one of them.* Notice that the chloroplast has an envelope, just as do the nucleus and mitochondria.
4. With the help of Figure 6-15 and any transmission electron micrographs and text in your textbook, list the function of the following structures.

   (a) cell wall _____
   _____

   (b) chloroplast _____
   _____

   (c) vacuole _____
   _____

   (d) vacuolar membrane _____
   _____

   (e) plasma membrane _____
   _____

   (f) cytoplasm _____
   _____

   (g) nucleus _____
   _____

Figure 6-15 Three-dimensional representation of a plant cell as seen with the electron microscope.

Labels in figure:

Golgi body

vesicle

microfilaments (components of cytoskeleton)

mitochondrion

chloroplast

microtubules (components of cytoskeleton)

central vacuole

rough endoplasmic reticulum (rough ER)

ribosomes (attached to rough ER)

ribosomes (free in cytoplasm)

smooth endoplasmic reticulum (smooth ER)

DNA + nucleoplasm

nucleolus — NUCLEUS

nuclear envelope

plasma membrane

cell wall

(From Starr, 2000.)

(h) nuclear envelope _____
_____

(i) nuclear pore _____
_____

(j) chromatin _____
_____

(k) nucleolus _____
_____

(l) rough endoplasmic reticulum (RER) _____
_____

(m) smooth endoplasmic reticulum (SER) _____
_____

(n) Golgi body _____
_____

(o) mitochondrion _____
_____

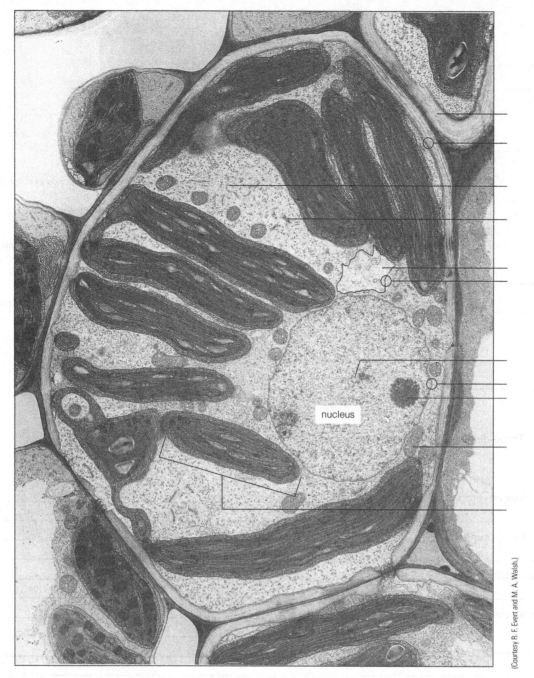

nucleus

Figure 6-16   Electron micrograph of a corn leaf cell (2700×).
Labels: cell wall, chloroplast, vacuole, vacuolar membrane, plasma membrane, nuclear envelope, chromatin, nucleolus, endoplasmic reticulum (ER), Golgi body, mitochondrion

_____ 1. The person who first used the term *cell* was
   (a) Darwin
   (b) Leeuwenhoek
   (c) Hooke
   (d) Watson

_____ 2. All cells contain
   (a) a nucleus, plasma membrane, and cytoplasm
   (b) a cell wall, nucleus, and cytoplasm
   (c) DNA, plasma membrane, and cytoplasm
   (d) mitochondria, plasma membrane, and cytoplasm

_____ 3. Prokaryotic cells *lack*
   (a) DNA
   (b) a true nucleus
   (c) a cell wall
   (d) none of the above

_____ 4. The word *eukaryotic* refers specifically to a cell containing
   (a) photosynthetic membranes
   (b) a true nucleus
   (c) a cell wall
   (d) none of the above

_____ 5. A bacterium is an example of a
   (a) prokaryotic cell
   (b) eukaryotic cell
   (c) plant cell
   (d) all of the above

_____ 6. Methylene blue
   (a) is used to kill cells that are moving too quickly to observe
   (b) renders cells nontoxic
   (c) is a portion of the electromagnetic spectrum used by green plant cells
   (d) is a biological stain used to increase contrast of cellular constituents

_____ 7. Components typical of plant cells but not of animal cells are
   (a) nuclei
   (b) cell walls
   (c) mitochondria
   (d) ribosomes

_____ 8. A central vacuole
   (a) is found only in plant cells
   (b) may take up between 50% and 90% of the cell's interior
   (c) is both of the above
   (d) is none of the above

_____ 9. The intercellular spaces between plant cells
   (a) contain air
   (b) are responsible for cytoplasmic streaming
   (c) are nonexistent
   (d) contain chloroplasts

_____ 10. An envelope
   (a) surrounds the nucleus
   (b) surrounds mitochondria
   (c) consists of two membranes
   (d) does all of the above

EXERCISE 6

Structure and Function of Living Cells

POST-LAB QUESTIONS

6.1 Prokaryotic Cells

1. Did all living cells that you saw in lab contain mitochondria?

2. Below is a high-magnification photomicrograph of an organism you observed in this exercise. Each rectangular box is a single cell. What organelle is absent from each cell that makes it "prokaryotic?"

(750×).

6.2 Eukaryotic Cells

3. Is it possible for a cell to contain more than one nucleus? Explain.

4. When students are asked to distinguish between an animal cell and a plant cell, they typically answer that plant cells contain chloroplasts and animal cells do not. If you were the professor reading that answer, what sort of credit would you give and why?

5. Describe a major distinction between most plant cells and animal cells.

6. Observe the electron micrograph to the right. Is the cell prokaryotic or eukaryotic?

Identify the labeled structures.

A. _____

B. _____

C. _____

(4800×).

7. Look at the photomicrograph to the right, which was taken with a technique that gives a three-dimensional impression. Identify the structures labeled A, B, and C.

A. _____

B. _____

C. _____

(Photo by J. W. Perry.)

8. Is the electron micrograph below a plant or an animal cell?

_____

Identify structures labeled A and B.

A. _____   (750×).

B. _____

9. What are the numerous "wavy lines" within the cell (labeled C)? _____

_____

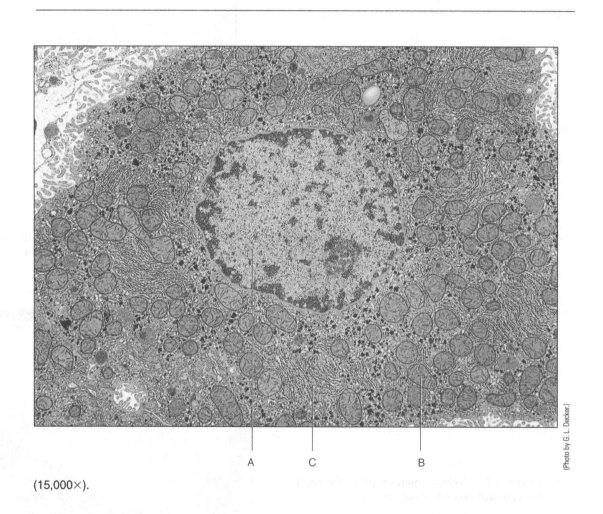

(15,000×).

(Photo by G. L. Decker.)

10. What structure(s) found in plant cells is (are) primarily responsible for cellular support?

11. What structural differences did you observe between prokaryotic and eukaryotic cells?

12. Are the cells in the electron micrograph below prokaryotic or eukaryotic? How do you know?

(Photo by J. J. Cardamone, Jr., University of Pittsburgh/BPS.)

Diffusion, Osmosis, and the Functional Significance of Biological Membranes

OBJECTIVES

After completing this exercise, you will be able to

1. define *solvent, solute, solution, selectively permeable, diffusion, osmosis, concentration gradient, equilibrium, turgid, plasmolyzed, plasmolysis, turgor pressure, tonicity, hypertonic, isotonic, hypotonic;*
2. describe the structure of cellular membranes;
3. distinguish between diffusion and osmosis;
4. determine the effects of concentration and temperature on diffusion;
5. describe the effects of hypertonic, isotonic, and hypotonic solutions on red blood cells and *Elodea* leaf cells.

INTRODUCTION

Water is a great environment. Earthly life is believed to have originated in the water. Without it, life as we know it would cease to exist. Recently, the discovery of water in meteorites originating within our solar system has fueled speculation that life may not be unique to earth.

Living cells are made up of 75–85% water. Virtually all substances entering and leaving cells are dissolved in water, making it the **solvent** most important for life processes. The substances dissolved in water are called **solutes** and include such substances as salts and sugars. The combination of a solvent and dissolved solute is a **solution.** The cytoplasm of living cells contains numerous solutes, like sugars and salts, in solution.

All cells possess membranes composed of a phospholipid bilayer that contains different kinds of embedded and surface proteins. Look at Figure 7-1 to get an idea of the complexity of a cellular membrane.

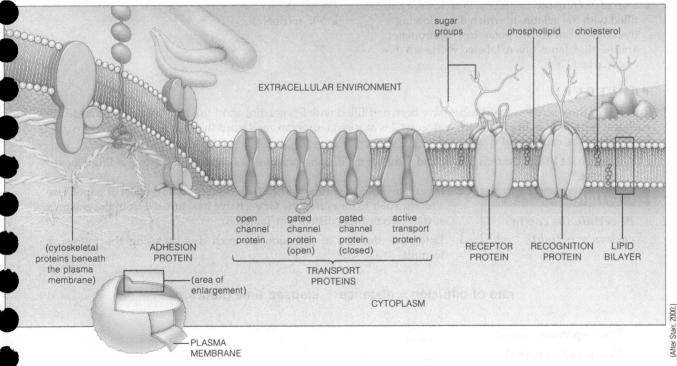

Figure 7-1 Artistic rendering of cutaway view of part of the plasma membrane.

(After Starr, 2000.)

Membranes are boundaries that solutes must cross to reach the cellular site where they will be utilized in the processes of life. These membranes regulate the passage of substances into and out of the cell. They are **selectively permeable,** allowing some substances to move easily while completely excluding others.

The most simple means by which solutes enter the cell is **diffusion,** the movement of solute molecules from a region of high concentration to one of lower concentration. Diffusion occurs without the expenditure of cellular energy. Once inside the cell, solutes move through the cytoplasm by diffusion, sometimes assisted by cytoplasmic streaming.

Water (the solvent) also moves across the membrane. **Osmosis** is the movement of *water* across selectively permeable membranes. Think of osmosis as a special form of diffusion, one occurring from a region of higher *water* concentration to one of lower *water* concentration.

The difference in concentration of like molecules in two regions is called a **concentration gradient.** Diffusion and osmosis take place *down* concentration gradients. Over time, the concentration of solvent and solute molecules becomes equally distributed, the gradient ceasing to exist. At this point, the system is said to be at **equilibrium.**

Molecules are always in motion, even at equilibrium. Thus, solvent and solute molecules continue to move because of randomly colliding molecules. However, at equilibrium there is no *net change* in their concentrations.

This exercise introduces you to the principles of diffusion and osmosis.

Note: If Sections 7.2 and 7.3 are to be done during this lab period, start them before doing any other activity in this exercise.

| 7.1 | **Experiment: Rate of Diffusion of Solutes** (*About 10 min.*) |

Solutes move within a cell's cytoplasm largely because of diffusion. However, the rate of diffusion (the distance diffused in a given amount of time) is affected by such factors as temperature and the size of the solute molecules. In this experiment, you will discover the effects of these two factors in gelatin (the substance of Jell-O®), a substance much like cytoplasm and used to simulate it in this experiment.

MATERIALS

Per student:
- metric ruler

Per student group (table):
- 1 set of 3 screw-cap test tubes, in rack, each half-filled with 5% gelatin, to which the following dyes have been added: potassium dichromate, aniline blue, Janus green; labeled with each dye and marked "5°C"

- 1 set of 3 screw-cap test tubes, in rack, as above but marked "Room Temperature"

Per lab room:
- 5°C refrigerator

PROCEDURE

Two sets of three screw-cap test tubes have been half-filled with 5% gelatin; and 1 mL of a dye has been added to each test tube. Set 1 is in a 5°C refrigerator; set 2 is at room temperature. Record the time at which your instructor tells you the experiment was started: _____

1. Remove set 1 from the refrigerator and compare the distance the dye has diffused in corresponding tubes of each set.

Caution
Be certain the cap to each tube is tight!

2. Invert and hold each tube vertically in front of a white sheet of paper. Use a metric ruler to measure how far each dye has diffused from the gelatin's surface. Record this distance in Table 7-1.

3. Determine the *rate* of diffusion for each dye by using the following formula:

rate of diffusion = distance ÷ elapsed time (hours)

Time experiment ended: _____

Time experiment started: _____

Elapsed time: _____ hours

TABLE 7-1 Effect of Temperature on Diffusion Rates of Various Solutes

Solute (dye)	Set 1 (5°C)		Set 2 (Room Temp.)	
	Distance (mm)	Rate	Distance (mm)	Rate
Potassium dichromate (MW = 294)[a]				
Janus green (MW = 511)				
Aniline blue (MW = 738)				

[a]MW = molecular weight, a reflection of the mass of a substance. To determine MW, add the atomic weights of all elements in a compound.

Which of the solutes diffused the slowest (regardless of temperature)? _____

Which diffused the fastest? _____

What effect did temperature have on the rate of diffusion? _____

Make a conclusion about the diffusion of a solute in a gel, relating the rate of diffusion to the molecular weight of the solute and to temperature.

_____

_____

Note: Return set 1 to the refrigerator.

7.2   Experiment: Osmosis *(About 20 min. for setup)*

Osmosis occurs when different concentrations of water are separated by a selectively permeable membrane. One example of a selectively permeable membrane within a living cell is the plasma membrane. In this experiment, you will learn about osmosis using dialysis membrane, a selectively permeable cellulose sheet that permits the passage of water but obstructs passage of larger molecules. If you examined the membrane with a scanning electron microscope, you would see that it is porous; it thus prevents molecules larger than the pores from passing through the membrane.

MATERIALS

Per student group (4):
- four 15-cm lengths of dialysis tubing, soaking in dH$_2$O
- eight 10-cm pieces of string or waxed dental floss
- ring stand and funnel apparatus (Figure 7-2)
- 25-mL graduated cylinder
- 4 small string tags
- china marker
- four 400-mL beakers

Per student group (table):
- dishpan half-filled with dH$_2$O
- paper toweling
- balance

Per lab room:
- source of dH$_2$O (at each sink)
- 15% and 30% sucrose solutions
- scissors (at each sink)

PROCEDURE

Work in groups of four for this experiment.

1. Obtain four sections of dialysis tubing, each 15 cm long, that have been presoaked in dH$_2$O. Recall that the dialysis tubing is permeable to water molecules but not to sucrose.
2. Fold over one end of each tube and tie it tightly with string or dental floss.
3. Attach a string tag to the tied end of each bag and number them 1–4.

4. Slip the open end of the bag over the stem of a funnel (Figure 7-2). Using a graduated cylinder* to measure volume, fill the bags as follows:

Bag 1. 10 mL of dH$_2$O   Bag 3. 10 mL of 30% sucrose
Bag 2. 10 mL of 15% sucrose   Bag 4. 10 mL of dH$_2$O

5. As each bag is filled, force out excess air by squeezing the bottom end of the tube.
6. Fold the end of the bag and tie it securely with another piece of string or dental floss.
7. Rinse each filled bag in the dishpan containing dH$_2$O; gently blot off the excess water with paper toweling.
8. Weigh each bag to the nearest 0.5 g.
9. Record the weights in the column marked "0 min." in Table 7-2.
10. Number four 400-mL beakers with a china marker.
11. Add 200 mL of dH$_2$O to beakers 1–3.
12. Add 200 mL of 30% sucrose solution to beaker 4.
13. Place bags 1–3 in the correspondingly numbered beakers.
14. Place bag 4 in the beaker containing 30% sucrose.
15. After 15 minutes, remove each bag from its beaker, blot off the excess fluid, and weigh each bag.

Figure 7-2 Method for filling dialysis bags.

16. Record the weight of each bag in Table 7-2.
17. Return the bags to their respective beakers immediately after weighing.
18. Repeat steps 15–17 at 30, 45 and 60 minutes from time zero.

At the end of the experiment, take the bags to the sink, cut them open, pour the contents down the drain, and discard the bags in the wastebasket. Pour the contents of the beakers down the drain and wash them according to the instructions given on page x.

Make a *qualitative* statement about what you have observed. _____

_____

_____

_____

Was the direction of *net* movement of water in bags 2–4 into or out of the bags? _____

_____

_____

Which bag gained the most weight? Why? _____

_____

_____

_____

*Be sure to rinse the cylinder if it has been used to measure sucrose.

TABLE 7-2   Change in Weight as a Consequence of Osmosis

Bag	Bag Contents	Beaker Contents	0 min.	15 min.	30 min.	45 min.	60 min.	Weight Change (g)
					Bag Weight (g)			
1	dH_2O	dH_2O						
2	15% sucrose	dH_2O						
3	30% sucrose	dH_2O						
4	dH_2O	30% sucrose						

7.3 Experiment: Selective Permeability of Membranes *(About 15 min. for setup)*

Dialysis tubing is a selectively permeable material that provides a means to demonstrate the movement of substances through cellular membranes.

MATERIALS

Per student group (4):

- 1 25-cm length of dialysis tubing, soaking in dH_2O
- two 10-cm pieces of string or waxed dental floss
- bottle of 1% soluble starch in 1% sodium sulfate (Na_2SO_4)
- dishpan half-filled with dH_2O
- 400-mL graduated beaker
- ring stand and funnel apparatus (Figure 7-2)
- bottle of 1% albumin in 1% sodium chloride (NaCl)
- 8 test tubes
- test tube rack
- china marker

- 25-mL graduated cylinder
- iodine (I_2KI) solution in dropping bottle
- 2% barium chloride ($BaCl_2$) in dropping bottle
- 2% silver nitrate ($AgNO_3$) in dropping bottle
- Biuret reagent in dropping bottle
- albustix reagent strips (optional)
- scissors

Per lab room:

- series of 4 test tubes in test tube rack demonstrating positive tests for starch, sulfate ion, chloride ion, protein

PROCEDURE

Work in groups of four.

1. Obtain a 25-cm section of dialysis tubing that has been soaked in dH_2O.
2. Fold over one end of the tubing and tie it securely with string or dental floss to form a leakproof bag (Figure 7-2).
3. Slip the open end of the bag over the stem of a funnel and fill the bag approximately half full with 25 mL of a solution of 1% soluble starch in 1% sodium sulfate (Na_2SO_4).
4. Remove the bag from the funnel; fold and tie the open end of the bag.
5. Rinse the tied bag in a dishpan partially filled with dH_2O.
6. Pour 200 mL of a solution of 1% albumin (a protein) in 1% sodium chloride (NaCl) into a 400-mL beaker.
7. Place the bag into the fluid in the beaker.
8. Record the time: _____
9. With a china marker, label eight test tubes, numbering them 1–8.
10. Seventy-five minutes after the start of the experiment, pour 20 mL of the *beaker contents* into a *clean* 25-mL graduated cylinder.
11. Decant (pour out) 5 mL from the graduated cylinder into each of the first four test tubes.

12. Perform the following tests, recording your results in Table 7-3. Your instructor will have a series of test tubes showing positive tests for starch, sulfate and chloride ions, and proteins. You should compare your results with the known positives.

   (a) *Test for starch.* Add several drops of iodine solution (I_2KI) from the dropper bottle to test tube 1. If starch is present, the solution will turn blue-black.

   (b) *Test for sulfate ion.* Add several drops of 2% barium chloride ($BaCl_2$) from the dropper bottle to test tube 2. If sulfate ions (SO^{-4}) are present, a white precipitate of barium sulfate ($BaSO_4$) will form.

   (c) *Test for chloride ion.* Add several drops of 2% silver nitrate ($AgNO_3$) from the dropper bottle to test tube 3. A milky-white precipitate of silver chloride ($AgCl$) indicates the presence of chloride ions (Cl^2).

   (d) *Test for protein.* Add several drops of Biuret reagent from the dropper bottle to test tube 4. If protein is present, the solution will change from blue to pinkish-violet. The more intense the violet hue, the greater the quantity of the protein.

   An alternative method for determining the presence of protein is the use of albustix reagent strips. Presence of protein is indicated by green or blue-green coloration of the paper.

13. Wash the graduated cylinder, using the technique described on page x.
14. Thoroughly rinse the bag in the dishpan of dH_2O.
15. Using scissors, cut the bag open and empty the contents into the 25-mL graduated cylinder.
16. Decant 5-mL samples into each of the four remaining test tubes.
17. Perform the tests for starch, sulfate ions, chloride ions, and protein on tubes 5–8, respectively.
18. Record the results of this series of tests in Table 7-4.

To which substances was the dialysis tubing permeable?

_____

What physical property of the dialysis tubing might explain its differential permeability?

_____

19. Discard contents of test tubes and beaker down sink drain. Wash glassware by using the technique described on page x.
20. Discard dialysis tubing in wastebasket.

TABLE 7-3 Results of Tests for Substances in Beaker[a]		
	At Start of Experiment	**After 75 min.**
Starch	–	
Sulfate ion	–	
Chloride ion	+	
Albumin	+	

[a]Contents of beaker: (+) = presence, (−) = absence.

TABLE 7-4 Results of Tests for Substances in Dialysis Bag[a]		
	At Start of Experiment	**After 75 min.**
Starch	+	
Sulfate ion	+	
Chloride ion	–	
Albumin	–	

[a]Contents of dialysis bag: (+) = presence, (–) = absence.

Plant cells are surrounded by a rigid cell wall, composed primarily of the glucose polymer, cellulose. Recall from Exercise 6 that many plant cells have a large central vacuole surrounded by the vacuolar membrane. The vacuolar membrane is selectively permeable. Normally, the solute concentration within the cell's central vacuole is greater than that of the external environment. Consequently, water moves into the cell, creating **turgor pressure,** which presses the cytoplasm against the cell wall. Such cells are said to be **turgid.** Many nonwoody plants (like beans and peas) rely on turgor pressure to maintain their rigidity and erect stance.

In this experiment, you will discover the effect of external solute concentration on the structure of plant cells.

MATERIALS

Per student:

- forceps
- 2 microscope slides
- 2 coverslips
- compound microscope

Per student group (table):

- *Elodea* in tap water
- 2 dropping bottles of dH_2O
- 2 dropping bottles of 20% sodium chloride (NaCl)

PROCEDURE

1. With a forceps, remove two young leaves from the tip of an *Elodea* plant.
2. Mount one leaf in a drop of distilled water on a microscope slide and the other in 20% NaCl solution on a second microscope slide.
3. Place coverslips over both leaves.
4. Observe the leaf in distilled water with the compound microscope. Focus first with the medium-power objective and then switch to the high-dry objective.
5. Label the photomicrograph of turgid cells (Figure 7-3).
6. Now observe the leaf mounted in 20% NaCl solution. After several minutes, the cell will have lost water, causing it to become **plasmolyzed.** (This process is called **plasmolysis.**) Label the plasmolyzed cells shown in Figure 7-4.

Figure 7-3   Turgid *Elodea* cells (400×). (Photo by J. W. Perry.)
Labels: cell wall, chloroplasts in cytoplasm, central vacuole

nucleus

Tonicity describes one solution's solute concentration compared to that of another solution. The solution containing the lower concentration of solute molecules than another is **hypotonic** *relative to the second solution.* Solutions containing equal concentrations of solute are **isotonic** to each other, while one containing a greater concentration of solute relative to a second one is **hypertonic.**

Were the contents of the vacuole in the *Elodea* leaf in distilled water hypotonic, isotonic, or hypertonic compared to the dH_2O? _____

Was the 20% NaCl solution hypertonic, isotonic, or hypotonic relative to the cytoplasm? _____

_____

If a hypotonic and a hypertonic solution are separated by a selectively permeable membrane, in which direction will the water move? _____

Figure 7-4 Plasmolyzed *Elodea* cells (400×). (Photo by J. W. Perry.) **Labels:** cell wall, chloroplasts in cytoplasm, plasma membrane, space (between cell wall and plasma membrane)

Name two selectively permeable membranes that are present within the *Elodea* cells and that were involved in the plasmolysis process.

1. _____

2. _____

7.5   **Experiment: Osmotic Changes in Red Blood Cells** *(About 15 min.)*

Animal cells lack the rigid cell wall of a plant. The external boundary of an animal cell is the selectively permeable plasma membrane. Consequently, an animal cell increases in size as water enters the cell. However, since the plasma membrane is relatively fragile, it ruptures when too much water enters the cell. This is because of excessive pressure pushing out against the membrane. Conversely, if water moves out of the cell, it becomes plasmolyzed and looks spiny.

In this experiment, you will use red blood cells to discover the effects of osmosis in animal cells.

MATERIALS

Per student:
- compound microscope

Per student group (4):
- 3 clean screw-cap test tubes
- test tube rack
- metric ruler
- china marker
- bottle of 0.9% sodium chloride (NaCl)
- bottle of 10% NaCl
- bottle of dH$_2$O

- 3 disposable plastic pipets
- 3 clean microscope slides
- 3 coverslips

Per student group (table):
- bottle of sheep blood (in ice bath)

Per lab room:
- source of dH$_2$O

PROCEDURE

Work in groups of four for this experiment, but do the microscopic observations individually.

1. Observe the scanning electron micrographs in Figure 7-5.

Figure 7-5a illustrates the normal appearance of red blood cells. They are biconcave disks; that is, they are circular in outline with a depression in the center of both surfaces. Cells in an isotonic solution will appear like these blood cells.

Figure 7-5b shows cells that have been plasmolyzed. (In the case of red blood cells, plasmolysis is given a special term, *crenation;* the blood cell is said to be *crenate*.)

Figure 7-5c represents cells that have taken in water but have not yet burst. (Burst red blood cells are said to be *hemolyzed,* and of course they can't be seen.) Note their swollen, spherical appearance.

2. Obtain three clean screw-cap test tubes.
3. Lay test tubes 1 and 2 against a metric ruler and mark lines indicating 5 cm *from the bottom of each tube.*
4. Fill each tube as follows:
   Tube 1: 5 cm of 0.9% sodium chloride (NaCl)
           5 drops of sheep blood
   Tube 2: 5 cm of 10% NaCl
           5 drops of sheep blood
5. Lay test tube 3 against a metric ruler and mark lines indicating 0.5 cm and 5 cm *from the bottom of the tube.*
6. Fill tube 3 to the 0.5-cm mark with 0.9% NaCl, and to the 5-cm mark with dH_2O. Then add 5 drops of sheep blood. Enter the contents of each tube in the appropriate column of Table 7-5.

a Red blood cells in an isotonic solution ("normal")

b Red blood cells in a hypertonic solution ("crenate")

c Red blood cells in a hypotonic solution

Figure 7-5 Scanning electron micrographs of red blood cells. (Photos from M. Sheetz, R. Painter, and S. Singer. Reproduced from *The Journal of Cell Biology,* 1976, 70:193, by copyright permission of the Rockefeller University Press and M. Sheetz.)

7. Replace the caps and mix the contents of each tube by inverting several times (Figure 7-6a).
8. Hold each tube flat against the printed page of your lab manual (Figure 7-6b). *Only if the blood cells are hemolyzed should you be able to read the print.*
9. In Table 7-5, record your observations in the column "Print Visible?"
10. Number three clean microscope slides.
11. With three *separate* disposable pipets, remove a small amount of blood from each of the three tubes. Place 1 drop of blood from tube 1 on slide 1, 1 drop from tube 2 on slide 2, and 1 drop from tube 3 on slide 3.
12. Cover each drop of blood with a coverslip.
13. Observe the three slides with your compound microscope, focusing first with the medium-power objective and finally with the high-dry objective. (Hemolyzed cells are virtually unrecognizable; all that remains are membranous "ghosts," which are difficult to see with the microscope.)
14. In Figure 7-7, sketch the cells from each tube. Label the sketches, indicating whether the cells are normal, plasmolyzed (crenate), or hemolyzed.

a

b

(After Abramoff and Thomson, 1982.)

Figure 7-6 Method for studying effects of different solute concentrations on red blood cells.

15. Record the microscopic appearance in Table 7-5.
16. Record the relative tonicity of the sodium chloride solutions you added to the test tubes in Table 7-5.

Why do red blood cells burst when put in a hypotonic solution whereas *Elodea* leaf cells do not?

_____

_____

_____

Figure 7-7 Microscopic appearance of red blood cells in different solute concentrations (_____×).
Labels: normal, plasmolyzed (crenate), hemolyzed

After completing all experiments, take your dirty glassware to the sink and wash it as directed on page x. Invert the test tubes in the test tube rack so they drain. Reorganize your work area, making certain all materials used in this exercise are present for the next class.

TABLE 7-5 Effect of Salt Solutions on Red Blood Cells

Tube	Contents	Print Visible?	Microscopic Appearance of Cells	Tonicity of External Solutiona
1				
2				
3				

aWith respect to that inside the red blood cell at the start of the experiment.

7.6 Experiment: Determining the Concentration of Solutes in Cells
(About 20 min. for setup)

If you've done the previous experiments of this exercise, you now know that water flows into or out of cells in response to the concentration of solutes within the cells. But you might logically ask at this point how much solute is present in a typical cell. While the answer varies from cell to cell, a simple experiment enables you to determine the osmotic concentration in the cells of a potato tuber.

MATERIALS

Per student group (4):

- five 250-mL beakers
- large potato tuber
- china marker
- single-edge razor blades *or* paring knife
- metric ruler
- potato peeler

Per table:

- balance
- paper toweling
- bottles containing solutions of 0.15, 0.20, 0.25, 0.30, and 0.35 M sucrose

PROCEDURE

1. With the china marker, label the five 250-mL beakers with the concentrations of sucrose solution.
2. Pour about 100 mL of each solution into its respective beaker.
3. Peel the potato and then cut it into five 3-cm cubes (3 cm on each side).
4. Without delay, weigh each cube to the nearest 0.01 g. Record the weights in Table 7-6.
5. Place one cube in each beaker and allow it to remain there for a minimum of 30 minutes, longer if time is available.

6. After the experimental period has elapsed, remove each cube, one at a time, and blot it lightly but thoroughly with the paper toweling.
7. Weigh each cube and record its final weight in Table 7-6. Then calculate and record the weight loss or gain.
8. Calculate the percent change in weight by dividing the *initial weight* by the *final weight*.

TABLE 7-6 Determining the Solute Concentration in Potato Tuber Cells

| Solution | Weight | | | |
	Initial	Final	Change	Percent Change
0.15 M				
0.20 M				
0.25 M				
0.30 M				
0.35 M				

The cube with the lowest percentage of weight loss or gain is in a solution that most closely approximates the solute concentration of the cells within the potato tuber. Of course, most of the solute within the tuber is in the form of starch, and our experimental solution is sucrose. The results of this experiment indicate that the *concentration* of the solute, but not the *type* of solute, is important for osmosis to occur.

What was the approximate concentration of solute in the potato tuber? _____

_____

Which concentration resulted in the *greatest* percentage change? _____

_____

Make a statement that relates the amount of water loss or gain to the concentration of the solute. _____

_____

_____

_____

_____ 1. If one were to identify the most important compound for sustenance of life, it would probably be
    (a) salt
    (b) $BaCl_2$
    (c) water
    (d) I_2KI

_____ 2. A solvent is
    (a) the substance in which solutes are dissolved
    (b) a salt or sugar
    (c) one component of a biological membrane
    (d) selectively permeable

_____ 3. Diffusion
    (a) is a process requiring cellular energy
    (b) is the movement of molecules from a region of higher concentration to one of lower concentration
    (c) occurs only across selectively permeable membranes
    (d) is none of the above

_____ 4. Cellular membranes
    (a) consist of a phospholipid bilayer containing embedded proteins
    (b) control the movement of substances into and out of cells
    (c) are selectively permeable
    (d) are all of the above

_____ 5. An example of a solute would be
    (a) Janus green B
    (b) water
    (c) sucrose
    (d) both a and c

_____ 6. Dialysis membrane is
    (a) selectively permeable
    (b) used in these experiments to simulate cellular membranes
    (c) permeable to water but not to sucrose
    (d) all of the above

_____ 7. Specifically, osmosis
    (a) requires the expenditure of cellular energy
    (b) is diffusion of water from one region to another
    (c) is diffusion of water across a selectively permeable membrane
    (d) is none of the above

_____ 8. Which of the following reagents does *not* fit with the substance being tested for?
    (a) Biuret reagent protein
    (b) $BaCl_2$ starch
    (c) $AgNO_3$ chloride ion
    (d) albustix protein

_____ 9. When the cytoplasm of a plant cell is pressed against the cell wall, the cell is said to be
    (a) turgid
    (b) plasmolyzed
    (c) hemolyzed
    (d) crenate

_____ 10. If one solution contains 10% NaCl and another contains 30% NaCl, the 30% solution is
    (a) isotonic
    (b) hypotonic
    (c) hypertonic
    (d) plasmolyzed, with respect to the 10% solution

EXERCISE 7

Diffusion, Osmosis, and the Functional Significance of Biological Membranes

POST-LAB QUESTIONS

7.1 Experiment: Rate of Diffusion of Solutes

1. You want to dissolve a solute in water. Without shaking or swirling the solution, what might you do to increase the rate at which the solute would go into solution? Relate your answer to your method's effect on the motion of the molecules.

7.2 Experiment: Osmosis

2. If a 10% sugar solution is separated from a 20% sugar solution by a selectively permeable membrane, in which direction will there be a net movement of water?

3. Based on your observations in this exercise, would you expect dialysis membrane to be permeable to sucrose? Why?

7.4 Experiment: Plasmolysis in Plant Cells

4. You are having a party and you plan to serve celery, but your celery has gone limp, and the stores are closed. What might you do to make the celery crisp (turgid) again?

5. Why don't plant cells undergo osmotic lysis?

6. This drawing represents a plant cell that has been placed in a solution.
   a. What *process* is taking place in the direction of the arrows? What is happening at the cellular level when a wilted plant is watered and begins to recover from the wilt?

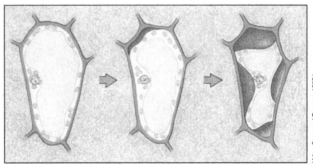

(After Starr and Taggart, 1989.)

   b. Is the solution in which the cells have been placed hypotonic, isotonic, or hypertonic relative to the cytoplasm?

7.5 Experiment: Osmotic Changes in Red Blood Cells

7. A human lost at sea without fresh drinking water is effectively lost in an osmotic desert. Why would drinking salt water be harmful?

Food for Thought

8. How does diffusion differ from osmosis?

9. Plant fertilizer consists of numerous different solutes. A small dose of fertilizer can enhance plant growth, but overfertilization can kill the plant. Why might overfertilization have this effect?

10. What does the word *lysis* mean? (*Now* does the name of the disinfectant Lysol® make sense?)

Enzymes: Catalysts of Life

OBJECTIVES

After completing this exercise, you will be able to

1. define *catalyst, enzyme, activation energy, enzyme–substrate complex, substrate, product, active site, denaturation, cofactor;*

2. explain how an enzyme operates;

3. recognize benzoquinone as a brown substance formed in damaged plant tissue;

4. indicate the substrates for the enzyme catechol oxidase;

5. describe the effect of temperature on the rate of chemical reactions in general and on enzymatically controlled reactions in particular;

6. describe the effect that an atypical pH may have on enzyme action;

7. indicate how a cofactor might operate and identify a cofactor for catechol oxidase.

INTRODUCTION

Life as we know it is impossible without enzymes. The energy required by your muscles simply to open your lab manual would take years to accumulate without enzymes. Due to the presence of enzymes, the myriad chemical reactions occurring in your cells at this very moment are being completed in a fraction of a second rather than the years or even decades that would be otherwise required.

Enzymes are proteins that function as biological catalysts. A **catalyst** is a substance that lowers the amount of energy necessary for a chemical reaction to proceed. You might think of this so-called **activation energy** as a mountain to be climbed. Enzymes decrease the size of the mountain, in effect turning it into a molehill (Figure 8-1).

By lowering the activation energy, an enzyme affects the *rate* at which reaction occurs. Enzyme-boosted reactions may proceed from 100,000 to 10 million times faster than they would without the enzyme.

In an enzyme-catalyzed reaction, the reactant (the substance being acted upon) is called the **substrate.** Substrate molecules combine with enzyme molecules to form a temporary **enzyme–substrate complex. Products** are formed, and the enzyme molecule is released unchanged. Thus, the enzyme is not used up in the process and is capable of catalyzing the same reaction again and again. This can be summarized as follows:

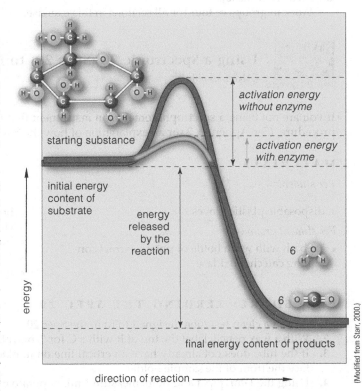

Figure 8-1 Enzymes and activation energy.

$$\text{substrate} \xrightarrow{\text{enzyme}} \text{enzyme–substrate complex} \longrightarrow \text{products + enzyme}$$

Before we proceed, let's visualize an enzyme. Look at Figure 8-2. Using common, everyday items, think of an enzyme as a key that unlocks a lock. Imagine that you have a number of locks, and all use the same key. You would only need one key to unlock them.

Figure 8-2 Action of an enzyme.

substrate   enzyme   enzyme–substrate complex   products   enzyme

Changing the shape of the key just a tiny bit may still allow the key to function in the lock, but you may have to fumble with the key a bit to get the lock open. Changing the key more results in an inability to open the lock. Similarly, a change in the shape of an enzyme alters its function. We will examine a number of factors in this exercise to determine their effects on enzyme action, including

1. temperature
2. pH (hydrogen-ion concentration of the environment)
3. specificity (how discriminating the enzyme is in catalyzing different potential substrates)
4. cofactor necessity (the need for a metallic ion for enzyme activity)

Although thousands of enzymes are present within cells, we'll examine only one: catechol oxidase (also known as tyrosinase).

Work in groups of four for all sections in this exercise.

8.1   Using a Spectronic 20 (Spec 20) to Determine Color Changes
(About 15 min.)

If you are not using a spectrophotometer, an instrument that measures color change, skip the following 11-step procedure. (See Appendix 2 for an explanation of how the Spec 20 works.)

MATERIALS

Per student:

- disposable plastic gloves

Per student group (4):

- ice bath with wash bottle of potato extract containing catechol oxidase

- bottle of dH₂O
- china marker
- Spec 20 spectrophotometer
- 1-mL pipet and bulb
- 5-mL pipet and bulb

PROCEDURE: ZEROING THE SPEC 20

1. Obtain a clean test tube designed to fit in the Spec 20.
2. With a wax pencil, label the top of it with a C for "control."
3. If the tube does not already have a vertical line on it, place one on it with the wax pencil. This mark must face the front of the sample holder.
4. Using the 1-mL pipet and bulb, measure 1 mL of potato extract into test tube C.
5. Using the 5-mL pipet and bulb, add 5 mL of dH₂O to the test tube.
6. Place your gloved thumb over the mouth of the test tube and invert the tube to mix the contents.
7. Adjust the wavelength knob (top, right) of the Spec 20 to 540 nm.
8. Rotate the lower *left* absorbance adjustment so the needle reads infinity (∞) on the bottom scale.
9. Clean the surface of the tube by wiping it with a tissue and insert the tube into the Spec 20 sample holder with the vertical mark facing front (toward you).
10. Rotate the lower *right* absorbance adjustment so the needle reads zero.
11. You have now zeroed the Spec 20 for this exercise. Remove tube C and set it aside.

The previous procedure is done to account for the fact that the potato extract has color and absorbs light. In your experiments, you will be measuring the change in the amount of light absorbed by potato extract before and after various experimental treatments.

Formation and Detection of Benzoquinone *(About 20 min.)*

Catechol oxidase is an enzyme that catalyzes the production of benzoquinone and water from catechol:

$$\text{catechol} + \tfrac{1}{2}\,O_2 \xrightarrow{\text{catechol oxidase}} \text{benzoquinone} + H_2O$$

(substrates)   (enzyme in potato extract)   (product)

This is an oxidation reaction, with catechol and oxygen as the substrates. Hence, the enzyme gets its preferred name, *catechol oxidase*. (This suffix *-ase* is a tipoff that the substance is an enzyme.)

Catechol and catechol oxidase are present in the cells of many plants, although in undamaged tissue they are separated in different compartments of the cells. Injury causes mixing of the substrate and enzyme, producing benzoquinone, a brown substance.

You've probably noticed the brown coloration of a damaged apple or the blackening of an injured potato tuber (Figure 8-3). Benzoquinone inhibits the growth of certain microorganisms that cause rot.

In this section, you will form the product, benzoquinone, and establish a color intensity scale or absorbance standard that you will use in subsequent experiments.

(Photo by J. W. Perry.)

Figure 8-3 Potato showing browning due to benzoquinone production. The potato on the left was sliced immediately before this photo was taken. The one on the right had been cut and exposed to the oxygen in the air for several minutes before being photographed.

MATERIALS

Per student:
- disposable plastic gloves

Per student group (4):
- 3 test tubes
- test tube rack
- metric ruler
- ice bath with wash bottle of potato extract containing catechol oxidase
- wash bottle containing 1% catechol solution

- bottle of dH₂O
- china marker
- warmed up and zeroed Spec 20, optional; see Appendix 2

Per lab room:
- 40°C waterbath
- vortex mixer (optional)

PROCEDURE

1. With a china marker, label three test tubes 2_A, 2_B, and 2_C. Place your initials on each test tube for later identification.
2. Lay the test tubes against a metric ruler and mark lines on the tubes corresponding to 1 cm and 2 cm *from the bottom* of each tube.
3. Fill each tube as follows:
   Tube 2_A: 1 cm of potato extract containing catechol oxidase
          1 cm of 1% catechol solution
   Tube 2_B: 1 cm of potato extract containing catechol oxidase
          1 cm of dH₂O
   Tube 2_C: 1 cm of 1% catechol solution
          1 cm of dH₂O

> **Caution**
>
> *Some of the chemicals (catechol, hydroquinone) used in these experiments can be hazardous to your health if they are ingested or taken in through your skin. Wear disposable plastic gloves for all experiments.*

Note: Be certain to return potato extract to ice bath IMMEDIATELY after use in this and subsequent experiments.

4. Shake all tubes (using a vortex mixer if available).
5. Record the color of the solution in each tube in the "time 0" spaces of Table 8-1.
6. Place the tubes in a 40°C waterbath.
7. After 10 minutes, the catechol should be completely oxidized. Remove the tubes from the waterbath. Record the *color* of the substance in each test tube in Table 8-1.
   What you do next depends on whether you're using a spectrophotometer. Proceed with *either* step 8 *or* 9.
8. *Color-intensity method:* Consider the color of the product in tube 2_A to be a 5 on a color intensity scale of 0–5, while the color of the substance in tubes 2_B and 2_C is a 0. In Table 8-2, record the color intensity for tubes 2_B and 2_C as 0, and that of tube 2_A as 5.
   You will use this scale to make comparisons in Sections 8.3–8.6. Keep the contents in tubes 2_A, 2_B, and 2_C, and refer to them as you make comparisons in subsequent experiments.
9. *Spec 20 method:*
   (a) Pipet 6 mL of the contents of each tube into six separate Spec 20 tubes.
   (b) Clean off each tube.
   (c) Zero the Spec 20 using the contents of tube 2_C.
   (d) Insert tubes containing the contents of tube 2_A and then tube 2_B, determine the absorbance of each, and record them in Table 8-2.

TABLE 8-1	Formation and Detection of Benzoquinone: Record Color		
Time	Tube 2_A: Potato Extract and Catechol	Tube 2_B: Potato Extract and Water	Tube 2_C: Catechol and Water
0 min.			
10 min.			

What is the brown-colored substance that appeared in tube 2_A? _____

What is the substrate for the reaction that occurred in tube 2_A? _____

What is the product of the reaction in tube 2_A? _____

What substances do tubes 2_B and 2_C lack that account for the absence of the brown-colored substance?
2_B _____ 2_C _____

What is the purpose of tubes 2_B and 2_C? _____

TABLE 8-2	Color-Intensity Scale or Absorbance	
Intensity/Absorbance	Tube	Color of Product
	2_C	
	2_B	
	2_A	

8.3 Experiment: Enzyme Specificity (*About 20 min.*)

Generally, enzymes are substrate-specific, acting on one particular substrate or a small number of structurally similar substrates. This specificity is due to the three-dimensional structure of the enzyme. For the enzyme–substrate complex to form, the structure of the substrate must very closely complement that of the enzyme's

active site. The active site is a special region of the enzyme where the substrate binds. The active site has a small amount of moldability, so that the active site and substrate become fully complementary to each other, as shown in Figure 8-4.

Think again about the lock and key analogy (Figure 8-2). If the lock and key are not complementary, the lock won't open. But how exact a fit is necessary?

In this experiment, you will determine the ability of the enzyme catechol oxidase to catalyze the oxidation of two different but structurally similar substrates: catechol and hydroquinone. First, examine the chemical structure of each compound:

catechol   hydroquinone

You need not memorize these structural formulas, but do notice that both are ring structures with two hydroxyl (—OH) groups attached.

Keep this in mind as you do the next experiment, in which you will determine how specific (discriminating) catechol oxidase is for particular substrates.

two substrate molecules

substrates contacting active site of enzyme

active site

TRANSITION STATE (tightest binding but least stable)

end product

enzyme unchanged by the reaction

(After Starr, 2000.)

Figure 8-4 Induced-fit model of enzyme–substrate interactions.

MATERIALS

Per student group (4):

- 3 test tubes
- test tube rack
- metric ruler
- china marker
- wash bottle containing 1% catechol
- wash bottle containing 1% hydroquinone
- ice bath with wash bottle of potato extract containing catechol oxidase
- warmed up and zeroed Spec 20, optional; see Appendix 2

Per lab room:

- 40°C waterbath
- vortex mixer (optional)

PROCEDURE

1. With a china marker, label three clean test tubes 3_A, 3_B, and 3_C. Include your initials for identification.
2. Lay the test tubes against a metric ruler and mark lines indicating 1 cm and 2 cm *from the bottom* of each test tube.
3. Fill each tube as follows:
   Tube 3_A: 1 cm of potato extract containing catechol oxidase
   1 cm of 1% catechol
   Tube 3_B: 1 cm of potato extract containing catechol oxidase
   1 cm of 1% hydroquinone
   Tube 3_C: 1 cm of potato extract containing catechol oxidase
   1 cm of dH_2O
4. Gently shake the test tubes to mix the contents.
5. Compare the color intensity of the solution in each test tube *with the standards produced in Section 8.2* and record them at time 0 in Table 8-3.
6. Place the test tubes in a 40°C waterbath.

This experiment addresses the hypothesis that *the structure of a substrate determines how well an enzyme acts upon the substrate.*

7. While you wait for the experiment to run its course, write your prediction of the outcome in Table 8-3.
8. After 10 minutes, remove the test tubes from the water bath and examine them. Choose step 9 *or* 10 and proceed.
9. *Color-intensity method:* Record the color intensity (scale 0–5) of each tube's contents in Table 8-3.

TABLE 8-3 Specificity of Catechol Oxidase for Different Substrates

Prediction:

	Relative Color Intensity or Absorbance		
Time	Tube 3$_A$: Catechol	Tube 3$_B$: Hydroquinone	Tube 3$_C$: dH$_2$O
0 min.			
10 min.			
Conclusion:			

10. *Spec 20 method:*
    (a) Pipet 6 mL of the contents of each tube into three labeled Spec 20 tubes.
    (b) Clean off each tube.
    (c) Zero the Spec 20 using the contents of tube 3$_C$.
    (d) Insert tubes containing the contents of tube 3$_A$ and then tube 3$_B$, determine the absorbance of each, and record them in Table 8-3.
11. Upon which substrate does catechol oxidase work best, forming the most benzoquinone in the shortest amount of time?

    _____

12. Based on your knowledge of the structures of the two substrates, what apparently determines the specificity of catechol oxidase?

    _____

    _____

13. Why was tube 3$_C$ included in this experiment?

    _____

    _____

14. Record your conclusion in Table 8-3, either accepting or rejecting the hypothesis.

8.4 Experiment: Effect of Temperature on Enzyme Activity *(25 min.)*

The rate at which chemical reactions take place is largely determined by the temperature of the environment. *Generally, for every 10°C rise in temperature, the reaction rate doubles.* Within a rather narrow range, this is true for enzymatic reactions also. However, because enzymes are proteins, excessive temperature alters their structure, destroying their ability to function. When an enzyme's structure is changed sufficiently to destroy its function, the enzyme is said to be **denatured.** Most enzymatically controlled reactions have an *optimum* temperature and pH—that is, one temperature and pH where activity is maximized.

In this experiment, you will determine the temperature range over which the enzyme catechol oxidase is able to catalyze its substrate. You will also determine the best (optimum) temperature for the reaction.

MATERIALS

Per student group (4):

- 6 test tubes
- test tube rack
- metric ruler
- china marker
- wash bottle containing 1% catechol
- ice bath with wash bottle of potato extract containing catechol oxidase
- three 400-mL graduated beakers

- heat-resistant glove
- Celsius thermometer
- warmed up and zeroed Spec 20, optional; see Appendix 2

Per student group (table):

- hot plate *or* burner, tripod support, wire gauze, and matches or striker
- boiling chips

Per lab room:

- source of room-temperature water
- three waterbaths: 40°C, 60°C, 80°C
- vortex mixer (optional)

PROCEDURE

1. Half fill one 400-mL beaker with tap water. Add a few boiling chips and turn on the hotplate to the highest temperature setting, *or,* if your lab is equipped with burners, light the burner. Bring the water to a boil, then turn the heat down so that the water just continues to boil.
2. Put 150 mL of tap water into a second beaker and add ice to the water.
3. Half fill a third beaker with water from the source at room temperature.
4. With a china marker, label six test tubes 4$_A$–4$_F$. Include your initials for identification.
5. Lay the test tubes against a metric ruler and mark off lines indicating 1 cm and 2 cm *from the bottom* of each tube.
6. Fill each tube to the 1-cm mark with potato extract containing catechol oxidase.
7. **(a)** Place tube 4$_A$ in the 400-mL beaker of ice water.
   Measure and record the water temperature: _____°C
   (b) Place tube 4$_B$ in the 400-mL beaker containing room-temperature water.
   Room temperature: _____°C
   (c) Place tube 4$_C$ in the 40°C waterbath.
   (d) Place tube 4$_D$ in the 60°C waterbath.
   (e) Place tube 4$_E$ in the 80°C waterbath.
   (f) Place tube 4$_F$ in the 400-mL beaker containing boiling water.
   Temperature of boiling water: _____°C
8. Allow the test tubes to remain at the various temperatures for 5 minutes.
9. Remove the tubes and add catechol to the 2-cm line on each. Agitate the tubes (with a vortex mixer if available) to mix the contents.
10. *Color-intensity method:* In Table 8-4, record the relative color intensity (scale 0–5) of the solution in each tube, using the standard established in Section 8.2. Return each tube to its respective temperature bath immediately after recording.

This experiment addresses the hypothesis that *the temperature of a substrate and an enzyme determines the amount of product that is formed.*

Caution
Wear a heat-resistant glove when handling heated glassware.

11. While you wait for the experiment to run its course, write your prediction of the outcome of the experiment in Table 8-4.
12. Shake periodically (by hand) all tubes over the next 10 minutes.
13. After 10 minutes, remove the test tubes from the water baths. Choose step 14 *or* 15 and proceed.
14. *Color-intensity method:* Record the color intensity (scale 0–5) of each tube's contents in Table 8-4.

TABLE 8-4   Effect of Temperature on Enzyme Activity

Prediction:

	Relative Color Intensity or Absorbance					
Time	Tube 4$_A$	Tube 4$_B$	Tube 4$_C$	Tube 4$_D$	Tube 4$_E$	Tube 4$_F$
0 min.						
10 min.						
Conclusion:						

15. *Spec 20 method:*
    (a) Pipet 6 mL of the contents of each tube into six labeled Spec 20 tubes.
    (b) Clean off each tube.
    (c) Zero the Spec 20 using the contents of tube 2_C.
    (d) Insert tubes containing the contents of each tube, recording them in Table 8-4.
16. Plot the data from Table 8-4 for the 10-minute reading in Figure 8-5.
17. Over what temperature *range* is catechol oxidase active?

_____

18. What is the *optimum* temperature for activity of this enzyme?

_____

19. What happens to enzyme activity at very high temperatures?

_____

_____

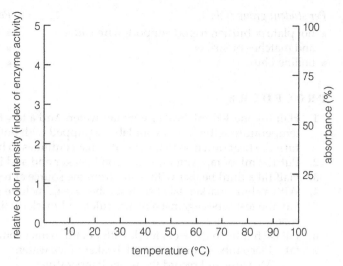

Figure 8-5 Effect of temperature on catechol oxidase activity.

20. Record your conclusion in Table 8-4, either accepting or rejecting the hypothesis.

8.5 Experiment: Effect of pH on Enzyme Activity *(25 min.)*

Another factor influencing the rate of enzyme catalysis is the hydrogen-ion concentration (pH) of the solution. Like temperature, pH affects the three-dimensional shape of enzymes, thus regulating their function. Most enzymes operate best when the pH of the solution is near neutrality (pH 7). Others, however, have pH optima in the acidic or basic range, corresponding to the environment in which they normally function.

In this experiment, you will determine the pH range over which the enzyme catechol oxidase is able to catalyze its substrate. You will also determine the optimum pH for the reaction.

MATERIALS

Per student group (4):
- 7 test tubes
- test tube rack
- metric ruler
- china marker
- wash bottle containing 1% catechol
- ice bath with wash bottle of potato extract containing catechol oxidase
- warmed up and zeroed Spec 20, optional; see Appendix 2

Per lab room:
- 40°C waterbath
- phosphate buffer series, pH 2–12 (2, 4, 6, 7, 8, 10, 12)
- vortex mixer (optional)

PROCEDURE

1. With a china marker, label seven test tubes 5_A–5_G. Include your initials for identification.
2. Lay the test tubes against a metric ruler and mark lines indicating 4 cm, 5 cm, and 6 cm *from the bottom* of each tube.
3. Take your test tubes to the location of the phosphate buffer series and fill each tube according to the following directions:

4. Return to your work area and add 1 cm of potato extract containing catechol oxidase to each of the seven tubes (thus bringing the total volume of each to the 5-cm mark). Agitate the tubes by hand.
5. Add 1% catechol to each of the seven tubes, bringing the total volume to the 6-cm mark. Agitate the contents of the tubes, using a vortex mixer if available.
6. In Table 8-5 at time 0, record the relative color intensity of each tube *immediately after adding the 1% catechol*.
7. Place the tubes in the 40°C waterbath.
8. Agitate the tubes periodically over the next 10 minutes.

Tube	Fill to the 4-cm Mark with Buffer of
5$_A$	pH 2
5$_B$	pH 4
5$_C$	pH 6
5$_D$	pH 7
5$_E$	pH 8
5$_F$	pH 10
5$_G$	pH 12

This experiment addresses the hypothesis that *the pH of a substrate and an enzyme determines the amount of product that is formed.*

9. While you wait for the experiment to run its course, write your prediction of the outcome in Table 8-5.
10. After 10 minutes, remove the test tubes from the water baths. Choose step 11 *or* 12 and proceed.
11. *Color-intensity method:* Record the color intensity (scale 0–5) of each tube's contents in Table 8-5.

TABLE 8-5 Effect of pH on Enzyme Activity

Prediction:

	Relative Color Intensity or Absorbance						
Time	Tube 5$_A$ (pH 2)	Tube 5$_B$ (pH 4)	Tube 5$_C$ (pH 6)	Tube 5$_D$ (pH 7)	Tube 5$_E$ (pH 8)	Tube 5$_F$ (pH 10)	Tube 5$_G$ (pH 12)
0 min.							
10 min.							

Conclusion:

---

12. *Spec 20 method:*
   (a) Pipet 6 mL of the contents of each tube into seven labeled Spec 20 tubes.
   (b) Clean off each tube.
   (c) Zero the Spec 20 using the contents of tube 2$_C$ from Section 8.2.
   (d) Insert each tube, determine the absorbance, and record it in Table 8-5.
13. Plot the data from Table 8-5 for your 10-minute reading in Figure 8-6.
14. Over what pH *range* does catechol oxidase catalyze catechol to benzoquinone?

_____

15. What is the *optimum* pH for catechol oxidase activity?

_____

16. Record your conclusion in Table 8-5, either accepting or rejecting the hypothesis.

Figure 8-6 Effect of pH on catechol oxidase activity.

Some enzymatic reactions occur only when the proper *cofactors* are present. **Cofactors** are nonprotein organic molecules and metal ions that are part of the structure of the active site, making the formation of the enzyme–substrate complex possible.

In this experiment, you will use phenylthiourea (PTU), which binds strongly to copper, to remove copper ions. Thus, you'll be able to determine whether copper is a necessary cofactor necessary for producing benzo-quinone from catechol.

MATERIALS

Per student group (4):

- 2 test tubes
- test tube rack
- metric ruler
- china marker
- ice bath with wash bottle of potato extract con-taining catechol oxidase
- wash bottle containing 1% catechol solution
- bottle of dH_2O
- china marker
- scoopula (small spoon)

- phenylthiourea crystals in small screw-cap bottle
- warmed up and zeroed Spec 20, optional; see Appendix 2

Per lab room:

- 40°C waterbath
- vortex mixer (optional)
- bottle of 95% ethanol (at each sink)
- tissues (at each sink)

PROCEDURE

1. With a china marker, label two test tubes 6_A and 6_B. Include your initials for identification.
2. Lay the test tube against a metric ruler and mark lines indicating 1 cm and 2 cm *from the bottom* of each tube.
3. Add potato extract containing catechol oxidase to the 1-cm mark of each test tube.
4. Using a scoopula, add five crystals of phenylthiourea (PTU) to tube 6_A. Do not add anything to tube 6_B.

Caution
PTU is poisonous.

5. Agitate the contents of both test tubes frequently by hand during the next 5 minutes.
6. Add 1% catechol to the 2-cm mark of both test tubes and agitate the con-tents of the tubes, using a vortex mixer if available.
7. *Color-intensity method:* In Table 8-5 at time 0, record the relative color in-tensities (scale of 0–5).

TABLE 8-6 Is Copper a Cofactor for Catechol Oxidase?

	Relative Color Intensity or Absorbance	
Time	**Tube 6_A: with PTU**	**Tube 6_B: without PTU**
0 min.		
10 min.		
Conclusion:		

Prediction:

8. Place the tubes in a 40°C waterbath. Agitate the tubes several times during the next 10 minutes.

This experiment addresses the hypothesis that *a cofactor is necessary for the action of the enzyme catecol oxidase*.

9. While you wait for the experiment to run its course, write your prediction of the outcome in Table 8-6.
10. After 10 minutes, remove the test tubes from the water baths. Choose step 11 *or* 12 and proceed.
11. *Color-intensity method:* Record the color intensity (scale 0–5) of each tube's contents in Table 8-6.

12. *Spec 20 method:*
    (a) Pipet 6 mL of the contents of each tube into seven separate Spec 20 tubes.
    (b) Clean off each tube.
    (c) Zero the Spec 20 using the contents of tube 2_C from Section 8.2.
    (d) Insert each tube in the Spec 20, determine the absorbance, and record it in Table 8-6.

13. Did benzoquinone form in tube 6_A? In tube 6_B? _____

14. From this experiment, what can you conclude about the necessity for copper for catechol oxidase activity?
    _____

15. What substance used in this experiment contained copper?
    _____

16. Record your conclusion in Table 8-5, either accepting or rejecting the hypothesis.

Note: After completing all experiments, take your dirty glassware to the sink and wash it following directions on page x. Use 95% ethanol to remove the china marker. Invert the test tubes in the test tube racks so they drain. Tidy up your work area, making certain all materials used in this exercise are there for the next class.

_____ 1. Enzymes are
  (a) biological catalysts
  (b) agents that speed up cellular reactions
  (c) proteins
  (d) all of the above

_____ 2. Enzymes function by
  (a) being consumed (used up) in the reaction
  (b) lowering the activation energy of a reaction
  (c) combining with otherwise toxic substances in the cell
  (d) adding heat to the cell to speed up the reaction

_____ 3. The substance that an enzyme combines with is
  (a) another enzyme
  (b) a cofactor
  (c) a coenzyme
  (d) the substrate

_____ 4. Enzyme specificity refers to the
  (a) need for cofactors for some enzymes to function
  (b) fact that enzymes catalyze one particular substrate or a small number of structurally similar substrates
  (c) effect of temperature on enzyme activity
  (d) effect of pH on enzyme activity

_____ 5. For every 10°C rise in temperature, the rate of most chemical reactions will
  (a) double
  (b) triple
  (c) increase by 100 times
  (d) stop

_____ 6. When an enzyme becomes denatured, it
  (a) increases in effectiveness
  (b) loses its requirement for a cofactor
  (c) forms an enzyme–substrate complex
  (d) loses its ability to function

_____ 7. An enzyme may lose its ability to function because of
  (a) excessively high temperatures
  (b) a change in its three-dimensional structure
  (c) a large change in the pH of the environment
  (d) all of the above

_____ 8. pH is a measure of
  (a) an enzyme's effectiveness
  (b) enzyme concentration
  (c) the hydrogen-ion concentration
  (d) none of the above

_____ 9. Catechol oxidase
  (a) is an enzyme found in potatoes
  (b) catalyzes the production of catechol
  (c) has as its substrate benzoquinone
  (d) is a substance that encourages the growth of microorganisms

_____ 10. The relative color intensity used in the experiments of this exercise
  (a) is a consequence of production of benzoquinone
  (b) is an index of enzyme activity
  (c) may differ depending on the pH, temperature, or presence of cofactors, respectively
  (d) is all of the above

EXERCISE 8

Enzymes: Catalysts of Life

POST-LAB QUESTIONS

8.4 *Experiment: Effect of Temperature on Enzyme Activity*

1. Eggs can contain bacteria such as *Salmonella*. Considering what you've learned in this exercise, explain how cooking eggs makes them safe to eat.

2. As you demonstrated in this experiment, high temperatures inactivate catechol oxidase. How is it that some bacteria live in the hot springs of Yellowstone Park at temperatures as high as 73°C?

3. Why do you think high fevers alter cellular functions?

4. Some surgical procedures involve lowering a patient's body temperature during periods when blood flow must be restricted. What effect might this have on enzyme-controlled cellular metabolism?

5. At one time, it was believed that individuals who had been submerged under water for longer than several minutes could not be resuscitated. Recently this has been shown to be false, especially if the person was in cold water. Explain why cold-water "drowning" victims might survive prolonged periods under water.

8.5 Experiment: Effect of pH on Enzyme Activity

6. Explain what happens to catechol oxidase when the pH is on either side of the optimum.

7. What would you expect the pH optimum to be for an enzyme secreted into your stomach?

Food for Thought

8. Is it necessary for a cell to produce one enzyme molecule for every substrate molecule that needs to be catalyzed? Why or why not?

9. Explain the difference between *substrate* and *active site*.

10. The photo shows slices of two apples. The one on the left sat on the counter for 15 minutes prior to being photographed. The one on the right was sliced immediately prior to the photo being taken.

    a. Explain as thoroughly as possible what you see and why the two slices differ.

(Photo by J. W. Perry.)

    b. If you don't want a cut apple to brown, what can you do to prevent it?

Photosynthesis: Capture of Light Energy

OBJECTIVES

After completing this exercise, you will be able to

1. define *photosynthesis, autotroph, heterotroph, chlorophyll, chromatogram, absorption spectrum, carotenoid;*

2. describe the role of carbon dioxide in photosynthesis;

3. determine the effect of light and carbon dioxide on photosynthesis;

4. determine the wavelengths absorbed by pigments;

5. identify the pigments in spinach chloroplast extract;

6. identify the carbohydrate produced in geranium leaves during photosynthesis;

7. identify the structures composing the chloroplast and indicate the function of each structure in photosynthesis.

INTRODUCTION

Photosynthesis is the process by which light energy converts inorganic compounds to organic substances with the subsequent release of elemental oxygen. It may very well be the most important biological event sustaining life. Without it, most living things would starve, and atmospheric oxygen would become depleted to a level incapable of supporting animal life. Ultimately, the source of light energy is the sun, although on a small scale we can substitute artificial light.

Nutritionally, two types of organisms exist in our world, autotrophs and heterotrophs. **Autotrophs** (*auto* means self, *troph* means feeding) synthesize organic molecules (carbohydrates) from inorganic carbon dioxide. The vast majority of autotrophs are the photosynthetic organisms that you're familiar with—plants, as well as some protistans and bacteria. These organisms use light energy to produce carbohydrates. (A few bacteria produce their organic carbon compounds chemosynthetically, that is, using chemical energy.)

By contrast, **heterotrophs** must rely directly or indirectly on autotrophs for their nutritional carbon and metabolic energy. Heterotrophs include animals, fungi, many protistans, and most bacteria.

In both autotrophs and heterotrophs, carbohydrates originally produced by photosynthesis are broken down by *cellular respiration* (Exercise 10), releasing the energy captured from the sun for metabolic needs.

The photosynthetic reaction is often conveniently summarized by the equation:

$$12H_2O + 6CO_2 \xrightarrow{\text{light energy}} 6O_2 + C_6H_{12}O_6 + 6H_2O$$

water carbon   oxygen glucose water
dioxide

Although glucose is often produced during photosynthesis, it is usually converted to another transport or storage compound unless it is to be used immediately for carbohydrate metabolism. In plants and many protistans, the most common storage carbohydrate is *starch*, a compound made up of numerous glucose units linked together. Starch is designated by the chemical formula $(C_6H_{12}O_6)_n$, where *n* indicates a large number. Most plants transport carbohydrate as sucrose.

The following experiments will acquaint you with the principles of photosynthesis.

9.1   Test for Starch *(About 10 min.)*

As indicated by the overall formula of photosynthesis, one end product is a carbohydrate (CH_2O). But a number of different carbohydrates have the empirical formula CH_2O. In this section, you will perform a simple test to visually distinguish between two different carbohydrates and water.

MATERIALS

Per student group (4):

- 1 dropper bottle each of
  iodine (I_2KI) solution
  starch solution

glucose solution
dH$_2$O
- depression (spot) plate

PROCEDURE

1. Place a couple drops of starch, glucose, and distilled water in three different depressions of the spot plate. Now add a drop of iodine solution to each.
2. Record your observations. How can you identify the presence of starch?

   Observations: _____

   _____

   _____

9.2   Experiment: Effects of Light and Carbon Dioxide on Starch Production
(*About 30 min.*)

In this experiment, you will perform a test to determine the environmental conditions necessary for photosynthesis and starch production. This experiment addresses the hypothesis that *photosynthesis proceeds only in the presence of light and carbon dioxide.*

MATERIALS

Per student group (4):

- two 400-mL beakers
- square of aluminum foil
- hot plate in fume hood
- heat-resistant glove
- petri dish halves
- bottle of iodine solution
- bottle of 95% ethanol (EtOH)
- forceps

Per lab room:

- source of dH$_2$O
- Fast Plants™, 9–10 days old, grown for 4 days in three different environments:
  - I. normal conditions with both light and carbon dioxide
  - II. in dark, with normal carbon dioxide
  - III. in light, but with carbon dioxide removed

PROCEDURE

1. Carefully observe and record any differences in appearance among the three sets of plants in Table 9-1.
2. Write a prediction regarding starch presence, and thus photosynthesis activity, for each growing condition in Table 9-1.
3. Pigments present in the plants must be removed before a test for starch presence can be performed. Kill the plants and extract the pigments:
   - **(a)** With a china marker, label the beakers A (for alcohol) and dH$_2$O.
   - **(b)** Add about 150 mL distilled water to the dH$_2$O beaker, set it on the hot plate, and turn on the hot plate to the highest setting. Allow the water to come to a boil.
   - **(c)** Completely remove 1–2 plants of each treatment from its growing container. Wash off all soil from the roots. Keep plants of each treatment separate and labeled.
   - **(d)** Alcohol has a much lower boiling point than water, and so takes very little time to come to a boil. When the water is boiling, put about 150 mL of alcohol in the A beaker, set it also on the hot plate and bring to a boil. Keep the alcohol beaker covered with aluminum foil as much as possible throughout the lab to prevent excess evaporation.

   > ### Caution
   >
   > *Ethanol is highly flammable. Use only electric hot plates, never open flame. Also, never let a beaker boil dry. Add more liquid, or remove the beaker from the burner, and place it on a pad of folded paper towels.*

   - **(e)** Place the plants from one treatment in the beaker of boiling water for about 1 minute. This kills the tissue and breaks down internal membranes.
   - **(f)** Use the long forceps to move the wilted plants from the water into the boiling alcohol. This will extract the photosynthetic pigments from the plant tissues. When the pigments have been extracted, the liquid will appear green, and the plant will appear to be mostly bleached.

TABLE 9-1	Effect of Light and Carbon Dioxide on Starch Presence		
Fast Plants™ Growing Condition	Appearance	Prediction	Starch Presence and Location
I. Normal conditions with both light and carbon dioxide			
II. In dark, with normal carbon dioxide			
III. In light, but with carbon dioxide removed			

(g) Remove the plants from the alcohol with forceps, and dip momentarily in the boiling water to soften.

4. Test the plants for the presence and localization of starches:
   (a) Place killed, depigmented plants in petri dishes filled with iodine solution.
   (b) Let the plants soak in the iodine solution for a couple minutes, rinse, and float in water in another petri dish in order to observe the pattern of staining.

5. Repeat the pigment extraction and staining process for plants of the other two treatments, being careful to keep the treatments separate and identified.

6. Remove the A beaker from the hot plate, and turn the heat off.

7. In Figure 9-1, sketch a plant from each experimental treatment, shading in the portions that stained dark. Be careful to note where any dark staining occurs. Record your written observations in Table 9-1.

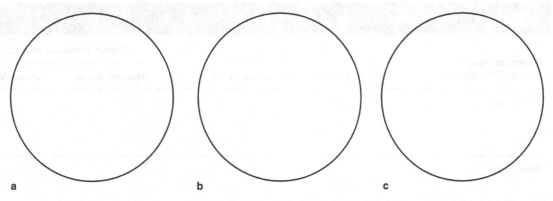

a   b   c

Figure 9-1 Distribution of starch in Fast Plants™. (a) Normal light and CO_2; (b) dark, normal CO_2; (c) light, no CO_2.

8. What does this staining pattern in plants of the three treatments indicate?

_____

_____

_____

9. What conclusion can you draw about the effect of light on the presence of starch?

_____

_____

10. What conclusion can you draw about the effect of carbon dioxide on the presence of starch?

_____

_____

11. Write a conclusion either accepting or rejecting the hypothesis.

_____

| 9.3 | **Experiment: Relationship Between Light and Photosynthetic Products**
(About 15 min.) |

This experiment addresses the hypothesis that _light is necessary for photosynthesis to proceed._

MATERIALS

Per student group (4):
- china marker
- two 400-mL graduated beakers
- hot plate in fume hood
- heat-resistant glove
- bottle of 95% ethanol
- forceps
- 2 petri dishes
- I₂KI solution in foil-wrapped stock bottle

Per lab room:
- source of dH_2O
- light-grown geranium plant or leaves of geranium plant with "masks"
- dark-grown geranium plant or leaves of geranium plant with "masks" (kept in dark place)

PROCEDURE

Work in groups of four.

1. Observe the two geranium plants available. One plant has been growing in bright light for several hours; the other has been kept in the dark for a day or more. Both leaves have had an area of the lamina (blade) masked by an opaque design.
2. Write a prediction regarding starch presence, and thus photosynthesis activity, for each growing condition and leaf treatment area in Table 9-2.

TABLE 9-2 Relationship Between Light and Starch Production

Geranium Plant Growing Condition	Prediction		Starch Presence and Location	
	Masked Areas	Unmasked Areas	Masked Areas	Unmasked Areas
Light-grown				
Dark-grown				

3. Select a leaf from one of the two geranium plants. Pigments present in the plants must be removed before a test for starch presence can be performed. Kill the leaf and extract the pigments:
   (a) With a china marker, label the beakers A (for alcohol) and dH_2O.
   (b) Add about 150 mL distilled water to the dH_2O beaker, set it on the hot plate, and turn on the hot plate to the highest setting. Allow the water to come to a boil.
   (c) Remove a treated leaf from each plant. Keep each separate and labeled. Remove the opaque cover from the leaf before proceeding.

(d) Alcohol has a much lower boiling point than water, and so takes very little time to come to a boil. When the water is boiling, put about 150 mL of alcohol in the A beaker, set it also on the hot plate, and bring to a boil. Keep the alcohol beaker covered with aluminum foil as much as possible throughout the lab to prevent excess evaporation.

(e) Place the leaf from one treatment in the beaker of boiling water for about 1 minute. This kills the tissue and breaks down internal membranes.

4. Test the plants for the presence and localization of starches:

(a) Place killed, depigmented leaf in a petri dish filled with iodine solution.

(b) Let the leaf soak in the iodine solution for a couple minutes, rinse, and float in water in another petri dish in order to observe the pattern of staining.

5. Show the distribution of the stain in the leaf by shading in and labeling Figure 9-2. In the blank provided in the legend for Figure 9-2, record the *substance* that I_2KI stains.

6. Repeat the pigment extraction and staining process for a leaf of the other treatment. Show the distribution of stain in this leaf by shading in and labeling Figure 9-2.

7. Remove the A beaker from the hot plate, and turn the heat off.

(f) Use the long forceps to move the wilted leaf from the water into the boiling alcohol. This will extract the photosynthetic pigments from the plant tissues. When the pigments have been extracted, the liquid will appear green, and the leaf will appear to be mostly bleached.

(g) Remove the leaf from the alcohol with forceps, dip momentarily in the boiling water to soften.

leaf kept in light   leaf placed in dark

Figure 9-2 Distribution of the photosynthetic product _____.

What does the blue-black coloration of the leaf indicate? _____

_____

Why did the masked area fail to stain? _____

_____

Write a conclusion accepting or rejecting the hypothesis. _____

_____

9.4 Experiment: Necessity of Photosynthetic Pigments for Photosynthesis
(About 15 min.)

Coleus plants are widely planted ornamentals that are popular for their striking foliage color patterns. Observe the plants available in the lab and note their wide variety and attractiveness. This experiment addresses the hypothesis that *chlorophyll is necessary for photosynthesis to occur.*

MATERIALS

Per student group (4):
- colored pencils or pens
- two 400-mL beakers
- hot plate in fume hood
- heat-resistant glove
- petri dish halves
- bottle of iodine solution

- bottle of 95% ethanol (EtOH)
- forceps

Per lab room:
- source of dH_2O
- variegated *Coleus* plants

PROCEDURE

1. **Obtain a leaf of variegated** *Coleus.* In the left-hand circle, carefully sketch the leaf, indicating the distribution of each color on the leaf with colored pencils or pens. Green coloration is due to chlorophyll, the major photosynthetic pigment. Pink colors are caused by water-soluble anthocyanin pigments (not involved in photosynthesis), and yellows are formed by carotenoid pigments. Be sure that you look at both surfaces of the leaf in case pigment distribution differs.

   Make a prediction regarding starch presence and photosynthetic activity for each pigmentation area:

   _____

   _____

2. Kill and extract the pigments from the leaf:
   (a) With a china marker, label the beakers A (for alcohol) and dH$_2$O.
   (b) Add about 150 mL distilled water to the dH$_2$O beaker, set it on the hot plate, and turn on the hot plate to the highest setting. Allow the water to come to a boil.
   (c) Alcohol has a much lower boiling point than water, and so takes very little time to come to a boil. When the water is boiling, put about 150 mL of alcohol in the A beaker, set it also on the hot plate, and bring to a boil. Keep the alcohol beaker covered with aluminum foil as much as possible throughout the lab to prevent excess evaporation.

Caution

   Ethanol is highly flammable. Use only electric hot plates, never open flame. Also, never let a beaker boil dry. Add more liquid, or remove the beaker from the burner, and place it on a pad of folded paper towels.

   (d) Place the leaf from one treatment in the beaker of boiling water for about 1 minute. This kills the tissue and breaks down internal membranes.
   (e) Use the long forceps to move the wilted leaf from the water into the boiling alcohol. This will extract the photosynthetic pigments from the plant tissues. When the pigments have been extracted, the liquid will appear green, and the leaf will appear to be mostly bleached.
   (f) Remove the leaf from the alcohol with forceps, and dip momentarily in the boiling water to soften.

3. Test the leaf for the presence and localization of starch:
   (a) Place the killed, depigmented leaf in a petri dish filled with iodine solution.
   (b) Let the leaf soak in the iodine solution for a couple minutes, rinse, and float in water in another petri dish in order to observe the pattern of staining.

4. On the right-hand side of the space below, resketch the leaf, indicating the pattern of staining with iodine.

5. How does the pattern of starch storage relate to the distribution of chlorophyll?

   _____

   _____

6. Write a conclusion either accepting or rejecting the hypothesis.

   _____

   _____

We tend to think of sunlight as being white. However, as you will see in this experiment, white light consists of a continuum of wavelengths. If we see light of just one wavelength, that light will appear colored.

When light hits a pigmented surface, some of the wavelengths are absorbed and others are reflected or transmitted. In this experiment, you will discover *which* wavelengths are absorbed, transmitted, or reflected by *particular* pigments, among them the photosynthetic pigment **chlorophyll.**

MATERIALS

Per lab room:

- several spectroscope setups (Figure 9-3a)
- sets of colored pencils (violet, blue, green, yellow, orange, red)
- colored filters (blue, green, red)
- small test tube containing pigment extract

Per student:

- hand-held spectroscope (optional; Figure 9-3b)

Figure 9-3 Use of a spectroscope. (**a**) Table-mounted. (After Abramoff and Thomson, 1982.) (**b**) Hand-held. (Photo by J. W. Perry.)

PROCEDURE

Work alone.

One way to separate light into its component parts is to view the light through a spectroscope. The spectroscope contains a prism that causes a spectrum of colors to form. A nanometer scale is imposed on the spectrum to indicate the wavelength of each component of white light.

1. Observe the spectrum of white light given off by an incandescent bulb through the spectroscope. With the colored pencils provided, record the positions of the colors violet, blue, green, yellow, orange, and red on the scale in Figure 9-4.
2. Observe the spectrum produced by the three colored filters using the spectroscope.

Which color or colors are absorbed when a red filter is placed between the light and the prism?

_____

_____

Figure 9-4 Spectrum of white light.

When a blue filter is used? _____

A green filter? _____

Make a general statement concerning the color of a pigment (filter) and the absorption of light by that pigment.

_____

_____

3. Now obtain a small test tube containing spinach chloroplast pigment extract and place it between the light source and the spectroscope. By adjusting the height of the tube so that the upper portion of the light passes through the pigment extract and the lower portion is white light, you can compare the absorption spectrum of the pigment extract with the spectrum of white light.

An **absorption spectrum** is a spectrum of light waves absorbed by a particular pigment. By contrast, the wavelengths that pass through the pigment extract and are visible in the spectroscope make up the *transmission spectrum* of the pigment.

4. Using the colored pencils, record the transmission spectrum of the chloroplast extract on the scale in Figure 9-5.

How does the absorption spectrum of the chloroplast extract compare with the absorption spectrum of the green filter?

_____

_____

300 nm   400 nm   500 nm   600 nm   700 nm   800 nm

Figure 9-5 Transmission spectrum of chloroplast extract.

How might you explain the difference in absorption by the green filter and by the chloroplast pigment extract? (You might want to do Section 9.6 before answering this question.)

_____

_____

9.6 Separation of Photosynthetic Pigments by Paper Chromatography
(15 min.)

Paper chromatography allows substances to be separated from one another on the basis of their physical characteristics. A chloroplast pigment extract has been prepared for you by soaking spinach leaves in cold acetone and ethanol. Although the extract appears green, other pigments present may be masked by the chlorophyll. In this activity, you will use paper chromatography to separate any pigments present. Separation occurs due to the solubility of the pigment in the chromatography solvent and the affinity of the pigments for absorption to the paper surface. The finished product, showing separated pigments, is called a **chromatogram.**

MATERIALS

Per student:

- chromatography paper, 3 cm × 15 cm sheet
- metric ruler

Per student pair:

- chloroplast pigment extract in foil-wrapped dropping bottle
- chromatography chamber containing solvent
- colored pencils (green, blue-green, yellow, orange)

PROCEDURE

1. Obtain a 3 cm × 15 cm sheet of chromatography paper. *Touch only the edges of the paper,* because oil from your fingers can interfere with development of the chromatogram.
2. Using a ruler, make a *pencil* line (do *not* use ink) about 2 cm from the bottom of the paper.
3. Load the paper by applying a droplet of the chloroplast pigment extract near the center of the pencil line. Allow the pigment spot to dry for about 30 seconds. Five to eight applications of extract on the same spot are necessary to get enough pigment for a good chromatogram. Be certain to allow the pigment to air-dry between applications.

4. Insert your "loaded" chromatography paper, spot-side down, into a chromatography chamber—a bottle containing a solvent consisting of 10% acetone in petroleum ether. The level of the solvent should cover the bottom of the strip but no portion of the pigment spot. Seal the chromatography chamber and allow the solvent to rise on the paper. (Two chromatograms can be inserted in a single bottle, but attempt to keep each separate.)

Caution

Avoid inhaling the solvent vapors. Keep the chamber tightly capped whenever possible.

5. Watch the separation take place over the next 10 minutes. When the solvent is within about 1 cm of the top of the paper, the separation is complete. Remove the strip, close the chromatography chamber, and allow the chromatogram to dry.
6. Using colored pencils, sketch the results in Figure 9-6, showing the relative position of the colors along the paper.
7. Beginning nearest the original pigment spot, identify and label the yellow-green pigment **chlorophyll b.**
8. Moving upward, find the blue-green **chlorophyll a,** two yellow-orange **xanthophylls** in the middle, and an orange **carotene** at the top. Xanthophylls and carotenes belong to the class of pigments called **carotenoids.**
9. You may preserve your chromatogram for future reference by keeping it in a dark place (for example, between the pages of your textbook). Light causes the chromatogram to fade.

Figure 9-6 Chloroplast pigment chromatogram.
Labels: chlorophyll b, chlorophyll a, xanthophylls, carotene

What pigments are contained within the chloroplasts of spinach leaves? _____

_____

What common "vegetable" is particularly high in carotenes? _____
(Are you familiar with the medical condition called "carotenosis"? If not, go to the library and look it up in a medical dictionary.)

9.7   Structure of the Chloroplast *(15 min.)*

Work alone.

The chloroplast is the organelle concerned with photosynthesis. Study Figure 9-7, an artist's conception of the three-dimensional structure of a chloroplast.

Like the mitochondrion and the nucleus, the chloroplast is surrounded by two membranes. Within the **stroma** (semifluid matrix), identify the **thylakoid disks** stacked into **grana** (a single stack is a **granum**). The chloroplast pigment molecules are located on the surface of the thylakoid disks. Hydrogen ion buildup occurs within the interior of the disks. As these ions are expelled back into the stroma, ATP is formed. Within the stroma, the ATP is used to generate organic compounds. These compounds are converted to carbohydrates, lipids, and amino acids from carbon dioxide, water, and other raw materials.

Now examine Figure 9-8, a high-magnification electron micrograph of a chloroplast. With the aid of Figure 9-7, label the electron micrograph.

If the plant is killed and fixed for electron microscopy after being exposed to strong light, the chloroplasts will contain **starch grains.** Note the large starch grain present in this chloroplast. (Starch grains appear as ellipsoidal white structures in electron micrographs.)

Figure 9-7 The arrangement of membranes and compartments inside a chloroplast.

Figure 9-8 Electron micrograph of chloroplast (10,000×). Inset: a single granum (20,000×). **Labels:** chloroplast membrane, thylakoid disks, stroma, starch

PRE-LAB QUESTIONS

_____ 1. The raw materials used for photosynthesis include
(a) O_2
(b) $C_6H_{12}O_6$
(c) $CO_2 + H_2O$
(d) CH_2O

_____ 2. A device useful for viewing the spectrum of light is a
(a) spectroscope
(b) volumeter
(c) chromatogram
(d) chloroplast

_____ 3. Products and byproducts of photosynthesis do NOT include
(a) O_2
(b) $C_6H_{12}O_6$
(c) CO_2
(d) H_2O

_____ 4. A paper chromatogram is useful for
(a) measuring the amount of photosynthesis
(b) determining the amount of gas evolved during photosynthesis
(c) separating pigments based on their physical characteristics
(d) determining the distribution of chlorophyll in a leaf

_____ 5. Which of the following pigments would you find in a geranium leaf?
(a) chlorophyll, xanthophyll, phycobilins
(b) chlorophyll a, chlorophyll b, carotenoids
(c) phycocyanin, xanthophyll, fucoxanthin
(d) carotenoids, chlorophylls, phycoerythrin

_____ 6. Which reagent would you use to determine the distribution of the carbohydrate stored in leaves?
(a) starch
(b) Benedict's solution
(c) chlorophyll
(d) I_2KI

_____ 7. An example of a heterotrophic organism is
(a) a plant
(b) a geranium
(c) a human
(d) none of the above

_____ 8. Organisms capable of producing their own food are known as
(a) autotrophs
(b) heterotrophs
(c) omnivores
(d) herbivores

_____ 9. Grana are
(a) the same as starch grains
(b) the site of ATP production within chloroplasts
(c) part of the outer chloroplast membrane
(d) contained within mitochondria and nuclei

_____ 10. The ultimate source of energy trapped during photosynthesis is
(a) CO_2
(b) H_2O
(c) O_2
(d) sunlight

EXERCISE 9

Photosynthesis: Capture of Light Energy

POST-LAB QUESTIONS

9.2 Experiment: Effects of Light and Carbon on Starch Production

1. Is starch stored in the leaves of some plants? Would you expect leaves in a temperate climate plant to be the primary area for long-term starch storage? Why or why not? What part(s) of a plant might be better-suited for long-term starch storage?

9.3 Experiment: Relationship Between Light and Photosynthetic Products

2. Examine the photo at right, which shows the location of starch in two geranium leaves treated in much the same way as you did in Section 9.3. Explain the results you see.

(Photo by J.W. Perry.)

9.4 Experiment: Necessity of Photosynthetic Pigments for Photosynthesis

3. Examine the photo at right of a *Coleus* leaf. Describe an experiment that would allow you to determine whether the deep purple portion of the leaf is photosynthesizing.

(Photo by J.W. Perry.)

9.5 Experiment: Absorption of Light by Chloroplast Extract

4. The photo at right was taken through a spectroscope. What color was the pigment extract used to produce this spectrum? What color(s) did this extract absorb?

(Photo by J.W. Perry.)

5. Would you illuminate your house plants with a green light bulb? Why or why not?

9.7 Structure of the Chloroplast

6. Examine this electron micrograph of a chloroplast.

    a. Identify the stack of membranes labeled A.

    b. Identify the region labeled B.

    c. Would the production of organic compounds during the light-independent reactions occur in region B or on the membranes labeled A?

(17,257×).

(Photo by W. P. Wergin, courtesy E. H. Newcomb.)

    d. Would you expect the plant in which this structure was found to have been illuminated with strong light immediately before it was prepared for electron microscopy? Why or why not?

Food for Thought

7. Numerous hypotheses have been proposed for the extinction of the dinosaurs. Recently, evidence has been found of the impact of a large meteor at about the time of this mass extinction. The amount of dust and debris put into the atmosphere upon impact, as well as atmospheric heating, would have been enormous. Using your knowledge of photosynthesis, speculate as to why the dinosaurs subsequently became extinct.

8. Explain the statement: "Without autotrophic organisms, heterotrophic life would cease to exist."

9. Why do you suppose that a chloroplast kept in darkness for some time prior to being fixed for electron microscopy does not contain starch?

10. With the results of the preceding experiments in mind, what might you do to increase the vigor of your house plants?

Respiration: Energy Conversion

OBJECTIVES

After completing this exercise, you will be able to

1. define *metabolism, reaction, metabolic pathway, respiration, ATP, aerobic respiration, alcoholic fermentation;*

2. give the overall balanced equations for aerobic respiration and alcoholic fermentation;

3. distinguish among the inputs, products, and efficiency of aerobic respiration and those of fermentation;

4. explain the relationship between temperature and goldfish respiration rate;

5. identify the structures and list the functions of each part of a mitochondrion.

INTRODUCTION

The first law of thermodynamics states that energy can neither be created nor destroyed, only converted from one form to another. Because all living organisms have a constant energy requirement, they have mechanisms to gather, store, and use energy. Collectively, these mechanisms are called **metabolism.** A single, specific reaction that starts with one compound and ends up with another compound is a **reaction,** and a sequence of such reactions is a **metabolic pathway.**

In Exercise 9, we investigated the metabolic pathways by which green plants capture light energy and use it to make carbohydrates such as glucose. Carbohydrates are temporary energy stores. The process by which energy stored in carbohydrates is released to the cell is **respiration.**

Both autotrophs and heterotrophs undergo respiration. Photoautotrophs such as plants utilize the carbohydrates they have produced by photosynthesis to build new cells and maintain cellular machinery. Heterotrophic organisms may obtain materials for respiration in two ways: by digesting plant material or by digesting the tissues of animals that have previously digested plants.

Several different forms of respiration have evolved. The specific respiration pathway used depends on the specific organism and/or environmental conditions. In this exercise, we will consider two alternative pathways: (1) **aerobic respiration,** an oxygen-dependent pathway common in most organisms; and (2) **alcoholic fermentation,** an ethanol-producing process occurring in some yeasts.

Perhaps the most important aspect to remember about these two processes is that aerobic respiration is by far the most energy-efficient. **Efficiency** refers to the amount of energy captured in the form of ATP relative to the amount available within the bonds of the carbohydrate. **ATP, adenosine triphosphate,** is the so-called universal energy currency of the cell. Energy contained within the bonds of carbohydrates is transferred to ATP during respiration. This stored energy can be released later to power a wide variety of cellular reactions.

For aerobic respiration, the general equation is

$$C_6H_{12}O_6 + 6O_2 \xrightarrow{\text{enzymes}} 6CO_2 + 6H_2O + 36ATP^*$$

$$\text{glucose} \quad \text{oxygen} \qquad \text{carbon dioxide} \quad \text{water} \quad \text{chemical energy}$$

If glucose is completely broken down to CO_2 and H_2O, about 686,000 calories of energy are released. Each ATP molecule produced represents about 7500 calories of usable energy. The 36 ATP represent 270,000 calories of energy (36 × 7500 calories). Thus, aerobic respiration is about 39% efficient [(270,000/686,000) × 100%].

By contrast, fermentation yields only 2 ATP. Thus, these processes are only about 2% efficient [(2 × 7500/686,000) × 100%]. Obviously, breaking down carbohydrates by aerobic respiration gives a bigger payback than the other means.

---

*Depending on the tissue, as many as 38 ATP may be produced.

During the process of aerobic respiration, relatively high-energy carbohydrates are broken down in stepwise fashion, ultimately producing the low-energy products of carbon dioxide and water and transferring released energy into ATP. But what is the role of oxygen?

During aerobic respiration, the carbohydrate undergoes a series of oxidation–reduction reactions. Whenever one substance is oxidized (loses electrons), another must be reduced (accept, or gain, those electrons). The final electron acceptor in aerobic respiration is oxygen. Tagging along with the electrons as they pass through the electron transport process are protons (H^+). When the electrons and protons are captured by oxygen, water (H_2O) is formed:

$$2H^+ \ + \ 2e^- \ + \ \tfrac{1}{2} O_2 \longrightarrow H_2O$$

In the following experiments, we examine aerobic respiration in two sets of seeds.

A. Experiment: Carbon Dioxide Production *(About 25 min. for setup, 1 3/4 hr to complete)*

Seeds contain stored food material, usually in the form of some type of carbohydrate. When a seed germinates, the carbohydrate is broken down by aerobic respiration, liberating the energy (ATP) required for each embryo to grow into a seedling.

Two days ago, one set of dry pea seeds was soaked in water to start the germination process. Another set was not soaked. In this experiment, you will compare carbon dioxide production between germinating pea seeds, germinating pea seeds that have been boiled, and ungerminated (dry) pea seeds.

This experiment investigates the hypothesis that *germinating seeds produce carbon dioxide from aerobic respiration.*

MATERIALS

Per student group (4):
- 600-mL beaker
- hot plate *or* burner, wire gauze, tripod, and matches
- heat-resistant glove
- 3 respiration bottle apparatuses (Figure 10-1)
- china marker
- phenol red solution

Per lab room:
- germinating pea seeds
- ungerminated (dry) pea seeds

PROCEDURE

Work in groups of four.

1. Place about 250 mL of tap water in a 600-mL beaker, put the beaker on a heat source, and bring the water to a boil.
2. Obtain three respiration bottle setups (Figure 10-1). With a china marker, label one "Germ" for germinating pea seeds, the second "Germ-Boil" for those you will boil, and the third "Ungerm" for ungerminated seeds.
3. From the class supply, obtain and put enough germinating pea seeds into the two appropriately labeled respiration bottles to fill them approximately halfway. Fill the third bottle half full with ungerminated (dry) pea seeds.
4. Dump the germinating peas from the "Germ-Boil" bottle into the boiling waterbath; continue to boil for 5 minutes. After 5 minutes, turn off the heat source, put on a heat-resistant glove, and remove the water bath. Pour the

Figure 10-1   Respiration bottle apparatus.

water off into the sink and cool the boiled peas by pouring cold water into the beaker. Allow 5 minutes for the peas to cool to room temperature; then pour off the water. Now replace the peas into the "Germ-Boil" respiration bottle.
5. Fit the rubber stopper with attached glass tubes into the respiration bottles. Add enough water to the test tube to cover the end of the glass tubing that comes out of the respiration bottle. (This keeps gases from escaping from the respiration bottle.)
6. Insert rubber stoppers into the thistle tubes.
7. Set the three bottles aside for the next 1 1/4 hours and do the other experiments in this exercise.

8. Make a prediction about carbon dioxide production in each of the three bottles:

_____

_____

_____

Now start the next series of experiments while you allow this one to proceed.

9. After 1 1/4 hours, pour the water in each test tube into the sink and replace it with an equal volume of dilute phenol red solution. Phenol red solution, which should appear pinkish in the stock bottle, will be used to test for the presence of carbon dioxide (CO_2) within the respiration bottles. If CO_2 is bubbled through water, carbonic acid (H_2CO_3) forms:

$$CO_2 \;+\; H_2O \longrightarrow H_2CO_3$$

Phenol red solution is mostly water. When the phenol red solution is basic (pH > 7), it is pink; when it is acidic (pH < 7), the solution is yellow. The phenol red solution in the stock bottle is

_____ (color); therefore, the stock solution is

_____ (acidic/basic).

10. Put several hundred milliliters of tap water in the 600-mL beaker.
11. Remove the stopper plugging the top of the thistle tube and *slowly* pour water from the beaker into each thistle tube. The water will force out gases present in the bottles. If CO_2 is present, the phenol red will become yellow.
12. Record your observations in Table 10-1.

TABLE 10-1 CO_2 Evolution by Pea Seeds

Pea Seeds	Indicator Color (Phenol Red)	Conclusion (CO_2 Present or Absent)
Germinating—unboiled		
Germinating—boiled		
Ungerminated		

Which set(s) of seeds underwent respiration? _____

What happened during boiling that caused the results you found? (*Hint:* Think "enzymes.")

_____

Write a conclusion, accepting or rejecting the hypothesis.

_____

_____

B. Experiment: Oxygen Consumption (About 1 1/2 hr.)

One set of pea seeds has been soaked in water for the past 48 hours to initiate germination. In this section, you will measure oxygen consumption to answer the question, "Do germinating peas have a higher respiratory rate than ungerminated peas?"

MATERIALS

Per student group (4):

- volumeter (Figure 10-2)
- china marker
- 80 germinating pea seeds
- 80 ungerminated (dry) pea seeds
- glass beads

- nonabsorbent cotton
- metric ruler
- bottle of potassium hydroxide (KOH) pellets
- 1/4 teaspoon measure
- marker fluid in dropping bottle

PROCEDURE

Work in groups of four.

1. Obtain a volumeter set up as in Figure 10-2. Skip to step 6 if your instructor has already assembled the volumeters as described by steps 2–5.

2. Remove the test tubes from the volumeter. With a china marker, number the tubes and then fill as follows:

Tube 1: 80 germinating (soaked) pea seeds

Tube 2: 80 ungerminated (dry) pea seeds plus enough glass beads to bring the total volume equal to that in tube 1

Tube 3: Enough glass beads to equal the volume of tube 1

Figure 10-2 Volumeter.

Both temperature and pressure affect gas pressure within a closed tube. Tube 3 serves as a thermobarometer and is used as a control to correct experimental readings to account for changes in temperature and barometric pressure taking place during the experiment.

3. Pack cotton *loosely* into each tube to a thickness of about 1.5 cm above the peas/beads.

4. Measure out 1 cubic centimeter (cm^3) (about $^1/_4$ teaspoon) of KOH pellets and pour them atop the cotton.

Potassium hydroxide absorbs CO_2 given off during aerobic respiration. Since the volumeter measures change in gas volume, any gas *given off* during respiration must be removed from the tube so an accurate measure of O_2 consumption can be made.

> ### Caution
>
> *Potassium hydroxide can cause burns. Do not get any on your skin or clothing. If you do, wash immediately with copious amounts of water.*

5. Insert the stopper-syringe assembly in place.

6. Add a small drop of marker fluid to each side arm pipet by touching the dropper to the end of each. The drop should be taken into the side arm by capillary action. Gently withdraw the plunger of each syringe and adjust the position of the drop so it is between 0.80 and 0.90 cm^3 on the scale of the graduated pipet.

7. Adjust each side arm pipet so it is parallel to the table top. Wait 5 minutes before starting data collection.

8. In Table 10-2 at time 0, record the position of the marker droplet within each pipet. Record readings for each tube at 5-minute intervals for the next 60 minutes, keeping track of whether changes are positive (movement toward the test tube) or negative (movement away from the test tube).

If respiration is rapid and the marker drop moves too near the end of the scale to read, *carefully* use the syringe to readjust its position so it is between 0.80 and 0.90 cm^3 on the scale of the graduated pipet again. Note this in Table 10-2 and continue to record readings every 5 minutes.

9. To determine change in volume of gas within each tube at each sampling, subtract each subsequent reading from the previous reading.

10. Determine cumulative volume change (cumulative oxygen consumption) by adding each volume change to the previous volume-change measurement. The final figure represents the total oxygen consumption (in mL) in that tube.

11. At the end of the experiment, correct for any volume changes caused by changes in temperature or barometric pressure by using the reading obtained from the thermobarometer. If the thermobarometric marker moves *toward* the test tube (decrease in volume), *subtract* the volume change from the total oxygen consumption measurement of tubes 1 and 2. If the marker droplet moves *away* from the test tube (increase in volume), *add* the volume change to the last total oxygen consumption measurement for tubes 1 and 2.

12. In Figure 10-3, graph the consumption of oxygen over time. Use a + for data points of germinating peas, a • for dry peas.

How do the respiratory rates for germinating and nongerminating seeds compare?

_____

_____

How do you account for this difference?

_____

_____

It takes 820 cm^3 of oxygen to completely oxidize 1 g of glucose. How much glucose are the 80 germinating peas consuming per hour? (Recall that 1 cm^3 = 1 mL.)

TABLE 10-2 Respiratory Rate as Measured by Oxygen Consumption

Time (min.)	Tube 3: Thermobarometer		Tube 1: Germinating Peas			Tube 2: Dry Peas	
	Reading	Total Change in Volume	Reading	Total Change in Volume	Total Oxygen Consumption	Reading	Total Change in Volume	Total Oxygen Consumption
0		0		0	0		0	0
5								
10								
15								
20								
25								
30								
35								
40								
45								
50								
55								
60								

Figure 10-3 Oxygen consumption by germinating and nongerminating pea seeds.

10.2 Fermentation *(About 20 min. to set up, 1½ hr. to complete)*

Despite relatively low energy yield, fermentation provides sufficient energy for certain organisms to survive. Alcoholic fermentation by yeast is the basis for the baking, wine-making, and brewing industries. It's been said that yeast and alcoholic fermentation made Milwaukee famous.

The chemical equation for this process is

$$C_6H_{12}O_6 \longrightarrow 2CH_3CH_2OH + CO_2 + 2ATP$$

glucose   ethanol   carbon dioxide   energy

Starch (amylose), a common storage carbohydrate in plants, is a polymer consisting of a chain of repeating glucose ($C_6H_{12}O_6$) units. The polymer has the chemical formula ($C_6H_{12}O_6$)n,* where n represents a large number. Starch is broken down by the enzyme amylase into individual glucose units. To summarize:

$$(C_6H_{12}O_6)n \xrightarrow{\text{amylase}} C_6H_{12}O_6 + C_6H_{12}O_6 + C_6H_{12}O_6 + \ldots$$

starch   glucose

This section demonstrates the action of yeast cells on carbohydrates.

MATERIALS

Per student group (4):

- china marker
- three 50-mL beakers
- 25-mL graduated cylinder
- bottle of 10% glucose
- bottle of 1% starch
- 0.5% amylase in bottle fitted with graduated pipet
- 3 glass stirring rods

- 1/4 teaspoon measure (optional)
- 3 fermentation tubes
- 15-cm metric ruler

Per lab room:

- 0.5-g pieces of fresh yeast cake
- scale and weighing paper (optional)
- 37°C incubator

PROCEDURE

Work in groups of four.

1. Using a china marker, number three 50-mL beakers.
2. With a *clean* 25-mL graduated cylinder, measure out and pour 15 mL† of the following solutions into each beaker:

Note: Wash the graduated cylinder between solutions.

    Beaker 1: 15 mL of 10% glucose
    Beaker 2: 15 mL of 1% starch
    Beaker 3: 15 mL of 1% starch; then, using the graduated pipet to measure, add 5 mL of 0.5% amylase.

3. Wait 5 minutes and then to each beaker add a 0.5-g piece of fresh cake yeast. Stir with *separate* glass stirring rods.
4. When each is thoroughly mixed, pour the contents into three correspondingly numbered fermentation tubes (Figure 10-4). Cover the opening of the fermentation tube with your thumb and invert each fermentation tube so that the "tail" portion is filled with the solution.
5. Write a prediction about gas production in each tube.

_____

_____

_____

6. Place the tubes in a 37°C incubator.
7. At intervals of 20, 40, and 60 minutes after the start of the experiment, remove the tubes and, using a metric ruler, measure the distance from the tip of the tail to the fluid level. Record your results in Table 10-3. Calculate the volume of gas evolved using the formula below Table 10-3. (If time is short, do your calculations later.)

Figure 10-4 Fermentation tube.

---

*A number of carbohydrates share this same chemical formula but differ slightly in the arrangement of their atoms. These carbohydrates are called *structural isomers*.

†The amount of fluid needed to fill the fermentation tube depends on its size. Your instructor may indicate the required volume.

TABLE 10-3 Evolution of Gas by Yeast Cells

Tube	Solution	Distance from Tip of Tube to Fluid Level (mm) 20 min.	40 min.	60 min.	Volume of Gas Evolved (mm³)
1	10% glucose + yeast				
2	1% starch + yeast				
3	1% starch + yeast + amylase				

To calculate the volume of gas evolved, use the following equation: $V = \pi r^2 h$, where $\pi = 3.14$, r = radius of tail of fermentation tube [$r = \frac{1}{2} d$ (diameter)], h = distance from top of tail to level of solution.

Did your results conform to your predictions? If not, speculate on reasons why this might be so.

_____

_____

What gas accumulates in the tail portion of the fermentation tube?

_____

10.3   Experiment: Effect of Temperature on Goldfish Respiration *(About 1 hr.)*

All organisms respond to changes in their environment, often by changing their rate of respiration. Aerobic respiration is not completely efficient in converting glucose energy into ATP energy, and some energy is released as heat. Our bodies can respond to a decrease in environmental temperature (within limits) by increasing the rate of aerobic respiration in order to maintain a stable body temperature. We are considered *endothermic* animals, meaning that we control the heat balance from within our bodies.

Body temperature in *ectothermic* animals rises and falls with their surroundings and they are, figuratively speaking, at the mercy of their environment to a greater extent than endotherms. Activity levels may be closely associated with external temperatures. However, ectotherms may make behavioral changes to adjust to changing external temperatures.

Changes in behavior can be correlated with changes in carbohydrate metabolism. The previous experiments allowed you to determine which gases are used and produced during respiration. The respiratory cycle in fish, which accomplishes gas exchange between the environment and the fish, occurs when the water, laden with dissolved oxygen, enters the mouth and is forced out over the gill filaments when the mouth is closed. The oxygen dissolved in the water diffuses into the capillaries in the gill filaments and enters the blood.

Carbon dioxide, one of the products of respiration, diffuses from the blood across the gill filaments and into the water. The gill cover opens to allow the carbon dioxide–laden water to leave the gill chamber, thus completing the respiratory cycle.

By observing the action of the gill cover (determining the gill beat rate) in fishes (which are ectothermic animals) in this experiment, you will determine the effect of temperature on respiratory rate and the correlated metabolism rate. This experiment tests the hypothesis that *fish respiratory rates vary with temperature.*

MATERIALS

Per student group (4):
- aquarium (battery jar or 4-L beaker) filled with dechlorinated water at room temperature
- one goldfish
- Celsius thermometer with clip
- plastic dishpan
- crushed ice
- clock

PROCEDURE

1. Make a prediction regarding the outcome of your experiment. Identify the independent and dependent variables, and enter them in Table 10-4.

2. Place the goldfish in the aquarium with sufficient water to cover the dorsal (top) fin. Clip a thermometer on the edge of the container so you can read it without disturbing the fish. Take care to disturb the fish as little as possible.
3. Place the aquarium in the plastic dishpan. Determine the initial temperature of the water, and record it in Table 10-4.
4. Observe the movement of the operculum (gill cover). Count the movements of the operculum at the starting temperature for 1 minute. Repeat this procedure two more times. Record this gill beat rate data plus the average rate in Table 10-4.
5. Gradually add ice to the plastic container around the aquarium until the water temperature in it has been reduced to 25°C. If the starting temperature of the water is lower than 25°C, lower the temperature to 20°C. Wait 1 minute for the fish to adjust to the new temperature. Repeat step 4 and determine the gill beat rate.
6. Continue to lower the temperature of the water surrounding the fish with additional ice around the aquarium, waiting 1 minute each time a temperature is reached to allow acclimatization by the fish. Count operculum movements as described in step 5 at 15°C, 10°C, and 5°C. Record all data in Table 10-4.
7. At the end of the experiment, remove the aquarium containing the goldfish from the plastic container, and allow it to warm up gradually to room temperature.
8. Graph your average data points on Figure 10-5 to illustrate the manner in which goldfish gill beat rates ("breaths" per minute)—and hence cellular respiration—vary depending on water temperature.

TABLE 10-4 Operculum Movement of Goldfish as a Function of Temperature						
Prediction:						
Independent Variable:						
Dependent Variable:						
RESULTS:						
Trial	Starting Temperature ___°C	25°C	20°C	15°C	10°C	5°C
1						
2						
3						
Average						

9. Make a conclusion about your results, accepting or rejecting the hypothesis.

_____

_____

_____

What controls might you have used for this experiment?

_____

_____

_____

At which temperature was the gill beat rate highest?

_____

Figure 10-5 Relationship between gill beat rate and temperature in goldfish.

What is the relationship between the increase in water temperature and gill beat rate in goldfish? Why?

_____

_____

1. Study Figure 10-6b, which shows the three-dimensional structure of a mitochondrion, the respiratory organelle of all living eukaryotic cells. The mitochondrion has frequently been referred to as the "power-house of the cell," because most of the cell's chemical energy (ATP) is produced here.

Figure 10-6   **(a)** The pathways in aerobic respiration. **(b)** The membranes and compartments of a mitochondrion.

2. Now observe Figure 10-7, a high-magnification electron micrograph of a mitochondrion. Identify and label the **outer membrane** separating the organelle from the cytoplasm.

3. Note the presence of an inner membrane, folded into fingerlike projections. Each projection is called a **crista** (the plural is *cristae*). The folding of the inner membrane greatly increases the surface area on which many of the chemical reactions of aerobic respiration take place. Label the crista.

4. Identify and label the **outer compartment,** the space between the inner and outer membranes. The outer compartment serves as a reservoir for hydrogen ions.

5. Finally, identify and label the **inner compartment** (filled with the *matrix*), the interior of the mitochondrion.

6. Study Figure 10-6a, a diagram of the pathways in aerobic respiration.

Figure 10-7   Transmission electron micrograph of a mitochondrion (18,600×).
Labels: outer membrane, inner membrane, crista, intermembrane compartment, matrix

Now that you know the structure of the mitochondrion, you can visualize the events that take place to produce the chemical energy needed for life. Glycolysis, the first step in *all* respiration pathways, takes place in the cytoplasm. Pyruvate, a carbohydrate, and energy carriers formed during glycolysis enter the mitochondrion during aerobic respiration, moving through both the outer and inner membranes to the matrix within the inner compartment.

Within the inner compartment, the pyruvate is broken down in the Krebs cycle, forming more energy-carrier molecules as well as CO_2. A small amount of ATP is also produced during these reactions.

Electron transport molecules are embedded on the inner membrane, and ATP production occurs as hydrogen ions cross from the outer compartment to the inner compartment. Water is also formed. This accomplishes the third portion of aerobic respiration, electron transport phosphorylation.

Note: After completing all labs, take your dirty glassware to the sink and wash it following the directions given in *"Instructions for Washing Laboratory Glassware,"* page x. Invert the test tubes in the test tube racks so that they drain. Tidy up your work area, making certain all equipment used in this exercise is there for the next class.

PRE-LAB QUESTIONS

_____ 1. A metabolic pathway is
   (a) a single, specific reaction that starts with one compound and ends up with another
   (b) a sequence of chemical reactions that are part of the metabolic process
   (c) a series of events that occur only in autotrophs
   (d) all of the above

_____ 2. The "universal energy currency" of the cell is
   (a) O_2
   (b) $C_6H_{12}O_6$
   (c) ATP
   (d) H_2O

_____ 3. Products of aerobic respiration include
   (a) glucose
   (b) oxygen
   (c) carbon dioxide
   (d) starch

_____ 4. "Efficiency" of a respiration pathway refers to the
   (a) number of steps in the pathway
   (b) amount of CO_2 produced relative to the amount of carbohydrate entering the pathway
   (c) amount of H_2O produced relative to the amount of carbohydrate entering the pathway
   (d) amount of ATP energy produced relative to the energy content of the carbohydrate entering the pathway

_____ 5. The purpose of the thermobarometer in a volumeter is to
   (a) judge the amount of O_2 evolved during respiration
   (b) determine the volume changes as a result of respiration

   (c) indicate oxygen consumption by germinating pea seeds
   (d) indicate volume changes resulting from changes in temperature or barometric pressure

_____ 6. Phenol red is used in the experiments as
   (a) an O_2 indicator
   (b) a CO_2 indicator
   (c) a sugar indicator
   (d) an enzyme

_____ 7. As temperatures rise, the body temperatures of _____ organisms rise.
   (a) ectothermic
   (b) endothermic
   (c) autotrophic
   (d) heterotrophic

_____ 8. Which of the following enzymes breaks down starch into glucose?
   (a) kinase
   (b) maltase
   (c) fructase
   (d) amylase

_____ 9. Oxygen is necessary for life because
   (a) photosynthesis depends on it
   (b) it serves as the final electron acceptor during aerobic respiration
   (c) it is necessary for glycolysis
   (d) of all of the above

_____ 10. Yeast cells undergoing alcoholic fermentation produce
   (a) ATP
   (b) ethanol
   (c) CO_2
   (d) all of the above

EXERCISE 10

Respiration: Energy Conversion

POST-LAB QUESTIONS

10.1 *Aerobic Respiration*

1. Explain the role of the following components in the experiment on carbon dioxide production (page 132).

germinating pea seeds   _____

ungerminated (dry) pea seeds   _____

germinating, boiled pea seeds   _____

phenol red solution   _____

2. If you performed the experiment on oxygen consumption (page 133) without adding KOH pellets to the test tubes, what results would you predict? Why?

10.2 *Fermentation*

3. Sucrose (table sugar) is a disaccharide composed of glucose and fructose. Glycogen is a polysaccharide composed of many glucose subunits. Which of the following fermentation tubes would you expect to produce the greatest gas volume over a 1-hour period? Why?

Tube 1: glucose plus yeast

Tube 2: sucrose plus yeast

Tube 3: glycogen plus yeast

4. Bread is made by mixing flour, water, sugar, and yeast to form a dense dough. Why does the dough rise? What gas is responsible for the holes in bread?

10.3 *Experiment: Effect of Temperature on Goldfish Respiration*

5. Warmer water holds less dissolved oxygen than cooler water. Use this information plus that which you gleaned from this experiment to more fully explain why the gill beat rate of a fish increases as water temperature increases.

10.4 Ultrastructure of the Mitochondrion

6. Examine the electron micrograph of the mitochondrion on the right.

   a. What portions of aerobic respiration occur in
   region b?

   _____

   b. What substance is produced as hydrogen
   ions cross from the space between the inner
   and outer membranes into region b?

   _____

   c. What portion of cellular respiration takes
   place in the cytoplasm *outside* of this
   organelle?

   _____

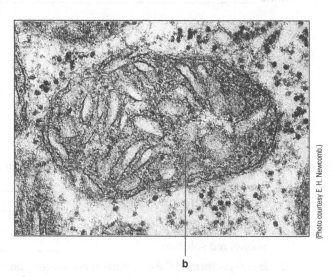

b

(20,000×).

(Photo courtesy E. H. Newcomb.)

Food for Thought

7. Oxygen is used during aerobic respiration. What biological process is the source of the oxygen?

8. Compare aerobic respiration and fermentation in terms of

   a. efficiency of obtaining energy from glucose

   b. end products

9. How would you explain this statement: "The ultimate source of our energy is the sun"?

10. The first law of thermodynamics seems to conflict with what we know about ourselves. For example, after
strenuous exercise we run out of "energy." We must eat to replenish our energy stores. Where has that
energy gone? What form has it taken?

Mitosis and Cytokinesis: Nuclear and Cytoplasmic Division

OBJECTIVES

After completing this exercise, you will be able to

1. define *fertilization, zygote, DNA, chromosome, mitosis, cytokinesis, nucleoprotein, sister chromatid, centromere, meristem;*

2. identify the stages of the cell cycle;

3. distinguish between mitosis and cytokinesis as they take place in animal and plant cells;

4. identify the structures involved in nuclear and cell division (those in **boldface**) and describe the role each plays.

INTRODUCTION

"All cells arise from preexisting cells." This is one tenet of the cell theory. It's easy to understand this concept if you think of a single-celled *Amoeba* or bacterium. Each cell divides to give rise to two entirely new individuals, and it is fascinating that each of us began life as *one* single cell and developed into this astonishingly complex animal, the human. Our first cell has *all* the hereditary information we'll ever get.

In higher plants and animals, **fertilization,** the fusion of egg and sperm nuclei, produces a single-celled **zygote**. The zygote divides into two cells, these two into four, and so on to produce a multicellular organism. During cell division, each new cell receives a complete set of hereditary information and an assortment of cytoplasmic components.

Recall from Exercise 6 that there are two basic cell types, prokaryotic and eukaryotic. The genetic material of both consists of **DNA (deoxyribonucleic acid).** In prokaryotes, the DNA molecule is organized into a single circular **chromosome.** Prior to cell division, the chromosome duplicates. Then the cell undergoes **fission,** the splitting of a preexisting cell into two, with each new cell receiving a full complement of the genetic material.

In eukaryotes, the process of cell division is more complex, primarily because of the much more complex nature of the hereditary material. Here the chromosomes consist of DNA and proteins complexed together within the nucleus. Cell division is preceded by duplication of the chromosomes and usually involves two processes: **mitosis** (nuclear division) and **cytokinesis** (cytoplasmic division). Whereas mitosis results in the production of two nuclei, both containing identical chromosomes, cytokinesis ensures that each new cell contains all the metabolic machinery necessary for sustenance of life.

In this exercise, we consider only what occurs in eukaryotic cells.

Dividing cells pass through a regular sequence of events called the cell cycle (Figure 11-1). Notice that the majority of the time is spent in interphase and that actual nuclear division—mitosis—is but a brief portion of the cycle.

Interphase is comprised of three parts (Figure 11-1): the G1 period, during which cytoplasmic growth takes place; the S period, when the DNA is duplicated; and the G2 period, when structures directly involved in mitosis are synthesized.

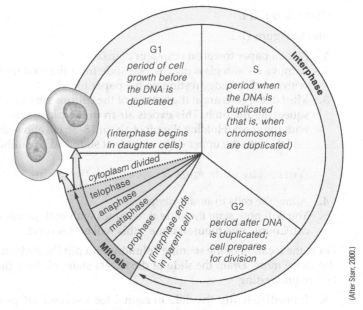

Figure 11-1 The eukaryotic cell cycle.

(After Starr, 2000.)

Unfortunately, because of the apparent relative inactivity that early microscopists observed, interphase was given the misnomer "resting stage." In fact, we know now that interphase is anything but a resting period. The cell is producing new DNA, assembling proteins from amino acids, and synthesizing or breaking down carbohydrates. In short, interphase is a very busy time in the life of a cell.

11.1   Chromosomal Structure *(About 25 min. without drying time)*

During much of a cell's life, each DNA–protein complex, the **nucleoprotein,** is extended as a thin strand within the nucleus. In this form, it is called **chromatin.** Prior to the onset of nuclear division, the genetic material duplicates itself. As nuclear division begins, the chromatin condenses. The two identical condensed nucleoproteins are called **sister chromatids** and are attached at the **centromere.** The centromere gives the appearance of dividing each chromatid into two "arms." Collectively, the two attached sister chromatids are referred to as a *duplicated chromosome.* Before looking at actual chromosomes, let's examine the background of the materials we'll use.

In 1951, Henrietta Lacks died from cervical cancer. Prior to her death, some of the cancerous (tumor) cells were removed from her body and grown in culture. The cells were allowed to divide repeatedly in this artificial culture environment and resulted in the formation of what is known as a *cell line.* These HeLa cells (the abbreviation coming from *He*nrietta *La*cks) live on today and are used for research on cell and tumor growth. They're also used to show chromosomal structure in the biology laboratory.

Normal human body cells contain 23 pairs of chromosomes (46 total chromosomes). Human cells of tumor origin (such as the HeLa cells) often produce greater chromosome numbers when grown in culture. Cells containing up to 200 chromosomes have been observed, although 50–70 per cell are most frequently found. In this section, you will observe the chromosomes of the descendant tumor cells of Henrietta Lacks.

Note: There is no danger from this activity. The tumor-producing properties are nontransmissible, and the cells have been killed and preserved.

MATERIALS

Per student:
- clean microscope slide prechilled in cold 40% methanol
- coverslip
- disposable pipet
- paper toweling
- compound microscope (with oil-immersion objective preferable)

Per student pair:
- metric ruler
- tube of HeLa cells
- dropper bottle containing Permount mounting medium or dH_2O

Per lab room:
- Coplin staining jars containing stains 1 and 2
- 1-L beaker containing dH_2O

PROCEDURE

Refer to Figure 11-2.

1. Place a paper towel on your work surface.
2. Remove a clean glass microscope slide from the cold methanol and lean it against a surface at a 45° angle, with one short edge resting on the paper towel.
3. Most of the cells are at the bottom of the culture tube. Gently resuspend the cells by inserting your pipet and squeezing the bulb. This expels air from the pipet, which disperses the cells. Remove a small cell sample with the pipet. Holding the pipet about 18–36 cm above the slide, allow 8–10 drops of the cell suspension to "splat" onto the upper edge of the wet slide and to tumble down the slide.

   Note: The slide must be wet when "splatting" takes place.

4. Allow the cells to *air-dry completely.*
5. You will now stain the slide three times with both stains, for *1 second each time.* The time in the stain is critical. Count "one thousand one"; this will be 1 second.

Go to the location of the staining solutions and dip the slide in stain 1 for 1 second. Withdraw the slide and then dip twice more. Drain the slide of the excess stain, blotting the bottom edge of the slide on the paper toweling before proceeding.

6. Immediately dip the slide in stain 2 for 1 second. (Repeat twice more.) Drain and blot the excess stain as before.

Figure 11-2 Applying HeLa cells to slide.

7. Rinse the slide in dH$_2$O by swishing it gently back and forth in the beaker.
8. Allow the slides to *air-dry completely*.
9. If making a permanent preparation, place 2 drops of Permount mounting medium on the slide in the region of the stained cells. Using the technique illustrated in Figure 3-9 (page 35), place a coverslip on the slide. (*Note:* Of course, you *do not* add the drop of water shown in Figure 3-9.) Squeeze out excess Permount by applying gentle pressure to the coverslip with the blunt eraser end of a pencil.

A nonpermanent preparation can be made by adding a drop of water to the preparation and making a traditional wet mount slide. Viewing may then proceed immediately.

10. Place the slide on the microscope stage and observe your chromosome spread, focusing first with the medium-power objective and then with the high-dry objective. Locate cells that appear to have burst and have the chromosomes spread out. The number of good spreads will be low; so careful observation of many cells is necessary.

    Note: If your microscope has an oil-immersion objective, proceed to step 11. If not, skip to step 12.

11. Once a good spread has been located, rotate the high-dry objective out of the light path and place a drop of immersion oil on that spot. Rotate the oil-immersion objective into the light path.
12. Observe the structure of the chromosomes, identifying sister chromatids and centromeres. Draw several of the chromosomes in Figure 11-3, labeling these parts.

> **Caution**
>
> *Allow Permount to dry for an hour before attempting to view if using an oil-immersion objective.*

Figure 11-3 Drawing of human chromosomes from HeLa cells. (_____×)
Labels: chromosome, sister chromatid, centromere

13. Select 10 cells in which the chromosomes are visible and count the number of chromosomes you observe in each cell, inserting your results in Table 11-1. When you have counted the chromosomes in 10 individual cells, calculate the average number of chromosomes per cell.

TABLE 11-1 Chromosome Numbers in HeLa Cells										
Cell	1	2	3	4	5	6	7	8	9	10	Average

Now examine Figure 11-4, an electron micrograph of a human chromosome. Label the two chromatids, the centromere, and the duplicated chromosome.

(Photo by E. J. DuPraw.)

Figure 11-4 Electron micrograph of a chromosome (26,000×).
Labels: chromatid (2), centromere, duplicated chromosome

Note: Use illustrations in your textbook to aid you in the following study.

11.2 The Cell Cycle in Plant Cells: Onion Roots *(About 45 min.)*

Nuclear and cell divisions in plants are, for the most part, localized in specialized regions called meristems. **Meristems** are regions of active growth. A meristem contains cells that have the capability to divide repeatedly.

Plants have two types of meristems: apical and lateral. Apical meristems are found at the tips of plant organs (shoots and roots) and increase length. Lateral meristems, located beneath the bark of woody plants, increase girth. In this section, you will examine structures related to the cell cycle in the apical meristem of onion roots.

MATERIALS

Per student:

- prepared slide of onion, *Allium*, root tip mitosis
- compound microscope

PROCEDURE

Obtain a prepared slide of a longitudinal section (l.s.) of an *Allium* (onion) root tip. This slide has been prepared from the terminal several millimeters of an actively growing root. It was "fixed" (killed) by chemicals to preserve the cellular structure and stained with dyes that have an affinity for the structures involved in nuclear division.

Focus first with the low-power objective of your compound microscope to get an overall impression of the root's morphology.

Concentrate your study in the region about 1 mm behind the actual tip. This region is the apical meristem of the root (Figure 11-5). Keep in mind that the cell cycle is a continuous cycle; we separate events into different stages as a convenience to aid in their study, but it is often difficult to say definitively when one phase begins and another ends.

1. **Interphase.** Use the medium-power objective to scan the apical meristem. Note that most of the nuclei are in interphase.

   Switch to the high-dry objective, focusing on a single interphase cell. Note the distinct **nucleus,** with one or more **nucleoli,** and the **chromatin** dispersed within the bounds of the **nuclear envelope.** Label these features in cell 1 of Figure 11-6.

2. **Mitosis.**

   (a) *Prophase.* During **prophase** the chromatin condenses, rendering the duplicated chromosomes visible as threadlike structures. At the same time, microtubules outside the nucleus are beginning to assemble into **spindle fibers.** Collectively, the spindle fibers make up the **spindle,** a three-dimensional structure widest in the middle and tapering to a point at the two **poles** (opposite ends of the cell). *You will not see the spindle during prophase.*

   Find a nucleus in prophase. Draw and label a prophase nucleus in cell 2 of Figure 11-6.

   The transition from prophase to metaphase is marked by the fragmentation and disappearance of the nuclear envelope. At about the same time, the nucleoli disappear.

   (b) *Metaphase.* When the nuclear envelope is no longer distinct, the cell is in **metaphase.** Identify a metaphase cell by locating a cell with the duplicated chromosomes, each consisting of two **sister chromatids,** lined up midway between the two poles. This imaginary midline is called the **spindle equator.** (You will not be able to distinguish the chromatids.) The spindle has moved into the space the nucleus once occupied. The microtubules have become attached to the chromosomes at the **kinetochores,** groups of proteins that form the outer faces of the centromeres. Find a cell in metaphase. Label cell 3 of Figure 11-6.

   (c) *Anaphase.* During **anaphase** sister chromatids of each chromosome separate, each chromatid moving toward an opposite pole.

   Find an early anaphase cell, recognizable by the slightly separated chromatids. Notice that the chromatids begin separating at the centromere. The last point of contact before separation is complete is at the ends of the "arms" of each chromatid. Although incompletely understood, the mechanism of chromatid separation is based on action of the spindle-fiber microtubules. Once separated, each chromatid is referred to as an individual daughter chromosome. Note that now the chromosome consists of a *single* chromatid.

   Find a late anaphase cell and draw it in cell 4 of Figure 11-6.

   (d) *Telophase.* When the daughter chromosomes arrive at opposite poles, the cell is in **telophase.** The spindle disorganizes. The chromosomes expand again into chromatin form, and a nuclear envelope re-forms around each newly formed daughter nucleus.

   Find a telophase cell and label individual chromosomes, nuclei, and nuclear envelopes on cell 5 of Figure 11-6.

apical meristem of root

root cap

(Photo by J. W. Perry.)

Figure 11-5 Root tip, l.s. (20×).

B. Cytokinesis in Onion Cells

Cytokinesis, division of the cytoplasm, usually follows mitosis. In fact, it often overlaps with telophase. Find a cell undergoing cytokinesis in the onion root tip. In plants, cytokinesis takes place by **cell plate formation** (Figure 11-7). During this process, Golgi body–derived vesicles migrate to the spindle equator, where they fuse. Their contents contribute to the formation of a new cell wall, and their membranes make up the new plasma membranes. In most plants, cell plate formation starts in the *middle* of the cell.

1. Examine Figure 11-7, an electron micrograph showing cell plate formation. Note the microtubules that are part of the spindle apparatus.
2. Find a cell undergoing cytokinesis on the prepared slide of onion root tips. With your light microscope, the developing **cell plate** appears as a line running horizontally between the two newly formed nuclei. Return to cell 5 of Figure 11-6 and label the developing cell plate.

Recently divided cells are often easy to distinguish by their square, boxy appearance. Find two recently divided **daughter cells**; then draw and label their contents in cell 6 of Figure 11-6. Include cytoplasm, nuclei, nucleoli, nuclear envelopes, and chromatin.

What is the difference between chromatin and chromosomes?

Figure 11-6 Interphase, mitosis, and cytokinesis in onion root tip cells.
Labels: interphase, cytoplasm, nucleus, nucleolus, chromatin, nuclear envelope, metaphase, spindle fibers, spindle, pole, spindle equator (between arrows), sister chromatids, telophase and cell plate formation, chromosome, cell plate, daughter cell
(*Note:* Some terms are used more than once.)

(Photo by W. P. Wergin, courtesy of E. H. Newcomb.)

daughter
nucleus
(portion)

cell wall

spindle
micro-
tubules

cell plate

daughter
nucleus
(portion)

Figure 11-7 Transmission electron micrograph of cytokinesis by cell plate formation in a plant cell (2000×).

Following cytokinesis, the cell undergoes a period of growth and enlargement, during which time the nucleus is in interphase. Interphase may be followed by another mitosis and cytokinesis, or in some cells interphase may persist for the rest of a cell's life.

C. Duration of Phases of the Cell Cycle

An onion root tip preparation can be thought of as a snapshot capturing cells in various phases of the cell cycle at a particular moment in time. The frequency of occurrence of a cell cycle phase is directly proportional to the length of a phase. You can therefore estimate the amount of time each phase takes by tallying the proportions of cells in each phase.

The length of the cell cycle for cells in actively dividing onion root tips is approximately 24 hours, with mitosis lasting for about 90 minutes.

1. Examine the meristem region of an onion root tip slide. Count the number of cells in each of the stages of mitosis plus interphase in one field of view. Repeat this procedure for other fields of view until you count 100 cells. Record your data in Table 11-2.
2. Now calculate the time spent in each stage based on a 24-hour cell cycle by dividing the number of cells in each stage by the total number of cells counted to determine percent of total cells in each stage.
3. Multiply the fraction obtained in step 2 by 24 to determine duration.
   Although your calculations are only a rough approximation of the time spent in each stage, they do illustrate the differences in duration of each stage in the cell cycle.

TABLE 11-2	Determining Duration of Cell Cycle Phases		
Phase	Number Seen	% of Total	Duration (hrs)
Interphase			
Prophase			
Metaphase			
Anaphase			
Telophase			
Total			

11.3   The Cell Cycle in Animal Cells: Whitefish Blastula *(About 20 min.)*

Fertilization of an ovum by a sperm produces a zygote. In animal cells, the zygote undergoes a special type of cell division, *cleavage*, in which no increase in cytoplasm occurs between divisions. A ball of cells called a blastula is produced by cleavage. Within the blastula, repeated nuclear and cytoplasmic divisions take place; consequently, the whitefish blastula is an excellent example in which to observe the cell cycle of an animal.

Note a key difference between plants and animals: Whereas plants have meristems where divisions continually take place, animals do not have specialized regions to which mitosis and cytokinesis are limited. Indeed, divisions occur continually throughout many tissues of an animal's body, replacing worn-out or damaged cells.

With several important exceptions, mitosis in animals is remarkably like that in plants. These exceptions will be pointed out as we go through the cell cycle.

MATERIALS

Per student:

- prepared slide of whitefish blastula mitosis
- compound microscope

PROCEDURE

Obtain a slide labeled "whitefish blastula." Scan it with the low-power objective and then at medium power. This slide has numerous thin sections of a blastula. Select one section (Figure 11-8) and then switch to the high-dry objective for detailed observation.

As you examine the slides, draw the cells to show the correct sequence of events in the cell cycle of whitefish blastula.

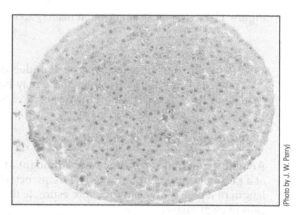

Figure 11-8   Section of a whitefish blastula (75×).

(Photo by J. W. Perry)

A. Interphase and Mitosis

1. **Interphase.** Locate a cell in **interphase**. As you observed in the onion root tip, note the presence of the nucleus and chromatin within it. Note also the absence of a cell wall.

    Draw an interphase cell above the word "Interphase" in Figure 11-9 and label the cytoplasm, nucleus, and plasma membrane.

2. **Mitosis.**

    (a) *Prophase.* The first obvious difference between mitosis in plants and animals is found in **prophase.** Unlike the onion cells, those of whitefish contain **centrioles** (Figure 11-10). As seen with the electron microscope, centrioles are barrel-shaped structures consisting of nine radially arranged triplets of microtubules.

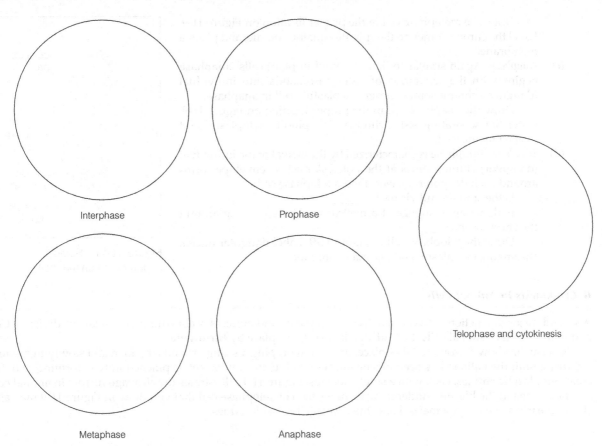

Interphase

Prophase

Telophase and cytokinesis

Metaphase

Anaphase

Figure 11-9 Drawings of cell cycle stages in whitefish blastula.
Labels: cytoplasm, nucleus, plasma membrane, spindle, chromosomes, spindle equator, sister chromatids, daughter nuclei, chromatin, furrow
(*Note:* Some terms are used more than once.)

One pair of centrioles was present in the cytoplasm in the G1 stage of interphase. These centrioles duplicated during the S stage of interphase. Subsequently, one new and one old centriole migrated to each pole.

Although the centrioles are too small to be resolved with your light microscope, you can see a starburst pattern of spindle fibers that appear to radiate from the centrioles. Other microtubules extend between the centrioles, forming the **spindle** (Figure 11-11). The chromosomes become visible as the chromatin condenses.

Find a prophase cell, identifying the spindle and starburst cluster of fibers about the centriole.

Draw the prophase cell in the proper location on Figure 11-9. Label the spindle, chromosomes, cytoplasm, and the position of the plasma membrane.

(b) *Metaphase.* As was the case in plant cells, during **metaphase** the spindle fiber microtubules become attached to the **kinetechore** of each centromere region, and the duplicated chromosomes (each consisting of two **sister chromatids**) line up on the **spindle equator.** Locate a metaphase cell.

triplet of microtubules

Figure 11-10
(a) Transmission electron micrograph (122,000×); **(b)** artist's drawing of centriole.

a

b

(Photo courtesy I. R. Gibbons.)

Draw the metaphase cell in the proper location on Figure 11-9. Label the chromosomes on the spindle equator, spindle, and plasma membrane.

(c) *Anaphase.* Again similar to that observed in plant cells, **anaphase** begins with the separation of sister chromatids into individual (daughter) chromosomes. Observe a blastula cell in anaphase.

Draw the anaphase cell in the proper location on Figure 11-9. Label the separating sister chromatids, spindle, cytoplasm, and plasma membrane.

(d) *Telophase.* **Telophase** is characterized by the arrival of the individual (daughter) chromosomes at the poles. A nuclear envelope forms around each daughter nucleus. Find a telophase cell.

Is the spindle still visible? _____

Is there any evidence of a nuclear envelope forming around the chromosomes?_____

Draw the telophase cell in Figure 11-9. Label daughter nuclei, chromatin, cytoplasm, and plasma membrane.

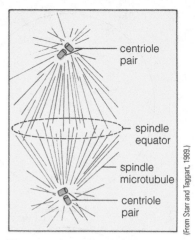

(From Starr and Taggart, 1989.)

Figure 11-11 Spindle apparatus in animal cell.

B. Cytokinesis in Animal Cells

A second major distinction between cell division in plants and animals occurs during cytoplasmic division. Cell plates are absent in animal cells. Instead, cytokinesis takes place by **furrowing.**

To visualize how furrowing takes place, imagine wrapping a string around a balloon and slowly tightening the string until the balloon has been pinched in two. In life, the animal cell is pinched in two, forming two discrete cytoplasmic entities, each with a single nucleus. Figure 11-12 illustrates the cleavage furrow in animal cell.

Find a cell in the blastula undergoing cytokinesis. The telophase cell that you drew in Figure 11-9 may also show an early stage of cytokinesis. Label the cleavage furrow if it does.

   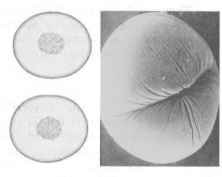

(a) Mitosis is completed and the bipolar spindle is starting to disassemble.

(b) At the former spindle equator, a ring of actin filaments attached to the plasma membrane contracts.

(c) The diameter of the contractile ring continues to shrink and pull the cell surface inward.

(d) The contractile mechanism continues to operate until the cytoplasm is partitioned.

(e)

(After Starr, 2000.) (Photo © D. M. Phillips, Visuals Unlimited.)

Figure 11-12 (a–d) Cytoplasmic division of an animal cell. **(e)** Scanning electron micrograph of the cleavage furrow at the plane of the former spindle equator.

11.4 Chromosome Squashes *(About 30 min.)*

You can make your own chromosome squash preparation quite simply. Cytologists and taxonomists do this routinely to count chromosomes. Observing whole sets of chromosomes is useful for studying chromosomal abnormalities and for determining if two organisms are different species.

MATERIALS

Per student:

- onion or daffodil root tips
- sharp razor blade
- 2 dissecting needles
- microscope slide and coverslip
- compound microscope

Per student pair:

- acetocarmine stain in dropping bottle
- iron alum in dropping bottle
- burner and matches

PROCEDURE

You will use onion or daffodil root tips that have been fixed, preserved, and softened to make squashes.

1. Obtain a single root and place it on a clean microscope slide. Notice that the terminal 2 mm or so is opaque white. This is the apical meristem.
2. With a sharp razor blade, separate the apical meristem from the rest of the root. Discard all *but* this meristem region.
3. Add a drop of acetocarmine stain and tease the tissue apart with dissecting needles.
4. Add a drop of iron alum. The iron intensifies the staining of the chromosomes.
5. Place a coverslip over the root tip. Spread the cells out by gently pressing down on the coverslip with your finger or a pencil eraser. Gently heat the slide over a flame.

> **Caution**
>
> *Be careful. You don't want to cause the fluid to boil away!*

6. Examine the preparation with your light microscope. Identify all stages of the cell cycle that have been described above.

   What do you notice about the shape of the cells after this preparation?

   _____

   _____

11.5   Simulating Mitosis *(About 20 min.)*

Understanding chromosome movements is crucial to understanding mitosis. You can simulate mitosis with a variety of materials. This is a simple activity, but a valuable one. It will be especially helpful when comparing the events of mitosis with those of meiosis in the next exercise.

MATERIALS

Per student pair:

- 44 pop beads each of two colors
- 8 magnetic centromeres

PROCEDURE

1. Build the components for two pairs of chromosomes by assembling strings of pop beads as follows:
   - **(a)** Assemble two strands of pop beads with 8 pop beads of one color on each arm, with a magnetic centromere connecting the two arms.
   - **(b)** Repeat step a, but use pop beads of the second color.
   - **(c)** Assemble two more strands of pop beads, but with 3 pop beads of one color on each arm.
   - **(d)** Repeat step c, using pop beads of the second color.

   You should have four long strings, two of each color, and four short strings, with two of each color. Each pop bead string should have a magnetic centromere at its midpoint. Note that pop bead strings can attach to each other at the magnetic centromere. Each pop bead string represents a single molecule of DNA plus proteins.
2. Place **one** of each kind of strand in the center of your workspace, which represents the nucleus. You have created a nucleus with four "chromosomes," two long and two short.
3. Manipulate these model chromosomes through the phases of the cell cycle, beginning in the G1 phase of interphase and proceeding through the rest of interphase, mitosis, and cytokinesis.

_____ 1. Reproduction in prokaryotes occurs primarily through the process known as
(a) mitosis
(b) cytokinesis
(c) furrowing
(d) fission

_____ 2. The genetic material (DNA) of eukaryotes is organized into
(a) centrioles
(b) spindles
(c) chromosomes
(d) microtubules

_____ 3. The process of cytoplasmic division is known as
(a) meiosis
(b) cytokinesis
(c) mitosis
(d) fission

_____ 4. The product of chromosome duplication is
(a) two chromatids
(b) two nuclei
(c) two daughter cells
(d) two spindles

_____ 5. The correct sequence of stages in _mitosis_ is
(a) interphase, prophase, metaphase, anaphase, telophase
(b) prophase, metaphase, anaphase, telophase
(c) metaphase, anaphase, prophase, telophase
(d) prophase, telophase, anaphase, interphase

_____ 6. During prophase, duplicated chromosomes
(a) consist of chromatids
(b) contain centromeres
(c) consist of nucleoproteins
(d) contain all of the above

_____ 7. During the S period of interphase
(a) cell growth takes place
(b) nothing occurs because this is a resting period
(c) chromosomes divide
(d) synthesis (or replication) of the nucleoproteins takes place

_____ 8. Chromatids separate during
(a) prophase
(b) telophase
(c) cytokinesis
(d) anaphase

_____ 9. Cell plate formation
(a) occurs in plant cells but not in animal cells
(b) usually begins during telophase
(c) is a result of fusion of Golgi vesicles
(d) is all of the above

_____ 10. Centrioles and a starburst cluster of spindle fibers would be found in
(a) both plant and animal cells
(b) only plant cells
(c) only animal cells
(d) none of the above

EXERCISE 11

Mitosis and Cytokinesis: Nuclear and Cytoplasmic Division

POST-LAB QUESTIONS

Introduction

1. Distinguish among interphase, mitosis, and cytokinesis.

11.1 Chromosomal Structure

2. Distinguish between the structure of a duplicated chromosome before mitosis and the chromosome produced by separation of two chromatids during mitosis.

11.2 The Cell Cycle in Plant Cells: Onion Roots

3. If the chromosome number of a typical onion root tip cell is 16 before mitosis, what is the chromosome number of each newly formed nucleus after nuclear division has taken place?

4. In plants, what name is given to a region where mitosis occurs most frequently?

5. The cells in the following photomicrographs have been stained to show microtubules comprising the spindle apparatus. Identify the stage of mitosis in each and label the region indicated on (**b**). (Photos by Andrew S. Bajer.)

  region? _____

a stage? _____   **b** stage? _____   **c** stage? _____

6. Name two features of animal cell mitosis and cytokinesis you can use to distinguish these processes from those occurring in plant cells.

   a.

   b.

Food for Thought

7. Observe photomicrographs (**a**) and (**b**) below. Is (**a**) from a plant or an animal?

   Note the double nature of the blue "threads." Each individual component of the doublet is called a _____. Is (**b**) from a plant or an animal? (Photos by Andrew S. Bajer.)

a plant or animal?

_____

structure?

_____

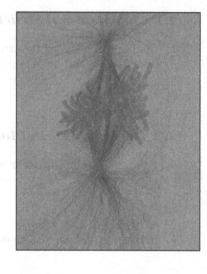

b plant or animal?

_____

8. Why do you suppose cytokinesis generally occurs in the cell's midplane?

9. Why must the DNA be duplicated during the S phase of the cell cycle, prior to mitosis?

10. What would happen if a cell underwent mitosis but not cytokinesis?

Meiosis: Basis of Sexual Reproduction

OBJECTIVES

After completing this exercise, you will be able to

1. define *meiosis, homologue (homologous chromosome), diploid, haploid, gene, gene pair, allele, gamete, ovum, sperm, fertilization, locus, synapsis, zygote, genotype, nondisjunction;*

2. indicate the differences and similarities between meiosis and mitosis;

3. describe the basic differences between the life cycles of higher plants and higher animals;

4. describe the process of meiosis, and recognize events that occur during each stage;

5. discuss the significance of crossing over, segregation, and independent assortment;

6. identify the meiotic products in male and female animals.;

7. describe the process of nondisjunction and chromosome number abnormalities in resulting gametes and zygotes.

INTRODUCTION

Like mitosis, meiosis is a process of nuclear division. During mitosis, the number of chromosomes in the daughter nuclei remains the same as that in the parental nucleus. In meiosis, however, the genetic complement is halved, resulting in daughter nuclei containing only one-half the number of chromosomes as the parental nucleus. Thus, while mitosis is sometimes referred to as an *equational division*, meiosis is often called *reduction division*. Moreover, while mitosis is completed after a single nuclear division, two divisions, called meiosis I and meiosis II, occur during meiosis. Table 12-1 summarizes the differences between mitosis and meiosis.

TABLE 12-1 Comparison of Mitosis and Meiosis	
Mitosis	**Meiosis**
Equational division: Amount of genetic material remains constant	Reduction division: Amount of genetic material is halved
Completed in one division cycle	Requires two division cycles for completion
Produces two genetically identical nuclei	Produces two to four genetically different nuclei
Generally produces cells not directly involved in sexual reproduction	Ultimately produces cells used for sexual reproduction

In the body cells of most eukaryotes, chromosomes exist in pairs called homologues (homologous chromosomes); that is, there are two chromosomes that are physically similar and contain genetic information for the same traits. To visualize this, press your palms together, lining up your fingers. Each "finger pair" represents one pair of homologues.

When both homologues are in the *same* nucleus, the nucleus is **diploid** (2n); when only one of the homologues is present, the nucleus is **haploid** (n). If the parental nucleus normally contains the diploid (2n) chromosome number before meiosis, all four daughter nuclei contain the haploid (n) number at the completion of meiosis.

The reduction in chromosome number is the basis for sexual reproduction. In animals, the cells containing the daughter nuclei produced by meiosis are called **gametes: ova** (singular is *ovum*) if the parent is female, **sperm** cells if male. As you probably know, gametes are produced in the gonads—ovaries and testes, respectively. In fact, this is the *only* place where meiosis occurs in higher animals. Figure 12-1 shows where meiosis occurs in humans, while Figure 12-2 shows the life cycle of a higher animal.

Note when meiosis occurs—during gamete production. During **fertilization** (the fusion of a sperm nucleus with an ovum nucleus), the diploid chromosome number is restored as the two haploid gamete nuclei fuse to form the **zygote,** the first cell of the new diploid generation.

What about plants? Do plants have sex? Indeed they do. However, the plant life cycle is a bit more complex than that of animals. Plants of a single species have two completely different body forms. The primary function of one is the production of gametes. This plant is called a *gametophyte* ("gamete-producing plant") and it is haploid. Because the entire plant is haploid, gametes are produced in specialized organs by mitosis.

Figure 12-1   Gamete-producing structures in humans. (**a**) Human male, (**b**) human female.

The other body form, a *sporophyte,* is diploid. This diploid sporophyte has specialized organs in which meiosis occurs, producing haploid spores (hence the name *sporophyte,* "spore-producing plant"). When spores germinate and produce more cells by mitosis, they grow into haploid gametophytes, completing the life cycle.

Figure 12-3 shows the structures in a typical flower that produce sperm and eggs.

Examine Figure 12-4, which shows the gametophyte and sporophyte of a fern plant. Remember, the gametophyte and sporophyte are different, free-living stages of the *same* species of fern. Now look at Figure 12-5, which diagrams a typical plant life cycle. Again, note the consequence of meiosis. In plants, it results in the production of **spores,** not gametes.

You should understand an important concept from these diagrams: *Meiosis always halves the chromosome number. The diploid chromosome number is eventually restored when two haploid nuclei fuse during fertilization.*

Figure 12-2   Life cycle of higher animals.

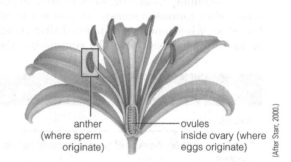

Figure 12-3   Gamete-producing structures in a flowering plant.

Figure 12-4   Gametophyte and sporophyte phases of the same fern species. Note size differences.

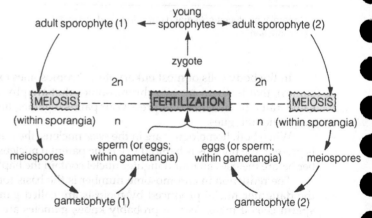

Figure 12-5   Life cycle of a plant.

Understanding meiosis is an absolute necessity for understanding the patterns of inheritance in Mendelian genetics. Gregor Mendel, an Austrian monk, spent years deciphering the complexity of simple genetics. Although he knew nothing of genes and chromosomes, he noted certain patterns of inheritance and formulated three principles, now known as Mendel's principles of recombination, segregation, and independent assortment. The following activities will demonstrate the events of meiosis and the genetic basis for Mendel's principles.

12.1   Demonstrations of Meiosis Using Pop Beads *(About 75 min.)*

MATERIALS

Per student pair:

- 44 pop beads each of two colors (red and yellow, for example)
- 8 magnetic centromeres
- marking pens
- 8 pieces of string, each 40 cm long
- meiotic diagram cards similar to those used here
- colored pencils

Per student group (table):

- bottle of 95% ethanol to remove marking ink
- tissues

PROCEDURE

Work in pairs.

Within the nucleus of an organism, each chromosome bears **genes,** which are units of inheritance. Genes may exist in two or more alternative forms called **alleles.** Each homologue bears *genes* for the same traits; these are the **gene pairs.** However, the homologues may or may not have the same *alleles*. An example will help here.

Suppose the trait in question is flower color and that a flower has only two possible colors, red or white (Figure 12-6a, b). The gene is coding (providing the information) for flower color. There are two homologues in the same nucleus, so each bears the gene for flower color. *But,* on one homologue, the *allele* might code for red flowers, while the allele on the other homologue might code for white flowers (Figure 12-6c). There are two other possibilities. The alleles on *both* homologues might be coding for red flowers (Figure 12-6d), or they *both* might be coding for white flowers (Figure 12-6e). Note that these three possibilities are mutually exclusive.

a Red flower   **b** White flower

c

or

e

d

Nuclei with one pair of homologous chromosomes. The alleles are *R* or *r*.

Figure 12-6 Chromosomal control of flower color. (c–e) show a nucleus with one pair of homologous chromosomes. The alleles for flower color are *R* or *r*.

1. Build the components for two pairs of homologous chromosomes by assembling strings of pop beads as follows:
   (a) Assemble two strands of pop beads with 8 pop beads of one color on each arm, with a magnetic centromere connecting the two arms.
   (b) Repeat step a, but use pop beads of the second color.
   (c) Assemble two more strands of pop beads, but with 3 pop beads of one color on each arm.
   (d) Repeat step c, using pop beads of the second color.
      You should have four long strings, two of each color, and two short strings, also two of each color. Each pop-bead string should have a magnetic centromere at its midpoint by which pop-bead strings can attach to each other. Each pop-bead string represents a single molecule of DNA plus proteins, with each bead representing a gene.
2. Place **one** of each kind of strand in the center of your workspace, which represents the interphase nucleus of a cell that will undergo meiosis. You have created a nucleus with four "chromosomes," two long and two short. The long strands represent one homologous pair, and the short strands represent a second homologous pair of chromosomes.

We start by assuming that these chromosomes represent the diploid condition. The two colors represent the origin of the chromosomes: One homologue (color _____) came from the male parent, and the other homologue (color _____) came from the female parent.

3. The four single-stranded chromosomes represent four unduplicated chromosomes. Now simulate DNA duplication during the S-phase of interphase (Figure 11-1), whereby each DNA molecule and its associated proteins are copied exactly. The two copies, called sister chromatids, remain attached to each other at their centromeres (Figure 12-7). During chromosome replication, the genes also duplicate. Thus, alleles on sister chromatids are identical.

Figure 12-7 One pair of homologous pop-bead chromosomes.

How many sister chromatids are there in a duplicated chromosome? _____

How many chromosomes are represented by four sister chromatids? _____ By eight? _____

What is the diploid number of the starting (parental) nucleus? (*Hint:* Count the number of homologues to obtain the diploid number.) _____

4. As mentioned previously, genes may exist in two or more alternative forms, called alleles. The location of an allele on a chromosome is its **locus** (plural: *loci*). Using the marking pen, mark two loci on each long chromatid with letters to indicate alleles for a common trait. Suppose the long pair of homologous chromosomes codes for two traits, skin pigmentation and the presence of attached earlobes in humans. We'll let the capital letter *A* represent the allele for normal pigmentation and a lowercase *a* the allele for albinism (the absence of skin pigmentation); *F* will represent free earlobes and *f* attached earlobes. A suggested marking sequence is illustrated in Figure 12-7.

5. Let's assign a gene to our second homologous pair of chromosomes, the short pair. We'll suppose this gene codes for the production of an enzyme necessary for metabolism. On one homologue (consisting of two chromatids) mark the letter *E*, representing the allele causing enzyme production. On the other homologue, *e* represents the allele that interferes with normal enzyme production.

6. Obtain a meiotic diagram card like the one in Figure 12-8. Manipulate your model chromosomes through the stages of meiosis described below, locating the chromosomes in the correct diagram circles (representing nuclei) as you go along. Reference to Figure 12-8 will be made at the proper steps. *DO NOT* draw on the meiotic diagram cards.

A. Meiosis Without Crossing Over

Although crossing over is a nearly universal event during meiosis, we will first work with a simplified model to illustrate chromosomal movements and separations during meiosis. Refer to Figure 12-9 as you manipulate your model.

1. **Late interphase.** During interphase, the nuclear envelope is intact and the chromosomes are randomly distributed throughout the nucleoplasm (semifluid substance within the nucleus). All duplicated chromosomes (eight chromatids) should be in the parental nucleus, indicating that DNA duplication has taken place. The sister chromatids of each homologue should be attached by their magnetic centromeres, but the four homologues should be separate. Your model nucleus contains a diploid number 2n = 4.

   The pop-bead chromosomes should appear during interphase in the parental nucleus as shown in Figure 12-8. Be sure to mark the location of the alleles. Use different pencil or pen colors to differentiate the homologues on your drawings.

2. **Meiosis I.** During meiosis I, homologues are separated from each other into different nuclei. Daughter nuclei created are thus haploid.

   (a) *Prophase I.* During the first prophase, the parental nucleus contains four duplicated homologous chromosomes, each comprised of two sister chromatids joined at their centromeres. The chromatin condenses to form discrete, visible chromosomes. The homologues pair with each other. This pairing is called *synapsis*. Slide the two homologues together.

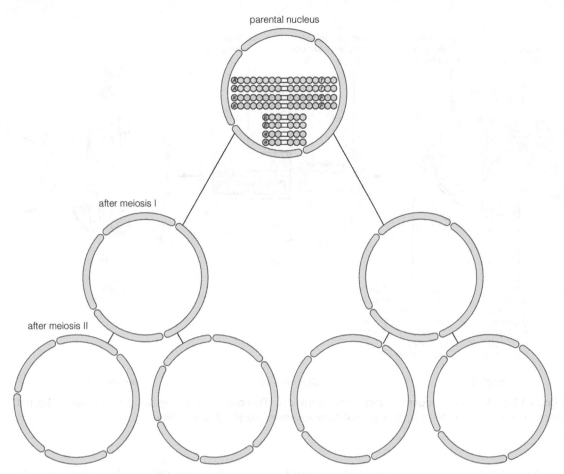

Figure 12-8 Meiosis without crossing over.

Twist the chromatids about one another to simulate synapsis.

The nuclear envelope disorganizes at the end of prophase I.

(b) *Metaphase I.* Homologous chromosomes now move toward the spindle equator, the centromeres of each homologue coming to lie *on either side of the equator.* Spindle fibers, consisting of aggregations of microtubules, attach to the centromeres. One homologue attaches to microtubules extending from one pole, and the other homologue attaches to microtubules extending from the opposite spindle pole.

To simulate the spindle fibers, attach one piece of string to each centromere. Then lay the free ends of strings from two homologues toward one spindle pole and the ends of the other homologues toward the opposite pole.

(c) *Anaphase I.* During anaphase I, the homologous chromosomes separate, one homologue moving toward one pole, the other toward the opposite pole. The movement of the chromosomes is apparently the result of shortening of some spindle fibers and lengthening of others. Each homologue is still in the duplicated form, consisting of two sister chromatids.

Pull the two strings of one homologous pair toward its spindle pole and the other toward the opposite spindle pole, separating the homologues from one another. Repeat with the second pair of homologues.

(d) *Telophase I.* Continue pulling the string spindle fibers until each homologue is now at its respective pole. The first meiotic division is now complete. You should have two nuclei, each containing two chromosomes (one long and one short) consisting of two sister chromatids.

Draw your pop-bead chromosomes as they appear after meiosis I on the two nuclei labeled "after meiosis I" of Figure 12-8. Depending on the organism involved, an interphase (interkinesis) and cytokinesis may precede the second meiotic division, *or* each nucleus may enter directly into meiosis II. The chromosomes decondense into chromatin form.

It is important to note here that DNA synthesis *does not* occur following telophase I (between meiosis I and meiosis II).

Before meiosis II, the spindle is rearranged into two spindles, one for each nucleus.

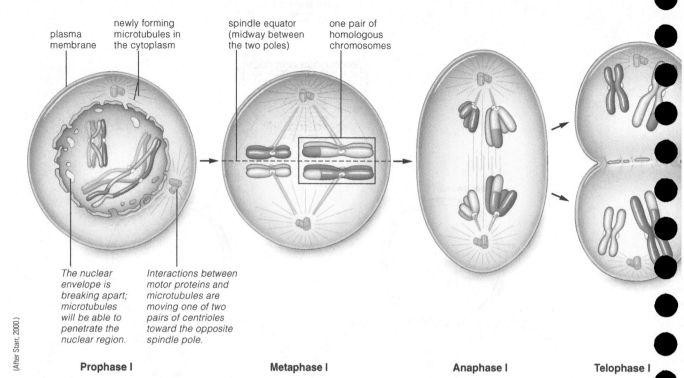

plasma membrane

newly forming microtubules in the cytoplasm

spindle equator (midway between the two poles)

one pair of homologous chromosomes

The nuclear envelope is breaking apart; microtubules will be able to penetrate the nuclear region.

Interactions between motor proteins and microtubules are moving one of two pairs of centrioles toward the opposite spindle pole.

Prophase I   **Metaphase I**   **Anaphase I**   **Telophase I**

Figure 12-9 Meiosis in a generalized animal germ cell. Two pairs of chromosomes are shown. Maternal chromosomes are shaded purple. Paternal chromosomes are shaded light blue.

3. **Meiosis II.** During meiosis II, sister chromatids are separated into different daughter nuclei. The result is four haploid nuclei.

    (a) *Prophase II.* At the beginning of the second meiotic division, the sister chromatids are still attached by their centromeres. During prophase II, the nuclear envelope disorganizes, and the chromatin recondenses.

    (b) *Metaphase II.* Within each nucleus, the duplicated chromosomes align with the equator, the centromeres lying *on the equator.* Spindle fiber microtubules attach the centromeres of each chromatid to opposite spindle poles.

    Your string spindle fibers should be positioned so that the two spindle fiber strings from sister chromatids lie toward opposite poles. Note that each nucleus contains only *two* duplicated chromosomes (one long and one short) consisting of *two* sister chromatids each.

    (c) *Anaphase II.* The sister chromatids separate, moving to opposite poles. Pull on the string until the two sister chromatids separate. After the sister chromatids separate, each is an individual (not duplicated) daughter chromosome.

    (d) *Telophase II.* Continue pulling on the string spindle fibers until the two daughter chromosomes are at opposite poles. The nuclear envelope re-forms around each chromosome and the chromosomes decondense back into chromatin form. Four daughter nuclei now exist. Note that each nucleus contains two individual unduplicated chromosomes (each formerly a chromatid) originally present within the parental nucleus. These nuclei and the cells they're in generally undergo a differentiation and maturation process to become gametes (in animals) or spores (in plants).

    Draw your pop-bead chromosomes as they appear after meiosis II in the "gamete nuclei" of Figure 12-8. Your diagram should indicate the genetic (chromatid) complement *before* meiosis and *after* each meiotic division, *not* the stages of each division.

    Remember that meiosis takes place in both male and female organisms. (See Figure 12-2.)

    If the parental nucleus was from a male, what is the gamete called? _____

    If female? _____

    Is the parental nucleus diploid or haploid? _____

    Are the nuclei produced after the *first* meiotic division diploid or haploid? _____

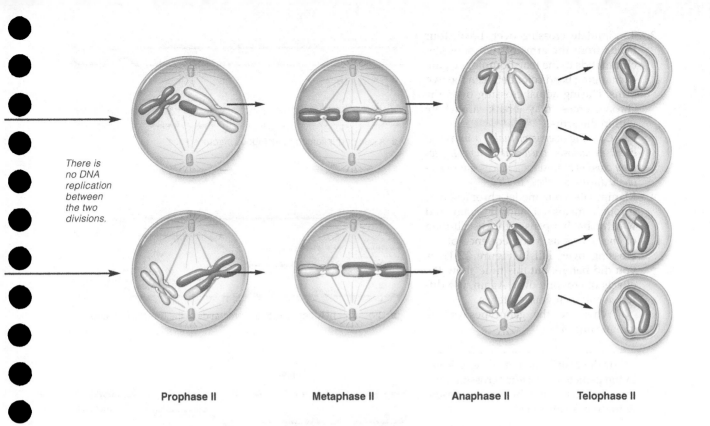

| Prophase II | Metaphase II | Anaphase II | Telophase II |

Are the nuclei of the gametes diploid or haploid? _____

What is the **genotype** of each gamete nucleus after meiosis II? (The genotype is the genetic composition of an organism, or the alleles present. Another way to ask this question is, What alleles are present in each gamete nucleus? Write these in the format: *AFE*, *afe*, and so on.)

_____

If you answered the preceding questions correctly, you might logically ask, "If the chromosome number of the gametes is the same as that produced after the first meiotic division, why bother to have two separate divisions? After all, the genes present are the same in both gametes and first-division nuclei."

There are two answers to this apparent paradox. The first, and perhaps the most obvious, is that the second meiotic division ensures that a *single* chromatid (nonduplicated chromosome) is contained within each gamete. After gametes fuse, producing a zygote, the genetic material duplicates prior to the zygote's undergoing mitosis. If gametes contained two chromatids, the zygote would have four, and duplication prior to zygote division would produce eight, twice as many as the organism should have. If DNA duplication within the zygote were not necessary for the onset of mitosis, this problem would not exist. Alas, DNA synthesis apparently is a necessity to initiate mitosis.

You can discover the second answer for yourself by continuing with the exercise, for although you have simulated meiosis, you have done so without showing what happens in *real* life. That's the next step . . .

B. Meiosis with Crossing Over

A very important event that results in a reshuffling of alleles on the chromatids occurs during prophase I. Recall that synapsis results in pairing of the homologues. During synapsis, the chromatids break, and portions of chromatids bearing genes for the same characteristic (but perhaps *different* alleles) are exchanged between *nonsister* chromatids. This event is called **crossing over**, and it results in recombination (shuffling) of alleles.

1. Look again at Figure 12-7. Distinguish between sister and nonsister chromatids. Now look at Figure 12-10, which demonstrates crossing over in one pair of homologues.
2. Return your chromosome models to the nucleus format with two pairs of homologues entering prophase I.

3. To simulate crossing over, break four beads from the arms of two nonsister chromatids in the long homologue pair, exchanging bead color between the two arms. During actual crossing over, the chromosomes may break anywhere within the arms.

   Crossing over is virtually a universal event in meiosis. Each pair of homologues may cross over in several places simultaneously during prophase I.

4. Manipulate your model chromosomes through meiosis I and II again and watch what happens to the distribution of the alleles as a consequence of the crossing over. Fill in Figure 12-11 as you did before, but this time show the effects of crossing over. Again, use different colors in your sketches.

   What are the genotypes of the gamete nuclei?

   _____

   Is the distribution of alleles present in the gamete nuclei after crossing over the same as that which was present without crossing over?

   _____

   Is the distribution of alleles present in the gamete nuclei after crossing over the same as that in the nuclei after the first meiotic division?

   _____

   Crossing over provides for genetic recombination, resulting in increased variety. How many different genetic *types* of daughter chromosomes are present in the gamete nuclei without crossing over (Figure 12-8)?

   _____

   How many different types are present with crossing over (Figure 12-11)?

   _____

   We think you would agree that a greater number of *types* of daughter chromosomes indicates greater *variety*.

   Recall that the parental nucleus contained a pair of homologues, each homologue consisting of two sister chromatids. Because sister chromatids are identical in all respects, they have the same alleles of a gene (see Figure 12-7). As your models showed, the alleles on nonsister chromatids may not (or may) be identical; they bear the same genes but may have different alleles, different forms of some genes.

   What is the difference between a gene and an allele?

   _____

   _____

   Let's look at a single set of alleles on your model chromosomes that are, say, the alleles for pigmentation, A and a. Both alleles were present in the parental nucleus. How many are present in the gametes?

   _____

a A pair of duplicated homologous chromosomes.

b Crossover between nonsister chromatids of the two chromosomes.

chiasma

c Nonsister chromatids exchange segments.

d Homologues have new combinations of alleles.

(After Starr, 2000.)

Figure 12-10 Crossing over in one pair of homologues. Maternal chromosomes are shaded purple. Paternal chromosomes are shaded light blue.

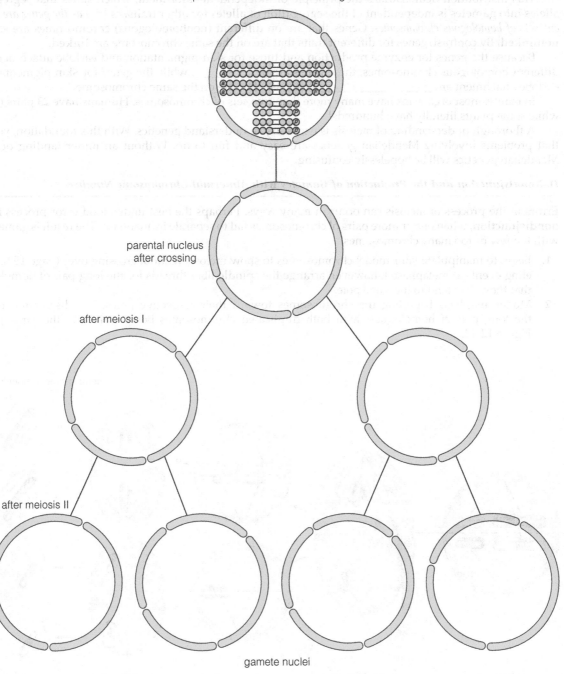

parental nucleus before crossing over

parental nucleus
after crossing

after meiosis I

after meiosis II

gamete nuclei

Figure 12-11 Meiosis with crossing over.

This illustrates Mendel's first principle, segregation. Segregation means that during gamete formation, pairs of alleles are separated (segregated) from each other and end up in different gametes.

C. Demonstrating Independent Assortment

Manipulate your model chromosomes again through meiosis with crossing over (Figure 12-11), searching for different possibilities in chromosome distribution that would make the gametes genetically different.

Does the distribution of the alleles for enzyme production to different gametes on the second set of homologues have any bearing on the distribution of the alleles on the first set (alleles for skin pigmentation and earlobe condition)? _____

This distribution demonstrates the principle of independent assortment, which states that segregation of alleles into gametes is independent of the segregation of alleles for other traits, *as long as the genes are on different sets of homologous chromosomes.* Genes that are on different (nonhomologous) chromosomes are said to be **nonlinked.** By contrast, genes for different traits that are on the same chromosome are **linked.**

Because the genes for enzyme production and those for skin pigmentation and earlobe attachment are on different homologous chromosomes, these genes are _____, while the genes for skin pigmentation and earlobe attachment are _____ because they are on the same chromosome.

In reality, most organisms have many more than two sets of chromosomes. Humans have 23 pairs (2n = 46), while some plants literally have hundreds!

A thorough understanding of meiosis is necessary to understand genetics. With this foundation, you'll find that problems involving Mendelian genetics are easy and fun to do. Without an understanding of meiosis, Mendelian genetics will be hopelessly confusing.

D. Nondisjunction and the Production of Gametes with Abnormal Chromosome Number

Errors in the process of meiosis can occur in many ways. Perhaps the best understood error process is that of **nondisjunction,** when one or more pairs of chromosomes fail to separate in anaphase. The result is gamete nuclei with too few or too many chromosomes.

1. Begin to manipulate your model chromosomes to show meiosis without crossing over (page 159). In modeling events at metaphase I, however, arrange the spindle fiber threads for the long pair of homologues so that they all extend to the same pole.
2. Model anaphase I, pulling the chromosomes toward their respective poles. Nondisjunction occurs in the long pair of homologues, with both duplicated chromosomes being pulled to the same pole. See Figure 12-12.

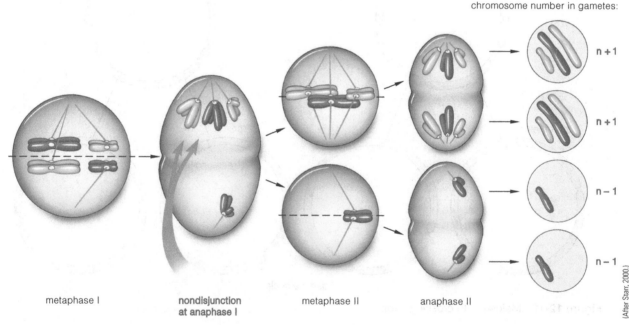

chromosome number in gametes:

n + 1

n + 1

n − 1

n − 1

metaphase I   nondisjunction at anaphase I   metaphase II   anaphase II

(After Starr, 2000.)

Figure 12-12   Nondisjunction. Of the two pairs of homologous chromosomes shown, one pair fails to separate at anaphase I of meiosis. The chromosome number changes in the gametes.

3. Continue to manipulate the model chromosomes through the remainder of the meiotic process.
    How many chromosomes are found in gamete nuclei? _____
    How does this compare to the chromosome number in normal gametes? _____
    Recall that each chromosome bears a unique set of genes and speculate about the effect of nondisjunction on the resulting zygotes formed from fertilization with such a gamete.

    _____

    _____

    _____

One of the most common human genetic disorders arises from nondisjunction during gamete (usually ovum) formation. Down syndrome results from nondisjunction in one of the 23 pairs of human chromosomes, chromosome 21. An individual with Down syndrome has three copies of chromosome 21 instead of the normal two copies. While symptoms of this genetic disorder vary greatly, most individuals show moderate to severe mental impairment and a host of associated physical defects. Relatively few other human genetic disorders arise from nondisjunction, probably because the consequences of abnormal chromosome number are often lethal.

Note: Remove marking ink from pop beads with 95% ethanol and tissues.

12.2   Meiosis in Animal and Plant Cells *(About 40 min.)*

Now that you have a conceptual understanding of meiosis, let's see the actual divisions as they occur in living organisms.

MATERIALS

Per lab room:
- set of demonstration slides of meiosis in animal testes and lily anther
- set of demonstration slides of meiosis in mammalian ovary

Per student pair:
- scissors
- tape or glue

PROCEDURE

A. Spermatogenesis in Male Animals

In animals, as mentioned previously, meiosis results in the production of gametes—ova in females and sperm in males.

1. Examine Figure 12-13, which depicts sperm formation in a seminiferous tubule within human testes. A diploid reproductive cell, the *spermatogonium*, first enlarges into a *primary spermatocyte*. The primary spermatocyte undergoes meiosis I to form two haploid *secondary spermatocytes*. After meiosis II, four haploid *spermatids* are produced, which develop flagella during differentiation into four *sperm cells*. This process is called *spermatogenesis*.
2. Examine the demonstration slide of spermatogenesis in animal testes. Under low power, note the many circular structures. These are the seminiferous tubules, where spermatogenesis takes place. See Figure 12-14.

Figure 12-13 Spermatogenesis within testes in male animals.

3. Switch to high power and focus on one seminiferous tubule for closer observation. Mature sperm appear as fine dark lines in the center of the tubule. Cells in progressively earlier stages of meiosis are seen as you move toward the outer wall of the tubule. Adjacent to the tubule wall, you can see diploid primary spermatocytes and spermatogonia. See Figure 12-15.

Figure 12-14 Section of mammalian testis (90×).

Figure 12-15 Light micrograph of cells inside three adjacent seminiferous tubules.

Can you identify any cells that appear to be undergoing meiotic divisions? _____

B. Oogenesis in Female Animals

In the ovaries of female animals, *ova* (eggs) are produced by meiosis during the process called oogenesis. Unlike spermatogenesis, only one of the meiotic products becomes a gamete.

1. Examine Figure 12-16, which depicts oogenesis in female animals.

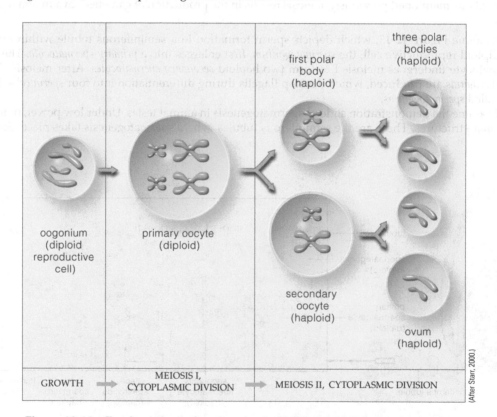

Figure 12-16 Egg formation in female animals. Unlike the sketch, the three polar bodies that actually form in meiosis are extremely small compared to the egg.

The diploid reproductive cell, called an *oogonium,* grows into a *primary oocyte.* The primary oocyte undergoes meiosis I, one product being the *secondary oocyte,* the other a *polar body.* Notice the difference in size of the secondary oocyte and the polar body. This is because the secondary oocyte ends up with nearly all of the cytoplasm after meiosis I.

In humans and other mammals, secondary oocytes are released from the ovary. If fertilization occurs, a sperm penetrates the secondary oocyte, which then continues through meiosis II. Following meiosis II, only the secondary oocyte becomes a mature, haploid *ovum;* depending on the species, the polar body may or may not undergo meiosis II. In any case, the polar bodies are extremely small and do not function as gametes.

2. Examine the demonstration slides of oogenesis in an animal. Identify the follicles within which oogenesis begins. Also identify oocytes that may be in various stages of development. (See Figures 12-17 and 12-18.)

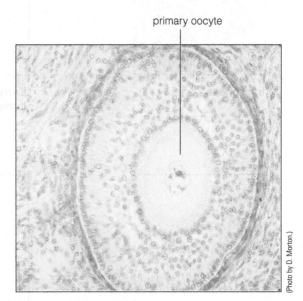

Figure 12-17 Section of mammalian ovary with primary follicles (220×).

Figure 12-18 Section of mammalian ovary with primary oocyte (376×).

C. Meiosis in Plants

For the sake of brevity, we will only examine meiosis in the male reproductive structure of flowering plants. Recall from our earlier discussion that meiosis in plants results in spore production, not directly into gametes. The details of the life cycle of flowering plants is considered in Exercise 25.

1. Examine the demonstration slides of meiosis beginning with the diploid *microsporocytes.* Microsporocytes are the cells within a flower that undergo meiosis to produce haploid *microspores.* Eventually these microspores develop into pollen grains, which in turn produce sperm.

2. As you examine the slides, cut out the photomicrographs on pages 175 and 177 and arrange them on Figure 12-19 to depict the meiotic events leading to microspore formation. Label each photo with the terms provided.

   (a) *Interphase.* During interphase, the *nucleus* of each diploid *microsporocyte* is distinct, containing granular-appearing chromatin. The cells are compactly arranged.

   (b) *Early prophase I.* Now the chromatin has begun to condense into discrete *chromosomes,* which have the appearance of fine threads within the nucleus.

   (c) *Mid-prophase I.* Additional condensation of the *chromosomes* has taken place. Pairing of homologous chromosomes is taking place.

   (d) *Late prophase I.* The chromosomes have condensed into short, rather fat structures. Synapsis and crossing over are taking place. Note that the nuclear envelope has disorganized.

   (e) *Metaphase I.* The homologous chromosomes lie in the region of the *spindle equator.* The *spindle,* composed of *spindle fibers,* can be discerned as fine lines running toward the *poles.* (Note the absence of centrioles in plant cells.)

   (f) *Early anaphase I.* Separation of homologous chromosomes is beginning to take place.

   (g) *Later anaphase I.* Homologous chromosomes have nearly reached the opposite poles. Reduction division has occurred.

Figure 12-19 Meiosis and microsporogenesis in the anther. Cut out the photomicrographs on pages 175 and 177 and arrange them in proper sequence here. (Photos by J. W. Perry.)

diploid
microsporocyte

nucleus

Interphase

Early Prophase I
Labels: nucleus, chromosomes

Mid-Prophase I
Label: chromosomes

Late Prophase I
Label: chromosomes

Metaphase I
Labels: spindle equator, spindle, spindle fibers, pole

Early Anaphase I
Label: spindle fibers

Later Anaphase I
Labels: pole, homologous chromosomes

Telophase I
Labels: pole, homologous chromosomes, spindle fibers

Cytokinesis I
Labels: cell plate

Interkinesis
Labels: nuclei, cell wall, daughter cells

Prophase II
Labels: daughter cells, nuclei

Metaphase II
Labels: chromosomes, spindle equator

Anaphase II
Labels: sister chromatids (unduplicated chromosomes)

Telophase II
Labels: cell plate, nuclei

Cytokinesis
Labels: cell plate, nuclei

(h) *Telophase I.* The homologous chromosomes have aggregated at opposite poles. The spindle remains visible.

(i) *Cytokinesis I.* The *cell plate* is forming in the midplane of the cell. Spindle fibers, which are aggregations of microtubules, are visible running perpendicularly through the cell plate. The microtubules are directing the movement of Golgi vesicles, which contain the materials that form the cell plate.

A nuclear envelope has re-formed about the chromosomes, resulting in a well-defined nucleus in each *daughter cell.*

(j) *Interkinesis.* In these plant cells, a short stage exists between meiosis I and II. Distinct nuclei are apparent in the two daughter cells. A cell wall has formed across the entirety of the midplane.

(k) *Prophase II.* The chromosomes in each nucleus of the two daughter cells condense again into distinct, threadlike bodies. As was the case at the end of prophase I, the nuclear envelope disorganizes.

(l) *Metaphase II.* Chromosomes consisting of sister chromatids line up on the spindle equator in both cells. (The photomicrograph shows the very early stages of separation of the chromatids.)

(m) *Anaphase II.* The sister chromatids (now more appropriately considered *unduplicated chromosomes*) are being drawn to their respective poles in each cell.

Before anaphase II begins, sister chromatids are attached to each other along their length. Shortening of the spindle fibers, which are attached to the chromatids at kinetochores within their centromeres, causes the chromatids to separate, beginning in the region of the centromere. This causes a V-shaped configuration of the chromosomes.

(n) *Telophase II and cytokinesis.* Nuclear envelopes are now re-forming around each of the four sets of chromosomes. Cell plate formation is occurring perpendicular to the cell wall that was formed after telophase I.

After cell wall formation is complete, the four haploid cells (microspores) will separate. Subsequently, each will develop into a pollen grain inside which sperm cells will form.

PRE-LAB QUESTIONS

_____ 1. In meiosis, the number of chromosomes _____, while in mitosis, it _____.
    (a) is halved/is doubled
    (b) is halved/remains the same
    (c) is doubled/is halved
    (d) remains the same/is halved

_____ 2. The term "2n" means
    (a) the diploid chromosome number is present
    (b) the haploid chromosome number is present
    (c) chromosomes within a single nucleus exist in homologous pairs
    (d) both a and c

_____ 3. In higher animals, meiosis results in the production of
    (a) egg cells (ova)
    (b) gametes
    (c) sperm cells
    (d) all of the above

_____ 4. Recombination of alleles on nonsister chromatids occurs during
    (a) anaphase I
    (b) meiosis II
    (c) telophase II
    (d) crossing over

_____ 5. Alternative forms of genes are called
    (a) homologues
    (b) locus
    (c) loci
    (d) alleles

_____ 6. If both homologous chromosomes of each pair exist in the same nucleus, that nucleus is
    (a) diploid
    (b) unable to undergo meiosis
    (c) haploid
    (d) none of the above

_____ 7. DNA duplication occurs during
    (a) interphase
    (b) prophase I
    (c) prophase II
    (d) interkinesis

_____ 8. Nondisjunction
    (a) results in gametes with abnormal chromosome numbers
    (b) occurs at anaphase
    (c) results when homologues fail to separate properly in meiosis
    (d) is all of the above

_____ 9. Humans
    (a) don't undergo meiosis
    (b) have 46 chromosomes
    (c) produce gametes by mitosis
    (d) have all of the above characteristics

_____ 10. Gametogenesis in male animals results in
    (a) four sperm
    (b) one gamete and three polar bodies
    (c) four functional ova
    (d) a haploid ovum and three diploid polar bodies

EXERCISE 12

Meiosis: Basis of Sexual Reproduction

POST-LAB QUESTIONS

Introduction

1. If a cell of an organism has 46 chromosomes before meiosis, how many chromosomes will exist in each nucleus after meiosis?

2. What basic difference exists between the life cycles of higher plants and higher animals?

3. In animals, meiosis results directly in gamete production, while in plants meiospores are produced. Where do the gametes come from in the life cycle of a plant?

4. How would you argue that meiosis is the basis for sexual reproduction in plants, even though the *direct* result is a spore rather than a gamete?

12.1 Demonstrations of Meiosis Using Pop Beads

5. Suppose one sister chromatid of a chromosome has the allele *H*. What allele will the other sister chromatid have? (Assume crossing over has not taken place.) _____

6. Suppose that two alleles on one homologous chromosome are *A* and *B*, and the other homologous chromosome's alleles are *a* and *b*.

   a. How many different genetic types of gametes would be produced *without* crossing over? _____

   b. What are the genotypes of the gametes? _____

   c. If crossing over were to occur, how many different genetic types of gametes could occur? _____

   d. List them. _____

7. Assume that you have built a homologous pair of *duplicated* chromosomes, one chromosome red and the other yellow. Describe or draw the appearance of two nonsister chromatids after crossing over.

8. Examine the meiotic diagram at right. Describe in detail what's wrong with it.

12.2 Meiosis in Animal and Plant Cells

9. Observe the photo at right, which shows a stage of meiosis occurring in a flower anther. Are the cells shown haploid or diploid?

(Photo by J. W. Perry.)

Food for Thought

10. From a genetic viewpoint, of what significance is fertilization?

Photomicrographs for Figure 12-19 Meiosis in anther of a flowering plant. Cut from this page and arrange in proper sequence in Figure 12-19. (1200×) Continues on next page. (Photos by J. W. Perry.)

EXERCISE 13
Heredity

OBJECTIVES

After completing this exercise you will be able to:

1. define *true-breeding, hybrid, monohybrid cross, diploid, haploid, genotype, phenotype, dominant, recessive, complete dominance, homozygous, heterozygous, incomplete dominance, codominance, sex-linked, dihybrid cross, probability, multiple alleles, chi-square test;*

2. solve problems illustrating monohybrid and dihybrid crosses, including those with incomplete dominance, codominance, sex-linkage, and problems involving multiple alleles;

3. Use a chi-square test to determine if observed results are consistent with expected results;

4. determine your phenotype for traits used in this exercise and give your probable genotype for these traits.

INTRODUCTION

In 1866 an Austrian monk, Gregor Mendel, presented the results of painstaking experiments on the inheritance of the garden pea. Those results were heard, but probably not understood, by Mendel's audience. Now, more than a century later, Mendel's work seems elementary to modern-day geneticists, but its importance cannot be overstated. The principles generated by Mendel's pioneering experimentation are the foundation for genetic counseling so important today to families with health disorders having a genetic basis. It's also the framework for the modern research that is making inroads in treating diseases previously believed to be incurable. In this era of genetic engineering — the incorporation of foreign DNA into chromosomes of unrelated species — it is easy to lose sight of the basics of the process that makes it all possible.

Recent advances in molecular genetics have resulted in the production of insulin and human growth hormone by genetic engineering techniques. Cancer patients are being treated with cells that have been removed from their own bodies, genetically altered to enhance their tumor-destroying capacity, and then reinserted in the hope that microscopic tumors escaping the surgeon's scalpel may be destroyed.

This newfound technology has not been without controversy, however. Release into the environment of genetically engineered microorganisms that may make crops resistant to disease-causing organisms (or even capable of withstanding temperatures that normally would freeze plants) has met with strong opposition.

In the future, *you* may be called upon to help make decisions about issues like these. To make an educated judgment, you must understand the basics, just as Mendel did. The genetics problems in this exercise should start you well on your way.

MATERIALS

Per student group (table):

- genetic corn ears illustrating monohybrid and dihybrid crosses

Optional:

- pop beads used in Exercise 10
- marking pen
- bottle of 70% ethanol
- simulated chromosomes, consisting of pop beads with magnetic centromeres, and meiotic diagram cards (see p. 116, Exercise 10)
- hand lens

I. Monohybrid Problems with Complete Dominance

Garden peas have both male and female parts in the same flower and are able to self-fertilize. For his experiments, Mendel chose parental plants that were **true-breeding,** meaning that all self-fertilized offspring displayed the same form of a trait as their parent. For example, if a true-breeding purple-flowered plant is allowed to self-fertilize, all of the offspring will have purple flowers.

When parents that are true-breeding for *different* forms of a trait are crossed — for example, purple flowers and white flowers — the offspring are called **hybrids.** When only one trait is being studied, the cross is called a **monohybrid cross.**

We'll look first at monohybrid problems.

1. Most organisms are diploid; that is, they contain homologous chromosomes with genes for the same traits. The location of a gene on a chromosome is its *locus* (plural: *loci*). Two genes at homologous loci are called a *gene pair*. Chromosomes have numerous genes, as illustrated in figure 11-1. Genes may exist in

Figure 11-1 Arrangement of genes on homologous chromosomes.

different forms, called *alleles*. Let's consider one gene pair at the *F* locus. There are three possibilities for the allelic makeup at the *F* locus:

Both alleles are *FF*.

```
                                    allele F
one chromosome    _____╱╲_____

...its homologue  _____╱╲_____
                                    allele F
```

Both alleles are *ff*.

```
                                    allele f
one chromosome    _____╱╲_____

...its homologue  _____╱╲_____
                                    allele f
```

One allele is *F*, and the other is *f*.

```
                                    allele F
one chromosome    _____╱╲_____

...its homologue  _____╱╲_____
                                    allele f
```

Gametes, on the other hand, are haploid, containing only one of the two homologues, and thus only one of the two alleles for a specific trait.

The **genotype** of an organism is its genetic constitution, that is, the alleles present.

For each of the following diploid genotypes, indicate the possible genotypes of the gametes.

Diploid genotype	Gamete genotype
FF	_____
ff	_____
Ff	_____, _____

If you don't understand the process that gives rise to the gamete genotypes, manipulate the pop-bead models that you used in the meiosis exercise. Using a marking pen, label one bead of each chromosome and go through the meiotic divisions that give rise to the gametes.

It is imperative that you understand meiosis before attempting to do genetics problems.

2. During fertilization, two gamete nuclei fuse, and the diploid condition is restored. Give the diploid genotype produced by fusion of the following gamete genotypes.

Gamete genotype ×	Gamete genotype →	Diploid genotype
f	*f*	_____
F	*f*	_____
F	*F*	_____

3. Now let's attach some meaning to genotypes. As you see from the previous problems, the genotype is an expression of the actual genetic makeup of the organism. The **phenotype** is the observable result of the genotype, that is, what the organism looks like because of its genotype. (Although phenotype is determined primarily by genotype, in many instances environmental factors can modify phenotype.)

Human earlobes are either attached or free (fig. 11-2). This trait is determined by a single gene consisting of two alleles, *F* and *f*. An individual whose genotype is *FF* or *Ff* has free earlobes. This is the **dominant** condition. Note that the presence of one *or* two *F* alleles results in the dominant phenotype, free earlobes. The allele *F* is said to be dominant over its allelic partner, *f*. The **recessive** phenotype, attached earlobes, occurs only when the genotype is *ff*. In the case of **complete dominance,** the dominant allele completely masks the expression or affect of the recessive allele.

When both alleles in a nucleus are identical, the nucleus is **homozygous.** Those having both dominant alleles are homozygous dominant.

When both recessives are present in the same nucleus, the individual is said to be *homozygous recessive* for the trait.

Suppose a man has the genotype *FF*. What is the genotype of his gamete (sperm) nuclei?

_____

Suppose a woman has attached earlobes. What is her genotype?

_____

Figure 11-2 Free and attached earlobes in humans.

What allele(s) do her gametes (ova) carry?

_____

Suppose these two individuals produce a child. Show the genotype of the child by doing the cross:

sperm genotype   x   ovum genotype

child's genotype

When both the dominant and recessive alleles are present within a single nucleus, the individual is **heterozygous** for that trait.

What is the phenotype of the child? (That is, does this child have attached or free earlobes?)

_____

4. In garden peas, purple flowers are dominant over white flowers. Let P represent the allele for purple flowers, p the allele for white flowers.

a. What is the phenotype (color) of the flowers with the following genotypes:

Genotype	Phenotype
PP	_____
pp	_____
Pp	_____

N O T E

Always be sure to distinguish clearly between upper- and lowercase letters.

A white-flowered garden pea is crossed with a homozygous dominant purple-flowered plant.

b. What is the genotype of the gametes of the white-flowered plant?

_____

c. What is the genotype of the gametes of the purple-flowered plant?

_____

d. What is the genotype of the plant produced by the cross?

_____

e. What is the phenotype of the plant produced by the cross?

_____

A convenient method of performing the mechanics of a cross is to use a Punnett square. The circles along the top and side of the Punnett square represent the gamete nuclei. Insert the proper letters indicating the genotypes of the gamete nuclei for the above cross in the circles and then fill in the Punnett square.

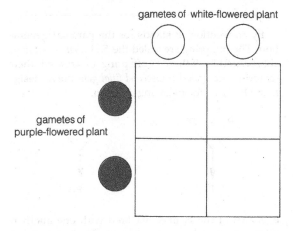

A heterozygous plant is crossed with a white-flowered plant. Fill in the Punnett square and give the genotypes and phenotypes of the offspring.

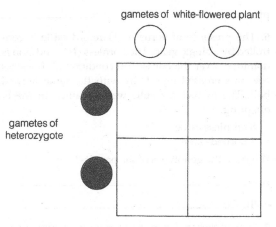

genotypes _____

phenotypes _____

(Draw a line from the genotype to its respective phenotype.)

For the remaining problems, you may wish to draw your own Punnett squares on a separate sheet of paper.

5. In mice, black fur (*B*) is dominant over brown fur (*b*). Breeding a brown mouse and a homozygous black mouse produces all black offspring.

a. What is the genotype of *the gametes* produced by the brown-furred parent?

_____

b. What is the genotype of the brown-furred parent?

_____

c. What is the genotype of the black-furred parent?

_____

d. What is the genotype of the black-furred offspring?

_____

By convention, P stands for the parental generation. The offspring are called the *first filial generation*, abbreviated F_1. If these F_1 offspring are crossed, their offspring are called the *second filial generation*, designated F_2. Note the following diagram.

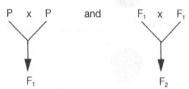

e. If two of the F_1 mice are bred with one another, what will the phenotype of the F_2 be, and in what proportion?

phenotype _____

proportion _____

6. The presence of horns on Hereford cattle is controlled by a single gene. The hornless (*H*) condition is dominant over the horned (*h*) condition. A hornless cow was crossed repeatedly with the same horned bull. The following results were obtained in the F_1 offspring:

    8 hornless cattle
    7 horned cattle

What are the genotypes of the parents?

cow _____

bull _____

7. In fruit flies, red eyes (*R*) are dominant over purple eyes (*r*). Two red-eyed fruit flies were crossed, producing the following offspring:

    76 red-eyed flies
    24 purple-eyed flies

a. What is the approximate ratio of red-eyed to purple-eyed flies?

_____

b. Based upon your experience with previous problems, what two genotypes give rise to this ratio?

_____

c. What are the genotypes of the parents?

_____

d. What is the genotypic ratio of the F_1?

_____

e. What is the phenotypic ratio of the F_1?

_____

II. Monohybrid Problems with Incomplete Dominance

8. Petunia flower color is governed by two alleles, but neither allele is truly dominant over the other. Petunias with the genotype R^1R^1 are red-flowered, those that are heterozygous (R^1R^2) are pink, and those with the R^2R^2 genotype are white. This is an example of **incomplete dominance.** (Note that superscripts are used rather than upper- and lowercase letters to describe the alleles.)

a. If a white-flowered plant is crossed with a red-flowered petunia, what is the genotypic ratio of the F_1?

_____

b. What is the phenotypic ratio of the F_1?

_____

c. If two of the F_1 offspring were crossed, what phenotypes would appear in the F_2?

_____

d. What would be the genotypic ratio in the F_2 generation?

_____

III. Monohybrid Problems Illustrating Codominance

9. Another type of monohybrid inheritance involves the expression of *both* phenotypes in the heterozygous situation. This is called **codominance.**

One of the well-known examples of codominance occurs in the coat color of Shorthorn cattle. Those with reddish-gray coats are heterozygous (*RR'*), and result from a mating between a red (*RR*) Shorthorn and one that's white (*R'R'*). Roan cattle do not have roan-colored hairs, as would be expected with incomplete dominance, but rather appear roan as a result of both red and white hairs being on the same animal. Thus the roan coloration is not a consequence of blending of pigments within each hair. Because the R and R' alleles are *both* fully expressed in the heterozygote, they are codominant.

a. If a roan Shorthorn cow is mated with a white bull, what will be the genotypic and phenotypic ratios in the F_1 generation?

genotypic ratio _____

phenotypic ratio _____

b. List the parental genotypes of crosses that could produce at least some:

white offspring _____

roan offspring _____

IV. Monohybrid, Sex-linked Problems

10. In humans, as well as in other primates, sex is determined by special sex chromosomes. An individual containing two X chromosomes is a female, while an individual possessing an X and a Y chromosome is a male. (Rare exceptions of XY females and XX males have recently been discovered.)

I am a male/female (circle one).

a. What sex chromosomes do you have?

_____

b. In terms of sex chromosomes, what type of gametes (ova) does a female produce?

_____

c. What are the possible sex chromosomes in a male's sperm cells?

_____

d. The gametes of which parent will determine the sex of the offspring?

_____

11. The sex chromosomes bear alleles for traits, just like the other chromosomes in our bodies. Genes that occur on the sex chromosomes are said to be **sex-linked.** More specifically, the genes present on the X chromosome are said to be X-linked. There are many more genes present on the X chromosome than are found on the Y chromosome. Nonetheless, those genes found on the Y chromosome are said to be Y-linked.

The Y chromosome is smaller than its homologue, the X chromosome. Consequently, some of the loci present on the X chromosome are absent on the Y chromosome.

In humans, color vision is X-linked; the gene for color vision is located on the X chromosome but is absent from the Y chromosome. Figure 11-3 illustrates

Figure 11-3 Diagrammatic representation of a sex-linked trait, *N*.

the appearance of duplicated sex chromosomes, each consisting of two sister chromatids.

In figure 11-4 sketch the appearance and distribution of the sex chromosomes as they would appear in gametes after meiosis.

Normal color vision (X^N) is dominant over color blindness (X^n). Suppose a color-blind man fathers children of a woman with the genotype $X^N X^N$.

a. What is the genotype of the father?

_____

b. What proportion of daughters would be color-blind?

_____

c. What proportion of sons would be color-blind?

_____

12. One of the daughters from the above problem marries a color-blind man.

a. What proportion of their sons will be color-blind? (Another way to think of this is to ask what the *chances* are that their sons will be color-blind.)

_____

b. Explain how a color-blind daughter might result from this couple.

_____

_____

V. An Observable Monohybrid Cross

Examine the monohybrid genetic corn demonstration. This illustrates a monohybrid cross between plants producing purple kernels and plants producing yellow kernels. Note that all the first-generation kernels (F_1) are purple, while the second-generation ear (F_2) has both purple kernels and yellow kernels. Count the purple kernels and then the yellow kernels. _____ *purple:* _____ *yellow.* When reduced to the lowest common denominator, is this ratio closest to 1:1, 2:1, 3:1, or 4:1? _____. This is called the *phenotypic ratio.*

13. A corncob represents the products of multiple instances of sexual reproduction. Each kernel represents a single instance; fertilization of one egg by one sperm produced *each* kernel. Thus each kernel represents a different cross.

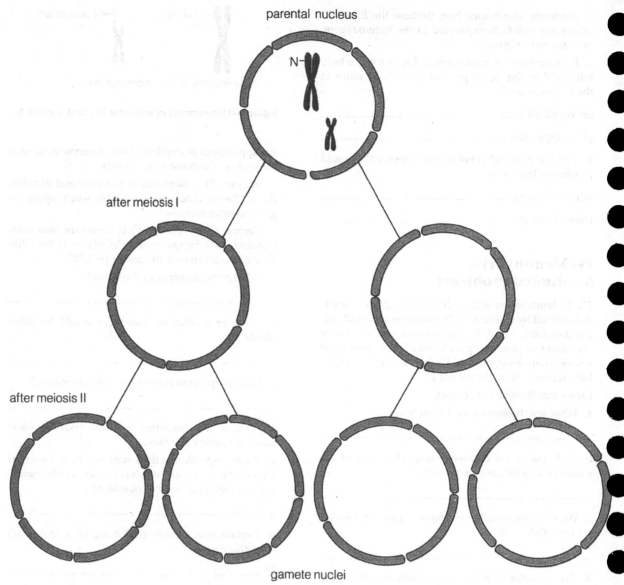

parental nucleus

N—

after meiosis I

after meiosis II

gamete nuclei

Figure 11-4 Distribution of sex chromosomes after meiosis.

a. What genotypes produce a purple phenotype?

_____

b. Which allele is dominant?

_____

c. What is the genotype of the yellow kernels on the F₂ ear?

_____

d. Suppose you were given an ear with purple kernels. How could you determine its genotype with a single cross?

_____

_____

VI. Dihybrid Problems

All the problems so far have involved the inheritance of only one trait; that is, they were monohybrid problems. We will now examine cases in which two traits are involved: **dihybrid problems.**

> **NOTE**
>
> **We will assume that the genes for these traits are carried on different (nonhomologous) chromosomes.**

Examine the demonstration of dihybrid inheritance in corn. Notice that not only are the kernels two different colors (one trait), but they are also differently shaped (second trait). Kernels with starchy endosperm (the carbohydrate-storing tissue) are smooth, while those with sweet endosperm are shriveled. Notice that all *four* possible phenotypic combinations of color and shape are present in the F_2 generation.

14. In humans, a pigment in the front part of the eye masks a blue layer at the back of the iris. The dominant allele *P* causes production of this pigment. Those who are homozygous recessive (*pp*) lack the pigment, and the back of the iris shows through, resulting in blue eyes. (Other genes determine the color of the pigment, but in this problem we'll consider only the presence or absence of *any* pigment at the front of the eye.)

Dimpled chins (*D* = allele for dimpling) are dominant over undimpled chins (*d* = allele for lack of dimple).

a. List all possible genotypes for an individual with pigmented iris and dimpled chin.

_____

b. List the possible genotypes for an individual with pigmented iris but lacking a dimpled chin.

_____

c. List the possible genotypes of a blue-eyed, dimple-chinned individual.

_____

d. List the possible genotypes of a blue-eyed individual lacking a dimpled chin.

_____

15. Suppose an individual is heterozygous for both traits (eye pigmentation and chin form).

a. What is the genotype of such an individual?

_____

b. What are the possible genotypes of that individual's gametes?

_____

If determining the answer for the last question was difficult, recall from Exercise 10 that the principle of independent assortment states that genes on different (nonhomologous) chromosomes are separated out independently of one another during meiosis. That is, the occurrence of an allele for eye pigmentation in a gamete has no bearing on which allele for chin form will occur in that same gamete.

There is a useful convention for determining possible gamete genotypes produced during meiosis from a given parental genotype. Using the genotype *PpDd* as an example, here's the method:

Follow the four arrows to determine the four gamete genotypes.

c. Suppose two individuals heterozygous for both eye pigmentation and chin form have children. What are the possible genotypes of their children?

_____

You can set up a Punnett square to do dihybrid problems just as you did with monohybrid problems. However, depending upon the parental genotypes, the square may have as many as sixteen boxes, rather than just four. Insert the possible genotypes of the gametes from one parent in the top circles and the gamete genotypes of the other parent in the circles to the left of the box.

Possible genotypes of children produced by two parents heterozygous for both eye pigmentation and chin form are

_____

d. What is the ratio of the genotypes?

_____

e. What is the phenotypic ratio?

_____

16. You would probably agree that it is unlikely that a family will have sixteen children. In fact, one of the most useful facets of problems such as these is that they allow you to *predict* what the chances are for a phenotype occurring. Genetics is really a matter of **probability,** the likelihood of the occurrence of any particular outcome.

To take a simple example, consider that the probability of coming up with heads in a single toss of a coin is one chance in two, or 1/2.

Now apply this example to the question of the probability of having a certain genotype. Look at your Punnett square in problem 15. The probability of having a genotype is the sum of all occurrences of that genotype. For example, the genotype *PPDD* occurs in one of the sixteen boxes. The probability of having the genotype *PPDD* is 1/16.

a. What is the probability of an individual from the above problem having the genotype:

ppDD _____

PpDd _____

PPDd _____

To extend this idea, let's consider the probability of flipping heads twice in a row with our coin. The chance of flipping heads the first time is 1/2. The same is true for the second flip. The chance (probability) that we will flip heads twice in a row is $1/2 \times 1/2 = 1/4$. The probability that we could flip heads three times in a row is $1/2 \times 1/2 \times 1/2 = 1/8$.

b. Returning to eye color and chin form, state the probability that three children born to these parents will have the genotype *ppdd*.

_____

c. What is the probability that three children born to these parents will have dimpled chins and pigmented eyes?

_____

d. What is the genotype of the F_1 generation when the father is homozygous for both pigmented eyes and dimpled chin, but the mother has blue eyes and no dimple?

_____

e. What is the phenotype of the individual(s) you determined in letter *d.* above?

_____

17. A pigment-eyed, dimple-chinned man marries a blue-eyed woman without a dimpled chin. Their first-born child is blue-eyed and has a dimpled chin.

_____

a. What are the possible genotypes of the father?

_____

b. What is the genotype of the mother?

_____

c. What alleles may have been carried by the father's sperm?

_____

18. Suppose a dimple-chinned, blue-eyed man whose father lacked a dimple marries a woman who is homozygous recessive for both traits.

a. What would be the expected genotypic ratio of children produced in this marriage?

_____

b. What would be the expected phenotypic ratio?

_____

19. In his original work on the genetics of garden peas, Mendel found that yellow seed color (*YY, Yy*) was dominant over green seeds (*yy*) and that round seed shape (*RR, Rr*) was dominant over shrunken seeds (*rr*). Mendel crossed pure-breeding (homozygous) yellow, round-seeded plants with green, shrunken-seeded plants.

a. What would be the genotype and phenotype of the F_1 produced from such a cross?

_____

b. If the F_1 plants are crossed, what would be the expected phenotypic ratio of the F_2?

_____

VII. Multiple Alleles

20. The major blood groups in humans are determined by **multiple alleles**, that is, there are *more than* two possible alleles, any one of which can occupy a locus.

In this ABO blood group system, a single gene can exist in any of three allelic forms: I^A, I^B, or *i*. The alleles *A* and *B* code for production of antigen A and antigen B (two proteins) on the surface of red blood cells. Alleles *A* and *B* are codominant, while allele *i* is recessive.

Four blood groups (phenotypes) are possible from combinations of these alleles (table 11-1).

a. Is it possible for a child with blood type O to be produced by two AB parents?

_____

Explain.

_____

_____

_____

Table 11-1 The ABO Blood Groups			
Blood Type	**Antigens Present**	**Antibody Present**	**Genotype**
O	neither A nor B	A and B	ii
A	A	B	$I^A I^A$ or $I^A i$
B	B	A	$I^B I^B$ or $I^B i$
AB	AB	neither A nor B	$I^A I^B$

b. In a case of disputed paternity, the child is type O, the mother type A. Could an individual of the following blood types be the father?

O _____

A _____

B _____

AB _____

VIII. Do Your Results Fit the Expected? Chi-square Analysis of Data

You have found that in monohybrid crosses, the expected phenotypic ratio of offspring produced by a cross between two heterozygous individuals is 3:1. Similarly, in dihybrid situations, the expected ratio would be 9:3:3:1. These are *expected* ratios. Stated in the manner described in the exercise on the scientific method (Exercise 1), it is your *hypothesis* that the ratio will be 3:1 or 9:3:3:1.

By now, you are probably wondering how this ratio can be interpreted if there are not exact multiples of four in the case of monohybrid problems, or of sixteen in the case of dihybrids. If the results don't fit exactly as expected, could the differences be due to chance variation? For example, if you crossed two heterozygous purple garden peas (question 4) and counted sixty-four purple and seventeen white offspring, is the deviation from the expected 3:1 ratio a result of chance or of some other factor?

You can determine whether experimentally obtained data are a satisfactory approximation of the expected data—or, stated another way, whether your hypothesis is correct—using a **chi-square test.**

The formula for chi square (χ^2) is

$$\chi^2 = \Sigma \frac{(O - E)^2}{E}$$

where

O = the *observed* number of individuals,

E = the *expected* number of individuals,

and

Σ = the sum of all values of $(O - E)^2/E$

for the various categories of phenotypes.

Let's see how we use this with our garden-pea example. Suppose eighty-one flowers are counted in a cross. Our hypothesis (expectation) is that three-fourths of them will be purple:

$$3/4 \times 81 = 60.75$$

Similarly, we expect one-fourth to be white:

$$1/4 \times 81 = 20.25$$

Examine table 11-2, noting how these values are used.

$$\chi^2 = \Sigma [0.174 + 0.522]$$
$$= 0.696$$

Now, how do we interpret the χ^2 value we found? Suppose that the expected and observed values were identical. Thus, χ^2 would equal zero. You might guess that a number very close to zero would indicate close agreement between observed and expected and that a large χ^2 would suggest that "something unusual" was taking place. But almost always there will be small deviations between observed and expected because of chance, *even when the hypothesis being tested is correct.*

When does the χ^2 value indicate that chance alone cannot explain this deviation? Statisticians have agreed that if the likelihood of deviation is more than one in twenty (or 5% = 0.05), then the disagreement between observed and expected cannot be explained by chance. Here we must consult a table of χ^2 values to make our decision (table 11-3).

In the example above, the χ^2 value is 0.696. Since this was a monohybrid problem with only two categories of possible outcomes (purple or white flowers) the number of degrees of freedom (n in the left hand column of table 11-3) is one. We read across the table until we come to 0.05 and find the number 3.841. Because 0.696, our calculated χ^2 value, is less than 3.841, it is likely that the variation in the observed and expected is the result of chance, and that our hypothesized outcome is correct. A value *greater than* 3.841, however, would indicate that chance alone could not explain the deviation between observed and expected, and we would reject our hypothesis.

Table 11-2 Summary of Calculations of Chi Square for Garden Peas						
Phenotype	**Genotype**	**O**	**E**	**(O − E)**	**(O − E)²**	**(O − E)²/E**
Purple	P_	64	60.75	3.25	10.56	0.174
White	pp	17	20.25	−3.25	10.56	0.522
Total		81	81	0		0.696

Table 11-3 Distribution of χ^2

n	Probability													
	.99	.98	.95	.90	.80	.70	.50	.30	.20	.10	.05	.02	.01	.001
1	.00016	.00063	.00393	.0158	.0642	.148	.455	1.074	1.642	2.706	3.841	5.412	6.635	10.827
2	.0201	.0404	.103	.211	.446	.713	1.386	2.408	3.219	4.605	5.991	7.824	9.210	13.815
3	.115	.185	.352	.584	1.005	1.424	2.366	3.665	4.642	6.251	7.815	9.837	11.345	16.268
4	.297	.429	.711	1.064	1.649	2.195	3.357	4.878	5.989	7.779	9.488	11.668	13.277	18.465
5	.554	.752	1.145	1.610	2.343	3.000	4.351	6.064	7.289	9.236	11.070	13.388	15.086	20.517
6	.872	1.134	1.635	2.204	3.070	3.828	5.348	7.231	8.558	10.645	12.592	15.033	16.812	22.457
7	1.239	1.564	2.167	2.833	3.822	4.671	6.346	8.383	9.803	12.017	14.067	16.622	18.475	24.322
8	1.646	2.032	2.733	3.490	4.594	5.527	7.344	9.524	11.030	13.362	15.507	18.168	20.090	26.125
9	2.088	2.532	3.325	4.168	5.380	6.393	8.343	10.656	12.242	14.684	16.919	19.679	21.666	27.877
10	2.558	3.059	3.940	4.865	6.179	7.267	9.342	11.781	13.442	15.987	18.307	21.161	23.209	29.588

The term *degrees of freedom* requires further explanation. The number of degrees of freedom is always one *less* than the number of categories of possible outcomes. Thus, you were dealing with a dihybrid problem with a ratio of 9:3:3:1 (four possible phenotypes), *n* would equal three.

Now let's put this test into practice.

21. In fruit flies, red eyes (*R*) are dominant over white eyes (*r*). A student performs a cross between a heterozygous red-eyed fly and a white-eyed fly. The student counts the offspring and finds sixty-five red-eyed flies and forty-nine white-eyed flies.

What is the expected phenotypic ratio of this cross?

_____

Using a χ^2 test, determine if the deviation between the observed and the expected is probably the result of chance.

$\chi^2 =$ _____

Conclusion _____

_____

22. Once again in fruit flies, gray body (*G*) is dominant over ebony body (*g*). A red-eyed, gray-bodied fly known to be heterozygous for both traits is mated with a white-eyed fly that is heterozygous for body color.

What is the expected phenotypic ratio for this mating?

_____

The observed offspring consisted of fifteen white-eyed, ebony-bodied flies; thirty-one white-eyed, gray-bodied flies; twelve red-eyed, ebony-bodied flies; and thirty-eight red-eyed, gray-bodied flies.

What is the χ^2 value for this cross?

_____

Is it likely that the observed results "fit" the expected?

_____

The chi-square technique is not restricted to monohybrid or dihybrid problems; it may be used to evaluate any cross in which an expected ratio can be determined.

IX. Some Readily Observable Human Traits

In the preceding problems, we examined several human traits that are fairly simple and that follow the Mendelian pattern of inheritance. Most of our traits are much more complex, involving many genes or interactions between genes. As an example, hair color is determined by at least four genes, each one coding for the production of melanin, a brown pigment. Because the effect of these genes is cumulative, hair color can range from blond (little melanin) to very dark brown (much melanin).

Clearly, human traits are most interesting to humans. A number of traits listed below exhibit Mendelian inheritance. For each, examine your phenotype and fill in table 11-4. List your possible genotype(s) for each trait. When convenient, examine your parents' phenotypes and attempt to determine your actual genotype.

1. *Mid-digital hair (fig. 11-5a).* Examine the joint of your fingers for the presence of hair, the dominant condition (*MM*, *Mm*). Complete absence of hair is due to the homozygous-recessive condition (*mm*). You may need a hand lens to determine your phenotype. Even the slightest amount of hair indicates the dominant condition.

2. *Tongue rolling (fig. 11-5b).* The ability to roll one's tongue is due to a dominant allele, *T*. The homozygous-recessive condition, *t*, results in inability to roll one's tongue.

3. *Widow's peak (fig. 11-5c).* Widow's peak describes a distinct downward point in the frontal hairline and is due to the dominant allele, *W*. The recessive allele, *w*, results in a continuous hairline. (Omit study of this trait if baldness is affecting the hairline.)

Table 11-4 Summary of My Mendelian Traits

Trait	My Phenotype	My Possible Genotype(s)	Mom's Phenotype	Mom's Possible Genotype	Dad's Phenotype	Dad's Possible Genotype	My Possible or Probable Genotype
Mid-digital hair							
Tongue rolling							
Widow's peak							
Earlobe attachment							
Hitchhiker's thumb							
Relative finger length							

Figure 11-5 Some readily observable human Mendelian traits.

4. *Earlobe attachment (fig. 11-5d).* Most individuals have free earlobes (*FF, Ff*). Homozygous recessives (*ff*) have earlobes attached directly to the head.

5. *Hitchhiker's thumb (fig. 11-5e).* Although considerable variation exists in this trait, we will consider those individuals who *cannot* extend their thumbs backward to approximately 45° to be carrying the dominant allele, *H.* Homozygous-recessive persons (*hh*) can bend their thumbs at least 45°, if not farther.

6. *Relative finger length (fig. 11-5f).* An interesting sex-influenced (*not sex-linked*) trait relates to the relative lengths of the index and ring finger. In males, the allele for a short index finger (*S*) is dominant. In females, it is recessive. In rare cases each hand may be different. If one or both index fingers are greater than or equal to the length of the ring finger, the recessive genotype is present in males, and the dominant present in females.

X. Experiment: Inheritance in a Fungus

Your instructor may provide you with an optional experiment about inheritance of spore color in the fungus *Sordaria*.

PRE-LAB QUESTIONS

____ 1. In a monohybrid cross (a) only one trait is being considered, (b) the parents are always homozygous, (c) the parents are always heterozygous, (d) no hybrid is produced.

____ 2. The genetic makeup of an organism is its (a) phenotype, (b) genotype, (c) locus, (d) gamete.

____ 3. An allele whose expression is completely masked by the expression or effect of its allelic partner is (a) incompletely dominant, (b) homozygous, (c) dominant, (d) recessive.

____ 4. The physical appearance of an organism, resulting from interactions of its genetic makeup and its environment, is (a) phenotype, (b) hybrid vigor, (c) dominance, (d) genotype.

____ 5. An organism that is heterozygous for a trait is (a) haploid, (b) homozygous, (c) diploid, (d) all of the above.

____ 6. Codominance occurs when (a) the phenotype for both (or all) alleles is expressed, (b) the individual is heterozygous, (c) the organism is homozygous recessive, (d) a and b above.

____ 7. A gene located only on the female (X) chromosome having no allelic partner on the Y chromosome would be (a) incompletely dominant, (b) codominant, (c) sex-linked, (d) heterozygous.

____ 8. The sex chromosome determining maleness is (a) the Y chromosome, (b) the X chromosome, (c) sex-linked, (d) heterozygous.

____ 9. A nucleus containing only one of the two homologues is (a) sex-linked, (b) an improbable event, (c) diploid, (d) haploid.

____ 10. An example of a trait controlled by multiple alleles is (a) baldness in males, (b) color blindness, (c) the ABO blood groups, (d) blue Andalusian chickens.

EXERCISE 13
Heredity

POST-LAB QUESTIONS

1. Explain the implications of the principle of independent assortment as it applies to distribution of alleles in gametes.

2. What does it mean to say that certain traits are sex-linked?

3. Distinguish between incomplete dominance and codominance.

4. Define the term *multiple alleles.*

5. Suppose you have two traits controlled by genes on separate chromosomes. If sexual reproduction occurs between two heterozygous parents, what will the genotypic ratio of all possible gametes be?

6. What is the probability that parents will bear five sons and no daughters?

7. How does probability differ from actuality?

8. Studies have suggested (although not proved) that whether you are right- or left-handed may be hereditary. Homozygous-dominant (*RR*) people are strongly right-handed and are not easily influenced to change preferences. Homozygous-recessive individuals are strongly left-handed. Heterozygous individuals are more variable. They are potentially ambidextrous but are easily influenced by environment or training.

   a. Would you characterize handedness as an example of complete dominance, incomplete dominance, or codominance?

   b. Would it be possible for a left-handed person to be heterozygous?

   c. Would it be possible for two left-handed parents to have a right-handed child? Explain.

9. For this problem, assume that one allele is completely dominant over the other.

   a. Suppose two individuals heterozygous for a *single* trait have children. What is the expected phenotypic ratio of the offspring?

   b. If two individuals heterozygous for *two* traits have children, what would be the expected phenotypic ratio of the offspring?

   c. Remember that the gene for each trait is located at a locus, a physical region on the chromosome. Suppose that crossing two individuals heterozygous for two traits resulted in the same phenotypic ratio as for a single trait. Are the genes for these two traits on separate chromosomes or on the same chromosome? Explain your answer.

10. Explain the usefulness of the chi-square test.

Evidences of Evolution

OBJECTIVES

After completing this exercise, you will be able to

1. define *evolution*, *natural selection*, *population*, *species*, *fitness*, *fossil*, *hominid*, *Australopithecus*, *Homo*, *Homo sapiens*;

2. explain how natural selection operates to alter the genetic makeup of a population over time;

3. describe the general sequence of evolution of life forms over geologic time;

4. recognize primitive and advanced characteristics of skull structure of human ancestors and relatives.

Introduction

The process by which the incredible diversity of mammals living and extinct species came to exist is called *evolution*, the focus of this exercise. **Evolution**, the process that results in changes in the genetic makeup of populations of organisms through time, is the unifying framework for the whole of biology. Less than 200 years ago, it seemed obvious to most people that living organisms had not changed over time—that oak trees looked like oak trees and humans looked like humans, year after year, generation after generation, without change. As scientists studied the natural world more closely, however, evidence of change and the relatedness of all living organisms emerged from geology and the fossil record, as well as from comparative morphology, developmental patterns, and biochemistry.

Charles Darwin (and, independently, Alfred Russel Wallace) postulated the major mechanism of evolution to be **natural selection**, the difference in survival and reproduction that occurs among individuals of a population that differ in one or more alleles. (Review Exercise 12 for the definition of *allele*.) A **population** is a group of individuals of the same species occupying a given area. A **species** is one or more populations that closely resemble each other, interbreed under natural conditions, and produce fertile offspring.

As we understand natural selection, genetic modifications that place an organism at a disadvantage in its environment will be "selected against," that is, those members of a population will die off, reproduce less, or both. Other individuals may have allele combinations that are advantageous; these are "selected for" and tend to live longer, have more offspring, or both. They have greater **fitness**. Their offspring will receive those advantageous alleles from their parents. As physical, chemical, or biological aspects of the populations' environment change, those modifications that are best adapted to that environment tend to be found more often within the population. The population evolves as some traits become more common and others decrease or disappear over time.

Many people think of evolution in historic terms—as something that produced the dinosaurs but that no longer operates in today's world. Remember, though, that *the process of genetic change in populations over time continues today* and is a dominant force shaping the living organisms of our planet.

The scientific evidence for evolution is overwhelming, although scientists continue to debate the exact mechanisms by which natural selection and other evolutionary agents change allele frequencies. In this exercise, you will track the effects of natural selection in a simulated population, consider the time over which evolution has occurred, and examine the fossil record for evidence of large-scale trends and change among our human ancestors and relatives.

17.1 How Natural Selection Works *(About 1 hour)*

In this activity, you will simulate interacting populations of predators and prey. You will study how predators exert selective pressure on prey populations and vice versa and consider how the environment affects the interaction. The simulated prey are populations of different dry beans, and the simulated predator populations are familiar utensils.

This experiment tests two hypotheses: (1) that *prey populations of different forms vary in fitness as a consequence of predation* and (2) *predator populations of different forms vary in fitness as a consequence of prey characteristics*. Each student group will act as one predator species and forage for prey over a short time period. Analysis of changes in prey population numbers will allow us to draw conclusions about the validity of these hypotheses.

MATERIALS

Per student group (4):

- predator utensils of one form (knife, fork, spoon, forceps, or chopsticks)
- collection of dry beans (50 each of five types)
- four cups to hold prey
- calculator

Per lab room:

- patterned fabric or carpet pieces
- reservoirs of additional beans of each type
- stopwatch or timer

PROCEDURE

1. Obtain a fabric or carpet piece to serve as the habitat. Scatter the beans randomly over the habitat. What prey species (bean type) do you expect to be most able to survive predation? Why?

   _____

   _____

   Which prey species do you expect to be least successful? Why?

   _____

   _____

   What predator species (utensil type) do you expect to be most successful in capturing prey? Why?

   _____

   _____

   Which predator do you expect to be least successful? Why?

   _____

   _____

2. At the signal from your instructor, students (predators) will collect prey for 30 seconds. Prey may be collected only with your predator utensil and only one at a time. Place each prey bean into your cup and continue foraging until the signal to stop.

3. Record the number of each kind of prey in your cup after this first round foraging session:

   Black bean prey _____

   Garbanzo prey _____

   Lentil prey _____

   Lima bean prey _____

   Navy bean prey _____

   In Table 17-1, in the "1st round" column, record the total number of each prey species taken by your whole group. Also record your group's results on the class master data sheets.

4. Calculate the number of each prey species remaining. These surviving prey reproduce so that the total number of each species in the habitat doubles. For example, if 10 garbanzo prey were captured from the habitat, the remaining 40 will reproduce and add 40 new garbanzo prey for a total of 80 in the habitat. Repeat this process for each species.

5. Repeat foraging and reproduction of the survivors for two more generations, entering group data in Table 17-1 and on class master data sheets. Double the number of surviving prey of each species in the habitat after each round of predation.

   My round two prey capture:

   Black bean prey _____

   Garbanzo prey _____

   Lentil prey _____

   Lima bean prey _____

   Navy bean prey _____

   My round three prey capture:

   Black bean prey _____

   Garbanzo prey _____

   Lentil prey _____

   Lima bean prey _____

   Navy bean prey _____

TABLE 17-1	Group Totals: Prey Population Changes Caused by Predation by ▭ (Predator Species)										
	Black		Garbanzo		Lentil		Lima		Navy		
Prey Species	Number Captured	Number Remaining	Number Captured	Number Remaining	Number Captured	Number Remaining	Number Captured	Number Remaining	Number Captured	Number Remaining	Total Prey Captured
1st round											
2nd round											
3rd round											
Total											

6. Graph the total population size over time for each prey species in Figure 17-1. Be sure to distinguish among the five species by using different symbols or colors for the trend lines for each.

Do your group's results support the hypothesis that *prey populations of different forms vary in fitness as a consequence of predation*? Write a conclusion accepting or rejecting the hypothesis and explaining your reasoning.

_____

_____

Which prey species was most vulnerable to your team's predator species?

_____

Which prey species was least vulnerable to your predator?

Figure 17-1 Prey population sizes after predator foraging rounds.

How well do these results agree with your expectations?

_____

Study the class total results. Did any prey species become extinct? _____ If so, speculate why.

_____

_____

Which prey species appears to be most fit in all environments with all predator species? What trait(s) may contribute to that fitness?

_____

_____

Which predator species appears to be most fit? Which predator species appears to be least fit? Explain.

_____

_____

What effect did the habitat characteristics have on your group's results? If the habitat had been uniformly white, speculate on the effect of this environmental change on the outcome for predator and prey species.

_____

_____

If you failed to detect any differences in fitness among prey species, speculate on the reason(s) for this failure. Does this failure necessarily mean that natural selection would not occur in these populations?

_____

_____

Explain the results of this activity in terms of the effects of natural selection on the genetic makeup of the five prey populations.

_____

_____

_____

_____

17.2 Geologic Time (*About 30 min.*)

Earth is an ancient planet that formed from a cloud of dust and gas approximately 4.6 billion years ago. Life formed relatively quickly on the young planet, and the first cells emerged in the seas by 3.8 billion years ago. Initially, the only living organisms on Earth were prokaryotic bacteria and bacteria-like cells. Eventually, though, more complex, eukaryotic organisms evolved. The seas were colonized by single-celled organisms first followed by multicelled and colonial plants and animals (Figure 17-2). Only much later did life move onto the land.

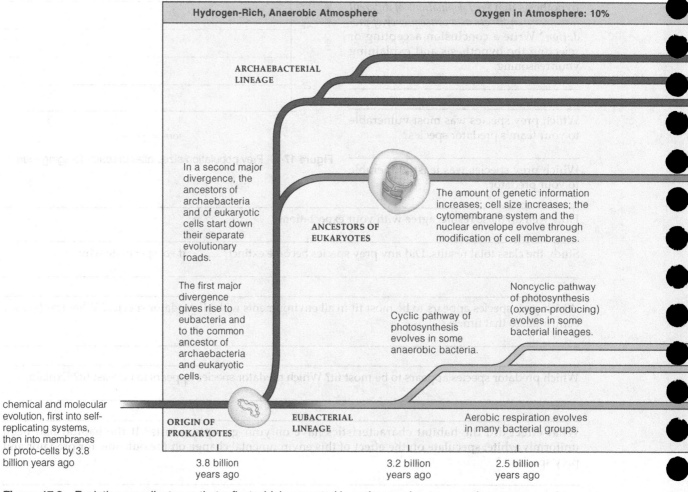

Figure 17-2 Evolutionary milestones that reflect widely accepted hypotheses about connections among major groups of organisms. (Timeline not shown to scale.)

Geologic time, "deep time," is difficult for humans to grasp given our recent evolution and 75-year life spans. In this section, you will construct a geologic timeline to help you gain perspective on the almost incomprehensible sweep of time over which evolution has operated.

MATERIALS

Per student pair:

- one 4.6-m rope or string
- meter stick or metric ruler (or both)
- masking tape
- calculator

PROCEDURE

1. Obtain a 4.6 m length of rope or string. The string represents the entire length of time (4.6 billion years) since the Earth was formed. On this timeline, you will attach masking tape labels to mark the points when the events below occurred. Measure from the starting point with the meter stick or metric ruler.
2. Locate and mark with tape on the timeline the events listed in Table 17-2 (bya = billion years ago, mya = million years ago, ya = years ago).
   Over what *proportion* of the Earth's history were there only single-celled living organisms? _____
   Over what *proportion* of the Earth's history have multicelled organisms existed? _____
   Over what *proportion* of the Earth's history have mammals been a dominant part of the fauna?

   _____
   Over what *proportion* of the Earth's history have modern humans existed? _____

   _____

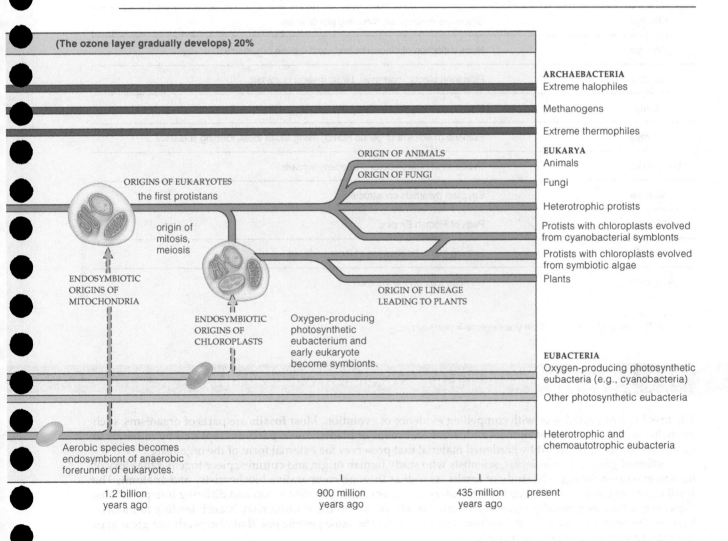

(The ozone layer gradually develops) 20%

ARCHAEBACTERIA
Extreme halophiles

Methanogens

Extreme thermophiles

EUKARYA
Animals

ORIGIN OF ANIMALS

ORIGIN OF FUNGI

Fungi

ORIGINS OF EUKARYOTES
the first protistans

Heterotrophic protists

Protists with chloroplasts evolved from cyanobacterial symbionts

origin of mitosis, meiosis

Protists with chloroplasts evolved from symbiotic algae

Plants

ENDOSYMBIOTIC ORIGINS OF MITOCHONDRIA

ORIGIN OF LINEAGE LEADING TO PLANTS

ENDOSYMBIOTIC ORIGINS OF CHLOROPLASTS

Oxygen-producing photosynthetic eubacterium and early eukaryote become symbionts.

EUBACTERIA
Oxygen-producing photosynthetic eubacteria (e.g., cyanobacteria)

Other photosynthetic eubacteria

Heterotrophic and chemoautotrophic eubacteria

Aerobic species becomes endosymbiont of anaerobic forerunner of eukaryotes.

1.2 billion years ago   900 million years ago   435 million years ago   present

TABLE 17-2 Events in Evolution of Life on Earth

Time Frame	Event
4.6 bya*	Formation of Earth
3.8 bya	First living prokaryotic cells
2.5 bya	Oxygen-releasing photosynthetic pathway
1.2 bya	Origin of eukaryotic cells
580 mya	Origin of multicellular marine plants and animals
500 mya	First vertebrate animals (marine fishes)
435 mya	First vascular land plants and land animals
345 mya	Great coal forests; amphibians and insects undergo great diversification
240 mya	Mass extinction of nearly all living organisms
225 mya	Origin of mammals, dinosaurs; seed plants dominate
135 mya	Dinosaurs reach peak; flowering plants arise
65 mya	Mass extinction of dinosaurs and most marine organisms
63 mya	Flowering plants, mammals, birds, insects dominate
6 mya	First hominid (upright walking) human ancestors
2 mya	Humans (members of genus *Homo*) using stone tools, forming social life
200,000 ya	Evolution of *Homo sapiens* (modern humans)
6400 ya	Egyptian pyramids constructed
2000 ya	Peak of Roman Empire
A.D. 1776	Signing of the Declaration of Independence
A.D. 1969	Humans step on Earth's moon

bya = billion years ago, mya = million years ago, ya = years ago

© Cengage Learning 2013

17.3 The Fossil Record and Human Evolution (*About 30 min.*)

The fossil record provides us with compelling evidence of evolution. Most **fossils** are parts of organisms, such as shells, teeth, and bones of animals and stems and seeds of plants. These parts are replaced by minerals to form stone or are surrounded by hardened material that preserves the external form of the organism.

Anthropologists and *archeologists*, scientists who study human origin and cultures, piece together the story of human evolution through the study of fossils, as well as through comparative biochemistry and anatomy. The fossil record of our human lineage is fragmentary and generates much discussion and differing interpretations. However, scientists generally agree that **hominids**, all species on the evolutionary branch leading to modern humans, arose in Africa by about 7 million years ago from the same genetic line that also produced great apes (gorillas, orangutans, and chimpanzees).

Many anatomic changes occurred in the course of evolution from hominid ancestor to modern humans. Arms became shorter, feet flattened and then developed arches, and the big toe moved in line with the other toes. The legs moved more directly under the pelvis. These features allowed upright posture and bipedalism (walking on two legs), and they also allowed the use of the hands for tasks other than locomotion.

Still other anatomic changes were associated with the head. In this section, you will observe some of the evolutionary trends associated with skull structure by studying images or reproductions of the skulls of several ancestors and relatives of modern humans.

MATERIALS

Per laboratory room:

- images or sets of skull reproductions and replicas, including *Australopithecus afarensis*, *Homo habilis*, *Homo erectus*, *Homo sapiens*, and chimpanzee (*Pan troglodytes*)
- collection of fossil plants and animals (optional)

PROCEDURE

1. If available, examine the fossil collection. Note which fossils lived in the seas and which lived on land.
   (a) Do any of the fossils resemble organisms now living? If so, describe the similarities between fossil and current forms.

   _____

   _____

   _____

   (b) Are there any fossils in the collection that are unlike any organisms currently living? If so, describe the features that appear to be most unlike today's forms.

   _____

   _____

2. Examine the hominid skulls in the laboratory or images available online as instructed. (Be aware that physical skull specimens are not actual fossils, but are plaster or plastic restoration designed partly from fossilized remains and partly from reconstruction. The *Homo sapiens* and chimpanzee skulls are replicas of modern specimens.)
3. Identify the scientific name of each organism and their approximate date of origin. As you can see, some of these hominids appear to have lived during the same approximate time span.
4. Study the skull specimens and Figure 17-3. For each skull, rate the characteristic listed in Table 17-3 (use a scale of (– – –) for the most primitive and (+ + +) for the most advanced). Record your observations of the changes that occurred over time in Table 17-4.

| A. afarensis | H. habilis | H. erectus | H. sapiens | P. troglodytes |

Figure 17-3 Comparison of skull shapes of hominid relatives and ancestors.

TABLE 17-3	**Primitive and Advanced Characteristics of Primate Skulls**	
Characteristic	**Primitive Form**	**Advanced Form**
Teeth	Many large, specialized	Fewer, smaller, less specialized
Jaw	Jaw and muzzle long	Jaw and muzzle short
Cranium (braincase)	Cranium small, forehead receding	Cranium large, prominent vertical forehead
Muscle attachments	Prominent eyebrow ridges and cranial keel (ridge)	Much reduced eyebrow ridges, no keel
Nose	Nose not protruding from face	Prominent nose with distinct bridge

© Cengage Learning 2013

TABLE 17-4	Skull Characteristics of Human Ancestors and Relatives, from (– – –) = Most Primitive to (+ + +) = Most Advanced					
Genus and species	Teeth	Jaw	Structure	Cranium	Muscle Attachments	Nose
Australopithecus afarensis						
Homo habilis						
Homo erectus						
Homo sapiens						
Pan troglodytes						

© Cengage Learning 2013

5. The first true hominids found in the fossil record have been assigned to the genus *Australopithecus* (from the Greek *australis* for "southern" and *pithecus* for "ape" because the first specimens were found in southern Africa). Some of the oldest known fossils of *Australopithecus* are of the species *A. afarensis*. The most famous skeleton has been named Lucy. Lucy and others of her species lived approximately 3.6 to 2.9 million years ago.

6. Now turn your attention to the skulls of the *Homo* lineage. There is debate about the lineage of our own genus, *Homo* ("Man"). *Homo habilis*, the early toolmaker, lived in eastern and southern Africa from about 1.9 to 1.6 million years ago. *Homo erectus* ("upright man") also arose in Africa. However, it was *Homo erectus* whose populations left Africa in waves between 2 million and 500,000 years ago. Some still lived in southeast Asia until at least 53,000 years ago. Our own species, *Homo sapiens* ("wise man"), seems to have evolved from *Homo erectus* ancestors by 100,000 years ago.

(a) What changes from primitive to advanced characteristics do you see in the evolution from *A. afarensis* to *Homo habilis*?

_____

_____

_____

(b) What is the trend in cranial capacity between the ancestral *A. afarensis* and *Homo erectus*?

_____

_____

_____

(c) Between *Homo erectus* and *Homo sapiens*?

_____

_____

_____

7. Finally, study the skulls of the modern human form (*Homo sapiens*) and our nearest living relative, the chimpanzee (*Pan troglodytes*). Fossil evidence, biochemistry, and genetic analyses indicate that chimpanzees and humans are the most closely related of all living primates. In fact, comparisons of amino acid sequences of proteins and DNA sequences show that chimpanzees and humans share about 99% of their genes! Other evidence shows that the separation from the hominid line of the lineage that led to chimpanzees and other great apes occurred about 6 million years ago.

(a) How does the chimpanzee skull compare with the skull of *Australopithecus afarensis*? What features are most alike? Which are most different?

_____

_____

(b) How does the chimpanzee skull compare with the human skull with respect to primitive and advanced anatomical features?

_____

_____

_____

_____ 1. Evolution is
  (a) the survival of populations.
  (b) the process that results in changes in the genetic makeup of a population over time.
  (c) a group of individuals of the same species occupying a given area.
  (d) change in an individual's genetic makeup over its lifetime.

_____ 2. The major mechanism of evolution is
  (a) species development.
  (b) predation.
  (c) fitness.
  (d) natural selection.

_____ 3. An organism whose genetic makeup allows it to produce more offspring than another of its species is said to have greater
  (a) fitness.
  (b) evolution.
  (c) foraging.
  (d) selection.

_____ 4. The Earth formed approximately
  (a) 4600 years ago.
  (b) 1 million years ago.
  (c) 1 billion years ago.
  (d) 4.6 billion years ago.

_____ 5. The first living organisms appeared on Earth approximately
  (a) 4.6 billion years ago.
  (b) 3.8 billion years ago.
  (c) 1 billion years ago.
  (d) 6400 years ago.

_____ 6. Modern humans evolved about
  (a) 200,000 years ago.
  (b) 2,000,000 years ago.
  (c) 2,000,000,000 years ago.
  (d) 4,600,000,000 years ago.

_____ 7. Fossils
  (a) are remains of organisms.
  (b) are formed when organic materials are replaced with minerals.
  (c) provide evidence of evolution.
  (d) are all of the above.

_____ 8. The first true hominids in the fossil record are
  (a) _Australopithecus._
  (b) _Homo habilis._
  (c) the chimpanzee.
  (d) _Homo sapiens._

_____ 9. Hominids with evolutionarily advanced skull characteristics would have
  (a) many large, specialized teeth.
  (b) a large cranium with prominent vertical forehead.
  (c) prominent eyebrow ridges.
  (d) a long jaw and muzzle.

_____ 10. The human ancestor whose populations dispersed from Africa to other parts of the world was
  (a) _Homo sapiens._
  (b) _Australopithecus afarensis._
  (c) _Pan troglodytes._
  (d) _Homo erectus._

EXERCISE **17**

Evidences of Evolution

Post-Lab Questions

Introduction

1. Define the following terms:
   (a) Evolution

   (b) Natural selection

17.1 How Natural Selection Works

2. Describe how natural selection might operate to change the genetic makeup of a population of rabbits if a new, faster predator was introduced into their habitat.

17.2 Geologic Time

3. Arrange the following events in their order of occurrence:
   (a) Photosynthesis *or* eukaryotic cells?
   (b) Vertebrate animals *or* flowering plants?
   (c) Extinction of dinosaurs *or* origin of hominids?

17.3 The Fossil Record and Human Evolution

4. What primitive characteristics are visible in the skull pictured here?

5. Describe anatomical changes in the skull that occurred in human evolution between an *Australopithecus afarensis*–like ancestor and *Homo sapiens.*

Photo by J. W. Perry.

6. Compare the slope of the forehead of chimpanzees with that of modern humans.

7. Compare the teeth of *Australopithecus afarensis* and *Homo sapiens*.
   (a) Describe similarities and differences between the two species.

   (b) Write a hypothesis about dietary differences between the two species based on their teeth.

Food for Thought

8. Why is the development of bipedalism considered to be a major advancement in human evolution?

9. Do you believe humans are still evolving? If not, why not? If yes, explain in what ways humans may be evolving.

10. Humans have selectively bred many radically different domestic animals (e.g., St. Bernard and Chihuahua dog breeds). Does this activity result in evolution? Why or why not?

Taxonomy: Classifying and Naming Organisms

After completing this exercise, you will be able to

1. define *common name, scientific name, binomial, genus, specific epithet, species, taxonomy, phylogenetic system, dichotomous key, herbarium;*

2. distinguish common names from scientific names;

3. explain why scientific names are preferred over common names in biology;

4. identify the genus and specific epithet in a scientific binomial;

5. write out scientific binomials in the form appropriate to the Linnean system;

6. construct a dichotomous key;

7. explain the usefulness of an herbarium;

8. use a dichotomous key to identify plants, animals, or other organisms as provided by your instructor.

Introduction

We are all great classifiers. Every day, we consciously or unconsciously classify and categorize the objects around us. We recognize an organism as a cat or a dog, a pine tree or an oak tree. But there are numerous kinds of oaks, so we refine our classification, giving the trees distinguishing names such as "red oak," "white oak," or "bur oak." These are examples of **common names**, names with which you are probably most familiar.

Scientists are continually exchanging information about living organisms. But not all scientists speak the same language. The common name "white oak," familiar to an American, is probably not familiar to a Spanish biologist, even though the tree we know as white oak may exist in Spain as well as in our own backyard. Moreover, even within our own language, the same organism can have several common names. For example, within North America a gopher is also called a ground squirrel, a pocket mole, and a groundhog. On the other hand, the same common name may describe many different organisms; there are more than 300 different trees called "mahogany"! To circumvent the problems associated with common names, biologists use **scientific names** that are unique to each kind of organism and that are used throughout the world.

A scientific name is two-parted, a **binomial**. The first word of the binomial designates the group to which the organism belongs; this is the **genus** name (the plural of genus is *genera*). All oak trees belong to the genus *Quercus*, a word derived from Latin. Each kind of organism within a genus is given a **specific epithet**. Thus, the scientific name for white oak is *Quercus alba* (specific epithet is *alba*), while that of bur oak is *Quercus macrocarpa* (specific epithet is *macrocarpa*).

Notice that the genus name is always capitalized; the specific epithet usually is not capitalized (although it can be if it is the proper name of a person or place). The binomial is written in *italics* (since these are Latin names); if italics are not available, the genus name and specific epithet are underlined.

You will hear discussion of "species" of organisms. For example, on a field trip, you may be asked "What species is this tree?" Assuming you are looking at a white oak, your reply would be "*Quercus alba.*" The scientific name of the **species** includes *both* the genus name and specific epithet.

If a species is named more than once within a document, it is accepted convention to write out the full genus name and specific epithet the first time and to abbreviate the genus name every time thereafter. For example, if white oak is being described, the first use is written *Quercus alba,* and each subsequent naming appears as *Q. alba.*

Similarly, when a number of species, all of the same genus, are being listed, the accepted convention is to write both the genus name and specific epithet for the first species and to abbreviate the genus name for each species listed thereafter. Thus, it is acceptable to list the scientific names for white oak and bur oak as *Quercus alba* and *Q. macrocarpa,* respectively.

Taxonomy is the science of classification (categorizing) and nomenclature (naming). Biologists prefer a system that indicates the evolutionary relationships among organisms. To this end, classification became a **phylogenetic system;** that is, one indicating the current understanding of evolutionary ancestry among organisms.

Current taxonomic thought separates all living organisms into six kingdoms:

1. Kingdom Bacteria (prokaryotic cells of great diversity, and that include pathogens)
2. Kingdom Archaea (prokaryotic organisms that are evolutionarily between eukaryotes and bacteria)
3. Kingdom Protista (as collection of lineages, some single-celled and some multi-celled; includes euglenoids, ciliates, dinoflagellates, amoebas, and many groups of "algae")
4. Kingdom Fungi (fungi)
5. Kingdom Plantae (plants)
6. Kingdom Animalia (animals)

Let's consider the scientific system of classification, using ourselves as examples. All members of our species belong to Kingdom Animalia (animals):

- Phylum Chordata (animals with a notochord)
- Class Mammalia (animals with mammary glands and skin with hair)
- Order Primates (mammals that walk upright on two legs)
- Family Hominidae (human forms, existing and extinct)
- Genus *Homo* (mankind)
- Specific epithet *sapiens* (wise)
- Species: *Homo sapiens*

The more closely related evolutionarily two organisms are, the more categories they share. You and I are different individuals of the same species. We share the same genus and specific epithet, *Homo* and *sapiens*. A creature believed to be a close, extinct ancestor walked the Earth 1.5 million years ago. That creature shared our genus name but had a different specific epithet, *erectus*. Thus, *Homo sapiens* and *H. erectus* are *different* species.

Like all science, taxonomy is subject to change as new information becomes available. Modifications are made to reflect revised interpretations.

18.1 Constructing a Dichotomous Key *(About 45 min.)*

To classify organisms, you must first identify them. A *taxonomic key* helps to identify an object or organism unknown to you but that someone else has described. The user chooses between alternative characteristics of the unknown object and, by making the correct choices, arrives at the name of the object.

Keys that are based on successive choices between two alternatives are known as **dichotomous keys** (*dichotomous* means "to fork into two equal parts"). When using a key, always read both choices even though the first appears to describe the subject. Don't guess at measurements; use a ruler. Since living organisms vary in their characteristics, don't base your conclusion on a single specimen if more are available.

MATERIALS

Per lab room:

- several meter sticks or metric height charts taped to a wall

PROCEDURE

1. Suppose the geometric shapes below have unfamiliar names. Look at the dichotomous key following the figures. Notice there is a 1a and a 1b. Start with 1a. If the description in 1a fits the figure you are observing better than description 1b, then proceed to the choices listed under 2, as shown at the end of line 1a. If 1a does *not* describe the figure in question, 1b does. Looking at the end of line 1b, you see that the figure would be called an Elcric.

2. Use the key provided to determine the hypothetical name for each object. Write the name beneath the object and then check with your instructor to see if you have made the correct choices.

Key		
1a.	Figure with distinct corners	2
1b.	Figure without distinct corners	Elcric
2a.	Figure with 3 sides	3
2b.	Figure with 4 or more sides	4
3a.	All sides of equal length	Legnairt
3b.	Only 2 sides equal	Legnairtosi
4a.	Figure with only right angles	Eraqus
4b.	Figure with other than right angles	Nogatco

3. Now you will construct a dichotomous key, using your classmates as subjects. The class should divide up into groups of eight (or as evenly as the class size will allow). Working with the individuals in your group, fill in Table 18-1, measuring height with a metric ruler or the scale attached to the wall.

4. To see how you might plan a dichotomous key, examine the following branch diagram below. If there are both men and women in a group, the most obvious first split is male/female (although other possibilities for the split could be chosen as well). Follow the course of splits for two of the men in the group.

Note that each choice has *only* two alternatives. Thus, we split into "under 1.75 m" and "1.75 m or taller." Likewise, our next split is into "blue eyes" and "nonblue eyes" rather than all the possibilities.

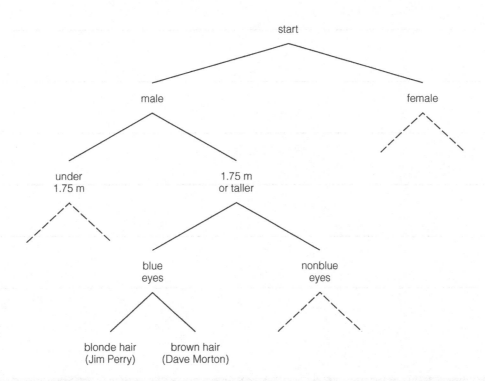

5. On a separate sheet of paper, construct a branch diagram for your group using the characteristics in Table 18-1 and then condense it into the dichotomous key that follows. When you have finished, exchange your key with that of an individual in another group. Key out the individuals in the other group without speaking until you believe you know the name of the individual you are examining. Ask that individual if you are correct. If not, go back to find out where you made a mistake, or possibly where the key was misleading. (Depending on how you construct your key, you may need more or fewer lines than have been provided.)

TABLE 18-1 Characteristics of Students

Student (name)	Sex (m/f)	Height (m)	Eye Color	Hair Color	Shoe Size
1.					
2.					
3.					
4.					
5.					
6.					
7.					
8.					

© Cengage Learning 2013

Key to Students in Group _____

1a.

1b.

2a.

2b.

3a.

3b.

4a.

4b.

5a.

5b.

6a.

6b.

7a.

7b.

8a.

8b.

18.2 Using a Taxonomic Key

A. Some Microscopic Members of the Freshwater Environment (About 30 min.)

Suppose you want to identify the specimens in some pond water. The easiest way is to key them out with a dichotomous key, now that you know how to use one. In this section, you will do just that.

MATERIALS

Per student:
- compound microscope
- microscope slide
- coverslips
- dissecting needle

Per student group (table):
- cultures of freshwater organisms
- one disposable plastic pipet per culture
- methylcellulose in dropping bottle

PROCEDURE

1. Obtain a clean glass microscope slide and clean coverslip.
2. Using a disposable plastic pipet or dissecting needle, withdraw a small amount of the culture provided.
3. Place *one* drop of the culture on the center of the slide.
4. Gently lower the coverslip onto the liquid.
5. Using your compound light microscope, observe your wet mount. Focus first with the low-power objective and then with the medium or high-dry objective, depending on the size of the organism in the field of view.
6. Concentrate your observation on a single specimen, keying out the specimen using the Key to Selected Freshwater Inhabitants that follows.
7. In the space provided, write the scientific name of each organism you identify. After each identification, have your instructor verify your conclusion.
8. Clean and reuse your slide after each identification.

Key to Selected Freshwater Inhabitants

1a.	Filamentous organism consisting of green, chloroplast-bearing threads	2
1b.	Organism consisting of a single cell or nonfilamentous colony	4
2a.	Filament branched, each cell mostly filled with green chloroplast	*Cladophora*
2b.	Filament unbranched	3
3a.	Each cell of filament containing 1 or 2 spiral-shaped green chloroplasts	*Spirogyra*
3b.	Each cell of filament containing 2 star-shaped green chloroplasts	*Zygnema*
4a.	Organism consisting of a single cell	5
4b.	Organism composed of many cells aggregated into a colony	6
5a.	Motile, teardrop-shaped or spherical organism	*Chlamydomonas*
5b.	Nonmotile, elongate cell on either end; clear, granule-containing regions at ends	*Closterium*
6a.	Colony a hollow round ball of more than 500 cells; new colonies may be present inside larger colony	*Volvox*
6b.	Colony consisting of less than 50 cells	7
7a.	Organism composed of a number of tooth-shaped cells	*Pediastrum*
7b.	Colony a loose square or rectangle of 4–32 spherical cells	*Gonium*

Organism 1 is _____

Organism 2 is _____

Organism 3 is _____

Organism 4 is _____

Organism 5 is _____

Organism 6 is _____

Organism 7 is _____

Organism 8 is _____

Suppose you want to identify the trees growing on your campus or in your yard at home. Without having an expert present, you can now do that, because you know how to use a taxonomic key. But how can you be certain that you have keyed your specimen correctly?

Typically, scientists compare their tentative identifications against *reference specimens*—that is, preserved organisms that have been identified by an expert *taxonomist* (a person who names and classifies organisms). If you are identifying fishes or birds, the reference specimen might be a bottled or mounted specimen with the name on it. In the case of plants, reference specimens most frequently take the form of *herbarium mounts* (Figure 18-1) of the plants. An **herbarium** (plural, *herbaria*) is a repository, a museum of sorts, of preserved plants. The taxonomist flattens freshly collected specimens in a plant press. They are then dried and mounted on sheets of paper.

Herbarium labels are affixed to the sheets, indicating the scientific name of the plant, the person who collected it, the location and date of collection, and often pertinent information about the habitat in which the plant was found.

It is likely that your school has an herbarium. If so, your instructor may show you the collection. To some, this endeavor may seem boring, but herbaria serve a critical function. The appearance or disappearance of plants from the landscape often gives a very good indication of environmental change. An herbarium records the diversity of plants in the area, at any point in history since the start of the collection.

MATERIALS

Per student group (table):

- set of eight tree twigs with leaves (fresh or herbarium specimens) *or*
- trees and shrubs in leafy condition (for an outdoor lab)

PROCEDURE

Use the appropriate following key to identify the tree and shrub specimens that have been provided in the lab or that you find on your campus. Refer to the *Glossary to Tree Key* (page 236) and Figures 18-2 through 18-9 (pages 230–232) when you encounter an unfamiliar term. When you have finished keying a specimen, confirm your identification by checking the herbarium mounts or asking your instructor.

Note: Some descriptions within the key have more characteristics than your specimen will exhibit. For example, the key may describe a fruit type when the specimen doesn't have a fruit on it. However, other specimen characteristics are described, and these should allow you to identify the specimen in most cases.

Note: The keys provided are for *selected* trees of your area. In nature, you will find many more genera than can be identified by these keys.

Figure 18-1 A typical herbarium mount.

Figure 18-2 Structure of a typical plant (bean).

Common names within parentheses follow the scientific name. A metric ruler is provided below for use where measurements are required.

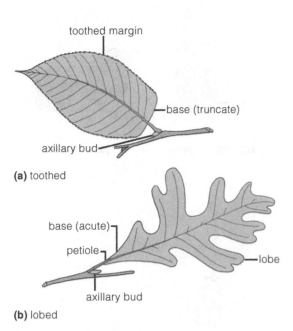

(a) toothed

(b) lobed

Figure 18-3 Simple leaves.

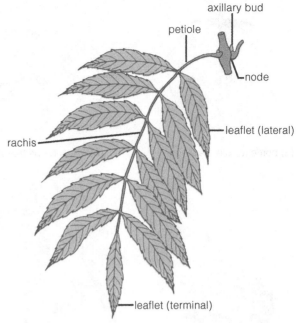

Figure 18-4 Pinnately compound leaf.

Figure 18-5 Simple leaves—alternating.

Figure 18-6 Simple leaves—opposite.

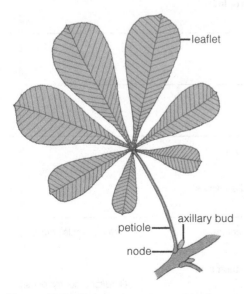

Figure 18-7 Palmately compound leaf.

(a) pith chambered **(b)** pith solid

Figure 18-8 Pith types.

Taxonomy: Classifying and Naming Organisms **231**

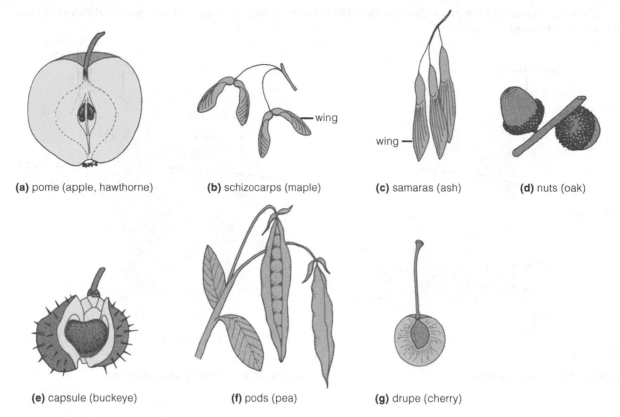

(a) pome (apple, hawthorne) **(b)** schizocarps (maple) **(c)** samaras (ash) **(d)** nuts (oak)

(e) capsule (buckeye) **(f)** pods (pea) **(g)** drupe (cherry)

Figure 18-9 Fruit types.

centimeters

Key to Some Common Genera of Trees of the Midwestern and Eastern United States and Canada	
1a. Leaves broad and flat; plants producing flowers and fruits (angiosperms)	2
1b. Leaves needlelike or scalelike; plants producing cones, but no flowers or fruits (gymnosperms)	22
2a. Leaves compound	3
2b. Leaves simple	9
3a. Leaves alternate	4
3b. Leaves opposite	7
4a. Leaflets short and stubby, less than twice as long as broad; branches armed with spines or thorns; fruit a beanlike pod	5
4b. Leaflets long and narrow, more than twice as long as broad; trunk and branches unarmed; fruit a nut	6
5a. Leaflet margin without teeth; terminal leaflet present; small deciduous spines at leaf base	*Robinia* (black locust)
5b. Leaflet margin with fine teeth; terminal leaflet absent; large permanent thorns on trunk and branches	*Gleditsia* (honey locust)

6a.	Leaflets usually numbering less than 11; pith of twigs solid	*Carya* (hickory)
6b.	Leaflets numbering 1 or more; pith of twigs divided into chambers	*Juglans* (walnut, butternut)

7a.	Leaflets pinnately arranged; fruit a light-winged samara	8
7b.	Leaflets palmately arranged; fruit a heavy leathery spherical capsule	*Aesculus* (buckeye)

8a.	Leaflets mostly 3–5; fruit a schizocarp with curved wings	*Acer* (box elder)
8b.	Leaflets mostly more than 5; samaras borne singly, with straight wings	*Fraxinus* (ash)

9a.	Leaves alternate	10
9b.	Leaves opposite	21

10a.	Leaves very narrow, at least 3 times as long as broad; axillary buds flattened against stem	*Salix* (willow)
10b.	Leaves broader, less than 3 times as long as broad	11

11a.	Leaf margin without small, regular teeth	12
11b.	Leaf margin with small, regular teeth	13

12a.	Fruit a pod with downy seeds; leaf blade obtuse at base; petioles flattened, or if rounded, bark smooth	*Populus* (poplar, popple, aspen)
12b.	Fruit an acorn; leaf blade acute at base; petioles rounded; bark rough	*Quercus* (oaks)

13a.	Leaves (at least some of them) with lobes or other indentations in addition to small, regular teeth	14
13b.	Leaves without lobes or other indentations except for small, regular teeth	16

14a.	Lobes asymmetrical, leaves often mitten-shaped	*Morus* (mulberry)
14b.	Lobes or other indentations fairly symmetrical	15

15a.	Branches thorny (armed); fruit a small applelike pome	*Crataegus* (hawthorne)
15b.	Branches unarmed	17

16a.	Bark smooth and waxy, often separating into thin layers; leaf base symmetrical	*Betula* (birch)
16b.	Bark rough and furrowed; leaf base asymmetrical	*Ulmus* (elm)

17a.	Leaf base asymmetrical, strongly heart-shaped, at least on one side	*Tilia* (basswood or linden)
17b.	Leaf base acute, truncate, or slightly cordate	18

18a.	Leaf base asymmetrical; bark on older stems (trunk) often warty	*Celtis* (hackberry)
18b.	Leaf base symmetrical	19

19a.	Leaf blade usually about twice as long as broad, generally acute at base; fruit fleshy	20
19b.	Leaf not much longer than broad, generally truncate at base; fruit a dry pod	*Populus* (poplar, popple, aspen)

20a.	Leaf tapering to a pointed tip, glandular at base	*Prunus* (cherry)
20b.	Leaf spoon-shaped with a rounded tip, no glands at base	*Crataegus* (hawthorne)

21a.	Leaf margins with lobes and points; fruit a schizocarp	*Acer* (maple)
21b.	Leaf margins without lobes or points; fruit a long capsule	*Catalpa* (catalpa)

22a.	Leaves needlelike, with 2 or more needles in a cluster	23
22b.	Leaves needlelike or scalelike, occurring singly	24
23a.	Leaves more than 5 in a cluster, soft, deciduous, borne at the ends of conspicuous stubby branches	*Larix* (larch, tamarack)
23b.	Leaves 2–5 in a cluster	*Pinus* (pines)
24a.	Leaves soft, not sharp to the touch	25
24b.	Leaves stiff or sharp and often unpleasant to touch	27
25a.	Leaves about 0.2 cm and scalelike, overlapping	*Thuja* (white cedar, arbor vitae)
25b.	Leaves needlelike, appear to form two ranks on twig	26
26a.	Leaves with distinct petioles, 0.8–1.5 cm long; twigs rough; female cones drooping from branches	*Tsuga* (hemlock)
26b.	Leaves without distinct petioles, 1–3 cm long; twigs smooth; female cones erect on branches	*Abies* (firs)
27a.	Leaves appear triangular-shaped, about 0.5 cm, and tightly pressed to twig; cone blue, berrylike	(juniper, Eastern red cedar)
27b.	Leaves elongated and needlelike	28
28a.	Tree; leaves 4-sided, protrude stiffly from twig; female cones droop from branch	*Picea* (spruces)
28b.	Shrub; leaves flattened, pressed close to twig at base; seed partially covered by a fleshy coat, usually red	*Taxus* (yew)

Key to Some Common Genera of Trees of the Pacific Region of the United States and Canada

1a.	Leaves broad and flat; plants producing flowers and fruits (angiosperms)	2
1b.	Leaves needlelike or scalelike; plants producing cones, but no flowers or fruits (gymnosperms)	15
2a.	Leaves compound	3
2b.	Leaves simple	6
3a.	Leaves pinnately arranged	4
3b.	Leaves palmately arranged	5
4a.	Leaflets numbering 7; fruit a samara	*Fraxinus* (ash)
4b.	Leaflets 15–17; fruit a nut	*Juglans* (walnut)
5a.	Leaflets numbering 3, lobed; fruit a schizocarp	*Acer* (box elder)
5b.	Leaflets numbering more than 3; fruit a smooth or spiny capsule	*Aesculus* (buckeye)
6a.	Three or more equal-sized veins branching from leaf base	7
6b.	Leaf with single large central vein with other main veins branching from the central vein	9
7a.	Leaves opposite; fruit a schizocarp	*Acer* (maple)
7b.	Leaves alternate	8

8a.	Leaves nearly round in outline; fruit a pod	*Cercis* (redbud)
8b.	Leaves deeply lobed, very hairy beneath; fruit consisting of an aggregation of many 1-seeded nutlets surrounded by long hairs	*Platanus* (sycamore)
9a.	Leaf lobed; fruit a nut	*Quercus* (oak)
9b.	Leaf not lobed	10
10a.	Leaves opposite; fruit a drupe; halves of leaf remain attached by "threads" after blade has been creased and broken	*Cornus* (dogwood)
10b.	Leaves alternate	11
11a.	Upon crushing, blade gives off strong, penetrating odor	*Eucalyptus* (eucalyptus)
11b.	Blade not strongly odiferous upon crushing	12
12a.	Branch bark smooth, conspicuously red-brown; fruit a red or orange berry	*Arbutus* (madrone)
12b.	Branch rough, not colored red-brown	13
13a.	Undersurface of leaves golden-yellow; fruit a spiny, husked nut	*Catanopsis* (golden chinquapin)
13b.	Leaves green beneath	14
14a.	Petiole hairy; leathery blade with a stubby spine at end of each main vein; fruit a nut	*Lithocarpus* (tanoak)
14b.	Petiole and leaf lacking numerous hairs, leaves long and narrow, more than twice as long as wide	*Salix* (willow)
15a.	Leaves needlelike	16
15b.	Leaves scalelike	23
16a.	Leaves needlelike, with 2 or more needles in a cluster	17
16b.	Leaves needlelike, occurring singly	18
17a.	Needles 2–5 in a cluster	*Pinus* (pine)
17b.	Needles 6 or more per cluster, soft, deciduous, borne at the ends of stubby, conspicuous branches	*Larix* (larch)
18a.	Round scars on twigs where old needles have fallen off; twigs smooth; needles soft to the grasp; cones pointing upward with reference to stem	*Abies* (fir)
18b.	Twigs rough, with old needle petioles remaining	19
19a.	Needles angled, stiff, sharp, pointed, unpleasant to grasp; cones hanging	*Picea* (spruce)
19b.	Needles soft, not sharp when grasped	20
20a.	Needles round in cross section, can be rolled easily between thumb and index finger; needles less than 1.3 cm long; cones small, less than 1.5 cm	*Tsuga* (hemlock)
20b.	Needles too flat to be rolled easily	21
21a.	Tips of needles blunt or rounded, undersurface with 2 white bands; cones with long, conspicuous, 3-lobed bracts	*Pseudotsuga* (Douglas fir)
21b.	Tips of needles pointed	22
22a.	Tops of needles grooved; woody seed cones broadly oblong in outline	*Sequoia* (redwood)
22b.	Tops of needles with ridges; lacking in cones, instead having a red, fleshy, cuplike seed covering	*Taxus* (yew)

| 23a. | Twig ends appear as if jointed | *Calocedrus* (incense cedar) |
| 23b. | Tips of branches flattened, not jointed in appearance | 24 |

| 24a. | Leaves glossy and fragrant | *Thuja* (Western red cedar) |
| 24b. | Leaves awl-shaped, arranged spirally on twig | *Sequoiadendron* (giant sequoia) |

Glossary to Tree Key

- *Acorn*—The fruit of an oak, consisting of a nut and its basally attached cup (Figure 18-9d)
- *Acute*—Sharp-pointed (Figure 18-2)
- *Alternate*—Describing the arrangement of leaves or other structures that occur singly at successive nodes or levels; not opposite or whorled (Figure 18-5)
- *Angiosperm*—A flowering seed plant (e.g., bean plant, maple tree, grass)
- *Armed*—Possessing thorns or spines
- *Asymmetrical*—Not symmetrical
- *Axil*—The upper angle between a branch or leaf and the stem from which it grows
- *Axillary bud*—A bud occurring in the axil of a leaf (Figures 18-3 through 18-7)
- *Basal*—At the base
- *Blade*—The expanded, more or less flat portion of a leaf (Figure 18-2)
- *Bract*—A much reduced leaf
- *Capsule*—A dry fruit that splits open at maturity (e.g., buckeye; Figure 18-9e)
- *Compound leaf*—Blade composed of two or more separate parts (leaflets) (Figures 18-4, 18-7)
- *Cordate*—Heart-shaped (Figure 18-2)
- *Deciduous*—Falling off at the end of a functional period (such as a growing season)
- *Drupe*—Fleshy fruit containing a single hard stone that encloses the seed (e.g., cherry, peach, or dogwood; Figure 18-9g)
- *Fruit*—A ripened ovary, in some cases with associated floral parts (Figure 18-9a–g)
- *Glandular*—Bearing secretory structures (glands)
- *Gymnosperm*—Seed plant lacking flowers and fruits (e.g., pine tree)
- *Lateral*—On or at the side (Figure 18-4)
- *Leaflet*—One of the divisions of the blade of a compound leaf (Figures 18-4, 18-7)
- *Lobed*—Separated by indentations (sinuses) into segments (lobes) larger than teeth (Figure 18-3b)
- *Node*—Region on a stem where leaves or branches arise (Figures 18-2 through 18-7)
- *Nut*—A hard, one-seeded fruit that does not split open at maturity (e.g., acorn; Figure 18-9d)
- *Obtuse*—Blunt (Figure 18-6)
- *Opposite*—Describing the arrangement of leaves of other structures that occur two at a node, each separated from the other by half the circumference of the axis (Figure 18-6)
- *Palmately compound*—With leaflets all arising at apex of petiole (Figure 18-7)
- *Petiole*—Stalk of a leaf (Figures 18-2, 18-3, 18-4, 18-7)
- *Pinnately compound*—A leaf constructed somewhat like a feather, with the leaflets arranged on both sides of the rachis (Figure 18-4)
- *Pith*—Internally, the centermost region of a stem (Figure 18-8a, b)
- *Pod*—A dehiscent, dry fruit; a rather general term sometimes used when no other more specific term is applicable (Figure 18-9f)
- *Pome*—Fleshy fruit containing several seeds (e.g., apple or pear; Figure 18-9a)
- *Rachis*—Central axis of a pinnately compound leaf (Figure 18-4)
- *Samara*—Winged, one-seeded, dry fruit (e.g., ash fruits; Figure 18-9c)
- *Schizocarp*—Dry fruit that splits at maturity into two one-seeded halves (Figure 18-9b)
- *Simple leaf*—One with a single blade, not divided into leaflets (Figures 18-3, 18-5, 18-6)
- *Spine*—Strong, stiff, sharp-pointed outgrowth on a stem or other organ (Figure 18-6)
- *Symmetrical*—Capable of being divided longitudinally into similar halves
- *Terminal*—Last in a series (Figure 18-4)
- *Thorn*—Sharp, woody, spinelike outgrowth from the wood of a stem; usually a reduced, modified branch
- *Tooth*—Small, sharp-pointed marginal lobe of a leaf (Figure 18-3a)
- *Truncate*—Cut off squarely at end (Figure 18-3a)
- *Unarmed*—Without thorns or spines
- *Whorl*—A group of three or more leaves or other structures at a node

Each year millions of "evergreen" trees become the center of attraction in human dwellings during the Christmas season. The process of selecting the all-important tree is the same whether you reside in the city where you buy your tree from a commercial grower, or whether you cut one off your "back forty." You ponder and evaluate each specimen until, with the utmost confidence, you bring home that perfect tree. Now that you have it, just what kind of tree stands in your home, looking somewhat like a cross between Old Glory and the Sistine Chapel? This key contains most of the trees that are used as Christmas trees; other gymnosperm trees are included, too. The common "Christmas trees" have an asterisk after their scientific name. Note that this key, unlike those in the preceding sections, indicates actual species designations.

1a.	Tree fragrant, boughs having supported (on clear moonlit nights) masses of glistening snow on their green needles; tree a product of nature	2
1b.	Tree not really a tree but rather a product of a cold and insensitive society; tree never giving life and never having life	17
2a.	Leaves persistent and green throughout the winter, needlelike, awl-shaped, or scalelike	3
2b.	Leaves deciduous; for this reason not a desirable Christmas tree	4
3a.	Leaves in clusters of 2–5, their bases within a sheath	5
3b.	Leaves borne singly, not in clusters	9
4a.	Cones 1.25–1.8 cm long, 12–15 scales making up cone	*Larix laricina* (tamarack)
4b.	Cones 1.8–3.5 cm long, 40–50 scales comprising cone	*Larix decidua* (larch)
5a.	Leaves 5 in a cluster, cones 10–25 cm long	*Pinus strobus* (white pine)
5b.	Leaves 2 in a cluster, cones less than 10 cm long	6
6a.	Leaves 2.5–7.5 cm long	7
6b.	Leaves 7.5–15 cm long	8
7a.	Leaves with a bluish cast; cones with a stout stalk, pointing away from the tip of the branch; bark orange in the upper part of the tree	*Pinus sylvestris** (scotch pine)
7b.	Leaves 1.25–3.75 cm long; cones stalkless, pointing forward toward the tip of branch	*Pinus banksiana* (jack pine)
8a.	Leaves slender, shiny; bark of trunk red-brown; cones 5–7.5 cm long; scales of cones without any spine at tip	*Pinus resinosa** (red pine)
8b.	Leaves thickened, dull; bark of trunk gray to nearly black; cones 5 to 7.5 cm long; scales of cone armed with short spine at tip	*Pinus nigra** (Austrian pine)
9a.	Leaves scalelike or awl-shaped	10
9b.	Leaves needlelike	11
10a.	Twigs flattened, leaves all of one kind, scalelike, extending down the twig below the point of attachment	*Thuja occidentalis* (white cedar, arbor vitae)
10b.	Twigs more or less circular in cross section; leaves of two kinds, either scalelike or awl-shaped, often both on same branch, not extending down the twig; coneless but may have a blue berrylike structure	*Juniperus virginiana* (red cedar)
11a.	Leaves with petioles	12
11b.	Leaves lacking petioles, leaf tip notched, needles longer than 1.25 cm	*Abies balsamea** (balsam fir)

| 12a. | Leaves angular, 4-sided in cross section, harsh to the touch; petiole adheres to twig | 13 |
| 12b. | Leaves flattened | 15 |

| 13a. | Leaves 3–10 mm long, blunt-pointed; twigs rusty and hairy | *Picea mariana** (black spruce) |
| 13b. | Leaves 2 cm long, sharp-pointed; twigs smooth | 14 |

| 14a. | Cones 2.5–5 cm long; leaves ill-scented when bruised or broken; smaller branches mostly horizontal | *Picea glauca** (white spruce) |
| 14b. | Cones 7.5–15 cm long; scales comprising cone with finely toothed markings; leaves not ill-scented when bruised or broken; smaller branches drooping | *Picea abies** (Norway spruce) |

| 15a. | Leaves pointed, over 1.25 cm long; red fleshy, berrylike structures present | 16 |
| 15b. | Leaves rounded at tip, less than 1.25 cm long, with two white lines on underside | *Tsuga canadensis* (hemlock) |

| 16a. | Leaves 2–2.5 cm long, dull dark green on top, with two broad yellow bands on undersurface; petiole yellowish | *Taxus cuspidata* (Japanese yew) |
| 16b. | Leaves 1.25–2 cm long, without yellow bands on underside | *Taxus canadensis* (American yew) |

| 17a. | Tree a glittering mass of structural aluminum, sometimes illuminated by multicolored floodlights | *Aluminous ersatzenbaum** (aluminum substitute) |
| 17b. | Tree green, made from petroleum products; used year after year; exactly like all others of its manufacture | *Plasticus perfectus** (plastic substitute) |

_____ **1.** The name "human" is an example of a
   (a) common name.
   (b) scientific name.
   (c) binomial.
   (d) polynomial.

_____ **2.** Current scientific thought places organisms in one of ___ kingdoms.
   (a) two
   (b) four
   (c) five
   (d) six

_____ **3.** The scientific name for the ruffed grouse is *Bonasa umbellus. Bonasa* is
   (a) the family name.
   (b) the genus.
   (c) the specific epithet.
   (d) all of the above

_____ **4.** A binomial is always a
   (a) genus.
   (b) specific epithet.
   (c) scientific name.
   (d) two-part name.

_____ **5.** The science of classifying and naming organisms is known as
   (a) taxonomy.
   (b) phylogeny.
   (c) morphology.
   (d) physiology.

_____ **6.** Which scientific name for the wolf is presented correctly?
   (a) Canis lupus
   (b) canis lupus
   (c) *Canis lupus*
   (d) Canis Lupus

_____ **7.** A road that dichotomizes is
   (a) an intersection of two crossroads.
   (b) a road that forks into two roads.
   (c) a road that has numerous entrances and exits.
   (d) a road that leads nowhere.

_____ **8.** Most scientific names are derived from
   (a) English.
   (b) Latin.
   (c) Italian.
   (d) French.

_____ **9.** One problem with using common names is that
   (a) many organisms may have the same common name.
   (b) many common names may exist for the same organism.
   (c) the common name may not be familiar to an individual not speaking the language of the common name.
   (d) all of the above are true.

_____ **10.** Phylogeny is the apparent
   (a) name of an organism.
   (b) ancestry of an organism.
   (c) nomenclature.
   (d) dichotomy of a system of classification.

EXERCISE **18**

Taxonomy: Classifying and Naming Organisms

Post-Lab Questions

Introduction

1. If you were to use a binomial system to identify the members of your family or the family of a friend, (mother, father, sisters, brothers), how would you write their names so that your system would most closely approximate that used to designate species?

2. Describe several advantages of using scientific names instead of common names.

3. Based on the following classification scheme, which two organisms are most closely phylogenetically related? Why?

	Organism 1	Organism 2	Organism 3	Organism 4
Kingdom	Animalia	Animalia	Animalia	Animalia
Phylum	Arthopoda	Arthropoda	Arthropoda	Arthropoda
Class	Insecta	Insecta	Insecta	Insecta
Order	Coleoptera	Coleoptera	Coleoptera	Coleoptera
Genus	*Caulophilus*	*Sitophilus*	*Latheticus*	*Sitophilus*
Specific epithet	*oryzae*	*oryzae*	*oryzae*	*zeamaize*
Common name	Broadnosed grain weevil	Rice weevil	Longheaded flour beetle	Maize weevil

Consider the drawing of plants A and B in answering questions 4–6.

fruit

plant A

cone

plant B

4. Using the taxonomic key in the exercise, identify the two plants as either angiosperms or gymnosperms.

   Plant A is a (an) _____.

   Plant B is a (an) _____.

5. To what genus does plant A belong? What is its common name?

   genus: _____

   common name: _____

6. To what genus does plant B belong? What is its common name?

   genus: _____

   common name: _____

Consider the drawing of plants C and D in answering questions 7–9.

plant C

plant D

7. As completely as possible, describe the leaf of plant C.

8. To what genus does plant C belong? What is its common name?

        genus: _____

common name: _____

9. Using the taxonomic key to freshwater organisms in the exercise, identify the genus of the organism below.

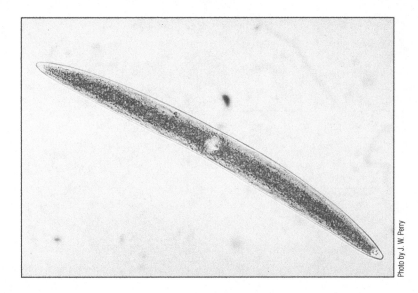

Photo by J. W. Perry

        genus: _____

Food for Thought

10. If you owned a large, varied music collection, how might you devise a key to keep track of all your different kinds of music?

Bacteria and Protists I

OBJECTIVES

After completing this exercise, you will be able to

1. define *prokaryotic, eukaryotic, pathogen, decomposer, coccus, bacillus, spirillum, Gram stain, antibiotic, symbiosis, parasitism, commensalism, mutualism, nitrogen fixation, monoecious, dioecious, obligate mutualism, gametangia, vector, agar, fucoxanthin, algin, kelp;*

2. describe characteristics distinguishing bacteria from protists;

3. identify and classify the organisms studied in this exercise;

4. identify structures (those in **boldface** in the procedure sections) in the organisms studied;

5. distinguish Gram-positive and Gram-negative bacteria, indicating their susceptibility to certain antibiotics;

6. suggest measures that might be used to control malaria.

Introduction

The bacteria (Domain Bacteria, Kingdom Bacteria) and archaea (Domain Archaea, Kingdom Archaea) and protists (Domain Eukarya, Kingdom Protista) are among the simplest of living organisms. These have unicellular organisms within them, but that's where the similarity ends.

Bacteria and archaea are **prokaryotic** organisms, meaning that their DNA is free in the cytoplasm, unbounded by a membrane. They lack organelles (cytoplasmic structures surrounded by membranes). By contrast, the protists are **eukaryotic** organisms: the genetic material contained within the nucleus and many of their cellular components are compartmentalized into membrane-bound organelles.

Both bacteria and archaea, and unicellular protists, are at the base of the food chain. From an ecological standpoint, these simple organisms are among the most important organisms on our planet. Ecologically, they're much more important than we are.

19.1   Domain Bacteria, Kingdom Bacteria *(About 40 min.)*

The Kingdom Bacteria consists of bacteria and cyanobacteria. Most bacteria are heterotrophic, dependent upon an outside source for nutrition, while cyanobacteria are autotrophic (photosynthetic), able to produce their own carbohydrates.

Some heterotrophic bacteria are **pathogens**, causing plant and animal diseases, but most are **decomposers**, breaking down and recycling the waste products of life. Others are nitrogen fixers, capturing the gaseous nitrogen in the atmosphere and making it available to plants via a symbiotic association with their roots.

A. Bacteria: Are Bacteria Present in the Lab? *(About 15 min.)*

MATERIALS

Per student group (4):

- dH$_2$O in dropping bottle
- four nutrient agar culture plates
- two bottles labeled A and B (A contains tap water, B contains 70% ethyl alcohol)
- sterile cotton swabs
- transparent adhesive tape
- china marker
- paper towels

PROCEDURE

Work in groups of four.

1. Obtain four petri dishes containing sterile nutrient agar. Using a china marker, label one dish "Dish 1: Control." Label the others "Dish 2: Dry Swab," "Dish 3: Treatment A," and "Dish 4: Treatment B." Also include the names of your group members.
2. Run a sterile cotton swab over a surface within the lab. Some examples of things you might wish to sample include the surface of your lab bench, the floor, and the sink. Be creative!
3. Lift the lid on Dish 2 as little as is necessary to run the swab over the surface of the agar.

   Note: Be careful that you don't break the agar surface.

4. Tape the lid securely to the bottom half of the dish.
5. Soak one paper towel with liquid A and a second paper towel with liquid B.
6. Wipe down one-half of the surface you just sampled with liquid A (tap water), the other half with liquid B (70% ethyl alcohol). After the areas have dried, using dishes 3 and 4, repeat the procedures described in step 2. Place the cultures in a desk drawer to incubate until the next lab period. At that time, examine your culture for bacterial colonies, noting the color and texture of the bacterial growth.
7. Make a prediction of what you will find in the culture plates after the next lab period.

   _____

   _____

8. Describe what you see.

   Source of sample: _____

   Dish 1: Control. _____

   _____

   _____

   Dish 2: Dry Swab. _____

   _____

CAUTION

Leave the lid on as you examine the cultures to prevent the spread of any potentially pathogenic (disease-causing) organisms. While the probability is small that pathogens are present, you should always err on the side of caution.

   Dish 3: Treatment A. _____

   _____

   _____

   Dish 4: Treatment B. _____

   _____

9. Make a conclusion about the usefulness of tap water and 70% ethyl alcohol as disinfectants.

   _____

   _____

B. Bacteria: Bacterial Shape and Sensitivity to Antibiotics (About 10 min.)

MATERIALS

Per student:
- bacteria type slide
- compound microscope

Per lab room:
- Gram-stained bacteria (three demonstration slides)

Work alone for this and the rest of these activities.

Bacteria exist in three shapes: **coccus** (plural, *cocci;* spherical), **bacillus** (plural, *bacilli;* rods), and **spirillum** (plural, *spirilla;* spirals).

PROCEDURE

1. Study a bacteria type slide illustrating these three shapes. You'll need to use the highest magnification available on your compound microscope. In Figure 19-1, draw the bacteria you are observing.

In addition to being differentiated by shape, bacteria can be separated according to how they react to a staining procedure called **Gram stain,** named in honor of a nineteenth-century microbiologist, Hans Gram. *Gram-positive* bacteria are purple after being stained by the Gram stain procedure, while *Gram-negative* bacteria appear pink. The Gram stain reaction is important to bacteriologists because it is one of the first steps in identifying an unknown bacterium. Furthermore, the Gram stain reaction indicates a bacterium's susceptibility or resistance to certain **antibiotics**, substances that inhibit the growth of bacteria.

2. Examine the *demonstration slides* illustrating Gram-stained bacteria. Gram-positive bacteria are susceptible to penicillin, while Gram-negative bacteria are not. In Table 19-1, list the species of bacteria that you have examined and their staining characteristics.

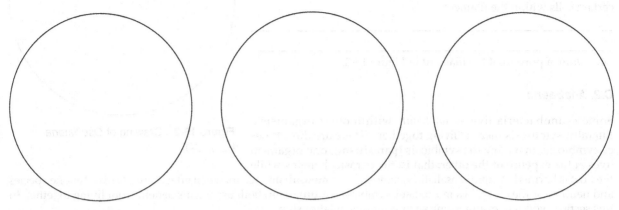

Figure 19-1   Drawings of three bacterial shapes (_____×).

TABLE 19-1	Gram Stain Reaction of Various Bacteria
Bacterial Species	**Gram Reactions (+ or –)**

© Cengage Learning 2013

C. Cyanobacteria (Blue-Green Algae) (About 15 min.)

The cyanobacteria (sometimes called blue-green algae) are distinguished from the heterotrophic bacteria by being photosynthetic (photoautotrophic).

C.1. Oscillatoria

MATERIALS

Per student:
- microscope slide
- coverslip
- dissecting needle
- compound microscope

Per lab room:
- *Oscillatoria*—living culture; disposable pipet

PROCEDURE

1. Examine the culture provided of *Oscillatoria*. Describe what the culture looks like, including the texture and the color.

_____

_____

The color of the culture is a consequence of the photosynthetic accessory pigments that for the most part mask the chlorophyll.

(If you have immediate access to a greenhouse, you might walk through it now to see if you can find any *Oscillatoria* growing on the flowerpots or even the floor.)

2. Using a dissecting needle, scrape some of the culture from the surface and prepare a wet mount slide.
3. Examine your preparation with your compound microscope, starting with the medium-power objective and finally with the highest magnification available (oil immersion, if possible). Note that the individual cells are joined and so form the filament.

Do all the *Oscillatoria* cells look alike, or is there differentiation of certain cells within the filament?

_____

_____

4. Draw a portion of the filament in Figure 19-2.

C.2. Anabaena

Some cyanobacteria live as *symbionts* within other organisms. Literally, **symbiosis** means "living together." There are three types of symbiosis. In a parasitic symbiosis (**parasitism**), one organism lives at the expense of the other; that is, the parasite benefits while the host is harmed. A commensalistic symbiosis (**commensalism**) occurs when effects are positive for one species and neutral for the other. In a mutualistic symbiosis (**mutualism**) both organisms benefit from living together. In this section, you will examine one such symbiotic relationship.

Figure 19-2 Drawing of *Oscillatoria* (_____×).

MATERIALS

Per student:
- microscope slide
- coverslip
- dissecting needle
- compound microscope

Per lab room:
- *Azolla*—living plants

PROCEDURE

1. Place a leaf of the tiny water fern *Azolla* on a clean glass slide. Use a dissecting needle to crush the leaf into very small pieces. Now add a drop of water and a coverslip.
2. Scan your preparation with the medium-power objective of your compound microscope, looking for long chains (composed of numerous beadlike cells) of the filamentous cyanobacterium *Anabaena*. Switch to higher magnification when you find *Anabaena*.
3. Within the filament, locate the **heterocysts,** cells that are a bit larger than the other cells.
4. Draw what you see in Figure 19-3 and label it.
5. Examine the very high magnification electron micrograph of *Anabaena* in Figure 19-4. Identify the heterocyst with its distinctive *polar nodules* at either end of the cell. In the other cells, note the numerous wavy **thylakoids**, membranes on and in which the photosynthetic pigments are found. Identify the large electron-dense carbohydrate **storage granules** within the cytoplasm and the cell wall.

Figure 19-3 Drawing of *Anabaena* that was within *Azolla* leaves (_____×).
Label: heterocyst

Is a nucleus present within the cells of *Anabaena?* Explain.

_____

Based upon this electron micrograph, would you hypothesize that the heterocyst is photosynthetic?

_____

6. Now look again at your microscope slide of *Anabaena*. Find the polar nodules, appearing as bright spots within the heterocysts.

Heterocysts convert nitrogen in the air (or water) to a form that the cyanobacterium can use for cellular metabolism. This process is called **nitrogen fixation**. Nitrogen-containing compounds accumulate in the water fern, some of it being used for its own metabolic needs. There is also an advantage to the *Anabaena*: it not only gets a place to live, but by being within the water fern leaf it is shielded from very high light levels that would otherwise do it damage.

Which type of symbiosis is the association between *Anabaena* and the water fern?

_____

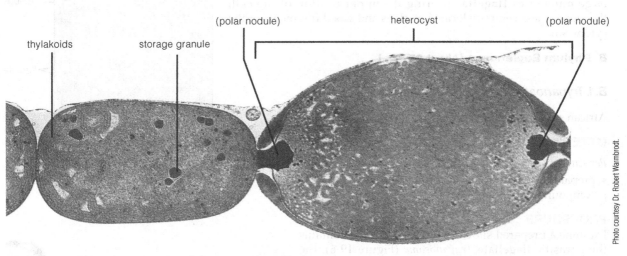

Figure 19-4　Electron micrograph of *Anabaena* (14,220×).

| 19.2 | Domain Eukarya, Kingdom Protista *(About 2 hours)* |

The protists are a diverse assemblage of organisms, both photoautotrophic and heterotrophic. They are so diverse that different protists have previously been classified as fungi, animals, and plants! The following organisms are examined in this, the first of two protist exercises:

Phylum	Common Name
Parabasalia	Parabasalids
Euglenozoa	Trypanosomes and euglenoids
Alveolata	Ciliates, dinoflagellates, apicomplexans
Stramenophila	Water molds, diatoms, and brown algae

A. Phylum Parabasalia (About 5 min.)

These protistans have one or more flagella to provide motility. The group includes some fairly notorious human parasites that cause disease, including giardiasis (from drinking water contaminated with the causal protozoans) and some sexually transmitted diseases (caused by *Trichomonas vaginalis*).

MATERIALS

Per student:

■ prepared slide of *Trichonympha*
■ compound microscope

PROCEDURE

Trichonympha

The flagellated protozoan *Trichonympha* (Figure 19-5) inhabits the gut of termites. The association of the termite and *Trichonympha* is an example of **obligate mutualism,** in which neither organism is capable of surviving without the other. Termites lack the enzymes to metabolize cellulose, a major component of wood. Wood particles ingested by termites are engulfed by *Trichonympha*, whose enzymes break the cellulose into soluble carbohydrates that are released for use by the termite.

Study a prepared slide of these organisms. Examine the gut of the termite with the high-dry objective to find *Trichonympha*. Note the large number of **flagella** covering the upper portion of the cell, the more or less centrally located **nucleus** and wood fragments in the cytoplasm.

B. Phylum Euglenozoa (About 25 min.)

B.1. *Trypanosoma*

African sleeping sickness is caused by *Trypanosoma brucei*.

MATERIALS

Per student:

- prepared slide of *Trypanosoma* in blood smear
- compound microscope

PROCEDURE

Examine a prepared slide of human blood that contains the parasitic flagellate *Trypanosoma* (Figure 19-6), the cause of African sleeping sickness. This flagellate is transmitted from host to host by the bloodsucking tsetse fly. Note the **flagellum** arising from one end of the cell.

B.2. Euglenoids

Euglenoids are motile, unicellular protists. Most species are photosynthetic, but there are also some heterotrophic species.

MATERIALS

Per student:

- microscope slide
- coverslip
- compound microscope

Per group (table):

- methylcellulose in two dropping bottles
- dH$_2$O in two dropping bottles

Per lab room:

- *Euglena*-living culture; disposable pipet

PROCEDURE

1. From the culture provided, prepare a wet mount slide of *Euglena*.
2. Observe with the medium-power objective of your compound microscope. Notice the motion of these green cells as they swim through the medium. If they're swimming too rapidly, prepare another slide, but add a drop of methylcellulose to the cell suspension before adding a coverslip.
3. Switch to the high-dry objective for more detailed observation. Figure 19-7a will serve as a guide in your study. This specimen was photographed by a special technique to give it a three-dimensional appearance.
4. Within the **cytoplasm,** identify the green **chloroplasts** and, if possible, the centrally located **nucleus.**
5. By closing the microscope's diaphragm to increase the contrast, you may be able to locate the **flagellum** at one end of the cell.
6. Search for the orange **eyespot**, a photoreceptive organelle located within the cytoplasm at the base of the flagellum.

In the world of microscopic swimmers, there are two types of flagella. One type, the *whiplash flagellum*, pushes the organism through the medium. An example of this is a human sperm cell. The other type, with which you're probably less familiar, is the *tinsel flagellum*, which pulls the organism through its watery environment. Tinsel flagella have tiny hairlike projections, visible only with the electron microscope.

7. Notice the direction of motion of the *Euglena* cells. Which type of flagellum does *Euglena* have? _____

Figure 19-5 *Trichonympha* (900×).

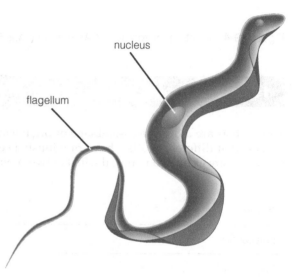

Figure 19-6 Artist's rendering of *Trypanosoma*, the causal agent of African sleeping sickness.

Besides seeing the swimming motion caused by the flagellum, you may observe a contractionlike motion of the entire cell (*euglenoid movement*). *Euglena* is able to contort like this because it lacks a rigid cell wall. Instead, flexible helical interlocking proteinaceous strips within the cell membrane delimit the cytoplasm. These strips plus the cell membrane form the **pellicle**. Euglenoid movement provides a means of locomotion for mud-dwelling organisms.

8. Examine Figure 19-7b, a scanning electron micrograph showing the *flagellum* and the helical strips of the pellicle.
9. In Figure 19-8, make a series of sketches showing the different shapes *Euglena* takes during euglenoid movement.

C. Phylum Alveolata

C.1. Ciliated Protozoans (About 20 min.)

Ciliates are covered with numerous short locomotory structures called *cilia*. In this section, you will examine one of the largest ciliates, the predatory *Paramecium caudatum*.

Paramecium

MATERIALS

Per student:

- microscope slide
- coverslip
- compound microscope

Per group (table):

- methylcellulose in two dropping bottles
- tissue paper
- acetocarmine stain in two dropping bottles
- box of toothpicks

Per lab room:

- *Paramecium caudatum*—living culture; disposable pipet
- Congo red—yeast mixture; disposable pipet

PROCEDURE

1. From the culture provided, prepare a wet mount of *Paramecium* on a clean microscope slide. Observe their rapid movement with the medium-power objective of your microscope. Look along the edge of the *Paramecium's* body to see evidence of the locomotory structures, the **cilia**. (Increasing the contrast by closing the microscope's iris diaphragm may help.)
2. Examine Figure 19-9, a scanning electron micrograph of *Paramecium*. Note the numerous **cilia** covering the body surface.

Figure 19-7 *Euglena.* (**a**) Light micrograph (1100×). (**b**) Scanning electron micrograph (1500×).

Figure 19-8 Different shapes possible in living *Euglena* exhibiting euglenoid movement.

Figure 19-9 Scanning electron micrograph of *Paramecium caudatum* (1170×).

3. Use Figure 19-10 as an aid as you proceed with your observation of your living specimen.

4. Prepare another wet mount of *Paramecium*, but before you place a coverslip on the slide, add a drop of acetocarmine stain and a drop of methylcellulose to slow the organisms' movement.

5. Find the large, centrally located **macronucleus**. It's likely that the sec-

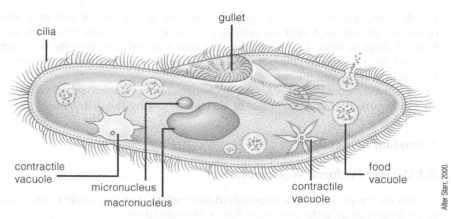

Figure 19-10 Artist's rendering of *Paramecium caudatum* (1700×).

ond, a smaller **micronucleus adjacent** to the macronucleus, will be difficult to see. Surprise! This eukaryotic cell is *binucleate*. Each nucleus has its own distinctive functions.

6. Make a third preparation. First place a drop of methylcellulose on the slide, then a drop of Congo red/yeast mixture. Stir the mixture with a toothpick. Now add a drop of *Paramecium* culture. Place a coverslip on your wet mount and observe with the medium-power objective.

7. Locate the **oral groove**, a depression in the body that leads to the **gullet**.

8. Observe the yeast cells as they are eaten by *Paramecium*. The yeast will be taken into **food vacuoles**, where they are digested. Congo red is a pH indicator. As digestion occurs within the food vacuoles, the indicator will turn blue because of the increased acidity.

9. At either end of the organism, find the **contractile vacuoles**, which regulate water content within the organism. Watch them in operation.

C.2. Dinoflagellates (About 15 min.)

Dinoflagellates spin as they move through the water due to the position of their flagellum. On occasion, populations of certain dinoflagellates may increase dramatically, causing the seas to turn red or brown. These are the **red tides**, which can devastate fish populations because neurotoxins produced by the dinoflagellates poison fish.

MATERIALS

Per student:

- prepared slide of a dinoflagellate (for example, *Gymnodinium*, *Ceratium*, or *Peridinium*)
- compound microscope

Per lab room:

- dinoflagellate—living culture; disposable pipet (optional)

Figure 19-11 Two representative dinoflagellates. (**a**) *Ceratium* (240×). (**b**) *Peridinium* (640×).

PROCEDURE

1. With the high-dry objective of your compound microscope, examine a prepared slide or living representative.
2. Compare what you are observing with Figures 19-11a and b.
3. Attempt to identify the stiff cellulosic plates encasing the cytoplasm.
4. Locate the two grooves formed by the junction of the plates. This is where the flagella are located. If you are examining living specimens, chloroplasts may be visible beneath the cellulose plates.
5. Examine the scanning electron micrograph of a dinoflagellate in Figure 19-12.

C.3. Apicomplexans (About 20 min.)

All apicomplexans are parasites, infecting a wide range of animals, including humans. *Plasmodium vivax* causes one type of malaria in humans. In this section, you will study its life cycle with demonstration slides. Refer to Figure 19-13 as you proceed.

Figure 19-12 Scanning electron micrograph of a dinoflagellate (1000×).

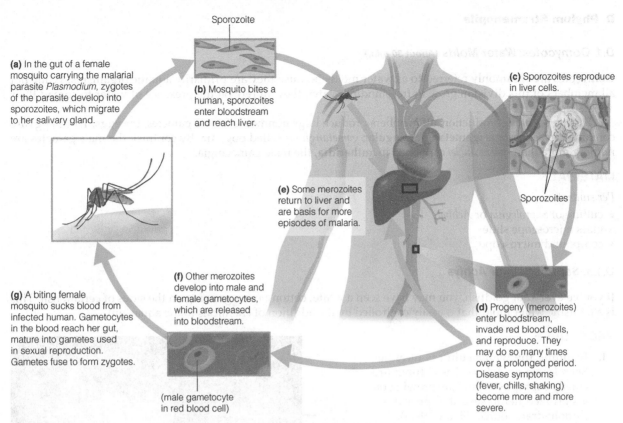

(a) In the gut of a female mosquito carrying the malarial parasite *Plasmodium*, zygotes of the parasite develop into sporozoites, which migrate to her salivary gland.

Sporozoite

(b) Mosquito bites a human, sporozoites enter bloodstream and reach liver.

(c) Sporozoites reproduce in liver cells.

Sporozoites

(e) Some merozoites return to liver and are basis for more episodes of malaria.

(g) A biting female mosquito sucks blood from infected human. Gametocytes in the blood reach her gut, mature into gametes used in sexual reproduction. Gametes fuse to form zygotes.

(f) Other merozoites develop into male and female gametocytes, which are released into bloodstream.

(d) Progeny (merozoites) enter bloodstream, invade red blood cells, and reproduce. They may do so many times over a prolonged period. Disease symptoms (fever, chills, shaking) become more and more severe.

(male gametocyte in red blood cell)

Figure 19-13 Life cycle of *Plasmodium vivax*, causal agent of malaria.

Plasmodium vivax

MATERIALS

Per lab room:

- demonstration slide of *Plasmodium vivax*, sporozoites
- demonstration slide of *P. vivax*, merozoites
- demonstration slide of *P. vivax*, immature gametocytes

PROCEDURE

1. Examine Figure 19-13a. *P. vivax* is transmitted to humans through the bite of an infected female *Anopheles* mosquito. The mosquito serves as a **vector**, a means of transmitting the organism from one host to another. Male mosquitos cannot serve as vectors, because they lack the mouth parts for piercing skin and sucking blood. If the mosquito carries the pathogen, **sporozoites** enter the host's bloodstream with the saliva of the mosquito.
2. Examine the demonstration slide of sporozoites (Figure 19-13b).
3. The sporozoites travel through the bloodstream to the liver, where they penetrate certain cells, grow, and multiply. When released from the liver cells, the parasite is in the form of a **merozoite** and infects the red blood cells. Figures 19-13c and 19-13d show this process.

(There are two intervening stages between sporozoites and merozoites. These are the *trophozoites* and *schizonts*, both developmental stages in red blood cells.)

4. Now examine the demonstration slide illustrating merozoites in red blood cells (Figure 19-13d).
5. Within the red blood cells, merozoites divide, increasing the merozoite population. At intervals of 48 or 72 hours, the infected red blood cells break down, releasing the merozoites. At this time, the infected individual has disease symptoms, including fever, chills, and shaking caused by the release of merozoites and metabolic wastes from the red blood cells. Some of these merozoites return to the liver cells, where they repeat the cycle and are responsible for recurrent episodes of malaria.
6. Merozoites within the bloodstream can develop into **gametocytes**. For development of a gametocyte to be completed, the gametocyte must enter the gut of the mosquito. This occurs when a mosquito feeds upon an infected (diseased) human.
7. Observe the demonstration slide of an **immature gametocyte** in a red blood cell (Figure 19-13f).
8. Within the gut of the mosquito, the gametocyte matures into a gamete (Figure 19-13g). When gametes fuse, they form a zygote that matures into an **oocyst**. Within each oocyst, sporozoites form, completing the life cycle of *Plasmodium vivax*. These sporozoites migrate to the mosquito's salivary glands to be injected into a new host.

D.1. Oomycotes: Water Molds *(About 30 min.)*

Oomycotes are commonly referred to as water molds because they are primarily aquatic organisms. While not all members of this division grow in freestanding water, they all rely on the presence of water to spread their asexual spores.

During sexual reproduction, all members produce large nonmotile female gametes, the eggs. These eggs are contained in sex organs (**gametangia**; singular, *gametangium*) called **oogonia**. By contrast, the male gametes are nothing more than *sperm nuclei* contained in **antheridia**, the male gametangia.

MATERIALS

Per student:

- culture of *Saprolegnia* or *Achlya*
- glass microscope slide
- compound microscope

D.1.a. Saprolegnia or Achlya

If you've ever kept goldfish, you may have seen a white, cottony mass growing on the sides of certain fish. This is a parasitic water mold that is easily controlled by the addition of chemicals to the aquarium.

PROCEDURE

1. Examine the water cultures of either *Saprolegnia* or *Achlya*. These fungi are chiefly saprophytes and are growing on a sterilized hemp seed that provides a carbohydrate source (Figure 19-14).
2. Examine its life cycle (Figure 19-15) as you study this organism.
3. Notice the numerous filamentous hyphae that radiate from the hemp seed. A **hypha** (plural, *hyphae*) is the basic unit of the fungal body. Collectively, all the hyphae constitute the **mycelium** (plural, *mycelia*).
4. Identify the hyphae and mycelium in Figures 19-14 and 19-15a.

Figure 19-14 Mycelium of water mold growing on hemp seed (3×).

The mycelium of the water mold is **multinucleate**, meaning that there are many nuclei in each cell, not just one. Each nucleus is diploid (2n). Moreover, cross walls separating the mycelium into distinct cells are infrequent, forming only when reproductive organs are formed.

5. Place a glass slide on the stage of your compound microscope. This slide will serve as a platform for the culture dish that contains the fungal culture, allowing you to use the mechanical stage of the microscope to move the culture (if the microscope is so equipped).
6. Remove the lid from the culture dish, carefully place the culture dish on the platform, and examine with the low-power objective. Look first at the edge of the mycelium—that is, at the tips of the youngest hyphae.
7. Find the tips that appear denser (darker) than the rest of the hyphae. These dense tips are cells specialized for asexual reproduction. They are the **zoosporangia** (singular, *zoosporangium*; Figures 19-16, 19-15b), which produce biflagellate **zoospores** (Figure 19-15c). Note the cross wall separating the zoosporangium from the rest of the hyphae.
8. Examine Figure 19-15d. Zoospores are released from the zoosporangia, swim about for a period of time, lose their flagella, and encyst, meaning that they form a thick wall around the cytoplasm.
9. Look at Figure 19-15e. When the encysted zoospore germinates, it produces a second type of zoospore. This one also will eventually encyst, as shown in Figure 19-15f.
10. Look at Figure 19-15g. When the second cyst stage germinates, it produces a hypha that proliferates into a new mycelium (Figure 19-15a). As you see, this is asexual reproduction; no sex organs were involved in the formation of zoospores.

Sexual reproduction in the water molds occurs in the older portion of the mycelium. In your culture the older portion is located nearer the hemp seed.

11. Scan the colony to find the spherical female gametangia, the oogonia (singular, **oogonium**; Figures 19-16, 19-15h). Meiosis takes place within the oogonium to form haploid eggs.

12. Switch to the medium-power objective and study a single oogonium in greater detail. Depending on the stage of development, you will find either **eggs** (Figure 19-15i) or **zygotes** (fertilized eggs) (Figures 19-16, 19-15j) within the oogonium.

13. Now you'll need to find the male gametangium, the **antheridium**. It's a short fingerlike hypha that attaches itself to the wall of the oogonium (Figures 19-17, 19-15i), much as you would wrap your finger around a baseball. Find an antheridium.

Because the nuclei of the antheridium have undergone meiosis, each nucleus is haploid.

14. Examine Figure 19-15i, which shows fertilization. Fertilization takes place when tiny fertilization tubes penetrate the wall of the oogonium. Rather than forming special male gametes, the haploid nuclei within the antheridium flow through the fertilization tubes to fuse with the egg nuclei.

15. Search your culture to see if you can locate any thick-walled zygotes within oogonia (Figures 19-18, 19-15j). Following a maturation period that can last several months, the zygote germinates by forming a germ tube (Figure 19-15k) that grows into a new mycelium (Figure 19-15a).

Figure 19-15 Life cycle of a water mold such as *Saprolegnia* or *Achyla*. (Structures colored green are 2n.)

Modified from artwork by Carolina Biological Supply Company.

Bacteria and Protists I   **255**

Notice that both male and female gametangia are produced on the same mycelium. The term describing this condition is **monoecious** (from the Greek words for "one house"). Organisms producing one type of sex organ on one body and the other type of sex organ on another body are **dioecious** (from the Greek words for "two" and "house").

Are humans monoecious or dioecious?

D.1.b. Phytophthora

Some of the most notorious and historically important plant pathogens known to humans are water molds. Included in this group is *Phytophthora infestans,* the fungus that causes the disease known as late blight of potato. This disease spread through the potato fields of Ireland between 1845 and 1847. Most of the potato plants died, and 1 million Irish working-class citizens who had depended on potatoes as their primary food source starved to death. Another 2 million emigrated, many to the United States.

Perhaps no other plant pathogen so poignantly illustrates the importance of environmental factors in causing disease. While *Phytophthora infestans* had been present previous to 1845 in the potato-growing fields of Ireland, it was not until the region experienced several consecutive years of wet and especially cool growing seasons that late blight became a major problem. We can easily observe the importance of these climate-associated factors by studying another *Phytophthora* species, *P. cactorum.*

MATERIALS

Per student:

- culture of *Phytophthora cactorum*
- glass microscope slide
- dissecting needle
- compound microscope

Per lab room:

- refrigerator
  or

Per student group (4):

- ice bath

PROCEDURE

1. Obtain a culture of *P. cactorum* that has been flooded with distilled water. Note that the agar has been removed from the edges of the petri dish and that the mycelium has grown from the agar edge into the water.
2. Place a glass slide on the stage of your compound microscope. This slide will serve as a platform for the culture, allowing you to use the mechanical stage of the microscope to move the culture (if the microscope is so equipped).

Figure 19-16   Water mold zoosporangium (272×).

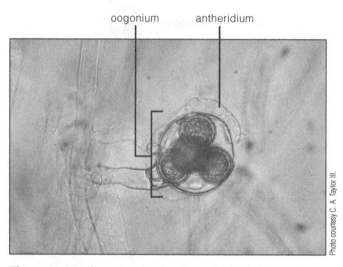

Figure 19-17   Gametangia of water mold (272×).

Figure 19-18   Water mold oogonium with zygotes (720×).

3. Remove the lid from the culture, carefully place the culture dish on the platform, and examine the culture with the low-power objective.

4. Search the surface of the mycelium, especially at the edges, until you find the rather *pear-shaped* **zoosporangia**. Switch to the medium-power objective for closer observation and then draw in Figure 19-19 a single zoosporangium.

5. Return your microscope to the low-power objective, remove the culture, replace the cover, and place it in a refrigerator or on ice for 15–30 minutes.

6. After the incubation time, again observe the zoosporangia microscopically. Find one in which the **zoospores** are escaping from the zoosporangium. Each zoospore has the potential to grow into an entirely new mycelium! Draw the zoospores in Figure 19-19.

Figure 19-19 Drawing of zoosporangium and zoospores of *Phytophthora cactorum* (_____×).
Labels: zoosporangium, zoospores

Like the other water molds, *Phytophthora* reproduces sexually. Your cultures contain the sexual structures as well as asexual zoosporangia.

7. Using a dissecting needle, cut a section about 1 cm square from the agar colony and *invert* it on a glass slide (so that the bottom side of the agar is now uppermost).

8. Place a coverslip on the agar block and observe with your compound microscope, first with the low-power objective, then with the medium-power, and finally with the high-dry objective.

9. Identify the spherical **oogonia** that contain **eggs** or thick-walled **zygotes** (depending on the stage of development). If present, the **antheridia** are club shaped and plastered to the wall of the oogonium.

10. In Figure 19-20, draw an oogonium, eggs (zygotes), and antheridia.

D.2. Chrysophytes: Diatoms (About 15 min.)

Diatoms are called the "organisms that live in glass houses" because their cell walls are composed largely of opaline *silica* (SiO_2 nH_2O). Diatoms are important as primary producers in the food chain of aquatic environments, and their cell walls are used for a wide variety of industrial purposes, ranging from the polishing agent in toothpaste to a reflective roadway paint additive. Massive deposits of cell walls of long-dead diatoms make up diatomaceous earth (Figure 19-21).

Figure 19-20 Drawing of gametangia of *Phytophthora cactorum* (_____×).
Labels: oogonium, eggs (zygotes), antheridium

MATERIALS

Per student:

- microscope slide
- coverslip
- dissecting needle
- prepared slide of freshwater diatom
- compound microscope

Per group (table):

- diatomaceous earth
- dH_2O in two dropping bottles

Per lab room:

- diatoms—living culture; disposable pipet

PROCEDURE

1. Using a dissecting needle, scrape a small amount of diatomaceous earth onto a microscope slide and prepare a wet mount slide.

Photo courtesy Daniel F. Williams.

Figure 19-21 Diatomaceous earth quarry near Quincy, Washington.

2. Examine your slide, starting with the low magnification objective, proceeding through the highest magnification available on your compound microscope. Close the iris diaphragm to increase the contrast.
3. You are looking at only the silica opaline shell. The cytoplasm of this organism disappeared hundreds of thousands, if not millions of years ago.
4. Note the tiny holes in the shells.
5. Now prepare a wet mount of living diatoms. Use the high-dry objective to note the golden brown chloroplasts within the cytoplasm and the numerous holes in the cell walls (shells).
6. In Figure 19-22, sketch several of the diatoms you are observing.
7. Now obtain a prepared slide of diatoms. These cells have been "cleaned," making the perforations in the cell wall especially obvious if you close the iris diaphragm on your microscope's condenser to increase the contrast. Study with the high-dry objective.

Figure 19-22 Drawing of diatoms (_____×).

The pattern of the holes in the walls is characteristic of a given species. Before the advent of electronic techniques, microscopists observed diatom walls to assess the quality of microscope lenses. The resolving power (see discussion of resolving power in Exercise 3) could be determined if one knew the diameter of the holes under observation.

D.3. Phaeophytes: Brown Algae *(About 10 min.)*

The vast majority of the brown algae are found in cold, marine environments. All members are multicellular, and most are macroscopic. Their color is due to the accessory pigment fucoxanthin, which is so abundant that it masks the green chlorophylls. Some species are used as food, while others are harvested for fertilizers. Of primary economic importance is **algin**, a cell wall component of brown algae that makes ice cream smooth, cosmetics soft, and paint uniform in consistency, among other uses.

D.3.a. Kelps—*Laminaria* and *Macrocystis*

Kelps are large (up to 100 m long), complex brown algae. They are common along the seashores in cold waters.

MATERIALS

Per lab room:

- demonstration specimen of *Laminaria*
- demonstration specimen of *Macrocystis*

PROCEDURE

Examine specimens of *Laminaria* (Figure 19-23) and *Macrocystis* (Figure 19-24). On each, identify the rootlike **holdfast** that anchors the alga to the substrate; the **stipe**, a stemlike structure; and the leaflike **blades**.

D.3.b. Rockweed—*Fucus*

Fucus is a common brown alga of the coastal shore, especially abundant attached to rocks where the plants are periodically wetted by splashing waves and the tides.

MATERIALS

Per lab room:

- demonstration specimen of *Fucus*

blade

stipe

holdfast

Photo by J. W. Perry

Figure 19-23 *Laminaria* (0.06×).

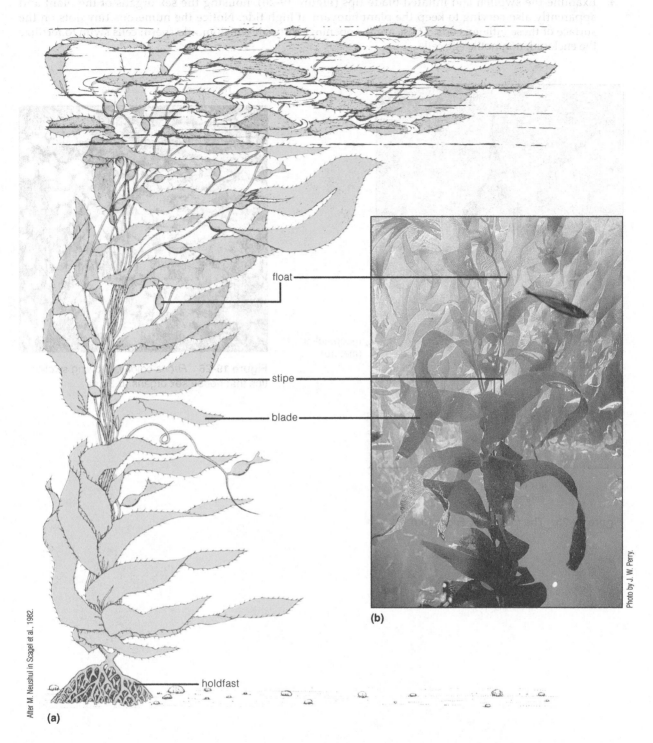

Figure 19-24 *Macrocystis.* (**a**) Artist's conception. (**b**) Photograph taken at Monterey Bay Aquarium, Monterey, CA. (Both about 0.01×.)

PROCEDURE

1. Examine demonstration specimens of *Fucus* (Figure 19-25), noting the branching nature of the body.
2. Locate the short **stipe** and **blade**.

3. Examine the swollen and inflated blade tips (Figure 19-26), housing the sex organs of the plant and apparently also serving to keep the plant buoyant at high tide. Notice the numerous tiny dots on the surface of these inflated ends. These are the openings through which motile sperm cells swim to fertilize the enclosed, nonmotile egg cells.

Figure 19-26   *Fucus* colony, showing swollen tips that house sex organs (0.35×).

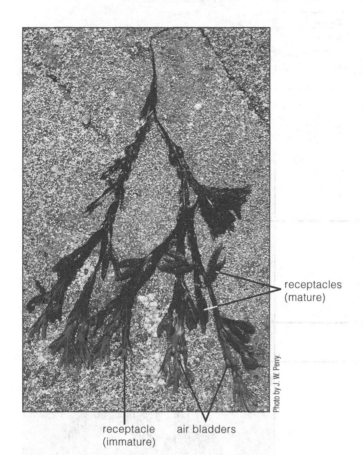

receptacles
(mature)

receptacle   air bladders
(immature)

Figure 19-25   The rockweed, *Fucus* (0.6×).

_____ 1. Some members of the Domain Bacteria have
(a) a nucleus.
(b) membrane-bound organelles.
(c) chloroplasts.
(d) photosynthetic ability.

_____ 2. A pathogen is
(a) a disease.
(b) an organism that causes a disease.
(c) a substance that kills bacteria.
(d) the same as a heterocyst.

_____ 3. Gram stain is used to distinguish between different
(a) bacteria.
(b) protistans.
(c) dinoflagellates.
(d) all of the above

_____ 4. Organisms capable of nitrogen fixation
(a) include some bacteria.
(b) include some cyanobacteria.
(c) may live as symbionts with other organisms.
(d) all of the above

_____ 5. Those organisms that are covered by numerous, tiny locomotory structures belong to the phylum
(a) Euglenozoa.
(b) Stramenopila.
(c) Parabasalia.
(d) Alveolata.

_____ 6. Which organisms cause "red tides?"
(a) bacteria
(b) cyanobacteria
(c) euglenoids
(d) dinoflagellates

_____ 7. If you found a fish floating on the water covered with a white fuzzy material and tiny dark spheres you would suspect that the fish has been infected by a(an)
(a) diatom.
(b) euglenoid.
(c) water mold.
(d) cynanobacterium.

_____ 8. A vector is
(a) an organism that causes disease.
(b) a disease.
(c) a substance that prevents disease.
(d) an organism that transmits a disease causing organism.

_____ 9. The organism that causes malaria is
(a) a pathogen.
(b) *Plasmodium vivax*.
(c) carried by a mosquito.
(d) all of the above

_____ 10. The cell wall component algin is
(a) found in the brown algae.
(b) used in the production of ice cream.
(c) used as a medium on which microorganisms are grown.
(d) both a and b

EXERCISE **19**

Bacteria and Protists I

Post-Lab Questions

Introduction

1. What major characteristic distinguishes bacteria from protists?

19.1.A. Bacteria

2. What form of bacterium is shown in this photomicrograph?

(1100×)

19.1.C. Cyanobacteria

3. Examine the photomicrograph on the right, taken using an oil-immersion objective, the highest practical magnification of a light microscope. (The final magnification is 770×.)

   (a) Based on your observation, identify the kingdom to which the organism belongs.

   (770×)

   (b) Justify your answer.

4. Observe the photomicrograph on the right of an organism that was found growing symbiotically within the leaves of the water fern *Azolla*.

   (a) What is the common name given to an organism of this type?

   (b) Give the name *and* function of the cell depicted by the line.

   (432×)

19.2.C. Phylum Alveolata

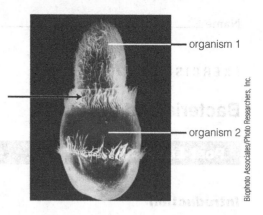

5. The scanning electron micrograph on the right contains two organisms in the phylum. What are the structures at the end of the arrow?

organism 1

organism 2

Biophoto Associates/Photo Researchers, Inc.

19.2.D. Phylum Stramenopila

6. You've never seen the protistan whose sexual structures appear here, but you have seen one very similar to it. What are the circular structures in the photo?

(287×)

Photo by J. W. Perry.

7. While the organism that resulted in the Irish potato famine of 1845–1847 had long been present, environmental conditions that occurred during this period resulted in the destructive explosion of disease. Indicate what those environmental conditions were and why they resulted in a major disease outbreak.

8. While walking along the beach at Point Lobos, California, the fellow pictured walks up to you with alga in hand. Figuring you to be a college student who has probably had a good introductory biology course, he asks if you know what it is.

   (a) What is the cell wall component of the organism that has commercial value?

   (b) Name three uses for that cell wall component.

(425×)

Photo by J. W. Perry.

9. If you were to travel to a region where rice is grown in paddies, you would see lots of the water fern *Azolla* growing in the water. A farmer would tell you this is done because *Azolla* is considered a "natural fertilizer." Explain why this is the case.

10. Based on your knowledge of the life history of *Plasmodium vivax*, suggest two methods for controlling malaria. Explain why each method would work.

Protists II

After completing this exercise, you will be able to

1. define *phytoplankton, phyt, phycobilin, agar, gametangium, oogonia, antheridia*;

2. recognize and classify selected members of the phyla represented in this exercise;

3. distinguish among the structures associated with asexual and sexual reproduction described in this exercise;

4. identify the structures of the algae (those in **boldface** in the procedure sections).

Introduction

The organisms in this exercise make an enormous impact on the biosphere, both positively and negatively. Among their greatest contribution is the production of oxygen, because most are the photosynthetic protistans. Many are given the common name "algae."

Pond scum, frog spittle, seaweed, the stuff that clogs your aquarium if it's not cleaned routinely, the debris on an ocean beach after a storm at sea, the nuisance organisms of a lake—these are the images that pop into our minds when we first think about the organisms called algae. But many algae are also **phytoplankton**, the weakly swimming or floating algae, at the base of the aquatic food chain.

Also included are amoebozoans, organisms lacking cell walls in their nonreproductive state that are the shape-shifters of the protistan world.

We'll examine the following organisms in this exercise:

Phylum	Common Name
Rhodophyta	Red algae
Chlorophyta	Green algae
Charophyta	Desmids and stoneworts
Amoebozoa	Amoebas and slime molds

Note the ending *-phyta* for several of the phylum names. This derives from the Greek root word *phyt*, which means "plant." In the not too distant past, these organisms were considered plants because they were photosynthetic. By contrast, the ending *-zoa* means "animal." While the endings remain, today these organisms are considered to be members of the kingdom Protista.

20.1 Phylum Rhodophyta: Red Algae *(About 15 min.)*

Although commonly called red algae, members of the Rhodophyta vary in color from red to green to purple to greenish-black. The color depends on the quantity of their photosynthetic accessory pigments, the **phycobilins**, which are blue and red. These accessory pigments allow capture of light energy across the entire visible spectrum. This energy is passed on to chlorophyll for photosynthesis. One phycobilin, the red phycoerythrin, allows some red algae to live at great depths where red wavelengths, those of primary importance for green and brown algae, fail to penetrate.

Which wavelengths (colors) would be absorbed by a red pigment?

_____

Most abundant in warm marine waters, red algae are the source of **agar** and carrageenan substances extracted from their cell walls. Agar is the solidifying agent in microbiological media and carrageenan is a thickener used in ice cream and to make beer clear by causing suspended proteins to precipitate out.

MATERIALS

Per lab room:

- culture dish containing dried agar and petri dish of hydrated agar
- demonstration slide of *Porphyridium*
- demonstration specimen and slide of *Porphyra* (nori)

PROCEDURE

1. Observe the dried agar that is on demonstration.
2. Now observe the petri dish containing agar that has been hydrated, heated, and poured into the dish.
3. Examine these cells of the unicellular *Porphyridium* at the demonstration microscope, noting the reddish chloroplast.
4. In Figure 20-1, sketch a cell of *Porphyridium*.
5. Examine a portion of the multicellular membranous *Porphyra* specimen on demonstration. Draw what you see in Figure 20-2.
6. Compare the specimen with the photo of live *Porphyra* (Figure 20-3).
7. In the adjacent demonstration microscope, note the microscopic appearance of *Porphyra* (Figure 20-4). Note that the clear areas are actually the cell walls.

Porphyra is used extensively as a food substance in Asia, where it's commonly sold under the name *nori*. In Japan, nori production is valued at $20 million annually.

Figure 20-1 Drawing of *Porphyridium* (_____×).

Figure 20-2 Drawing of the macroscopic appearance of *Porphyra* (nori) (_____×).

Figure 20-3 Living *Porphyra* (0.5×).

cell wall

Figure 20-4 Microscopic appearance of *Porphyra* (nori) (278×).

The Chlorophyta is a diverse assemblage of green organisms, ranging from motile and nonmotile unicellular forms to colonial, filamentous, membranous, and multinucleate forms. Not only do they include the most species, they are also important phylogenetically because ancestral green algae gave rise to the land plants. As you would expect, the photosynthetic pigments—both primary and accessory—and the stored carbohydrates are identical in the green algae and land plants.

In this section, you will examine the green algae from a morphological standpoint, starting with unicellular forms. For some, you'll also study their modes of reproduction and identify their characteristic sex organs, the gametangia (the singular is *gametangium*).

A. *Chlamydomonas*—A Motile Unicell

MATERIALS

Per student:

- microscope slide
- coverslip
- compound microscope

Per student pair:

- tissue paper
- I₂KI in dropping bottle

Per lab room:

- living culture of *Chlamydomonas*, disposable pipet

PROCEDURE

1. Prepare a wet mount of *Chlamydomonas* cells from the culture provided.
2. First examine with the low-power objective of your compound microscope. Notice the numerous small cells swimming across the field of view.
3. It will be difficult to study the fast-swimming cells, so kill the cells by adding a drop of I₂KI to the edge of the coverslip; draw the I₂KI under the coverslip by touching a folded tissue to the opposite edge. To observe the cells, switch to the highest power.
4. Identify the large, green cup-shaped **chloroplast** filling most of the cytoplasm.
5. *Chlamydomonas* stores its excess photosynthate as *starch grains*, which appear dark blue or black when stained with I₂KI. Locate the starch grains.
6. If the orientation of the cell is just right, you may be able to detect an orange **stigma** (eyespot) that serves as a light receptor.
7. Close the iris diaphragm to increase the contrast and find the two **flagella** at the anterior end of the cell.
8. Examine Figure 20-5, a transmission electron micrograph of *Chlamydomonas*. The electron microscope makes much more obvious the structures you can barely see with your light microscope. Notice the magnification.
9. The green algae have a specialized center for starch synthesis located within their chloroplast, the **pyrenoid**.

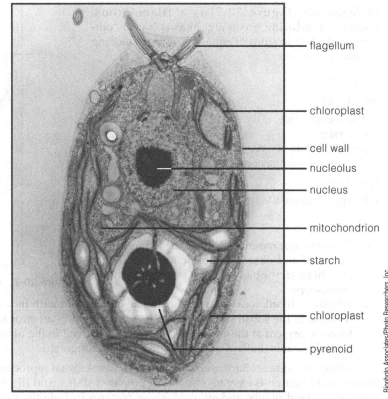

Figure 20-5 Transmission electron micrograph of *Chlamydomonas* (9750×).

B. *Volvox*—A Motile Colony

MATERIALS

Per student:
- depression slide
- compound microscope

Per lab room:
- living culture of *Volvox*, disposable pipet or prepared slide of *Volvox*

PROCEDURE

1. From the culture provided, place a drop of *Volvox*-containing culture solution on a depression slide. (A prepared slide may be substituted if living specimens are not available.)
2. Observe the large motile **colonies** (Figure 20-6), first with the microscope's low- and medium-power objectives. The colony is a hollow cluster of mostly identical, *Chlamydomonas*-like cells that are held together by a **gelatinous matrix**.
3. Identify the gelatinous matrix, which appears as the transparent region between individual cells.

Each cell possesses flagella. As the flagella beat, the entire colony rolls through the water. (The scientific name, *Volvox*, comes from the Latin word *volvere*, which means "to roll.")

4. Asexual reproduction takes place by **autocolony (daughter colony) formation**. Certain cells within the colony divide and then round up into a sphere called an **autocolony**. Find the autocolonies within your specimen.

Figure 20-6 *Volvox*, with autocolonies (56×).

C. *Oedogonium*—A Nonmotile Filament

Oedogonium (Figure 20-7) is a filamentous, zoospore-producing green alga that is found commonly attached to sides of aquaria and slow-moving freshwater streams.

MATERIALS

Per student:
- microscope slide
- coverslip
- prepared slide of *Oedogonium*
- compound microscope

Per lab room:
- living culture of *Oedogonium*

PROCEDURE

1. Prepare a wet mount slide from the living culture provided and observe with the medium-power and high-dry objectives of your compound microscope.

Figure 20-7 *Oedogonium*, with gametangia (250×).

2. Within each cell, locate the single, netlike **chloroplast** with its many **pyrenoids**. The cell that attaches the filament to the substrate is specialized as a **holdfast**. Scan your specimen to determine whether any holdfasts are present at the ends of the filaments. Each cell in the filament contains a single nucleus and a large central vacuole (both of which are difficult to distinguish).

Oedogonium reproduces both asexually and sexually. Asexual reproduction takes place by zoospore production. Sexual reproduction is easy to observe on prepared slides, and illustrates features commonly found in many other algae, land plants, and animals. These features include the presence of a very large nonmotile egg and motile sperm.

3. Obtain a prepared slide of a bisexual species of *Oedogonium*, which bears both male and female gametangia on the same filament. Examine with the medium-power objective of your compound microscope.
4. Find the large, spherical **oogonia**. These are the female sex organs. Within each oogonium locate a single, large **egg cell**, which virtually fills the oogonium.

Now find the male sex organs, the **antheridia**, which appear as short, boxlike cells. Each antheridium produces two *sperm*.

When the egg cell is fertilized by a sperm, a *zygote* is formed. The zygote develops a thick, heavy wall. Some oogonia on your slide may contain zygotes. When the zygote germinates, the diploid nucleus undergoes meiosis, producing motile spores. When the spore settles down, mitosis and cell division occur, producing the haploid filament you have examined.

Eventually, the two nuclei of each gamete fuse to form a **zygote**, which develops a thick wall. This thick-walled zygote serves as an overwintering structure. In the spring, the zygote nucleus undergoes meiosis. Three of the four nuclei die, leaving one functional, haploid nucleus. Germination of this haploid cell results in the formation of a haploid filament.

D. *Ulva*—A Membranous Form

A final representative of the green algae illustrates the fourth morphological form in the group, those having a membranous (tissuelike) body.

MATERIALS

Per lab room:

- demonstration specimen of *Ulva*

PROCEDURE

Examine living or preserved specimens of *Ulva*, commonly known as sea lettuce (Figure 20-8). The broad, leaflike body is called a *thallus*, a general term describing a vegetative body with relatively little cell differentiation. The *Ulva* body is only two cells thick!

Figure 20-8 The sea lettuce, *Ulva* (0.5×).

20.3 Phylum Charophyta: Desmids and Stoneworts

A. *Spirogyra*

A filamentous charophyte common to freshwater ponds is *Spirogyra*. This alga is often called pond scum because it forms a bright green, frothy mass on and just below the surface of the water.

MATERIALS

Per student:

- microscope slide
- coverslip
- dissecting needle
- prepared slide of *Spirogyra*
- compound microscope

Per student pair:

- diluted India ink in dropping bottle

Per lab room:

- living culture of *Spirogyra*

PROCEDURE

1. Observe the *Spirogyra* in the large culture dish. Pick up some of the mass, noting the slimy sensation. This is due to the watery sheath surrounding each filament.
2. Using a dissecting needle, place a few filaments on a slide and add a drop of diluted India ink before adding a coverslip. (Prepared slides may be used if living filaments are not available.)
3. Observe the filaments with the medium-power and high-dry objectives of your compound microscope (Figure 20-9).
4. Identify the **sheath**, which will appear as a bright area off the edge of the cell wall.
5. Note the spiral-shaped **chloroplast** with the numerous **pyrenoids**.
6. Each cell contains a large central **vacuole** and a single **nucleus**. Remember, the chloroplast is located within the cytoplasm, as is

pyrenoid within chloroplast · cell wall · strand of cytoplasm · nucleus within cytoplasm

Figure 20-9 *Spirogyra* (550×).

the nucleus. The nucleus, however, is suspended in strands of cytoplasm, much as a spider might be found in the center of a web. Look again at Figure 20-9 and locate the nucleus.

Asexual reproduction occurs when a small portion of the filament simply breaks off and continues to grow. Zoospores are not formed. Sexual reproduction is illustrated in Figure 20-9. Male and gametes, and for that matter sex organs, look identical to one another.

7. Obtain a prepared slide illustrating sexual reproduction in *Spirogyra*. Examine the slide with your medium or high-dry objective.
8. Find two filaments that are joined by cytoplasmic bridges known as **conjugation tubes**. The entire cytoplasmic contents serve as **isogametes** (that is, gametes of similar size) in *Spirogyra*, with one isogamete moving through the conjugation tube into the other cell, where it fuses with the other gamete.
9. Find stages illustrating conjugation as in Figure 20-10.

Figure 20-10 *Spirogyra*, stages in sexual reproduction (170×).

B. *Chara* or *Nitella*—Stoneworts

Stoneworts are within a green alga lineage that million of years ago gave rise to the land plants. They have a distinctive body form and sex organs, which are unlike those found in other green algae, and indeed remind one of tiny aquatic plants.

Stoneworts are interesting organisms found "rooted" in brackish and fresh waters, particularly those high in calcium. (Two of your lab manual authors—the Perrys—have ponds that are delightfully full of stoneworts.) They get their common names by virtue of being able to precipitate calcium carbonate over their surfaces, encrusting them and rendering them somewhat stony and brittle. (The suffix -*wort* is from a Greek word meaning "herb.")

MATERIALS

Per student:
- small culture dish
- dissecting microscope

Per lab room:
- living culture of (or preserved) *Chara* or *Nitella*
- demonstration slide of *Chara* with sex organs

PROCEDURE

1. From the classroom culture provided, obtain some of the specimen and place it in a small culture dish partially filled with water.
2. Observe the specimen with a dissecting microscope. Note that the stoneworts resemble what we would think of as a plant. They are divided into "stems" and "branches" (Figure 20-11).
3. Search for flask-shaped and spherical structures along the stem. These are the sex organs. If none is present on the specimen, observe the demonstration slide (Figure 20-12) that has been selected to show these structures.

4. The flask-shaped structures are **oogonia**, each of which contains a single, large egg (Figure 20-13). Notice that the oogonium is covered with cells that twist over the surface of the gametangium. Because of the presence of these cells, the oogonium is considered to be a *multicellular* sex organ. Multicellular sex organs are present in all land plants.

Based on your study of previously examined specimens, would you say the egg is motile or nonmotile?

_____

5. Now find a spherical **antheridium** (Figure 20-13). Like the oogonium, the antheridium is covered by cells and is also considered to be multicellular. Cells within the interior of the antheridium produce numerous flagellated sperm cells.

Figure 20-11 The stonewort, *Chara*, with sex organs (2×).

Fertilization of eggs by sperm produces a *zygote* within the oogonium. The zygote-containing oogonium eventually falls off from the parent plant. The zygote can remain dormant for some time before the nucleus undergoes meiosis in preparation for germination. Apparently, three of the four nuclei produced during meiosis disintegrate.

Figure 20-12 *Chara*, showing sex organs (30×).

Figure 20-13 Antheridia and oogonia of *Chara* (80×).

The slime molds have both plantlike and animal-like characteristics. They engulf their food and lack a cell wall in their nonreproductive state. However, when they reproduce, they produce spores with a rigid cell wall, similar to plants.

A. *Physarum*: A Plasmodial Slime Mold (About 15 min.)

The vegetative (nonreproductive) body of the plasmodial slime molds consists of a naked multinucleate mass of protoplasm known as a **plasmodium**.

MATERIALS

Per student:

- petri dish culture of slime mold (*Physarum*)
- compound microscope

Per lab room:

- demonstration of slime mold (*Physarum*) sporangia

PROCEDURE

1. Obtain a petri dish culture of *Physarum* (Figure 20-14) and remove the cover. After examining it with your unaided eye, place the culture dish on the stage of your compound microscope and examine it with the low-power objective.
2. Watch the cytoplasm. The motion that you see within the plasmodium is cytoplasmic streaming (Exercise 6). Is the cytoplasmic streaming unidirectional, or does the flow reverse? _____

As you noticed, the *Physarum* culture was stored in the dark. That's because light (along with other factors) stimulates the plasmodium to switch to the reproductive phase.

3. Examine the spore-containing sporangia of *Physarum* that are on demonstration (Figure 20-15). Spores released from the sporangia germinate, producing a new plasmodium.

Because the plasmodium is multinucleate (whereas the spores are uninucleate), what event must occur following spore germination?

_____

Figure 20-14   Culture dish containing the plasmodial slime mold, *Physarum* (0.7×).

Figure 20-15   Sporangia of the plasmodial slime mold, *Physarum* (1.5×).

B. *Amoeba* (About 20 min.)

Amoebas continually change shape by forming projections called *pseudopodia* (singular, *pseudopodium,* "false foot"). One notorious human pathogen is *Entamoeba histolytica,* the cause of amoebic dysentery.

MATERIALS

Per student:
- depression slide
- coverslip
- dissecting needle
- compound microscope

Per group (table):
- carmine, in two screw-cap bottles
- tissue paper

Per lab room:
- *Amoeba*—living culture on demonstration at dissecting microscope; disposable pipet

PROCEDURE

1. Observe the *Amoeba*-containing culture on the stage of a demonstration dissecting microscope. (One species of amoeba has the scientific name *Amoeba.*) The microscope has been focused on the bottom of the culture dish, where the amoebas are located. Look for gray, irregularly shaped masses moving among the food particles in the culture.
2. Using a clean pipet, remove an amoeba and place it, along with some of the culture medium, in a depression slide.
3. Examine it with your compound microscope using the medium-power objective. You will need to adjust the diaphragm to increase the contrast (see Exercise 3) because *Amoeba* is nearly transparent.
4. Refer to Figure 20-16. Locate the **pseudopodia**. At the periphery of the cell, identify the **ectoplasm,** a thin, clear layer that surrounds the inner, granular **endoplasm**. Watch the organism as it changes shape. Which region of the endoplasm appears to stream, the outer or the inner? _____

This region, called the *plasmasol,* consists of a fluid matrix that can undergo phase changes with the semisolid *plasmagel,* the outer layer of the endoplasm. Pseudopodium formation occurs as the plasmasol flows into new environmental frontiers and then changes to plasmagel.

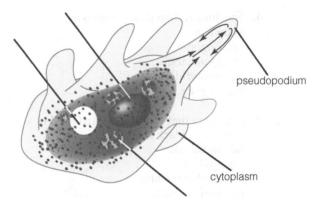

Figure 20-16 Artist's rendering of *Amoeba.*
Labels: ectoplasm, endoplasm, nucleus, contractile vacuole, food vacuole

Numerous granules will be found within the endoplasm. Some of these are organelles; others are food granules.

5. Within the endoplasm, try to locate the **nucleus**, a densely granular, spherical structure around which the cytoplasm is streaming.
6. Find the clear, spherical **contractile vacuoles**, which regulate water balance within the cell. Watch for a minute or two to observe the action of contractile vacuoles. Label Figure 20-16.

Amoeba feeds by a process called **phagocytosis**, engulfing its food. Pseudopodia form around food particles, and then the pseudopodia fuse, creating a **food vacuole** within the cytoplasm. Enzymes are then emptied into the food vacuole, where the food particle is digested into a soluble form that can pass through the vacuolar membrane. You can stimulate feeding behavior by drawing carmine under the coverslip.

7. Place a drop of distilled water against one edge of the coverslip.
8. Pick up some carmine crystals by dipping a dissecting needle into the bottle; and deposit them into the water droplet.
9. Draw the suspension beneath the coverslip by holding a piece of absorbent tissue against the coverslip on the side *opposite* the carmine suspension.
10. Observe the *Amoeba* with your microscope again—you may catch it in the act of feeding.

_____ **1.** Agar is derived from
   (a) red algae.
   (b) brown algae.
   (c) green algae.
   (d) all of the above

_____ **2.** Which is the correct plural form of the word for the organisms studied in this exercise?
   (a) alga
   (b) algae
   (c) algas
   (d) algaes

_____ **3.** Phycobilins are
   (a) photosynthetic pigments.
   (b) found in the red algae.
   (c) blue and red pigments.
   (d) all of the above

_____ **4.** Specifically, female sex organs are known as
   (a) oogonia.
   (b) gametangia.
   (c) antheridia.
   (d) zygotes.

_____ **5.** A reagent that stains the stored food of a green alga black is
   (a) India ink.
   (b) I_2KI.
   (c) methylene blue.
   (d) both a and b

_____ **6.** The starch production center within many algal cells is the
   (a) nucleus.
   (b) cytoplasm.
   (c) stipe.
   (d) pyrenoid.

_____ **7.** The phylum of organisms *most* closely linked to the evolution of land plants is the
   (a) Chlorophyta.
   (b) Charophyta.
   (c) Phaeophyta.
   (d) Euglenozoa.

_____ **8.** Gametangia are
   (a) chlorophyll-producing structures.
   (b) sex organs.
   (c) a name for colony-forming algae.
   (d) found in slime molds.

_____ **9.** Which of the following terms does **not** apply to organisms in the Phylum Amoeboza?
   (a) chlorophyll
   (b) phagocytosis
   (c) pseudopodia
   (d) slime mold

_____ **10.** Amoebic dysentery is caused by
   (a) *Ulva.*
   (b) *Volvox.*
   (c) a desmid.
   (d) *Entamoeba.*

EXERCISE **20**

Protists II

Post-Lab Questions

20.1 Phylum Rhodophyta: Red Algae

1. While wading in the warm salt water off the beaches of the Florida Keys on spring break, you stoop down to look at the feathery alga shown here.
   (a) What pigment gives this organism its coloration?

   (b) What commercial products are derived from this phylum?

20.2 Phylum Chlorophyta: Green Algae

2. What two characteristics found within the green algae are clues that this group of organisms is more closely related to the land plants than red algae?
   (a)

   (b)

20.3 Phylum Charophyta: Desmids and Stoneworts

3. Your class takes a field trip to a freshwater stream, where you collect the organism shown microscopically here.
   (a) What is the genus name of this organism?

   (b) Identify and give the function of the structure within the chloroplast at the end of the leader (line).

20.4 Phylum Amoebozoa: Slime Molds and Amoebas

4. This photomicrograph was taken from a prepared slide of a stained specimen. You observed unstained living specimens in lab. Describe the mechanism by which it moves from place to place.

5. What is phagocytosis? What function does it serve?

Food for Thought

6. Some botanists consider the stoneworts to be a link between the higher plants and the algae. As you will learn in future exercises, higher plants, such as the mosses, have both haploid and diploid stages that are *multicellular*.
    (a) Describe the multicellular organism in the charophytes.

    (b) Is this organism haploid or diploid?

    (c) Is the zygote haploid or diploid?

    (d) Is the zygote unicellular or multicellular?

7. (a) What color are the marker lights at the edge of an airport taxiway?

    (b) Are the wavelengths of this color long or short, relative to the other visible wavelengths?

    (c) Which wavelengths penetrate deepest into water, long or short?

    (d) Make a statement regarding why phycobilin pigments are present in deep-growing red algae.

    (e) What benefit is there to the color of airport taxiway lights for a pilot attempting to taxi during foggy weather?

8. Why do you suppose the Swedish automobile manufacturer Volvo chose this company name?

9. List two reasons why algae are useful and important to life.
    (a)

    (b)

10. It's generally accepted that the first life on Earth was unicellular and, while autotrophic, did not have chlorophyll. Later, multicellular, chlorophyll-bearing organisms evolved. Speculate on how amoeba-like organisms that lacked chlorophyll might have obtained the ability to use chlorophyll to capture the energy of the sun.

Bryophytes—Liverworts and Mosses

After completing this exercise, you will be able to

1. define *alternation of generations, isomorphic, heteromorphic, dioecious, antheridium, archegonium, hygroscopic, protonema;*

2. diagram the plant life cycle to show alternation of generations;

3. distinguish between alternation of isomorphic and heteromorphic alternation of generations;

4. list evidence supporting the evolution of land plants from green algae;

5. recognize charophytes, mosses, and liverworts;

6. identify the sporophytes, gametophytes, and associated structures of liverworts and mosses (those in **boldface** in the procedure sections);

7. describe the function of the sporophyte and the gametophyte;

8. postulate why bryophytes live only in environments where free water is often available.

Introduction

This is the first in a series of exercises that addresses true plants—the kingdom Plantae.

Plants evolved from the green algae, specifically now extinct relatives of living green algae called **charophytes**. Evidence for this includes identical food reserves (starch), the same photosynthetic pigments (chlorophylls *a* and *b*, carotenes, and xanthophylls), similarities in structure of their flagella, and the way cell division takes place. Some biologists have gone so far as to suggest that the land plants are nothing more than highly evolved green algae.

One major mystery is the origin of a feature common to *all* true plants (but *not* charophytes), **alternation of generations**. In alternation of generations, two distinct phases exist: a diploid **sporophyte** alternates with a haploid **gametophyte**, as summarized in Figure 21-1.

As animals, we find the concept of alternation of generations difficult to envision. But think of it as the existence of two body forms of the same organism. The primary reproductive function of one body form, the gametophyte, is to produce gametes (eggs and/or sperm) by *mitosis*. The primary reproductive function of the other, the sporophyte, is to produce spores by *meiosis*.

A fundamental distinction exists between the green algae and land plants with respect to alternation of generations. Although some green algae have alternation of generations, the sporophyte and gametophyte look *identical*. To the naked eye, they are indistinguishable. This is called alternation of **isomorphic** generations. (*Iso-* comes from a Greek word meaning "equal"; *morph-* is Greek for "form.")

By contrast, the alternation of generations in land plants is **heteromorphic** (*hetero-* is Greek for "different"). The sporophytes and gametophytes of land plants, including the bryophytes, are distinctly different from one another. The contrast between isomorphic and heteromorphic alternation of generations is modeled in Figure 21-2.

During the course of evolution, two major lines of divergence took place in the plant kingdom. In one line, the plants had as their dominant (most conspicuous) phase the gametophytic generation, meaning that the sporophyte was permanently attached to and dependent on the gametophyte for nutrition, never living an independent existence. Today these plants are represented by the bryophytes, mosses and liverworts. It seems that this line exemplifies *dead-end evolution*— no other group of plants present today arises from it.

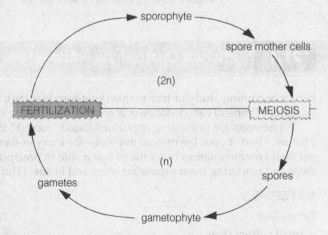

Figure 21-1 Summary of alternation of generations.

In the other line of evolution, the sporophyte led an independent existence, the gametophyte being quite small and inconspicuous. Figure 21-3 summarizes these two evolutionary lines.

As you will see in this exercise, the land plants known as liverworts and mosses are often fairly dissimilar in appearance. They do share similarities, including the following:

1. Both exhibit alternation of heteromorphic generations, in which the gametophyte is the dominant organism. The sporophyte remains attached to the gametophyte, deriving most of its nutrition from the gametophyte.
2. Both are dependent on water for fertilization, since their sperm must swim to a nonmotile egg.
3. Both lack true vascular tissues, xylem and phloem, and hence are relatively small organisms.

Figure 21-2 Types of alternation of generations. **(a)** Isomorphic. **(b)** Heteromorphic.

Figure 21-3 Evolution of land plants.

21.1 Phylum Charophyta—Ancestors of True Plants *(About 10 min.)*

Before beginning study of true plants (kingdom Plantae), let's look at their closest algal relatives. Charophytes (kingdom Protista) called stoneworts are within a lineage that millions of years ago gave rise to the land plants.

Stoneworts are interesting organisms found "rooted" in brackish and fresh waters, particularly those high in calcium. (Two of your lab manual authors—the Perrys—have ponds that are delightfully full of stoneworts.) They get their common names by virtue of being able to precipitate calcium carbonate over their surfaces, encrusting them and rendering them somewhat stony and brittle. (The suffix -*wort* is from a Greek word meaning "herb.")

MATERIALS

Per student:

- small culture dish
- dissecting microscope

Per lab room:

- living culture (or preserved) *Chara* or *Nitella*
- demonstration slide of *Chara* with sex organs

PROCEDURE

1. From the classroom culture provided, obtain some of the specimen and place it in a small culture dish partially filled with water.

2. Observe the specimen with a dissecting microscope. Note that the stoneworts resemble what we would think of as a plant. They are divided into "stems" and "branches" (Figure 21-4).

3. Search for flask-shaped and spherical structures along the stem. These are the sex organs. If none is present on the specimen, observe the demonstration slide (Figure 21-5) that has been selected to show these structures.

4. The flask-shaped structures are **oogonia**, each of which contains a single, large egg (Figure 21-6). Notice that the oogonium is covered with cells that twist over the surface of the gametangium. Because of the presence of these cells, the oogonium is considered to be a *multicellular* sex organ. Multicellular sex organs are present in all land plants.

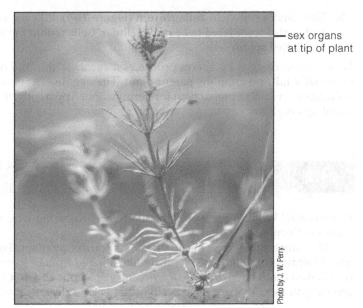

Figure 21-4 The stonewort, *Chara*, with sex organs (2×).

Based on your study of previously examined specimens, would you say the egg is motile or nonmotile?

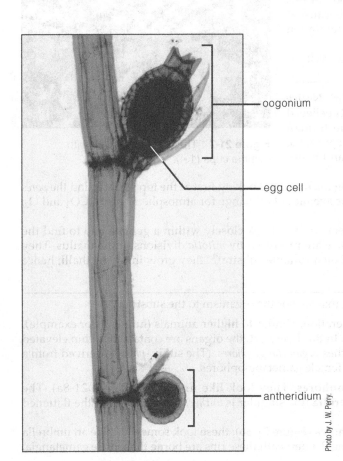

Figure 21-5 *Chara*, showing sex organs (30×).

Figure 21-6 Antheridia and oogonia of *Chara* (80×).

5. Now find a spherical **antheridium** (Figure 21-6). Like the oogonium, the antheridium is covered by cells and is also considered to be multicellular. Cells within the interior of the antheridium produce numerous flagellated sperm cells.

Fertilization of eggs by sperm produces a *zygote* within the oogonium. The zygote-containing oogonium eventually falls off from the parent plant. The zygote can remain dormant for some time before the nucleus undergoes meiosis in preparation for germination. Apparently, three of the four nuclei produced during meiosis disintegrate.

21.2   Phylum Hepatophyta: Liverworts *(About 20 min.)*

Liverworts!? What in the world is a liverwort? Knowing why these plants are called liverworts is a start to knowing them.

The Greek suffix *-wort* means "herb," a nonwoody plant. The "liver" portion of the common name comes about because the plants look a little like a lobed human liver. These are small plants that you have likely overlooked (until now!) because they're inconspicuous and don't look like anything important. You'll find them growing on rocks that are periodically wetted along clean freshwater streams.

MATERIALS

Per student:

- living or preserved *Marchantia* thalli, with gemma cups, antheridiophores, archegoniophores, and mature sporophytes
- dissecting microscope

PROCEDURE

1. Examine the living or preserved plants of the liverwort, *Marchantia,* that are on demonstration. The body of this plant is called a **thallus** (the plural is *thalli*), because it is flattened and has little internal tissue differentiation (Figure 21-7).
2. The thallus is the gametophyte portion of the life cycle.

Is it haploid or diploid? _____

3. Obtain and examine one thallus of the liverwort. Notice that the thallus is lobed. Centuries ago, herbalists believed that plants that looked like portions of the human anatomy could be used to treat ailments of that part of the body. This plant reminded them of the liver, and hence the plant was called a "liverwort."

thallus   gemma cup

Photo by J. W. Perry.

Figure 21-7   Thallus of a liverwort with gemma cups (1×).

4. Now place the thallus on the stage of a dissecting microscope. Looking first at the top surface, find the *pores* that lead to the interior of the plant and serve as avenues of exchange for atmospheric gases (CO_2 and O_2; Figure 21-7).
5. Identify **gemma cups** (Figure 21-7) on the upper surface. Look closely within a gemma cup to find the **gemmae** inside (the singular is *gemma*). Gemmae are produced by *mitotic* divisions of the thallus. They are dislodged by splashing water. If they land on a suitable substrate, they grow into new thalli; hence they are a means of asexual reproduction.
6. Are gemmae haploid or diploid? _____
7. Turn the plant over to find the hairlike **rhizoids** that anchor the organism to the substrate.

As noted above, the thalli are the gametophyte generation. Similar to higher animals (humans, for example), gametes are produced in special organs on the plant. In this liverwort, the organs are contained within elevated branches. The general name for these elevated branches is *gametangiophores.* (The suffix *-phore* is derived from a Greek word meaning "branch.") There are male and female gametangiophores.

8. On a male thallus, find the male **antheridiophores**. They look like umbrellas (Figure 21-8a). The sperm-producing male sex organs called **antheridia** (the singular is *antheridium*) are within the flattened splash platform of the umbrella.
9. On female plants, find the female **archegoniophores** (Figure 21-8b); these look somewhat like an umbrella that has lost its fabric and has only ribs remaining. Underneath these ribs are borne the female gametangia, **archegonia** (singular, *archegonium*).

Figure 21-8 Liverwort thalli with gametangiophores. (**a**) Male thalli with antheridiophores (0.25×). (**b**) Female thalli with archegoniophores (0.5×).

| 21.3 | Experiment: Effect of Photoperiod *(About 10 min. to set up; requires 6 weeks to complete)* |

Photoperiod, the length of light and dark periods, exerts a significant effect upon most living things. Flowering in many plants is dependent on photoperiod, some plants being classified as "long day (short night)," others as "short day (long night)," and still others as "day neutral." Flowering is a reproductive event. The reproductive behavior of many animals, such as deer, is also dependent on day length.

This experiment examines the effect of photoperiod on the production of gametangiophores and gemma cups in the liverwort, *Marchantia*. One possible experimental hypothesis is that *reproduction of* Marchantia *is stimulated by long days (short nights)*. You may wish to read the discussion in Exercise 1, "The Scientific Method," before proceeding.

MATERIALS

Per student group:

- vigorously growing colony of the liverwort *Marchantia polymorpha*
- pot label
- china or other marker

Per lab room:

- growth chambers set to long day (16 hr light, 8 hr darkness) and short day (8 hr light, 16 hr darkness) conditions

PROCEDURE

1. In Table 21-1, write a prediction about the effect of day length on *Marchantia* reproduction.
2. Obtain a colony of the liverwort, *Marchantia polymorpha*. On the pot label, write your name, date, and the experimental condition (long day or short day) to which you are going to subject the colony.
3. Place the colony in the growth chamber that is designated as "short day" or "long day," depending on which condition has been assigned to your experimental group. You will be responsible for watering the colonies on a regular basis. Failure to do so will result in unreliable experimental results and/or death of the plants.
4. Observe the colonies weekly over a period of 6 weeks, recording your observations in Table 21-1.
5. After 6 weeks of experimental treatment, compare observations with other experimental groups using the same and different independent variables.
6. List the results and make conclusions, writing them in Table 21-2.

Did the experimental results support your hypothesis? _____

Can you suggest any reasons why it might be beneficial to the liverwort to display the results that the different experimental groups found?

_____

_____

TABLE 21-1	The Effect of Photoperiod on the Reproduction of the Liverwort, *Marchantia polymorpha*

Prediction:

Week	Observations of the Effect of _____ (Long or Short) Day Illumination
1	
2	
3	
4	
5	
6	

TABLE 21-2	Summary of Results: The Effect of Photoperiod on the Reproduction of the Liverwort, *Marchantia polymorpha*

Photoperiod	Results
Long day	
Short day	

Conclusions:

21.4 Phylum Bryophyta: Mosses *(About 60 min.)*

Mosses are plants that you've probably noticed before. They grow on trees, rocks, and soil. Mosses have a wide variety of human uses, the most common ones being as a soil additive to potting soil and as a major component of peat, which is used for fuel in some parts of the world.

MATERIALS

Per student:

- *Polytrichum*, male and female gametophytes, the latter with attached sporophytes
- prepared slide of moss antheridial head, l.s.
- prepared slide of moss archegonial head, l.s.
- prepared slide of moss sporangium (capsule), l.s.
- glass microscope slide
- coverslip

- compound microscope
- dissecting microscope
- dissecting needle

Per student pair:

- dH$_2$O in dropping bottle

Per student group (table):

- moss protenemata growing on culture medium

PROCEDURE

Refer to Figure 21-15 as you study the life cycle of the mosses.

1. Obtain a living or preserved specimen of a moss that grows in your area. The hairy-cap moss, *Polytrichum*, is a good choice because one of the 10 species in this genus is certain to be found near wherever you live in North America.

Lacking vascular tissues, the mosses do not have true roots, stems, or leaves, although they do have structures that are rootlike, stemlike, and leaflike and perform the same functions as the true organs.

2. Identify the rootlike **rhizoids** at the base of the plant. What function do you think rhizoids perform?

_____

_____

3. Notice that the leaflike organs are arranged more or less radially about the stemlike *axis*. You are examining the **gametophyte generation** of the moss. In terms of the life cycle of the organism, what function does the gametophyte serve?

_____

_____

Figure 21-9   Colony of Polytrichum, male gametophytes (0.5×).

Polytrichum is **dioecious,** meaning that there are separate male and female plants. (Some other mosses are monoecious.) The male gametophyte can usually be distinguished by the flattened rosette of leaflike structures at its tip.

4. Examine a male gametophyte (Figures 21-9, 21-15a), noting this feature. Embedded within the rosette are the male sex organs, **antheridia** (singular, *antheridium*).

5. With the low- and medium-power objectives of your compound microscope, examine a prepared slide with the antheridia of a moss (Figure 21-15c). Identify the *antheridia* (Figure 21-10).

6. Study a single antheridium (Figure 21-10), using the high-dry objective. Locate the jacket layer surrounding the sperm-forming tissue that, with maturity, gives rise to numerous biflagellate *sperm.* Scattered among the antheridia, find the numerous sterile *paraphyses*. These do not have a reproductive role (and hence are called sterile) but instead function to hold capillary water, preventing the sex organs from drying out.

7. Examine a female gametophyte of *Polytrichum* (Figure 21-15b). Before the development of the sporophyte, the female gametophyte can usually be distinguished by the absence of the rosette at its tip. Nonetheless, the apex of the female gametophyte contains the female sex organs, **archegonia** (singular, *archegonium*).

(a)

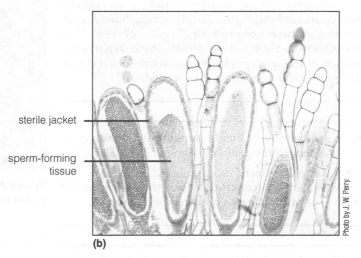

(b)

Figure 21-10   Longitudinal section of antheridial head of a moss (a) 8×. (b) 93×.

8. Obtain a prepared slide of the archegonial tip of a moss (Figures 21-11a, 21-15d). Start with the low-power objective of your compound microscope to gain an impression of the overall organization. Find the sterile *paraphyses* and the *archegonia*.

9. Switch to the medium-power objective to study a single archegonium, identifying the long **neck** and the slightly swollen base. Within the base, locate the **egg cell** (Figure 21-15d).

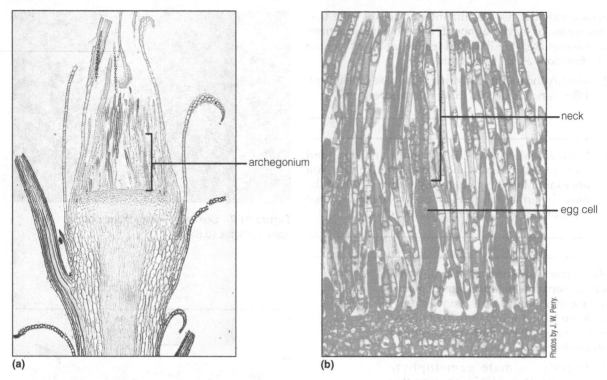

(a)   **(b)**

Figure 21-11 **(a)** Longitudinal section of archegonial head of a moss (22×). **(b)** Detail of archegonium (88×).

Remember, you are looking at a *section* of a three-dimensional object. The archegonium is very much like a long-necked vase, except that it's solid. The egg cell is like a marble suspended in the middle of the base.

The central core of the archegonial neck contains cells that break down when the egg is mature, liberating a fluid that is rich in sucrose and that attracts sperm that are swimming in dew or rainwater. (Sperm are capable of swimming only short distances and so male plants must be close by.) Fertilization of the egg produces the diploid zygote (Figure 21-15e), the first cell of the **sporophyte generation.**

Numerous mitotic divisions produce an **embryo** (embryo sporophyte, Figure 21-15f), which differentiates into the **mature sporophyte** (Figure 21-15g) that protrudes from the tip of the gametophyte. What is the function of the sporophyte (that is, what does it do, or what reproductive structures does it produce)?

_____

_____

10. Now examine a female gametophyte that has an attached *mature sporophyte* (Figures 21-12, 21-15g).

Is the sporophyte green? _____

What can you conclude about the sporophyte's ability to produce at least a portion of its own food?

_____

_____

Figure 21-12 Colony of Polytrichum, female gametophytes with attached sporophytes (0.25×).

11. Grasp the stalk of the sporophyte and detach it from the gametophyte. The base of the stalk absorbs water and nutrients from the gametophyte.
12. At the tip of the sporophyte, locate the **sporangium** covered by a papery hood. The cover is a remnant of the tissue that surrounded the archegonium and is covered with tiny hairs—hence the common name, hairy-cap moss, for *Polytrichum.*
13. Remove the hood to expose the sporangium (Figure 21-15h). Notice the small cap at the top of the sporangium.
14. Remove the cap and observe the interior of the sporangium with a dissecting microscope. Find the *peristomal teeth* that point inward from the margin of the opening.

The peristomal teeth are **hygroscopic**, meaning that they change shape as they absorb water. As the teeth dry, they arch upward, loosening the cap over the spore mass. The teeth may subsequently shrink or swell, thus regulating how readily the spores inside may escape.

15. Study a prepared slide of a longitudinal section of a sporangium (Figure 21-13). At the top, you will find sections of the peristomal teeth. Internally, locate the **sporogenous tissue**, which differentiates into *spores* when mature. The sporogenous tissue of the sporangium is diploid, but the spores are haploid and are the first cells of the gametophyte generation.

What type of nuclear division must take place for the sporogenous tissue to become spores?

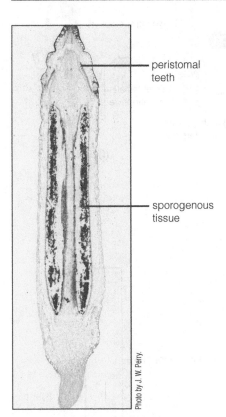

Figure 21-13 Longitudinal section of moss sporangium (12×).

When the spores are shed from the sporangium, they are carried by wind and water currents to new sites. If conditions are favorable, the spore germinates to produce a filamentous protonema (Figures 21-14, 21-15j; plural, *protonemata*) that looks much like a filamentous green alga.

Is the protonema part of the gametophyte or sporophyte generation?

Figure 21-14 Moss protonema, whole mount (70×).

16. Use a dissecting needle to remove a protonema from the culture provided and make a wet mount. Examine it with the medium-power and high-dry objectives of your compound microscope. Note the cellular composition and numerous green *chloroplasts*. If the protonema is of sufficient age, you should find *buds* (Figure 21-15k) that grow into the leafy gametophyte (Figures 21-15a, b, and l).

21.5 Experiment: Effect of Light Quality on Moss Spore Germination and Growth *(About 20 min. to set up; requires 8 weeks to complete)*

What causes plants to grow and reproduce? One significant environmental trigger is light. Both light *quantity* (the length of illumination) and light *quality* (the wavelengths or color of light) trigger growth and reproduction in organisms. In this experiment, you will grow moss protonemata from spores and examine the effect of different wavelengths of light on germination of spores and subsequent growth of the protonema. One hypothesis this simple experiment might address is that *moss spores germinate and protonemata grow best in short (blue) wavelength light.* You may wish to read the discussion in Exercise 1, "The Scientific Method," before proceeding.

(a) male gametophyte

(b) female gametophyte

antheridial head

archegonial head

rhizoids

(c) longitudinal section of antheridial head

paraphyses

antheridium

(d) longitudinal section of archegonial head

egg cell

paraphyses

archegonium

sperm

FERTILIZATION

neck

zygote

(e) archegonium after fertilization

calyptra

young sporophyte

tip of female gametophyte

(f) developing sporophyte

mature sporophyte

female gametophyte

MEIOSIS

(g) gametophyte with attached sporophyte

hood (removed from sporangium)

cap

peristomal teeth

(h) sporangium

(i) spores

germinating spore

(j) spore germination

protonemata

(k) old protonemata with bud

bud

rhizoid

(l) young gametophyte

Figure 21-15 Life cycle of representative moss. (Green structures are 2n.)

Modified from Carolina Biological Supply Company diagrams.

MATERIALS

Per student group:

- culture plate with moss agar
- water suspension containing moss spores
- china or other marker
- Pi-pump (1 mL or 10 mL)
- 1-mL pipet
- 8-cm strip of parafilm

- compound microscope
- glass microscope slide
- coverslip

Per lab room:

- four incubation chambers (one each for white, blue, green, and red light)

PROCEDURE

1. Obtain the following: one culture plate containing moss agar, china or other marker, a Pi-pump, a 1-mL pipet, and an 8-cm strip of parafilm.
2. Prepare a wet mount of the moss spore suspension provided by your instructor. Examine the spores with all magnifications available with your compound microscope.
3. Draw the spores in Figure 21-16, noting color.
4. Examine Figure 21-17, which shows you how to open the culture plate.
5. Pipet 1 mL of the spore suspension onto the culture plate.
6. Seal the culture plate with the strip of parafilm to prevent drying: remove the paper backing, place one end of the parafilm on the edge of the culture plate, hold the edge down with index finger pressure of the hand that is holding the culture plate, and stretch the parafilm around the circumference of the plate with a rolling motion.
7. With the marker, write your name, the date, and the light regime you will be using on the cover of the culture plate. Place the culture in the incubator with the proper light regime. Your instructor will designate the light regime (white, blue, green, or red) under which you should incubate your culture. This is the independent variable.
8. Formulate a prediction regarding this experiment. Write it in the proper space in Table 21-3.
9. Observe your cultures weekly: remove the lid (if necessary), place the culture on the stage of a dissecting microscope, and observe the spores. Record your observations in Table 21-3. Suggested dependent variables include percent germination, abundance of growth, color of protonemal cells, and formation of buds.
10. After 8 weeks, compare your results with other students using the same and different light regimes.
11. Summarize your observations and make conclusions in Table 21-4.

Was your hypothesis supported by the experimental results? _____

Figure 21-16 Drawing of ungerminated moss spores (_____×).

Figure 21-17 Method for inoculating petri plate culture so as to avoid contamination.

TABLE 21-3 Effect of Light Quality on Moss Spore Germination and the Growth of Protonemata

Prediction:

Week	Observations of Dependent Variables (list them here)
1	
2	
3	
4	
5	
6	
7	
8	

© Cengage Learning 2013

TABLE 21-4 Summary of Results on the Effect of Light Quality on the Germination of Moss Spores and Growth of Protonemata

Color of Light	Results
White	
Blue	
Green	
Red	

Conclusions:

© Cengage Learning 2013

_____ 1. Land plants are believed to have evolved from
   (a) mosses.
   (b) ferns.
   (c) charophytes.
   (d) fungi.

_____ 2. In the bryophytes, the sporophyte is
   (a) the dominant generation.
   (b) dependent on the gametophyte generation.
   (c) able to produce all of its own nutritional requirements.
   (d) both a and c

_____ 3. Liverworts and mosses utilize which of the following pigments for photosynthesis?
   (a) chlorophylls _a_ and _b_
   (b) carotenes
   (c) xanthophylls
   (d) all of the above

_____ 4. Which statement _best_ describes the concept of alternation of generations?
   (a) One generation of plants is skipped every other year.
   (b) There are two phases, a sporophyte and a gametophyte.
   (c) The parental generation alternates with a juvenile generation.
   (d) A green sporophyte phase produces food for a nongreen gametophyte.

_____ 5. Alternation of heteromorphic generations
   (a) is found only in the bryophytes.
   (b) is common to all land plants.
   (c) is typical of most green algae.
   (d) occurs in the liverworts but not mosses.

_____ 6. An organ that is hygroscopic
   (a) is sensitive to changes in moisture.
   (b) is exemplified by the peristomal teeth in the sporophyte of mosses.
   (c) may aid in spore dispersal in mosses.
   (d) is all of the above.

_____ 7. Gemmae function for
   (a) sexual reproduction.
   (b) water retention.
   (c) anchorage of a liverwort thallus to the substrate.
   (d) asexual reproduction.

_____ 8. Sperm find their way to the archegonium
   (a) by swimming.
   (b) due to a chemical gradient diffusing from the archegonium.
   (c) as a result of sucrose being released during the breakdown of the neck canal cells of the archegonium.
   (d) by all of the above.

_____ 9. A protonema
   (a) is part of the sporophyte generation of a moss.
   (b) is the product of spore germination of a moss.
   (c) looks very much like a filamentous brown alga.
   (d) produces the sporophyte when a bud grows from it.

_____ 10. The suffix _-phore_ is derived from a Greek word meaning
   (a) branch.
   (b) moss.
   (c) liverwort.
   (d) male.

EXERCISE 21

Bryophytes—Liverworts and Mosses

Introduction

1. Explain why water must be present for the bryophytes to complete the sexual portion of their life cycle.

2. Green algae are believed to be the ancestors of the bryophytes. Cite four distinct lines of evidence to support this belief.

   (a)

   (b)

   (c)

   (d)

3. Complete this diagram of a "generic" alternation of generations.

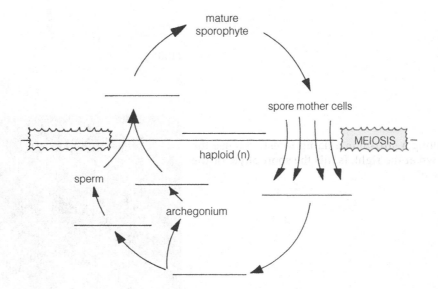

4. Describe in your own words the difference between a sporophyte and a gametophyte.

21.2 Phylum Hepatophyta: Liverworts

5. While the plant shown here is one that you didn't study specifically in lab, you should be able to identify it. Is this the gametophyte or the sporophyte of the plant?

(1×)

6. In what structure does meiosis occur in the bryophytes?

(150×)

21.4 Phylum Bryophyta: Mosses

7. Identify the type of gametangium shown here.

8. Walking along a stream in a damp forest, you see the plants shown at the right. Is this the sporophyte or the gametophyte?

(0.38×)

9. (a) What are the golden stalks seen in this photo?

   (b) Are they the products of meiosis or fertilization?

(0.25×)

10. Identify the plants in the photo at the right as male or female, gametophyte or sporophyte, moss or liverwort.

(0.25×)

Seedless Vascular Plants: Club Mosses and Ferns

OBJECTIVES

After completing this exercise, you will be able to

1. define *tracheophyte, rhizome, mutualism, sporophyte, sporangium, gametophyte, gametangium, antheridium, archegonium, epiphyte, strobilus, node, internode, frond, sorus, annulus, hygroscopic, chemotaxis;*

2. recognize whisk ferns, club mosses, horsetails, and ferns when you see them, placing them in the proper taxonomic phylum;

3. identify the structures of the fern allies and ferns in **boldface**;

4. describe the life cycle of ferns;

5. explain the mechanism by which spore dispersal occurs from a fern sporangium;

6. describe the significant differences between the life cycles of the bryophytes, and the club mosses and ferns.

Introduction

If you did the exercise on liverworts and mosses, you learned about alternation of generations. (If you did not do this exercise, you now need to read the Introduction for Exercise 21, pages 279–280.) Indeed, all plants have alternation of generations. However, a major distinction exists between the bryophytes (liverworts and mosses) and the fern allies, ferns, gymnosperms, and flowering plants: whereas the dominant and conspicuous portion of the life cycle in the bryophytes is the **gametophyte** (the gamete-producing part of the life cycle), in all other plants that you will examine in this and subsequent exercises, it is the **sporophyte** (that portion of the life cycle producing spores).

A second, and perhaps more important, distinction also exists between bryophytes and the fern allies, ferns, gymnosperms, and flowering plants: the latter group contains *vascular tissue*. Vascular tissues include phloem, the tissue that conducts the products of photosynthesis, and *xylem*, the tissue that conducts water and minerals. As a result of the presence of xylem and phloem, fern allies, ferns, gymnosperms, and flowering plants are sometimes called **tracheophytes**.

Push gently on the region of your throat at the base of your larynx (voicebox or Adam's apple). If you move your fingers up and down, you should be able to feel the cartilage rings in your *trachea* (windpipe). To visualize its structure, imagine that your trachea is a pipe with donuts inside of it (Figure 22-1). This same arrangement exists in some cell types within the xylem of plants. Thus, early botanical microscopists called plants having such an arrangement *tracheophytes*.

In this exercise, you will study the tracheophytes that lack seeds. Two phyla of plants make up the seedless vascular plants:

Phylum	Common Names
Lycophyta	Club mosses
Moniliophyta	Whisk ferns, horsetails

Figure 22-1 Three-dimensional representation of the cartilage in your trachea and some xylem cells of vascular plants.

We will study most closely the life cycle of the ferns, since they are common in our environment and have gametophytes and sporophytes that beautifully illustrate the concept of alternation of generations.

Lycopodium and *Selaginella* are the most commonly found genera in the phylum Lycophyta, the club mosses. The common name of this phylum comes from the presence of the so-called **strobilus** (plural, *strobili*), a region of the stem specialized for the production of spores. The strobilus looks like a very small club. Strobili are sometimes called cones.

MATERIALS

Per lab room:

- *Lycopodium*, living, preserved, or herbarium specimens with strobili
- *Lycopodium* gametophyte, preserved (optional)
- *Selaginella*, living, preserved, or herbarium specimens

- *Selaginella lepidophylla,* resurrection plant, two dried specimens
- culture bowl containing water

A. *Lycopodium*

The club moss *Lycopodium* is a small, forest-dwelling plant. These plants are often called ground pines or trailing evergreens. The scientific name comes from the appearance of the rhizome—it looked like a wolf's paw to early botanists. Lycos is Greek for "wolf," and *podium* means "foot."

PROCEDURE

1. Observe the living, preserved, or herbarium specimens of *Lycopodium* (Figure 22-2).
2. On your specimen, identify the true **roots**, **stems**, and **leaves**.
3. The adjective *true* is used to indicate that the organs contain vascular tissue—xylem and phloem.
4. Identify the **rhizome** to which the upright stems are connected. In the case of *Lycopodium*, the rhizome may be either beneath or on the soil surface, depending on the species. Notice that leaves cover the rhizome, as are the upright stems.
5. At the tip of an upright stem, find the **strobilus** (Figure 22-2). Look closely at the strobilus. As you see, it too is made up of leaves, but these leaves are much more tightly aggregated than the sterile (nonreproductive) leaves on the rest of the stem.

strobilus —

Figure 22-2 Sporophyte of *Lycopodium* (0.6×).

The leaves of the strobilus produce *spores* within a *sporangium*, the spore container. As was pointed out in the introduction, the plant you are looking at is a sporophyte.

Is the sporophyte haploid (n) or diploid (2n)? _____

Since the spores are haploid, what process must have taken place within the sporangium?

_____

As maturation occurs, the stem regions between the sporangium-bearing leaves elongate slightly, the sporangium opens, and the spores are carried away from the parent plant by wind. If they land in a suitable habitat, the spores germinate to produce small and inconspicuous subterranean gametophytes, which bear sex organs—antheridia and archegonia. For fertilization and the development of a new sporophyte to take place, free water must be available, since the sperm are flagellated structures that must swim to the archegonium.

6. If available, examine a preserved *Lycopodium* gametophyte (Figure 22-3).

B. *Selaginella*

Selaginella is another genus in the phylum Lycophyta. These plants are usually called spike mosses. (This points out a problem with common names—the common name for the phylum is club mosses, but individual genera have their own common names.) Some species are grown ornamentally for use in terraria.

PROCEDURE

1. Examine living representatives of *Selaginella* (Figure 22-4).
2. Look closely at the tips of the branches and identify the rather inconspicuous strobili.
3. Examine the specimens of the resurrection plant (yet another common name!), a species of *Selaginella* sold as a novelty, often in grocery stores. A native of the southwestern United States, this plant grows in environments that are subjected to long periods without moisture. It becomes dormant during these periods.
4. Describe the color and appearance of the dried specimen.

_____

_____

5. Now place a dried specimen in a culture bowl containing water. Observe what happens in the next hour or so, and describe the change in appearance of the plant.

_____

_____

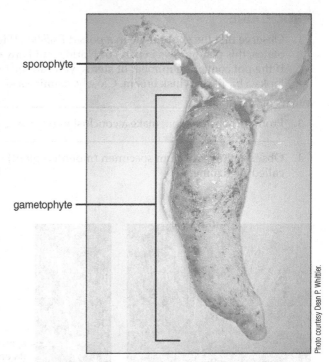

Figure 22-3 Gametophyte with young sporophyte of *Lycopodium* (2×).

(a)

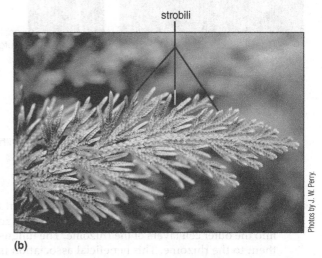

(b)

Figure 22-4 (a) Sporophyte of *Selaginella* (0.4×). (b) Higher magnification showing strobili at branch tips (0.9×).

22.2   Phylum Moniliophyta, Subphylum Psilophyta: Whisk Ferns
(About 15 min.)

The whisk ferns consist of only two genera of plants, *Psilotum* (the *P* is silent) and *Tmesipteris* (the T is silent). Neither has any economic importance, but they have intrigued botanists for a long time, especially because *Psilotum* resembles the first vascular plants that colonized the Earth. Current evidence indicates that the psilophytes are not directly related to those very early land plants, but instead are ferns. We'll examine only *Psilotum*.

MATERIALS

Per lab room:

- *Psilotum*, living plant
- *Psilotum*, herbarium specimen showing sporangia and rhizome

- *Psilotum* gametophyte
- dissecting microscope

PROCEDURE

1. Observe first the **sporophyte** in a potted *Psilotum* (Figure 22-5). Within the natural landscapes of the United States, this plant grows in parts of Florida and Hawaii.
2. If the pot contains a number of stems, you can see how it got its common name, the whisk fern, because it looks a bit like a whisk broom. Closely examine a single aerial stem.

What color is it? _____

3. From this observation, make a conclusion regarding one function of this stem.

_____

4. Observe the herbarium specimen (mounted plant) of *Psilotum*. Identify the nongreen underground stem, called a **rhizome**.

(a) (b) (c)

Photos by J. W. Perry.

Figure 22-5 Sporophytes of *Psilotum*. (**a**) Single stem without sporangia. (**b**) Portion of stem with sporangia (0.3×). (**c**) Sporangia (10×).

5. *Psilotum* is unique among vascular plants in that it lacks roots. Absorption of water and minerals takes place through small rhizoids attached to the rhizome. Additionally, a fungus surrounds and penetrates into the outer cell layers of the rhizome. The fungus absorbs water and minerals from the soil and transfers them to the rhizome. This beneficial association is similar to the mycorrhizal association between plant roots and fungi described in the fungi exercise (page 366). A beneficial relationship like that between the fungus and *Psilotum* is called a **mutualistic symbiosis** or, more simply, **mutualism**.
6. On either the herbarium specimen or the living plant, identify the tiny scalelike outgrowths that are found on the aerial stems. Because these lack vascular tissue, they are not considered true leaves. Their size precludes any major role in photosynthesis.
7. The plant you are observing is a sporophyte. Thus, it must produce spores. Find the three-lobed structures on the stem (Figure 22-5b). Each lobe is a single **sporangium** containing spores.
8. If these spores germinate after being shed from the sporangium, they produce a small and infrequently found gametophyte that grows beneath the soil surface. The gametophyte survives beneath the soil thanks to a symbiotic relationship similar to that of the sporophyte's rhizome.
9. If a gametophyte is available, observe it with the aid of a dissecting microscope (Figure 22-16). Note the numerous **rhizoids**. If you look very carefully, you may be able to distinguish **gametangia** (sex organs; singular, *gametangium*).
10. The male sex organs are **antheridia** (Figure 22-6b; singular, *antheridium*); the female sex organs are **archegonia** (singular, *archegonium*). Both antheridia and archegonia are on the same gametophyte.
11. Fertilization of an egg within an archegonium results in the production of a new sporophyte.

(a)

rhizoid

rhizoid   antheridium

(b)

Photos by J. W. Perry.

Figure 22-6 (**a**) *Psilotum* gametophyte (7.5×). (**b**) Higher magnification showing antheridia (23×).

22.3 Phylum Moniliophyta, Subphylum Sphenophyta: Horsetails
(About 15 min.)

During the age of the dinosaurs, tree-sized representatives of this phylum flourished. But like the dinosaurs, they too became extinct. Only one genus remains. However, the remnants of these plants, along with others that were growing at that time, remain in the form of massive coal deposits. *Speno-*, a Greek prefix meaning *"wedge,"* gives the phylum its name, presumably because the leaves of these plants are wedge shaped.

A single genus, *Equisetum*, is the only living representative of this subphylum. Different species of *Equisetum* are common throughout North America. Many are highly branched, giving the appearance of a horse's tail, and hence the common name. (Equus is Latin for "horse"; *saeta* means "bristle.") Horsetails are very unlike what we often think of as ferns, but molecular evidence confirms their relationship to more typical ferns.

MATERIALS

Per lab room:
- *Equisetum*, living, preserved, or herbarium specimens with strobili
- *Equisetum* gametophytes, living or preserved

PROCEDURE

1. Examine the available specimens of *Equisetum* (Figure 22-7). Depending on the species, it will be more or less branched.
2. Note that the plant is divided into **nodes** (places on the stem where the leaves arise) and **internodes** (regions on the stem between nodes). Identify the small leaves at the node.

If the specimen you are examining is a highly branched species, don't confuse the branches with leaves. The leaves are small, scale-like structures, often brown. (They *do* have vascular tissue, so they are true leaves.) Identify the leaves.

3. Look at the herbarium mount and identify the underground **rhizome** that bears **roots**.
4. Examine both the aerial stem and rhizome closely.

Do both have nodes? _____

Do both have leaves? _____

Which portion of *Equisetum* is primarily concerned with photosynthesis? _____

strobilius

leaves
at node

branches

Photo by J. W. Perry.

Figure 22-7 Sporophyte of the horsetail, *Equisetum* (0.2×).

5. Find the **strobilus** (Figure 22-7). Where on the plant is it located? _____

Based on the knowledge you've acquired in your study of *Lycopodium,* what would you expect to find within the strobilus? _____

When spores fall to the ground, what would you expect them to grow into after germination? _____

6. Now observe the horsetail gametophytes (Figure 22-8).

What color are they? _____

Would you expect them to be found on or below the soil surface? Why?

_____

_____

Figure 22-8 Horsetail gametophyte (5×).

22.4 Phylum Moniliophyta, Subphylum Pterophyta: Ferns *(About 60 min.)*

The variation in form of ferns is enormous, as is their distribution and ecology. We typically think of ferns as inhabitants of moist environments, but some species are also found in very dry locations. Tropical species are often grown as houseplants.

This subphylum gets its name from the Greek word pteri, meaning "fern."

MATERIALS

Per student:

- fern sporophytes, fresh, preserved, or herbarium specimens
- prepared slide of fern rhizome, c.s.
- fern gametophytes, living, preserved, or whole mount prepared slides
- fern gametophyte with young sporophyte, living or preserved
- microscope slide

- compound microscope
- dissecting microscope

Per lab room:

- squares of fern sori, in moist chamber (*Polypodium aureum* recommended)
- demonstration slide of fern archegonium, median l.s.
- other fern sporophytes, as available

PROCEDURE

1. Obtain a fresh or herbarium specimen of a typical fern **sporophyte**. As you examine the structures described in this experiment, refer to Figure 22-16, a diagram of the life cycle of a fern.

The sporophyte of many ferns (Figures 22-9, 22-16a) consists of true roots, stems, and leaves; that is, they contain vascular tissue.

2. Identify the horizontal stem, the **rhizome** (which produces true **roots**), and upright leaves. The leaves of ferns are called **fronds** and are often highly divided.

Ferns, unlike bryophytes, are vascular plants, their sporophytes containing xylem and phloem. Let's examine this vascular tissue.

3. Obtain a prepared slide of a cross section of a fern stem (rhizome). Study it using the low-power objective of your compound microscope. Use Figure 22-10 as a reference.
  (a) Find the epidermis, cortex, and vascular tissue.
  (b) Within the vascular tissue, distinguish between the **phloem** (of which there are outer and inner layers) and the thick-walled **xylem** sandwiched between the phloem layers.
4. Now examine the undersurface of the frond. Locate the dotlike **sori** (singular, *sorus*; Figure 22-9).
5. Each sorus is a cluster of sporangia. Using a dissecting microscope, study an individual sorus. Identify the sporangia (Figures 22-11, 22-16b).

Each sporangium contains spores (Figure 22-16c). Although the sporangium is part of the diploid (sporophytic) generation, spores are the first cells of the haploid (gametophytic) generation.

What process occurred within the sporangium to produce the haploid spores?

(a)   (b)

Figure 22-9 (a) Morphology of a typical fern (0.25×). (b) Enlargement showing the sori (0.5×).

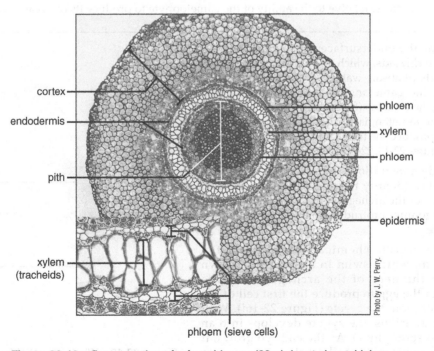

Figure 22-10 Cross section of a fern rhizome (29×). Inset shows higher magnification of vascular tissue (80×).

6. Obtain a single sorus-containing square of the hare's foot fern (*Polypodium aureum*).

   (a) Place it sorus-side up on a glass slide (DON'T ADD A COVERSLIP), and examine it with the low-power objective of your compound microscope.

   (b) Note the row of brown, thick-walled cells running over the top of the sporangium, the **annulus** (Figures 22-11, 22-16b).

The annulus is **hygroscopic**, meaning changes in moisture content within the cells of the annulus cause them to change shape, causing the sporangium to crack open. Watch what happens as the sporangium dries out.

As the water evaporates from the cells of the annulus, a tension develops that pulls the sporangium

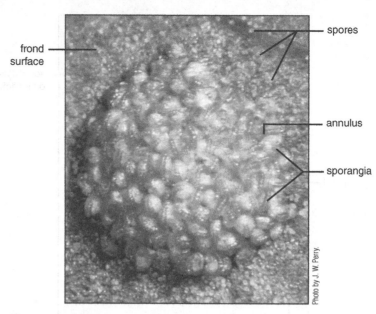

Figure 22-11 Sorus containing sporangia (30×).

apart. Separation of the halves of the sporangium begins at the thin-walled *lip cells*. As the water continues to evaporate, the annulus pulls back the top half of the sporangium, exposing the spores. The sporangium continues to be pulled back until the tension on the water molecules within the annulus exceeds the strength of the hydrogen bonds holding the water molecules together. When this happens, the top half of the sporangium flies forward, throwing the spores out. The fern sporangium is a biological catapult!

If spores land in a suitable environment, one that is generally moist and shaded, they germinate (Figures 22-16d and e), eventually growing into the heart-shaped adult gametophyte (22-16f).

7. Using your dissecting microscope, examine a living, preserved, or prepared slide whole mount of the gametophyte (Figures 22-12, 22-16f).

What color is the gametophyte? _____

What does the color indicate relative to the ability of the gametophyte to produce its own carbohydrates?

_____

   (a) Examine the undersurface of the gametophyte. Find the **rhizoids**, which anchor the gametophyte and perhaps absorb water.

   (b) Locate the gametangia (sex organs) clustered among the rhizoids (Figure 22-16f). There are two types of gametangia: **antheridia** (Figure 22-16g), which produce the flagellated *sperm*, and **archegonia** (Figures 22-13, 22-16h), which produce *egg cells*.

8. Study the demonstration slide of an archegonium (Figure 22-14). Identify the **egg** within the swollen basal portion of the archegonium. Note that the neck of the archegonium protrudes from the surface of the gametophyte.

The archegonia secrete chemicals that attract the flagellated sperm, which swim in a water film down a canal within the neck of the archegonium. One sperm fuses with the egg to produce the first cell of the sporophyte generation, the *zygote* (Figure 22-16i). With subsequent cell divisions, the zygote develops into an embryo (embryo sporophyte). As the embryo grows, it pushes out of the gametophyte and develops into a young sporophyte (Figure 22-16j).

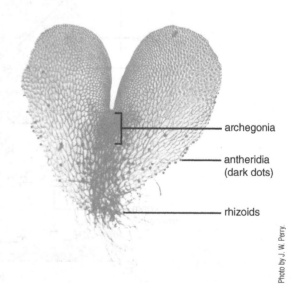

Figure 22-12 Whole mount of fern gametophyte, undersurface (10×).

9. Obtain a specimen of a young sporophyte that is attached to the gametophyte (Figures 22-15, 22-16j). Identify the **gametophyte** and then the *primary leaf* and *primary root* of the young sporophyte. As the sporophyte continues to develop, the gametophyte withers away.
10. Examine any other specimens of ferns that may be on demonstration, noting the incredible diversity in form. Look for sori on each specimen.

Figure 22-13 Gametangia (antheridia and archegonia) on undersurface of fern gametophyte (57×).

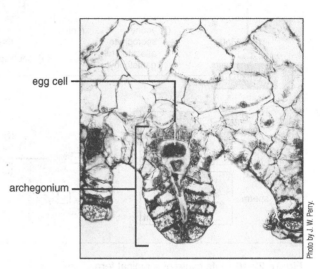

Figure 22-14 Longitudinal section of a fern archegonium (218×).

Figure 22-15 Fern gametophyte with attached sporophyte (12×).

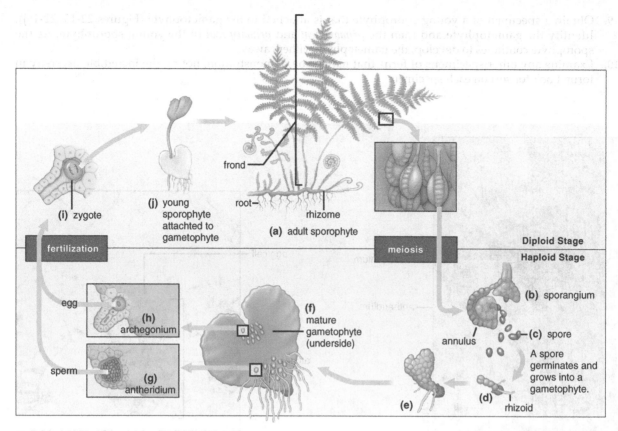

Figure 22-16   Life cycle of a typical fern.

22.5   Experiment: Fern Sperm Chemotaxis *(About 60 min.)*

Chemotaxis is a movement in response to a chemical gradient. This is an important biological process as it allows organisms to find their way or locate things. A dog following a scent is a common example of chemotaxis. How does a sperm cell shed from an antheridium find an archegonium-containing egg cell? The archegonium secretes a sperm-attracting chemical. The farther away the sperm from the archegonium, the more dilute the chemical. The sperm swim up the chemical concentration gradient, right to the egg cell.

In this experiment, you will determine whether certain chemical substances evoke a chemotactic response by fern sperm. This experiment addresses the hypothesis that *some chemicals will attract sperm more strongly and for greater duration than others.*

MATERIALS

Per experimental group (pair of students):

- sharpened toothpicks
- test solutions
- dissecting needle

- depression slide
- dissecting microscope
- petri dish culture containing *C-Fern*™ gametophytes

PROCEDURE

Work in pairs.

1. Obtain six wooden toothpicks whose tips have been sharpened to a fine point.

> **CAUTION**
>
> Do not touch the sharpened end with your fingers!

2. To identify the toothpicks, place one to five small dots along the side of the toothpicks near the unsharpened end so that each toothpick has a unique marking (one dot, two dots, and so on). One toothpick remains unmarked.

3. Dip the sharpened end of the toothpick with one dot into test solution 1. Insert it with the sharpened end up in the foam block toothpick holder.

4. Repeat step 3 with the four remaining toothpicks and four other test solutions. Leave the unmarked toothpick dry.

Which toothpick serves as the control? _____

5. Obtain a depression slide and pipet one drop of Sperm Release Buffer (SRB) into the depression.

6. Obtain a 12- to 18-day-old culture of *C-Fern*™ gametophytes. Remove the cover, place it on the stage of a dissecting microscope, and observe the gametophytes using transmitted light. (See Exercise 3, pages 28 and 35, if you need to learn how to choose transmitted light.)

7. Identify the two types of gametophytes present—the smaller thumb-shaped male gametophytes that have many bumps on them and the larger, heart-shaped bisexual gametophytes (Figure 22-17).

8. Using a dissecting needle, pick up 7–10 male gametophytes and place them into the SRB in the depression slide well. They don't need to be completely submerged.

9. Place the petri dish cover on the stage of the dissecting microscope, edges up, and then place the gametophyte-containing depression slide on the cover. (This keeps the gametophytes cooler, particularly important if your dissecting microscope has an incandescent light.) Adjust the magnification so it is at least 12×.

10. Within 5 minutes, you should be able to observe sperm being released from the antheridia.

11. Wait another 5 minutes to ensure that a sufficient number of sperm have been released, and then begin testing for chemotactic response by following steps 12–15.

12. While using 1220× magnification, focus on the TOP surface of the sperm suspension droplet in an area devoid of male gametophytes.

13. Remove one test toothpick from the block and, while looking through the oculars of the dissecting microscope, gently and briefly touch the sharpened end of the toothpick to the surface of the drop (Figure 22-18).

14. Observe whether any chemotactic response takes place. Record your observation in Table 22-1.

15. Repeat the procedure with the remaining toothpicks, stirring the sperm suspension (if necessary) with a dissecting needle after each test to redistribute the sperm.

16. Place your data on the lab chalk or marker board. Your instructor will pool the data for all experimental groups.

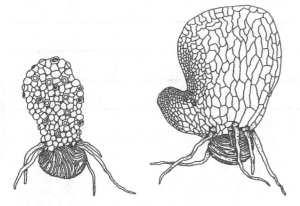

Figure 22-17 Mature male (left) and bisexual (right) *C-Fern*™ gametophytes.

Figure 22-18 Method for applying test substances. Proper technique is important. Gently and briefly touch the end of the toothpick to the surface of the sperm suspension. *Note:* The size of the drop of suspension is exaggerated to show detail.

17. Make a conclusion about the chemotactic properties of the various chemical test substances, and note it in Table 22-1.

Examine the chemical structures of each test solution (Figure 22-19). Relate the biological (chemotactic) response you observed to any of the chemical structural differences of the test substances. _____

_____

_____

What is the advantage to using the pooled data to draw your conclusion? _____

_____

_____

What do you hypothesize the naturally occurring chemical produced by mature archegonia to be? _____

_____

_____

COOH CH₂ CH₂ COOH	COOH HO—CH₂ CH₂ COOH	COOH HC—OH CH₂ COOH
1 succinic acid	2 L-malic acid	3 D-malic acid

4 fumaric acid   5 maleic acid

Figure 22-19   Chemical structures of test substance.

TABLE 22-1	My Data: Chemotactic Response of *C-Fern*™ Sperm

Prediction:

	Swarming Response[b]			
	Intensity (low, medium, high)		Duration (short, medium, long)	
Test Substance[a]	My Data	Pooled Data	My Data	Pooled Data
0				
1				
2				
3				
4				
5				

Conclusion:

[a]Identified by number of dots on toothpick.

[b]Quantify the response by using the symbols (0) for no response, (–) if the sperm move away from the test site, and (+, ++, +++) for varying degrees of attraction to the test site.

_____ 1. The sporophyte is the dominant and conspicuous generation in
   (a) the fern allies and ferns.
   (b) gymnosperms.
   (c) flowering plants.
   (d) all of the above

_____ 2. A tracheophyte is a plant that has
   (a) xylem and phloem.
   (b) a windpipe.
   (c) a trachea.
   (d) the gametophyte as its dominant generation.

_____ 3. *Psilotum* lacks
   (a) roots.
   (b) a mechanism to take up water and minerals.
   (c) vascular tissue.
   (d) alternation of generations.

_____ 4. Spore germination followed by cell divisions results in the production of
   (a) a sporophyte.
   (b) an antheridium.
   (c) a zygote.
   (d) a gametophyte.

_____ 5. Which phrase *best* describes a plant that is an epiphyte?
   (a) a plant that grows upon another plant
   (b) a parasite
   (c) a plant with the gametophyte generation dominant and conspicuous
   (d) a plant that has a mutually beneficial relationship with another plant

_____ 6. Club mosses
   (a) are placed in the subphylum Pterophyta.
   (b) are so-called because of the social nature of the plants.
   (c) do not produce gametophytes.
   (d) are so called because most produce strobili.

_____ 7. The resurrection plant
   (a) is a species of *Selaginella*.
   (b) grows in the desert Southwest of the United States.
   (c) is a member of the phylum Lycophyta.
   (d) all of the above

_____ 8. Which statement is **not** true?
   (a) Nodes are present on horsetails.
   (b) The rhizome on horsetails bears roots.
   (c) The internode of a horsetail is the region where the leaves are attached.
   (d) Horsetails are members of the subphylum Sphenophyta.

_____ 9. In ferns,
   (a) xylem and phloem are present in the sporophyte.
   (b) the sporophyte is the dominant generation.
   (c) the leaf is called a frond.
   (d) all of the above are true.

_____ 10. The spores of a fern are
   (a) produced by mitosis within the sporangium.
   (b) diploid cells.
   (c) the first cells of the gametophyte generation.
   (d) both a and b

EXERCISE **22**

Seedless Vascular Plants: Club Mosses and Ferns

Post-Lab Questions

Introduction

1. List two features that distinguish the seedless vascular plants from the bryophytes.
   (a)

   (b)

2. After consulting a biological or scientific dictionary, explain the derivation from the Greek of the word *symbiosis*.

22.1 Phylum Lycophyta: Club Mosses

3. Both *Lycopodium* and *Equisetum* have strobili, roots, and rhizomes. What did you learn in this exercise that enables you to distinguish these two plants?

4. Examine the photo at the right.
   (a) Give the genus of this plant.

   _____

   (b) Label the structure indicated.

5. Some species of *Lycopodium* produce gametophytes that grow beneath the surface of the soil, while others grow on the soil surface. Basing your answer on what you've learned from other plants in this exercise, predict how each respective type of *Lycopodium* gametophyte might obtain its nutritional needs.

(0.3×)

22.2 Phylum Moniliophyta, Subphylum Psilophyta: Whisk Ferns

6. Using a biological or scientific dictionary, or a reference in your textbook, determine the meaning of the root word *psilo*, and relate it to the appearance of *Psilotum*.

22.3 Phylum Moniliophyta, Subphylum Sphenophyta: Horsetails

7. Examine the photo on the right. You studied this genus in lab, but this is a different species. This species has two separate stems produced at different times in the growing season. The stem on the left is a reproductive branch, while that on the right is strictly vegetative. Based on the characteristics obvious in this photo, identify the plant, give its scientific name, and then identify the labeled structures.

   Scientific name _____

   A. _____

   B. _____

   C. _____

8. Explain the distinction between a node and an internode.

(0.75×)

22.4 Phylum Moniliophyta, Subphylum Pterophyta: Ferns

9. While rock climbing, you encounter the plant shown in the photo on the right growing out of a crevice.

   (a) Is this the sporophyte or the gametophyte?

   (b) What special name is given to the leaf of this plant?

(0.5×)

10. The environments in which ferns grow range from standing water to very dry areas. Nonetheless, all ferns are dependent upon free water in order to complete their life cycles. Explain why this is the case.

Seed Plants I: Gymnosperms

OBJECTIVES

After completing this exercise, you will be able to

1. define *gymnosperm, pulp, heterosporous, homosporous, pollination, fertilization, dioecious, monoecious;*

2. describe the characteristics that distinguish seed plants from other vascular plants;

3. produce a cycle diagram of heterosporous alternation of generations;

4. list human uses for conifers;

5. recognize the structures in **boldface** and describe the life cycle of a pine;

6. distinguish between a male and a female pine cone;

7. describe the method by which pollination occurs in pines;

8. describe the process of fertilization in pines;

9. recognize members of the four phyla: Coniferophyta, Cycadophyta, Ginkgophyta, and Gnetophyta.

Introduction

The development of the seed was a significant event in the evolution of vascular plants. Seeds have remarkable ability to survive under adverse conditions, a reason for the dominance of seed plants in today's flora.

Let's examine the characteristics of seeds and seed plants.

1. All seed plants produce **pollen grains**. Pollen grains are carriers for sperm, delivering the sperm to the egg-bearing female gametophyte. As a benefit of pollen production, the sperm of seed plants do *not* need free water to swim to the egg. Thus, seed plants can reproduce in harsh climates where nonseed plants are much less successful.

2. Seeds have some type of **stored food** for the embryo to use as it emerges from the seed during germination. (The sole exception is orchid seeds, which rely on symbiotic association with a fungus to obtain nutrients.)

3. All seeds have a **seed coat**, a protective covering enclosing the embryo and its stored food.

A seed coat and stored food are particularly important for survival. An embryo within a seed is protected from an inhospitable environment. Consider a seed produced during a severe drought. Water is necessary for the embryo to grow. If none is available, the seed can remain dormant until growing conditions are favorable. When germination occurs, a ready food source is present to get things underway, providing nutrients until the developing plant can produce its own carbohydrates by photosynthesis.

4. Like the bryophytes, fern allies, and ferns, seed plants exhibit **alternation of generations**.

5. All seed plants are **heterosporous**; that is, they produce *two* types of spores. Bryophytes and most fern allies and ferns are **homosporous**, producing only *one* spore type.

Examine Figure 23-1, a diagram of the heterosporous alternation of generations.

Gymnosperms are one of two groups of seed plants. *Gymnosperm* translates literally as "naked seed," referring to the production of seeds on the *surface* of reproductive structures. This contrasts with the situation in the angiosperms (see Exercise 24), whose seeds are contained within a fruit.

The general assemblage of plants known as gymnosperms contains plants in four separate phyla:

Phylum	Common Names
Coniferophyta	Conifers
Cycadophyta	Cycads
Ginkgophyta	Ginkgos
Gnetophyta	Gnetophytes or vessel-containing gymnosperms

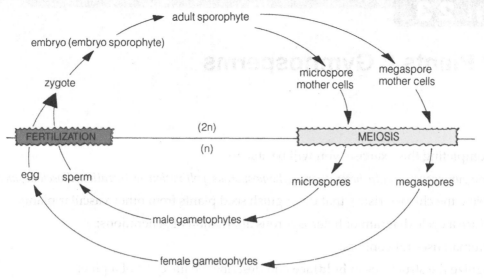

Figure 23-1 Heterosporous alternation of generations.

23.1   Phylum Coniferophyta: Conifers *(About 90 min.)*

By far the most commonly recognized gymnosperms are the conifers. Among the conifers, perhaps the most common is the pine (*Pinus*). Many people think of conifers and pines as one and the same. However, while all members of the genus *Pinus* are conifers, not all conifers are pines. Examples of other conifers include spruce (*Picea*), fir (*Abies*), and even some trees that lose their leaves in the fall such as larch (*Larix*).

The conifers are very important economically, because their wood is used in building construction. Millions of hectares (1 hectare = 2.47 acres) are devoted to growing conifers for this purpose, not to mention the numerous plantations that grow Christmas trees. In many areas conifers are used for **pulp**, the moistened cell wall–derived cellulose used to manufacture paper.

The structures and events associated with reproduction in pine (*Pinus*) will be studied here as a representative conifer.

MATERIALS

Per student:

- cluster of male cones
- prepared slide of male strobilus, l.s., with microspores
- young female cone
- prepared slide of female strobilus, l.s., with megaspore mother cell
- prepared slide of pine seed, l.s.
- compound microscope
- dissecting microscope
- single-edged razor blade

Per student group (table):

- young sporophyte, living or herbarium specimen

Per lab room:

- demonstration slide of female strobilus with archegonium
- demonstration slide of fertilization
- pine seeds, soaking in water
- pine seedlings, 12 weeks old
- pine seedlings, 36 weeks old

PROCEDURE

As you do this activity, examine Figure 23-12, representing the life cycle of a pine tree. To refresh your memory, look at a specimen of a small pine tree. This is the adult **sporophyte** (Figure 23-12a). Identify the stem and leaves. You probably know the main stem of a woody plant as the trunk. The leaves of conifers are often called needles because most are shaped like needles.

A. Male Reproductive Structures and Events

1. Obtain a cluster of **male cones** (Figures 23-2, 23-12b). The function of male cones is to produce **pollen**; consequently, male cones are typically produced at the ends of branches, where the wind currents can catch the pollen as it is being shed.

Figure 23-2 Cluster of male cones shedding pollen (0.75×).

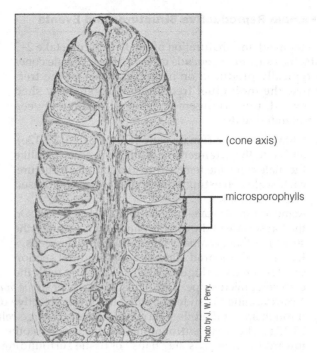

(cone axis)

microsporophylls

Figure 23-3 Male pine cone, l.s. (12×).

2. Note all the tiny scalelike structures that make up the male cones. These are *microsporophylls*.

Translated literally, a sporophyll would be a "spore-bearing leaf." The prefix *micro-* refers to "small." But the literal interpretation "small, spore-bearing leaf" does not convey the full definition; biologists use *microsporophyll* to mean a leaf that produces *male* spores, called *microspores*. These develop into winged, immature male *gametophytes* called **pollen grains**. (Why they are immature is a logical question. The male gametophyte is not mature until it produces sperm.)

3. Remove a single microsporophyll and examine its lower surface with a dissecting microscope. Identify the two **microsporangia**, also called **pollen sacs** (Figure 23-12c).
4. Study a prepared slide of a longitudinal section of a male cone (also called a male *strobilus*), first with a dissecting microscope to gain an impression of the cone's overall organization and then with the low-power objective of your compound microscope. Identify the *cone axis* bearing numerous **microsporophylls** (Figures 23-3).
5. Switch to the medium-power objective to observe a single microsporophyll more closely. Note that it contains a cavity; this is the **microsporangium** (also called a *pollen sac*), which contains numerous *pollen grains*.

As the male cone grows, several events occur in the microsporophylls that lead to the production of pollen grains. Microspore mother cells within the microsporangia undergo meiosis to form *microspores*. Cell division within the microspore wall and subsequent differentiation result in the formation of the pollen grain.

6. Examine a single **pollen grain** with the high-dry objective (Figures 23-4, 23-12d). Identify the earlike *wings* on either side of the body.
7. Identify the four cells that make up the body: the two most obvious are the **tube cell** and smaller **generative cell**. (The nucleus of the tube cell is almost as large as the entire generative cell.) Note that this male gametophyte is made up of only four cells!

In conifers, **pollination**, the transfer of pollen from the male cone to the female cone, is accomplished by wind and occurs during spring. Pollen grains are caught in a sticky *pollination droplet* produced by the female cone.

wing   tube cell   generative cell

Figure 23-4 Pine pollen grains (400×).

B. Female Reproductive Structures and Events

Development and maturation of the female cone take 2–3 years; the exact time depends on the species. Female cones are typically produced on higher branches of the tree. Because the individual tree's pollen is generally shed downward, this arrangement favors crossing between *different* individuals.

1. Obtain a young **female cone** (Figures 23-5, 23-12e), and note the arrangement of the cone scales. Unlike the male cone, the female cone is a complex structure, each scale consisting of an **ovuliferous** scale fused atop a *sterile bract.*
2. Remove a single scale-bract complex (Figure 23-12f). On the top surface of the complex find the two **ovules**, the structures that eventually will develop into the **seeds**.
3. Examine a prepared slide of a longitudinal section of a female cone (Figures 23-6, 23-12g) first with the

Figure 23-5 Female cones of pine (1×).

dissecting microscope. Distinguish the smaller *sterile bract* from the *ovuliferous scale.*

4. Now examine the slide with the low-power objective of your compound microscope. Look for a section through an ovuliferous scale containing a very large cell; this is the **megaspore mother cell** (Figures 23-7, 23-12g). The tissue surrounding the megaspore mother cell is the **megasporangium.** Protruding inward toward the cone axis are "flaps" of tissue surrounding the megasporangium, the **integument.** Find the integuments and the opening between them, the **micropyle.**

Figure 23-6 Female pine cone, l.s. (5×).

ovuliferous scale

ovule

sterile bract

integument megaspore mother cell

ovuliferous scale

microphyte megasporangium (sterile bract)

Figure 23-7 Portion of female cone showing megaspore mother cell (75×).

Think for a moment about the three-dimensional nature of the ovule: it's much like a short vase lying on its side on the ovuliferous scale. The neck of the vase is the integument, the opening of the micropyle. The integument extends around the base of the vase. If you poured liquid rubber inside the base of a vase, suspended a marble in the middle, and allowed the rubber to harden, you'd have a model of the megasporangium and the megaspore mother cell. Figure 23-8 gives you an idea of the three-dimensional structure.

The megaspore mother cell undergoes meiosis to produce four haploid *megaspores* (Figure 23-12h), but only one survives; the other three degenerate. The functional megaspore repeatedly divides mitotically to produce the multicellular **female gametophyte** (Figure 23-12i). At the same time, the female cone is continually increasing in size to accommodate the developing female gametophytes. (Remember, there are numerous ovuliferous scale/sterile bract complexes on each cone.)

The female gametophyte of pine is produced _____ (within *or* outside of) the megasporangium.

5. Examine the demonstration slide of **archegonia** (Figures 23-9, 23-12i) that have developed within the female gametophyte. Identify the single large **egg cell** that fills the entire archegonium. (The nucleus of the egg cell may be visible as well. The other generally spherical structures are protein bodies within the egg.)

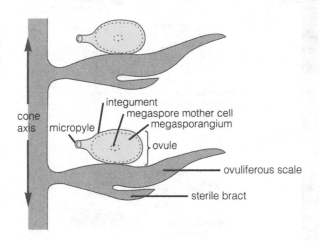

Figure 23-8 Ovule and ovuliferous scale/sterile bract complex.

Figure 23-9 Pine ovule with female gametophyte and archegonia, l.s. (12×).

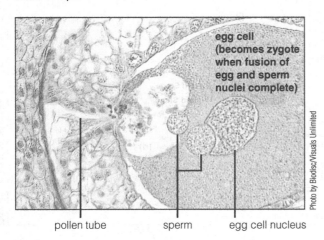

Figure 23-10 Fertilization in pine, l.s. (175×).

Recall that the pollen grains produced within male cones are caught in a sticky pollination droplet produced by the female cone. As the pollination droplet dries, the pollen grain is drawn through the micropyle and into a cavity called the *pollen chamber*.

Fertilization—the fusion of egg and sperm—occurs after the *pollen tube*, an outgrowth of the pollen grain's tube cell, penetrates the megasporangium and enters the archegonium. The generative cell of the pollen grain has divided to produce two sperm, one of which fuses with the egg. (The second sperm nucleus degenerates.)

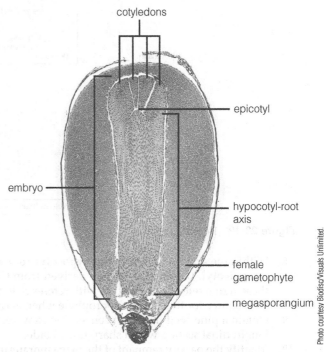

Figure 23-11 Pine seed, l.s. (24×).

6. Examine the demonstration slide of fertilization in *Pinus*. Identify the **zygote**, the product of fusion of egg and sperm (Figures 23-10, 23-12j).

After fertilization, numerous mitotic divisions of the zygote take place producing an **embryo** (*embryo sporophyte*). Fertilization also triggers changes in the integument, causing it to harden and become the seed coat.

7. With the low-power objective of your compound microscope, study a prepared slide of a longitudinal section through a pine seed (Figures 23-11, 23-12k). Starting from the outside, identify the **seed coat**, **megasporangium** (a very thin, papery remnant), the female gametophyte, and **embryo** (embryo sporophyte).

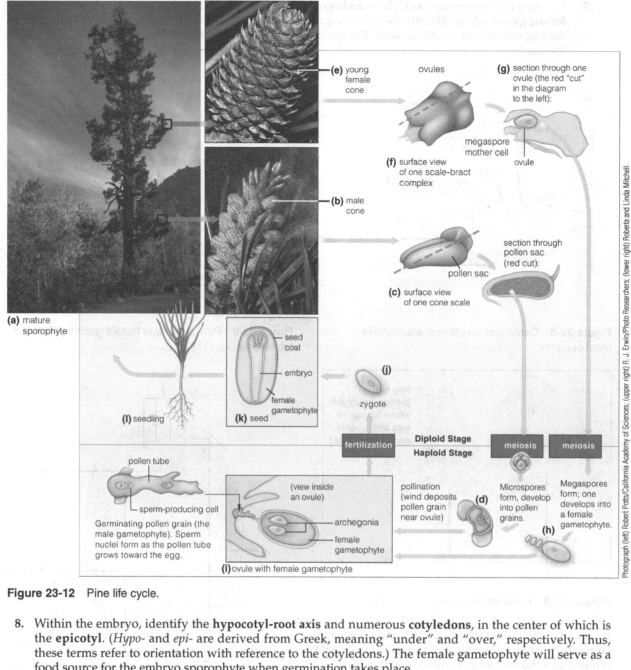

Figure 23-12 Pine life cycle.

8. Within the embryo, identify the **hypocotyl-root axis** and numerous **cotyledons**, in the center of which is the **epicotyl**. (*Hypo*- and *epi*- are derived from Greek, meaning "under" and "over," respectively. Thus, these terms refer to orientation with reference to the cotyledons.) The female gametophyte will serve as a food source for the embryo sporophyte when germination takes place.

9. Obtain a pine seed that has been soaked in water to soften the seed coat. Remove it and make a freehand longitudinal section with a sharp razor blade.

10. Identify the papery remnant of the **megasporangium**, the white **female gametophyte**, and **embryo** (embryo sporophyte).

How many cotyledons are present? _____

11. Examine the culture of pine seeds that were planted in sand 12 weeks ago. Note the germinating seeds (Figure 23-12l).

12. Identify the **hypocotyl-root axis, cotyledons, female gametophyte,** and **seed coat**.

The cotyledons serve two functions. One is to absorb the nutrients stored in the female gametophyte during germination. As the cotyledons are exposed to light, they turn green. What then is the second function of the cotyledons?

_____

_____

_____

13. Finally, examine the 36-week-old sporophyte seedlings. Notice that the cotyledons eventually wither away as the epicotyl produces new leaves.

During the age of the dinosaurs (240 million years ago), cycads were extremely abundant in the flora. In fact, botanists often call this "the age of the cycads."

Zamia and *Cycas* are two cycads most readily available in North America. In nature, these two species are limited to the subtropical regions.

They're often planted as ornamentals in Florida, Gulf Coast states, and California.

All cycads have separate male and female plants, unlike pine.

The female cones of some other genera become extremely large, weighing as much as 30 kg!

MATERIALS

Per lab room:

▪ demonstration specimens of *Zamia* and/or *Cycas*

PROCEDURE

1. Examine the demonstration specimen of *Zamia* and/or *Cycas* (Figure 23-13). Both have the common name *cycad*. Do these plants resemble any of the conifers you know? _____

_____

2. Notice the leaves of the cycads. They more closely resemble the leaves of the ferns than those of the conifers.

(a)

(b)

Figure 23-13   Two cycad species. (**a**) *Cycas* (0.01×). (**b**) *Zamia* (0.1×).

A single species of this phylum is all that remains of what was once a much more diverse assemblage of plants. *Ginkgo biloba* is sometimes called a living fossil because it has changed little in the last 80 million years. In fact, at one time it was believed to be extinct; the Western world knew it from the fossil record before living trees were discovered in Buddhist temple courtyards of remote China. Today *Ginkgo* is a highly prized ornamental tree that is commonly planted in our urban areas. The tree has a reputation for being resistant to most insect pests and atmospheric pollution. The seeds are ground up and sold as a memory-enhancing dietary supplement, although the supplement's ability to do that is in dispute.

MATERIALS

Per lab room:

▪ demonstration specimen of *Ginkgo* (living plant or herbarium specimen)

PROCEDURE

1. Examine the demonstration specimen of *Ginkgo biloba,* the maidenhair tree (Figure 23-14a)
2. Note the fan-shaped leaves (Figure 23-14b).

(a) (b)

Photos by J. W. Perry.

Figure 23-14 *Ginkgo.* **(a)** Tree. **(b)** Branch with leaves (0.5×).

23.4 Phylum Gnetophyta: Gnetophytes (Vessel-Containing Gymnosperms)
(About 10 min.)

The gnetophytes are a small assemblage of plants that have several characteristics found only in the flowering plants (angiosperms). Their reproductive structures look much more like flowers than cones. "Double fertilization" (pages 330 and 343), a feature thought to be unique to the flowering plants, has been reported in one gnetophyte species. And the water-conducting xylem tissue contains vessels in all species. Consequently, many scientists now believe these plants are very closely related to the flowering plants. Most species are found in desert or arid regions of the world. In the desert Southwest of the United States, *Ephedra* is a common shrub known as Mormon tea, because its stems were once harvested by Mormon settlers in Utah and used to make a tea.

MATERIALS

Per lab room:

■ demonstration specimen of *Ephedra* and/or *Gnetum* (living plant or herbarium specimen)

PROCEDURE

1. Examine the demonstration specimen of *Ephedra* (Figure 23-15).
2. A second representative gnetophyte is the genus *Gnetum* (pronounced "neat-um"). A few North American college and university greenhouses—and some tropical gardens—keep these specimens. *Gnetum* is native to Brazil, tropical west Africa, India, and Southeast Asia. Different species vary in form from vines to trees (Figures 23-16a, b). Examine the living specimen if one is on display, noting particularly the broad, flat leaves (Figure 23-16c).

(a)   (b)

Figure 23-15 *Ephedra.* (**a**) Several plants (1×). (**b**) Close-up of stems
(0.5×).

(a)   (b)   (c)

Figure 23-16 *Gnetum.* (**a**) A species that is a vine (0.02×). (**b**) A species that is a tree (0.02×). (**c**) Leaves
(0.38×).

_____ **1.** Which statement is *not* true about conifers?
  (a) Conifers are gymnosperms.
  (b) All conifers belong to the genus *Pinus*.
  (c) All conifers have naked seeds.
  (d) Conifers are heterosporous.

_____ **2.** Seed plants
  (a) have alternation of generations.
  (b) are heterosporous.
  (c) develop a seed coat.
  (d) are all of the above.

_____ **3.** A pine tree is
  (a) a sporophyte.
  (b) a gametophyte.
  (c) diploid.
  (d) both a and c

_____ **4.** The male pine cone
  (a) produces pollen.
  (b) contains a female gametophyte.
  (c) bears a megasporangium containing a megaspore mother cell.
  (d) gives rise to a seed.

_____ **5.** The male gametophyte of a pine tree
  (a) is produced within a pollen grain.
  (b) produces sperm.
  (c) is diploid.
  (d) is both a and b.

_____ **6.** Which of these are produced directly by meiosis in pine?
  (a) sperm cells
  (b) pollen grains
  (c) microspores
  (d) microspore mother cells

_____ **7.** An ovule
  (a) is the structure that develops into a seed.
  (b) contains the microsporophyll.
  (c) is produced on the surface of a male cone.
  (d) is all of the above.

_____ **8.** The process by which pollen is transferred to the ovule is called
  (a) transmigration.
  (b) fertilization.
  (c) pollination.
  (d) all of the above

_____ **9.** Which statement is true of the female gametophyte of pine?
  (a) It's a product of repeated cell divisions of the functional megaspore.
  (b) It's haploid.
  (c) It serves as the stored food to be used by the embryo sporophyte upon germination.
  (d) All of the above are true.

_____ **10.** The seed coat of a pine seed
  (a) is derived from the integuments.
  (b) is produced by the micropyle.
  (c) surrounds the male gametophyte.
  (d) is divided into the hypocotyl-root axis and epicotyl.

EXERCISE **2 3**

Seed Plants I: Gymnosperms

Post-Lab Questions

Introduction

1. What survival advantage does a seed have that has enabled the seed plants to be the most successful of all plants?

2. In the diagram below of a seed, give the ploidy level (n or 2n) of each part listed.

seed coat _____

megasporangium _____

female gametophyte _____

embryo sporophyte _____

3. Distinguish between a homosporous and a heterosporous type of life cycle.

23.1 Phylum Coniferophyta: Conifers

4. List four uses for conifers.

(a)

(b)

(c)

(d)

5. While snowshoeing through the winter woods, you stop to look at a tree branch pictured at the right. Specifically, what are the brown structures hanging from the branch?

6. Distinguish between *pollination* and *fertilization*.

(0.5×)

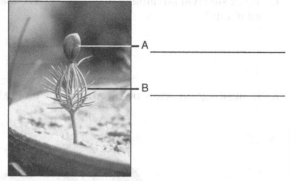

7. Are antheridia present in conifers? _____

   Are archegonia present? _____

8. Suppose you saw the seedling pictured at the right while walking in the woods.

   (a) To which gymnosperm phylum does the plant belong?

   A _____

   B _____

   (b) Identify structures A and B.

(0.5×)

23.2 Phylum Cycadophyta: Cycads

9. On spring break, you are strolling through a tropical garden in Florida and encounter the plant pictured at the right. Would the xylem of this plant contain tracheids, vessels, or both?

(0.01×)

23.3 Phylum Ginkgophyta: Ginkgo

10. A friend of yours picks up a branch like the one pictured at the right. Knowing that you have taken a biology course and studied plants, she asks you what the plant is. Identify this branch, giving your friend the full scientific name for the plant.

(0.75×)

Seed Plants II: Angiosperms

After completing this exercise, you will be able to

1. define *heterosporous, angiosperm, fruit, pollination, double fertilization, endosperm, seed, germination, annual, biennial, perennial;*

2. describe the significance of the flower, fruit, and seed for the success of the angiosperms;

3. identify the structures of the flower;

4. recognize the structures and events (those in **boldface**) that take place in angiosperm reproduction;

5. describe the origin and function of fruit and seed;

6. identify the characteristics that distinguish angiosperms from gymnosperms.

Introduction

The **angiosperms**, Phylum Anthophyta, are seed plants that produce flowers. "*Antho*" means flower, and "*phyta*" plant. The word *angiosperm* literally means "vessel seed" and refers to the seeds borne within a fruit.

There are more flowering plants in the world today than any other group of plants. Assuming that numbers indicate success, flowering plants are the most successful plants to have evolved thus far.

The most important characteristic that distinguishes the Anthophyta from other seed plants is the presence of flower parts that mature into a **fruit**, a container that protects the seeds and allows them to be dispersed without coming into contact with the rigors of the external environment. In many instances, the fruit also contributes to the dispersal of the seed. For example, some fruits stick to fur (or clothing) of animals and are brushed off some distance from the plant that produced them. Animals eat others; the undigested seeds pass out of the digestive tract and fall into environments often far removed from the seeds' source.

Our lives and diets revolve around flowering plants. Fruits enrich our diet and include such things as apples, oranges, tomatoes, beans, peas, corn, wheat, walnuts, pecans . . . the list goes on and on. Moreover, even when we are not eating fruits, we're eating flowering plant parts. Cauliflower, broccoli, potatoes, celery, and carrots all are parts of flowering plants.

Biologists believe that flower parts originated as leaves modified during the course of evolution to increase the probability for fertilization. For instance, some flower parts are colorful and attract animals that transfer the sperm-producing pollen to the receptive female parts.

As seed plants, and like gymnosperms, the angiosperms are **heterosporous**; that is, they produce *two* spore types. Review the diagram of heterosporous alternation of generations shown in Figure 23-1, page 314. Figure 24-15 depicts the life cycle of a typical flowering plant. Refer to it as you study the specimens in this exercise.

Note: This exercise provides two alternative paths to accomplish the objectives described above, a traditional approach (24.1–24.2) and an investigative one (24.3). Your instructor will indicate which alternative you will follow.

24.1 External Structure of the Flower *(About 20 min.)*

The number of different kinds of flowers is so large that it's difficult to pick a single example as representative of the entire phylum. Nonetheless, there is enough similarity among flowers that, once you've learned the structure of one representative, you'll be able to recognize the parts of most.

MATERIALS

Per student:

- flower for dissection (gladiolus or hybrid lily, for example)
- single-edged razor blade
- dissecting microscope

PROCEDURE

1. Obtain a flower provided for dissection.
2. At the base of the flower, locate the swollen stem tip, the **receptacle**, upon which the whorls of floral parts are arranged.
3. Identify the **calyx**, comprising the outermost whorl. Individual components of the calyx are called **sepals**. The sepals are frequently green (although not always). The calyx surrounds the rest of the flower in the bud stage (see Figure 24-15a).
4. Moving inward, locate the next whorl of the flower, the usually colorful **corolla** made up of **petals**.

It is usually the petals that we appreciate for their color. Remember, however, that the evolution of colorful flower parts was associated with the presence of color-visioned *pollinators*, animals that carry pollen from one flower to another. The colorful flowers attract those animals, enhancing the plants' chance of being pollinated, producing seeds, and perpetuating their species.

Both the calyx and corolla are sterile, meaning they do not produce gametes.

5. The next whorl of flower parts consists of the male, pollen-producing parts, the **stamens** (also called *microsporophylls*, "microspore-bearing leaves"; Figure 24-15b). Examine a single stamen in greater detail. Each stamen consists of a stalklike **filament** and an **anther.** The anther consists of four **microsporangia** (also called *pollen sacs*).
6. Next locate the female portion of the flower, the **pistil** (Figures 24-15a and c). A pistil consists of one or more **carpels**, also called *megasporophylls*, "megaspore-bearing leaves."

If the pistil consists of more than one carpel, they are usually fused, making it difficult to distinguish the individual components. However, you can usually determine the number of carpels by counting the number of lobes of the stigma.

7. How many carpels does your flower contain? _____
8. Identify the different parts of the pistil (Figure 24-15c): at the top, the **stigma**, which serves as a receptive region on which pollen is deposited; a necklike **style**; and a swollen **ovary.** The only members of the plant kingdom to have ovaries are angiosperms!
9. With a sharp razor blade, make a section of the ovary. (Some students should cut the pistil longitudinally; others should cut the ovary crosswise. Then compare the different sections.)
10. Examine the sections with a dissecting microscope, finding the numerous small **ovules** within the ovary. The diagram in Figure 24-15c is oversimplified; many flowers have more than one ovule per ovary.
11. In Figure 24-1, make and label two sketches: one of the cross section (c.s.) and the other of a longitudinal section (l.s.) of the ovary. Notice that the ovules are completely enclosed within the ovary. After fertilization, the ovules will develop into *seeds,* and the ovary will enlarge and mature into the *fruit.*

There are two groups of flowering plants, monocotyledons and dicotyledons. The number of flower parts indicates which group a plant belongs to. Generally, monocots have the flower parts in threes or multiples of three. Dicots have their parts in fours or fives or multiples thereof.

12. Count the number of petals or sepals in the flower you have been examining. Are you studying a monocot or dicot?

_____

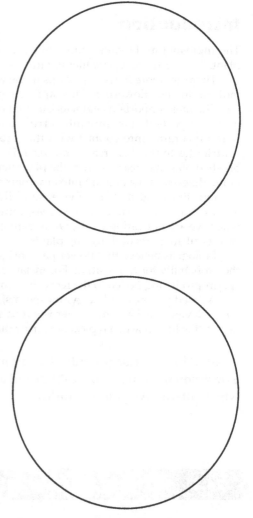

Figure 24-1 Drawings of cross section and longitudinal section of an ovary.
Label: ovules

A. Male Gametophyte (Pollen Grain) Formation in the Microsporangia (About 20 min.)

The male gametophyte in flowering plants is the pollen grain; a microscopic sperm-producing structure.

MATERIALS

Per student:

- prepared slide of young lily anther, c.s.
- prepared slide of mature lily anther (pollen grains), c.s.
- *Impatiens* flowers, with mature pollen
- glass microscope slide

- coverslip
- compound microscope

Per student pair:

- 0.5% sucrose, in dropping bottle

PROCEDURE

1. With the low-power objective of your compound microscope, examine a prepared slide of a cross section of an immature anther (Figures 24-2, 24-15d). Find sections of the four **microsporangia** (also called *pollen sacs*), which appear as four clusters of densely stained cells within the anther.

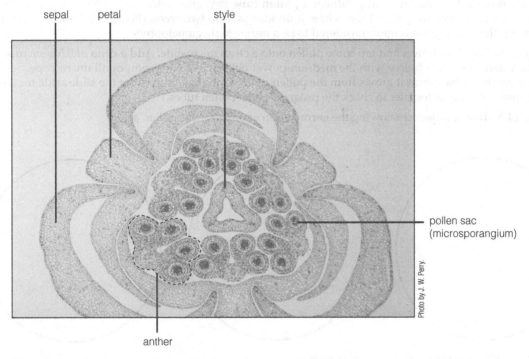

Figure 24-2 Immature anthers within flower bud, c.s. (4×).

2. Study the contents of a single microsporangium. Depending on the stage of development, you will find either diploid *microspore mother cells* (Figure 24-15e) or haploid *microspores* (Figures 24-15f and g).
3. Obtain a prepared slide of a cross section of a mature anther (Figure 24-3). Observe it first with the low-power objective, noting that the walls have split open to allow the pollen grains to be released, as shown in Figure 24-15i.
4. Pollen grains are immature *male gametophytes*, and very small ones at that. Switch to the high-dry objective to study an individual pollen grain more closely (Figure 24-4).
5. The pollen grain consists of only two cells. Identify the large **tube cell** and a smaller, crescent-shaped **generative cell** that floats freely in the cytoplasm of the tube cell (Figure 24-15h).
6. Note the ridged appearance of the outer wall layer of a pollen grain. Within the ridges and valleys of the wall, glycoproteins are present that appear to play a role in recognition between the pollen grain and the stigma.

generative cell nucleus   tube cell nucleus

generative cell   tube cell

Figure 24-3   Mature anther, c.s. (21×).

Figure 24-4   Pollen grain, c.s. (145×).

Transfer of pollen from the microsporangia to the stigma, called **pollination**, occurs by various means—wind, insects, and birds being the most common carriers of pollen. When a pollen grain lands on the stigma of a compatible flower, it germinates and produces a **pollen tube** that grows down the style (Figure 24-15j). The generative cell flows into the pollen tube, where it divides to form two *sperm* (Figure 24-15k). Because it bears two gametes, the pollen grain is now considered to be a *mature* male gametophyte.

7. Obtain an *Impatiens* flower and tap some pollen onto a clean microslide. Add a drop of 0.5% sucrose, cover with a coverslip, and observe with the medium-power objective of your compound microscope.
8. Look for the *pollen tube* as it grows from the pollen grain. (You may wish to set the slide aside for a bit and reexamine it 15 minutes later to check the progress of the pollen tubes.)

In Figure 24-5, draw a sequence showing the germination of an *Impatiens* pollen grain.

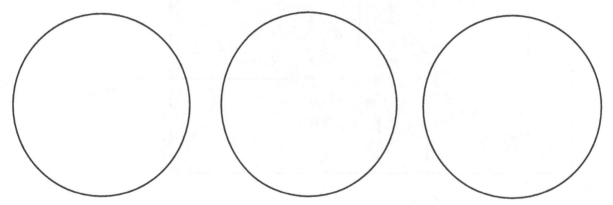

Figure 24-5   Germination of *Impatiens* pollen grain.

B. Female Gametophyte Formation in the Megasporangia (About 20 min.)

The female gametophyte is formed inside each ovule within the ovary of the flower. Like the male gametophyte, the female gametophyte in flowering plants consists of only a few cells.

MATERIALS

Per student:
- prepared slide of lily ovary, c.s., megaspore mother cell
- compound microscope

Per lab room:
- demonstration slide of lily ovary, c.s., seven-celled, eight-nucleate gametophyte
- demonstration slide of lily ovary, c.s., double fertilization

PROCEDURE

1. With the medium-power objective of your compound microscope, examine a prepared slide of a cross section of an ovary (Figures 24-6, 24-15l).

2. Find the several **ovules** that have been sectioned. One ovule will probably be sectioned in a plane so that the very large, diploid **megaspore mother cell** is obvious (Figures 24-7, 24-15m).

3. The megaspore mother cell is contained within the **megasporangium**, the outer cell layers of which form two flaps of tissue called **integuments**. Identify the structures in boldface print. After fertilization, the integuments develop into the *seed coat*.

4. Identify the **placenta**, the region of attachment of the ovule to the ovary wall.

As the megasporangium develops, the integuments grow, enveloping the megasporangium. However, a tiny circular opening remains. This opening is the **micropyle**. (The micropyle is obvious in Figure 24-15n.) Remember, the micropyle is an opening in the ovule. After pollination, the pollen grain germinates on the surface of the stigma, and the pollen tube grows down the style, through the space surrounding the ovule, through the micropyle, and penetrates the megasporangium (Figure 24-15p).

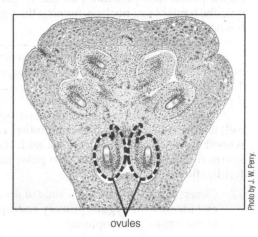

ovules

Figure 24-6 Lily ovary, c.s. (19×).

5. Identify the micropyle present in the ovule you are examining.

Considerable variation exists in the next sequence of events; we describe the pattern found in the lily.

The diploid megaspore mother cell undergoes meiosis, producing four haploid *nuclei* (Figure 24-15n). (Note that cytokinesis does *not* follow meiosis, and thus only nuclei—not cells—are formed.) The cell containing the four nuclei (the old megaspore mother cell) is now called the **female gametophyte** (also called the *embryo sac*).

Three of these four nuclei fuse. Thus, the female gametophyte contains one triploid (3n) nucleus and one haploid (n) nucleus (Figure 24-15o). Subsequently, the nuclei undergo two *mitotic* divisions, forming eight nuclei in the female gametophyte. Cell walls form around six of the eight nuclei; the large cell remaining—the **central cell**—contains two nuclei, one of which is triploid, the other haploid. These two nuclei are called the **polar nuclei**. At the micropylar end of the ovule there are three cells, all haploid. One of these is the **egg cell**. Opposite the micropylar end are three 3n cells. This stage of development is often called the *seven-celled, eight-nucleate female gametophyte* (Figures 24-8, 24-15p). Fertilization takes place at this stage.

6. Study the demonstration slide of the seven-celled, eight-nucleate female gametophyte. Identify the **placenta, integuments, micropyle, egg cell, central cell**, and **polar nuclei** (Figures 24-8, 24-15p).

integument

megasporangium

megaspore mother cell

Figure 24-7 Megaspore mother cell within megasporangium (94×).

polar nuclei of the central cell

female gametophyte

egg cell

Figure 24-8 Seven-celled, eight-nucleate female gametophyte (170×).

As the pollen tube penetrates the female gametophyte, it discharges the sperm; one of the sperm nuclei fuses with the haploid egg nucleus, forming the *zygote*. Figure 24-15q shows the female gametophyte after fertilization has occurred.

The zygote is a _____ (haploid, diploid) cell.

The other sperm nucleus enters the central cell and fuses with the two polar nuclei, forming the primary endosperm nucleus (Figure 24-15q). Thus, the primary endosperm nucleus is _____ (haploid, diploid, triploid, tetraploid, pentaploid).

The cell containing the primary endosperm nucleus (the old central cell) is now called the **endosperm mother cell**. Traditionally, the process whereby one sperm nucleus fuses with the egg nucleus and the other sperm nucleus fuses with the two polar nuclei has been called **double fertilization**.

7. Observe the demonstration slide of double fertilization (Figure 24-9), and identify the **zygote**, **primary endosperm nucleus**, and **central cell** of the female gametophyte.

Numerous mitotic and cytoplasmic divisions of the endosperm mother cell form the **endosperm**, a tissue used to nourish the embryo sporophyte as it develops within the seed.

central cell

primary endosperm nucleus

zygote

Photo courtesy Biodisc/Visuals Unlimited.

Figure 24-9 Double fertilization (170×).

C. Embryogeny (About 10 min.)

The zygote undergoes mitosis and cytokinesis to produce a two-celled **embryo** (also called the *embryo sporophyte*). Numerous subsequent divisions produce an increasingly large and complex embryo. This is the process of "embryogeny," literally embryo genesis.

MATERIALS

Per lab room:

■ demonstration slides of *Capsella* embryogeny: globular embryo, emerging cotyledons, torpedo-shaped embryo, mature embryo

PROCEDURE

1. Observe the series of four demonstration slides, which show the stages of embryo development in the female gametophyte of *Capsella* (Figure 24-10).
2. The first slide shows the so-called globular stage (Figure 24-10a), in which a chain of cells (the suspensor) attaches the embryo, a spherical mass of cells, to the wall of the female gametophyte (embryo sac). The very enlarged cell at the base of the suspensor is the *basal cell* and is active in uptake of nutrients that the developing embryo will use. Note the endosperm within the female gametophyte.
3. The second slide shows the heart-shaped stage (Figure 24-10b). Now you can distinguish the emerging **cotyledons** (seed leaves). In many plants, the cotyledons absorb nutrients from the endosperm and thus serve as a food reserve to be used during seed germination.
4. Further development of the embryo has occurred in the third slide, the torpedo stage (Figure 24-10c). Notice that the entire embryo has elongated. Find the *cotyledons*. Between the cotyledons, locate the **epicotyl**, which is the *apical meristem of the shoot*. Beneath the epicotyl and cotyledons find the **hypocotyl-root axis**. At the tip of the hypocotyl-root axis, locate the *apical meristem of the root* and the **root cap** covering it.
5. The final slide (Figure 24-10d) shows a mature embryo, neatly packaged inside the **seed coat**. Identify the seed coat and other regions previously identified in the torpedo stage.

How many cotyledons were there in the slides you examined? _____

Thus, is *Capsella* a monocot or dicot? _____

D. Fruit and Seed (About 20 min.)

Simply stated, a **fruit** is a matured ovary, while a **seed** is a matured ovule. Bear in mind that for each seed produced, a pollen grain had to fertilize the egg cells in the ovules. Fertilization not only causes the integuments of the ovule to develop into a seed coat, it also causes the ovary wall to expand into the fruit.

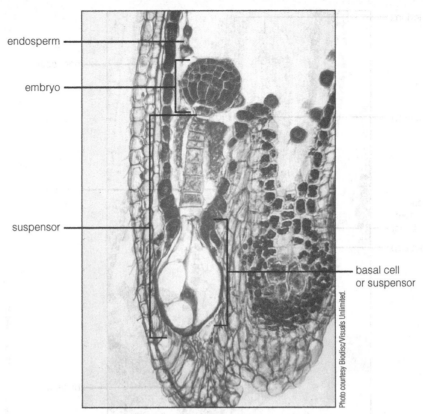

endosperm

embryo

suspensor

basal cell
or suspensor

Photo courtesy Biodisc/Visuals Unlimited.

(a) Globular embryo stage (232×).

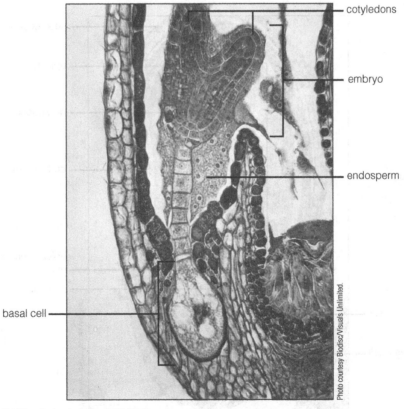

cotyledons

embryo

endosperm

basal cell

Photo courtesy Biodisc/Visuals Unlimited.

(b) Heart-shaped stage (240×).

Figure 24-10 Embryogeny in *Capsella* (shepherd's purse). *Continues on page 332.*

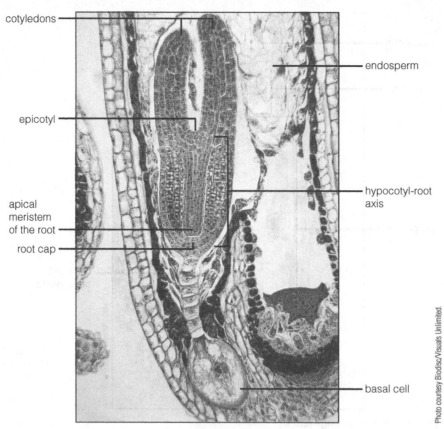

cotyledons

epicotyl

apical
meristem
of the root

root cap

endosperm

hypocotyl-root
axis

basal cell

Photo courtesy Biodisc/Visuals Unlimited.

(c) Torpedo stage (170×).

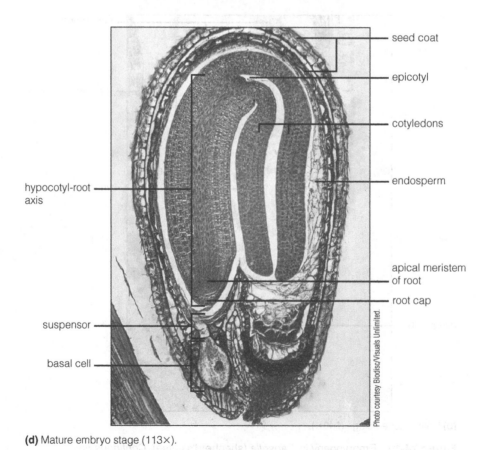

seed coat

epicotyl

cotyledons

endosperm

hypocotyl-root
axis

apical meristem
of root

root cap

suspensor

basal cell

Photo courtesy Biodisc/Visuals Unlimited.

(d) Mature embryo stage (113×).

Figure 24-10 Embryogeny in *Capsella* (shepherd's purse). *Continued.*

MATERIALS

Per student:

- bean fruits
- soaked bean seeds
- iodine solution (I₂KI), in dropping bottle

Per lab room:

- herbarium specimen of *Capsella*, with fruits
- demonstration slide of *Capsella* fruit, c.s.

PROCEDURE

1. Examine the herbarium specimen and demonstration slide of the fruits of *Capsella*. On the herbarium specimen, identify the **fruits**, which are shaped like the bag that shepherds carried at one time (Figure 24-11; the common name of this plant is "shepherd's purse").
2. Now study the demonstration slide of a cross section through a single fruit (Figure 24-12). Note the numerous **seeds** in various stages of embryo development.
3. Obtain a bean pod and carefully split it open along one seam.

   The pod is a matured ovary and thus is a _____.

   Find the *sepals* at one end of the pod and the shriveled *style* at the opposite end. The "beans" inside are

   _____

4. Note the point of attachment of the bean to the pod. This is the placenta, a term shared by the plant and animal kingdom that describes the nutrient bridge between the "unborn" offspring and parent.
5. In Figure 24-13, draw the split-open bean pod, labeling it with the correct scientific terms. Figure 24-15r shows a section of a typical fruit.

Figure 24-11 Herbarium specimen of *Capsella*, shepherd's purse (0.25×).

Figure 24-12 Cross section of *Capsella* fruit (8×).

Figure 24-13 Drawing of an open bean pod.
Labels: fruit, seeds, placenta

6. Closely study one of the beans from within the pod or a bean that has been soaked overnight to soften it. Find the scar left where the seed was attached to the fruit wall.
7. Near the scar, look for the tiny opening left in the seed coat.

What is this tiny opening? _____ (*Hint:* The pollen tube grew through it.)

8. Remove the seed coat to expose the two large **cotyledons**. Split the cotyledons apart to find the **epicotyl** and **hypocotyl-root axis**. During maturation of the bean embryo, the cotyledons absorb the endosperm. Thus, bean cotyledons are very fleshy because they store carbohydrates that will be used during seed germination. Add a drop of I₂KI to the cotyledon.

What substance is located in the cotyledon? _____
(*Hint:* Return to Exercise 7 if you've forgotten what is stained by I₂KI.)

E. Seedling (About 20 min.)

When environmental conditions are favorable for growth (adequate moisture, oxygen, and proper temperatures), the seed germinates; that is, the seedling (young sporophyte) begins to grow.

MATERIALS

Per student:

- germinating bean seeds
- bean seedlings

Per table:

- dishpan of water

PROCEDURE

1. Obtain a germinating bean seed from the culture provided (Figure 24-14). Wash the root system in the dishpan provided, *not* in the sink.
2. Identify the **primary root** with the smaller **secondary roots** attached to it. Emerging in the other direction will be the **hypocotyl**, the **cotyledons**, the **epicotyl** (above the cotyledons), and the first **true leaves** above the epicotyl. Identify these structures.

When some seeds (like the pea) germinate, the cotyledons remain *below* ground. Others, like the bean, emerge from the ground because of elongation of the hypocotyl-root axis.

3. Now, obtain a bean seedling from the growing medium. Be careful as you pull it up so as not to damage the root system. Wash the root system in the dishpan provided.

Your seedling should be in a stage of development similar to that shown in Figure 24-15s. Much of the growth that has taken place is the result of cellular elongation of the parts present in the seed.

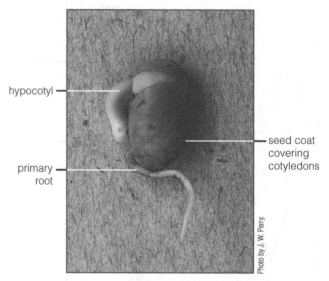

Figure 24-14 Germinating bean seed (2×).

4. On the root system, identify the **primary** and **secondary roots**. As the root system merges into the shoot (aboveground) system, find the **hypocotyl**. (The prefix *hypo-* is derived from Greek, meaning "below" or "underneath.")
5. Next, identify the cotyledons. Notice their shriveled appearance. Now that you know the function of the cotyledons from your previous study, why do you suppose the cotyledons are shriveled?

_____

6. Above the cotyledons, find that portion of the stem called the **epicotyl**.

Knowing what you do about the prefix *hypo-*, speculate on what the prefix *epi-* means.

_____

   As noted earlier, the seedling has *true leaves*. Contrast the function of the cotyledons ("seed leaves") with the true leaves. _____

_____

Depending on the stage of development, your seedling may have even more leaves that have been produced by the shoot apex.

The amount of time between seed germination and flowering largely depends on the particular plant. Some plants produce flowers and seeds during their first growing season, completing their life cycle in that growing season. These plants are called **annuals**. Marigolds are an example of an annual. Others, known as **biennials**, grow vegetatively during the first growing season and do not produce flowers and seeds until the second growing season (carrots, for example). Both annuals and biennials die after seeds are produced.

Perennials are plants that live several to many years. The time between seed germination and flowering (seed production) varies, some requiring many years. Moreover, perennials do not usually die after producing seed, but flower and produce seeds many times during their lifetime.

24.3 Experiment: An Investigative Study of the Life Cycle of Flowering Plants

Recent developments with a fast-growing and fast-reproducing plant in the mustard family allow you to study the life cycle of a flowering plant over the course of only 35 days. The plants were bred by a plant scientist at the University of Wisconsin—Madison and are sometimes called Wisconsin Fast Plants™. You will grow these rapid-cycling *Brassica rapa* (abbreviated RCBr for *R*apid *C*ycling *Brassica rapa*) plants from seeds, following the growth cycle and learning about plant structure, the life cycle of a flowering plant, and adaptive mechanisms for pollination.

Because this investigation occurs over several weeks, all Materials and Procedures are listed by the day the activity begins, starting from day 0. Record your measurements and observations in tables at the end of this exercise.

A. Germination

Day 0 (About 30 min.)

MATERIALS

Per student:

- one RCBr seed pod
- metric ruler
- 3 × 5 in. index card
- transparent adhesive tape
- petri dish
- paper toweling or filter paper disk to fit petri dish
- growing quad *or* two 35-mm film canisters
- 12 N-P-K fertilizer pellets (24 if using canister method)
- four paper wicks (growing quad) *or* two cotton string wicks (canister method)
- disposable pipet with bulb
- pot label (two if using canister method)
- marker

- forceps
- model seed
- 500-mL beaker
- two wide-mouth bottles (film canister method)

Per student group (4):

- 2-L soda bottle bottom or tray
- moistened soil mix
- watertight tray
- water mat

Per lab room:

- light bank

PROCEDURE

The life cycle of a seed plant has no beginning or end; it's a true cycle. For convenience, we'll start our examination of this cycle with germination of nature's perfect time capsule, the seed. **Germination** is the process of switching from dormancy to growth.

1. Obtain an RCBr seed pod that has been sandwiched between two strips of transparent adhesive tape. This pod is the **fruit** of the plant. A fruit is a matured ovary. Measure and record the length of the pod in Table 24-1.
2. Harvest the seeds by scrunching up the pod until the seeds come out. Then carefully separate the halves of the pod to expose the seeds.
3. Roll a piece of adhesive tape into a circle with the sticky side out. Attach the tape to an index card and then place the seeds on the tape. (This keeps the small seeds from disappearing.) You may wish to handle the seeds with forceps. Count the number of seeds and record the number in Table 24-1 on page 346.

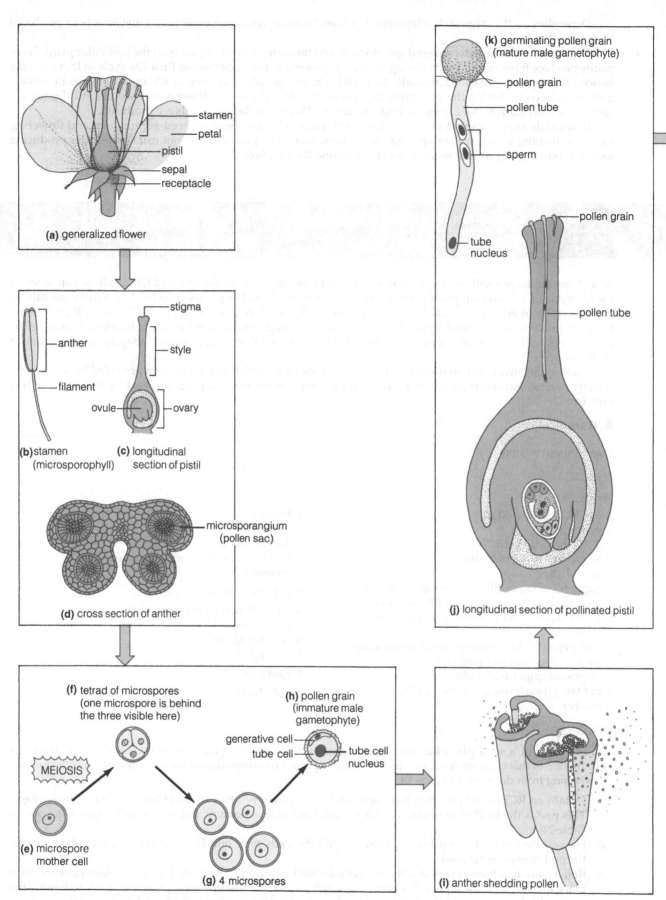

Figure 24-15 Life cycle of an angiosperm. [Color scheme: Haploid (n) structures are yellow, diploid (2n) are green, gold, or red; triploid (3n) are purple.]

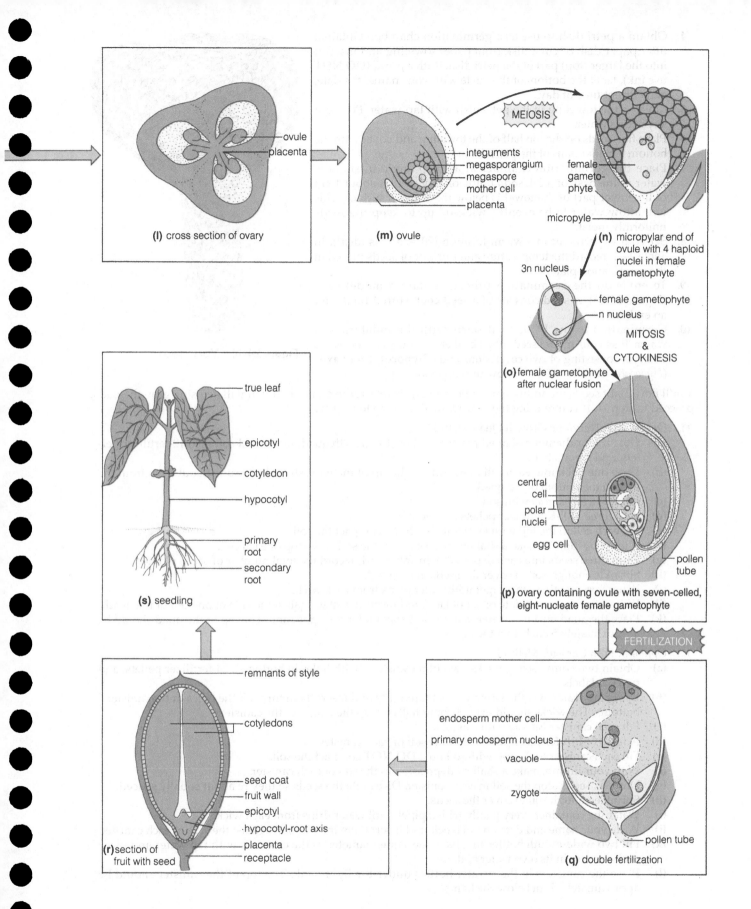

(l) cross section of ovary

ovule
placenta

(m) ovule

MEIOSIS

integuments
megasporangium
megaspore mother cell
placenta

female gametophyte

micropyle

(n) micropylar end of ovule with 4 haploid nuclei in female gametophyte

3n nucleus

female gametophyte

n nucleus

MITOSIS & CYTOKINESIS

(o) female gametophyte after nuclear fusion

central cell
polar nuclei
egg cell
pollen tube

(p) ovary containing ovule with seven-celled, eight-nucleate female gametophyte

FERTILIZATION

true leaf
epicotyl
cotyledon
hypocotyl
primary root
secondary root

(s) seedling

remnants of style
cotyledons
seed coat
fruit wall
epicotyl
hypocotyl-root axis
placenta
receptacle

(r) section of fruit with seed

endosperm mother cell
primary endosperm nucleus
vacuole
zygote
pollen tube

(q) double fertilization

4. Obtain a petri dish to use as a germination chamber. Obtain a filter paper disk or cut a disk from paper toweling and insert it into the larger (top) part of the petri dish. With a *pencil* (**DO NOT** use ink), label the bottom of the circle with your name, the date, and current time of day.

5. Moisten the toweling in the petri dish with tap water. Pour out any excess water.

6. Place five seeds on the top half of the toweling and cover with the bottom (smaller half) of the petri dish.

7. Place the germination chamber at a steep angle in shallow water in the base of a 2-L soda bottle or tray so that about 1 cm of the lower part of the towel is below the water's surface. This will allow water to be evenly "wicked" up to keep the seeds uniformly moist.

8. Set your experiment in a warm location (20°–25°C is ideal). In Table 24-1, record the temperature and number of seeds placed in the germination plate.

9. To envision the germination process, obtain a model seed (Figure 24-16). A **seed** consists of a **seed coat, stored food**, and an **embryo**.

10. Germination in the RCBr seed starts with the imbibition of water. Toss your model seed into a beaker of water. Out pops the embryo, consisting of two **cotyledons** and a **hypocotyl-root axis**. (*Hypocotyl* literally means "below the cotyledons.")

Figure 24-16 Model seed.

You'll now plant seeds for additional studies. If your instructor indicates that you will be using growth quads, proceed to step 11. If you're using the canister method, skip to step 12.

11. *Option A*: Polystyrene Growth Quad Method
    (a) Obtain four diamond-shaped paper towel wicks, growth quad, moistened soil mix, 12 fertilizer pellets, and a pot label.
    (b) Drop one wick into each cell in the quad. The tip of the wick should protrude about 1 cm from the hole in the bottom of the quad.
    (c) Fill each cell *halfway* with soil.
    (d) Add three N-P-K fertilizer pellets to *each* cell.
    (e) Fill each cell to the top with *loose* soil. **DO NOT** compact the soil.
    (f) With your thumb, make a shallow depression in the soil at the top of each cell.
    (g) Drop three seeds into each depression. In Table 24-1, record the total number of seeds planted.
    (h) Sprinkle enough soil to cover the seeds in each cell.
    (i) Water very gently with a pipet until water drips from each wick.
    (j) Write your name and date on a pot label and insert the label against the side of one cell of the quad.
    (k) Place the quad on a wet water mat inside a tray under the light bank. The top of the quad should be approximately 5 cm below the lights.

12. *Option B*: Film Canister Method
    (a) Obtain two cotton string wicks, two film canisters (with holes in bottoms), 24 fertilizer pellets, and two pot labels.
    (b) Using tap water, wet the string wicks thoroughly and insert them through the holes in the canisters' bottoms. The wicks should extend about halfway up the length of the canister.
    (c) Fill each canister *halfway* with soil mix.
    (d) Add 12 N-P-K fertilizer pellets atop the soil of each canister.
    (e) Fill each canister to the top with soil mix. **DO NOT** compact the soil.
    (f) With your thumb, make a shallow depression in the soil of each canister.
    (g) Drop six seeds atop the soil in each canister. Distribute the seeds so they're about equally spaced.
    (h) Sprinkle enough soil to cover the seeds.
    (i) Water the containers very gently with a pipet until water drips from each wick.
    (j) Write your name and date on pot labels and insert them into the soil against the side of each canister.
    (k) Fill two wide-mouth bottles that have the same diameter as the canisters with tap water and place each canister in its own water bottle.
    (l) Place the canisters in their water bottles under the light bank. The top of the canister should be approximately 5 cm below the lights.

Day 1 (About 10 min.)

MATERIALS

Per student:

- dissecting microscope
- tap water
- disposable pipet with bulb
- metric ruler

PROCEDURE

1. Water each quad cell or canister from the top using a pipet.
2. Observe your germination experiment in the petri dish chamber with a dissecting microscope. Note the **radicle** (primary root) and **hypocotyl** extending from a split in the brown **seed coat**. What colors are the radicle and the hypocotyl? _____
3. What does the color indicate about the source of carbohydrates for the germinating seeds?
   _____
4. Count the number of seeds that have germinated, and record it in Table 24-1. Measure the length of each hypocotyl and attached radicle. Record this in Table 24-1. Replace the cover and return your experiment to its place.

Day 2 (About 15 min.)

MATERIALS

Per student:

- germination experiment started on day 0
- disposable pipet with bulb
- tap water
- metric ruler
- forceps
- dissecting microscope
- two additional germination chambers (for gravitropism experiment)
- two RCBr seed pods

PROCEDURE

1. Water each quad cell or canister from the top using a pipet.
2. Observe your germination experiment. Count the number of germinated seeds and calculate the percentage of seeds that germinated. Record both numbers in Table 24-1. With a forceps, remove one of the germinating seeds from the toweling, place it on the stage of a dissecting microscope, and observe the numerous **root hairs** attached to the radicle. Root hairs greatly increase the surface area for absorption of water and minerals. Measure the lengths of the hypocotyls and attached radicles and record their average length in Table 24-1.

In what direction (up, down, or horizontal) are the hypocotyl and radicle growing?

   hypocotyl: _____

   radicle: _____

This directional growth is called **gravitropism**, a plant growth response to gravity.

Day 3 (About 10 min.)

MATERIALS

Per student:

- germination experiment started on day 0
- metric ruler
- disposable pipet with bulb
- tap water

PROCEDURE

1. Water your plants in the quads or canisters from the top using a pipet. Is any part of the plant visible yet? _____ (yes or no) If yes, which part? _____
2. Observe your germination experiment. By this time, the seed coat should be shed, and the **cotyledons**, the so-called seed leaves that were packed inside the seed coat, should be visible. The cotyledons absorb food stored within the seed, making the food available for initial stages of growth before photosynthesis starts to provide carbohydrates necessary for growth.

What color are the cotyledons? _____

    What function does this color indicate for the cotyledons? _____

3. Measure the length of the hypocotyls and attached radicles and record their average length in Table 24-1.

B. Growth

Day 4 or 5 (About 10 min.)

MATERIALS

Per student:

- forceps
- metric ruler
- dissecting microscope
- germination experiment started on day 0

PROCEDURE

1. Count the number of seedlings present, and record it in Table 24-1. Use a forceps to thin the plants to one per cell if you are using the quad growing method. If a cell has no plants, transplant one of the extra plants from another cell by inserting the tip of a pencil into the soil to form a hole and then inserting the transplant's root. Gently firm the soil around the transplant. Measure the height of each plant's shoot system—that is, from soil to the apex. Compute the average height and record it in Table 24-1.
2. Observe your germination experiment. Note that the radicle has produced additional roots. These are **lateral roots** (secondary roots). Remove one plant and observe it with the dissecting microscope.

Do lateral roots have root hairs? _____ (yes or no)

    At this time, you may discard your germination experiment. Your instructor will indicate what you should do with the materials.

Day 7 (About 10 min.)

MATERIALS

Per student:

- metric ruler

PROCEDURE

1. By now your plant should have its first **true leaves**. Describe how the true leaves differ from the cotyledons.

    _____

    _____

    _____

2. Measure the length of the true leaves, and record their average length in Table 24-1.
3. Measure the height of your plants from soil line to shoot apex, and record the average height in Table 24-1.

C. The Pollinator and Pollination

Pollen grains are actually sperm conveyors that deliver these male gametes to the egg-containing ovules within the ovary. Transfer of pollen from the anther to the stigma, called **pollination,** occurs by various means in different species of flowers, with wind, birds, and insects being the most common carriers of pollen. In the case of *Brassica,* the main pollinator is the common honeybee.

    Pollinators and flowers are probably one of the best-known examples of **coevolution**. Coevolution is the process of two organisms evolving together, their structures and behaviors changing to benefit both organisms. Flowering plants and pollinators work together in nearly perfect harmony: the bee receives the food it needs for its respiratory activities from the flower, and the plant receives the male gametes (delivered by the bee) directly to the female structure—it doesn't have to rely on the presence of water, which is necessary in lower plants, algae, and fungi, to get the gametes together.

    Flowering plants have considerable advantage over gymnosperms. While gymnosperms also produce pollen grains, the pollinator in these plants is the wind. No organism carries pollen directly to the female structure. Rather, chance and the production of enormous quantities of pollen (which takes energy that might be used otherwise for growth) are integral in assuring reproduction.

    In preparation for pollinating your plants' flowers, let's first study the pollinator, the common honeybee.

Day 10 (About 20 min.)

MATERIALS

Per student:

- metric ruler
- three toothpicks
- three dried honeybees
- dissecting microscope

Per student group (4):

- tube of glue
- scissors

PROCEDURE

1. Measure the lengths of the second set of true leaves and plant height, and record their averages in Table 24-1.
2. Obtain a dried honeybee and observe it with your dissecting microscope. Use Figure 24-2 to aid you in this study. Note the featherlike hairs that cover its body. As a bee probes for nectar, it brushes against the anthers and stigma. Pollen is entrapped on these hairs.
3. Closely study the foreleg of the bee, noticing the notch. This is the *antenna cleaner*. Quick movements over the antennae remove pollen from these sensory organs.
4. Examine the mid- and hind legs, identifying their *pollen brushes*, which are used to remove the pollen from the forelegs, thorax, and head.
5. On the hind leg, note the *pollen comb* and *pollen press*. The comb rakes the pollen from the midleg, and the press is a storage area for pollen collected.

Pollen is rich in the vitamins, minerals, fats, and proteins needed for insect growth. When the baskets are filled, the bee returns to the hive to feed the colony. Partially digested pollen is fed to larvae and to young, emerging bees.

As you can imagine, during pollen- and nectar-gathering at numerous flowers, cross-pollination occurs as pollen grains are rubbed off onto stigmas.

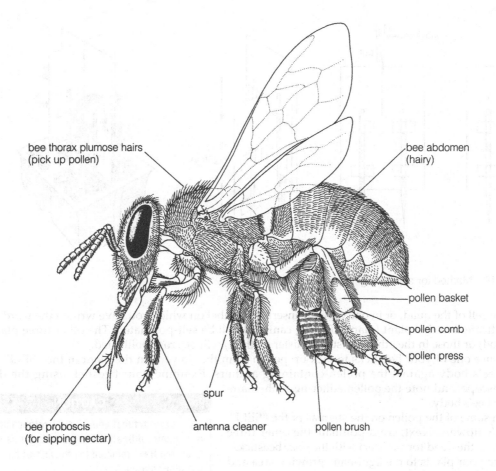

bee thorax plumose hairs (pick up pollen)

bee abdomen (hairy)

pollen basket

pollen comb

pollen press

spur

bee proboscis (for sipping nectar)

antenna cleaner

pollen brush

Figure 24-17 Structure of the honeybee.

On day 12, you will start pollinating your flowers. What better means to do it than to use a bee? (In this case, a dead bee that is attached to a stick.) Let's make some beesticks.

6. Add a drop of glue to one end of three round toothpicks. Insert the glue-bearing end of one stick into the top (dorsal) side of the thorax of a bee. Repeat with two more dried bees. Set your beesticks aside to dry.

D. Pollination

It's time to do a pollination study. Some species of flowers are able to **self-pollinate**, meaning that the pollen from one flower of a plant will grow on stigmas of other flowers of that same plant. Hence, the sperm produced by a single plant will fertilize its own flowers. Other species are **self-incompatible**. For fertilization to occur in the latter, pollen must travel from one plant to another plant of the same species. This is **cross-pollination**. In this portion of the exercise, you will determine whether RCBr is self-incompatible or is able to self-pollinate.

Day 12 (About 30 min.)

MATERIALS

Per student:

- beestick prepared on day 10
- index card divider
- metric ruler
- pot label
- forceps
- marker

PROCEDURE

1. Measure the height of each plant, and record the average height in Table 24-1.
2. Separate the cells of your quad or canister with a divider constructed with index cards as shown in Figure 24-18. This keeps the plants from brushing against each other.

Figure 24-18 Method for separating flowers for pollination study.

3. In one cell of the quad, or in one canister, insert a pot label on which you have written the word ("SELF"), to indicate that this plant (plants if using canister) will be self-pollinated. The other three plants (quad method) or those in the other canister (canister method) will be cross-pollinated.
4. Now use one of your beesticks to pick up pollen from the flowers on the plant in the "SELF" cell. Rub the bee's body against the pollen-containing anthers. Examine your beestick using the dissecting microscope, and note the pollen adhering to the hairs of the bee's body.
5. Brush some of the pollen on the stigmas of the "SELF" plant's flowers. Next, cross-pollinate the other three plants in the quad (or canister) with the *same* beestick.
6. Return your plants to the light-bank growing area and discard the beestick.

> **CAUTION**
>
> It is important that you DO NOT retouch any of the self-pollinated flowers with the beestick once you have touched the flowers of any of the other plants.

Day 14 (About 15 min.)

MATERIALS

Per student:

- metric ruler
- beestick

PROCEDURE

1. Measure the height of each plant, and record their average height in Table 24-1.
2. Pollinate the newly opened flowers using the same techniques as described for day 12.
3. Return your plants to the light-bank growing area.

Day 17 (About 15 min.)

MATERIALS

Per student:

- metric ruler
- beestick

PROCEDURE

1. Measure the height of each plant, and record their average height in Table 24-1.
2. Count the number of flowers on each plant (opened and unopened), calculate the average number per plant, and record it in Table 24-1. Pinch off the shoot apex of each plant to remove all unopened buds and pinch off any side shoots the plant has produced.
3. Do a final pollination of your flowers, using a fresh beestick and taking the same precautions as on days 12 and 14.
4. Return your plants to the light-bank growing area.

E. Fertilization and Seed Development

Within 24 hours of pollination, a pollen grain that has landed on a compatible stigma will produce a pollen tube that grows down the style and through the micropyle of the ovule.

Within the pollen tube are two **sperm**, the male gametes. As the pollen tube enters the ovule, the two sperm are discharged. One fertilizes the haploid egg nucleus, forming a diploid **zygote**. The second sperm unites with two other nuclei within the ovule, forming a triploid nucleus known as the **primary endosperm nucleus**.

The fusion of one sperm nucleus to form the zygote and the other to form the primary endosperm nucleus is called **double fertilization**.

1. Reexamine Figure 24-9, which illustrates double fertilization.

What is the fate of cells formed by double fertilization? The zygote undergoes numerous cell divisions during a process called **embryogeny** (the suffix *-geny* is derived from Greek, meaning "production") to form the diploid embryo. The triploid primary endosperm nucleus divides numerous times without cytokinesis. The result is the formation of a multinucleate milky **endosperm** (each nucleus is 3n), which serves as the food source for the embryo as it grows. At the same time, changes are taking place in the cell layers of the ovule—they are becoming hardened and will eventually form the seed coat. Also, the ovary is elongating as it matures into the **fruit**—in this case, a pod.

2. Examine your plants, looking for small, elongated pods.
3. At this time, you should be able to tell whether RCBr can self-pollinate or is self-incompatible, because the fruit—a pod—will develop only if fertilization has taken place. Do the cross-pollinated plants have pods? (yes or no) _____
4. Does the self-pollinated plant have pods? (yes or no) _____
5. Make a conclusion regarding the need for cross-pollination in RCBr. _____

_____

The young embryo goes through a continuous growth process, starting as a ball of cells (the globular stage) and culminating in the formation of a mature embryo. The early stages are somewhat difficult to observe, but the later stages can be seen quite easily with a microscope. By day 24, many of the ovules will be at the globular stage, similar to that seen in Figure 24-10a.

Day 26 (About 30 min.)

MATERIALS

Per student:

- dissecting microscope
- two dissecting needles
- dH$_2$O in dropping bottle

- glass microscope slide
- iodine solution (I$_2$KI) in dropping bottle

PROCEDURE

1. Remove a pod from one of the plants, place it on the stage of your dissecting microscope, and tease it open using dissecting needles. RCBr flowers have pistils consisting of two carpels; each carpel makes up one longitudinal half of the pod, and the "seam" represents where the carpels fuse.
2. Carefully remove the ovules (immature seeds) inside the pod, placing them in a drop of water on a clean microscope slide.
3. Rupture the ovule by mashing it with dissecting needles and place the slide on the stage of a dissecting microscope.
4. Attempt to locate the embryo, which should be at the heart-shaped stage, similar to Figure 24-10b, and which may be turning green. A portion of the endosperm has become cellular and may be green, too, so be careful with your observation. The "lobes" of the heart-shaped embryo are the young cotyledons. Identify these. Find the trailing **suspensor**, a strand of eight cells that serves as a sort of "umbilical cord" to transport nutrients from the endosperm to the embryo.
5. Add a drop of I$_2$KI to stain the endosperm. What color does the endosperm stain? _____
6. What can you conclude about the composition of the endosperm? (*Hint*: If you've forgotten, consult Exercise 7.)

_____

Day 29 (About 20 min.)

MATERIALS

Per student:

- dissecting microscope
- two dissecting needles

- dH$_2$O in dropping bottle
- glass microscope slide

PROCEDURE

1. Remove another pod from a plant and examine it as you did on day 26.
2. Attempt to find the torpedo stage of embryo development, similar to that illustrated in Figure 24-10c.
3. Describe the changes that have taken place in the transition from the heart-shaped to the torpedo stage.

_____

_____

Day 31 (About 20 min.)

MATERIALS

Per student:

- dissecting microscope
- two dissecting needles

- dH$_2$O in dropping bottle
- glass microscope slide

PROCEDURE

1. Again, remove and dissect a pod and ovules, and look for the embryo whose cotyledons have now curved, forming the so-called walking-stick stage.
2. Identify the **cotyledons** and the **hypocotyl-root axis** that has curved within the ovules' integuments.

Days 35–37 (About 20 min.)

MATERIALS

Per student:

- dissecting microscope
- two dissecting needles

PROCEDURE

The pods of your plants should be drying and have much the same appearance as the pod you started with about a month ago.

1. Remove seeds from mature pods and examine the seeds with your dissecting microscope. Note the bumpy **seed coat**, derived from the integument of the ovule. Look for a tiny hole in the seed coat. This is the **micropyle**!

2. Crack the seed coat and remove the embryo, identifying the cotyledons and hypocotyl-root axis. Separate the cotyledons and look between them, identifying the tiny **epicotyl**, which is the *apical meristem of the shoot*.

3. Harvest the remaining pods and count the number of seeds in each pod. Calculate the average number of seeds per pod and number of seeds per plant. Record this information in Table 24-1.

Congratulations! You have completed the life cycle study of a rapid cycling *Brassica rapa*. Virtually all of the 200,000 species of flowering plants have stages identical to that which you have examined over the course of the past 35–40 days. Most just take longer—from a few days to nearly a century longer!

Conclude your study by preparing the required graphs and answering the questions following Table 24-1.

4. In Figure 24-19, graph the increase in average length of the hypocotyl-root axis produced in the germination chamber.

Does length increase in a constant fashion (linearly), or does extension occur more quickly during a particular time period (logarithmically)? _____

Using the data from Table 24-1, graph in Figure 24-20 the rate of growth of your plants' shoot system as a function of time.

How does the number of seeds produced per pod compare with the number in the original pod from which you harvested your seed at the beginning of the study? _____

What is the *reproductive potential* (the number of possible plants coming from one parent plant) of your RCBr? _____

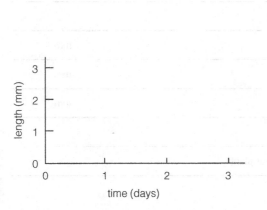

Figure 24-19 Growth of hypocotyl-root axis.

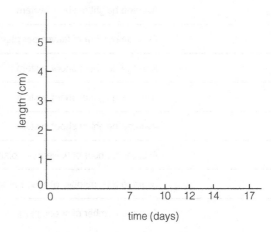

Figure 24-20 Growth of shoot system.

TABLE 24-1   Data for RCBr Life Cycle

Day	Parameter	Measurement
0	Pod length	mm
	Seed number (single pod)	
	Number of seeds sown in germination chamber	
	Temperature, °C	
	Number of seeds sown in quad (total)	
1	Germinated seeds (germination chamber)	
	Average length of hypocotyl-root axis	mm
2	Germinated seeds (germination chamber)	
	Percentage seeds germinated	
	Average length of hypocotyl-root axis	mm
3	Average length of hypocotyl-root axis	mm
4 or 5	Number of seedlings (quad)	
	Average height of shoot system	mm
7	Average length of first set of true leaves	mm
	Average height of shoot system	mm
10	Average length of second set of true leaves	mm
	Average height of shoot system	mm
12	Average number of leaves per plant	
	Average height of shoot system	mm
14	Average height of shoot system	mm
17	Average height of shoot system	mm
	Average number of flowers per plant	
35–37	Average total number of seeds produced per plant	
	Average number of seeds per pod	

_____ 1. Plants that produce flowers are
   (a) members of the Anthophyta.
   (b) angiosperms.
   (c) seed producers.
   (d) all of the above

_____ 2. All of the petals of a flower are collectively called the
   (a) corolla.
   (b) stamens.
   (c) receptacles.
   (d) calyx.

_____ 3. Which group of terms refers to the microsporophyll, the male portion of a flower?
   (a) ovary, stamens, pistil
   (b) stigma, style, ovary
   (c) anther, stamen, filament
   (d) megasporangium, microsporangium, ovule

_____ 4. A carpel is the
   (a) same as a megasporophyll.
   (b) structure producing pollen grains.
   (c) component making up the anther.
   (d) synonym for microsporophyll.

_____ 5. The portion of the flower containing pollen grains is
   (a) the pollen sac.
   (b) the microsporangium.
   (c) the anther.
   (d) all of the above

_____ 6. Which group of terms is in the correct developmental sequence?
   (a) microspore mother cell, meiosis, megaspore, female gametophyte
   (b) microspore mother cell, meiosis, microspore, pollen grain
   (c) megaspore, mitosis, female gametophyte, meiosis, endosperm mother cell
   (d) all of the above

_____ 7. Where does germination of a pollen grain occur in a flowering plant?
   (a) in the anther
   (b) in the micropyle
   (c) on the surface of the corolla
   (d) on the stigma

_____ 8. Double fertilization refers to
   (a) fusion of two sperm nuclei and two egg cells.
   (b) fusion of one sperm nucleus with two polar nuclei and fusion of another with the egg cell nucleus.
   (c) maturation of the ovary into a fruit.
   (d) none of the above

_____ 9. Ovules mature into _____, while ovaries mature into _____.
   (a) seeds/fruits
   (b) stamens/seeds
   (c) seeds/carpels
   (d) fruits/seeds

_____ 10. A bean pod is
   (a) a seed container.
   (b) a fruit.
   (c) a part of the stamen.
   (d) both a and b

EXERCISE **24**

Seed Plants II: Angiosperms

Post-Lab Questions

Introduction

1. There are two major groups of seed plants, gymnosperms (Exercise 23) and angiosperms. Compare these two groups of seed plants with respect to the following features:

Feature	Gymnosperms	Angiosperms
(a) type of reproductive structure	_____	_____
(b) source of nutrition for developing embryo	_____	_____
(c) enclosure of mature seed	_____	_____

24.1 External Structure of the Flower

2. What *event*, critical to the production of seeds, is shown at the right?

3. Distinguish between *pollination* and *fertilization*.

(0.84×)

4. Identify the parts of the trumpet creeper flower shown at the right.

   A.

   B.

   C.

   D.

   E.

(1×)

5. Examine the photo of the *Trillium* flower pictured at the right.

   (a) Is *Trillium* a monocotyledon or dicotyledon?

   (b) Justify your answer.

(0.75×)

6. Based on your observation of the stigma of the daylily flower in the photo at the right, how many carpels would you expect to comprise the ovary?

(1×)

24.2 The Life Cycle of a Flowering Plant

7. The photo is a cross section of a (an) _____

   _____.

   The numerous circles within the four cavities are

   _____.

(74×)

8. The photo shows a flower of the pomegranate some time after fertilization. Identify the parts shown.

A. _____

B. _____

C. _____

D. _____

(2×)

9. Some biologists contend that the term *double fertilization* is a misnomer and that the process should be called *fertilization* and *triple fusion*. Why do they argue that the fusion of the one sperm nucleus and the two polar nuclei is *not* fertilization?

Food for Thought

10. Your roommate says that you need vegetables and asks you to pick up tomatoes at the store. To your roommate's surprise, you say a tomato is not a vegetable, but a fruit. Explain.

Fungi

OBJECTIVES

After completing this exercise, you will be able to

1. define *parasite, saprobe, mutualist, gametangium, hypha, mycelium, multinucleate, sporangium, rhizoid, zygosporangium, ascus, conidium, ascospore, ascocarp, basidium, basidiospore, basidiocarp, lichen, mycorrhiza;*

2. recognize representatives of the major phyla of fungi;

3. distinguish structures that are used to place various representatives of the fungi in their proper phyla;

4. list reasons why fungi are important;

5. distinguish between the structures associated with asexual and sexual reproduction described in this exercise;

6. identify the structures (in **boldface**) of the fungi examined;

7. determine the effect of light on certain species of fungi.

Introduction

As you walk in the woods following a warm fall rain, you are likely to be met by a vast assemblage of colorful fungi. Some grow on dead or diseased trees, some on the surface of the soil, others in pools of water. Some are edible, some deadly poisonous.

Fungi (kingdom Fungi) are *heterotrophic* organisms; that is, they are incapable of producing their own food material. They secrete enzymes from their bodies that digest their food externally. The digested materials are then absorbed into the body.

Depending on the relationship between the fungus and its food source, fungi can be characterized in one of three ways:

1. Parasitic fungi (**parasites**) obtain their nutrients from the organic material of another *living* organism, and in doing so adversely affect the food source, sometimes causing death.

2. Saprotrophic fungi (**saprobes**) grow on nonliving organic (carbon-containing) matter.

3. Mutualistic fungi (**mutualists**) form a partnership *beneficial* to both the fungus and its host.

Fungi, along with the bacteria, are essential components of the ecosystem as decomposers. These organisms recycle the products of life, making the products of death available so that life may continue. Without them we would be hopelessly lost in our own refuse. Fungi and fungal metabolism are responsible for some of the food products that enrich our lives—the mushrooms of the field, the blue cheese of the dairy case, even the citric acid used in making soft drinks.

The kingdom Fungi is divided into four separate phyla, based on structures formed during sexual reproduction (Table 25-1). Certain fungi (the Imperfect Fungi) do not reproduce sexually; hence they are considered an informal "group."

TABLE 25-1	Classification of the Fungi
Phylum	**Common Name**
Chytridiomycota	Chytrids
Zygomycota	Zygosporangium-forming fungi
Ascomycota	Sac fungi
Basidiomycota	Club fungi
"Imperfect Fungi"	Fungi without sexual reproduction

© Cengage Learning 2013

25.1 Phylum Chytridiomycota (*About 5 min.*)

Commonly known as chytrids, these fungi are among the most simple in body form. While most live on dead organic matter, some are parasitic on economically important plants, resulting in damage and/or death of the host plant. Parasitic organisms that cause disease are called **pathogens**.

MATERIALS

Per lab room:

- preserved specimen of potato tuber with black wart disease

PROCEDURE

1. Examine the preserved specimen (if available) of the potato tuber that exhibits the disease known as "black wart." Notice the warty eruptions on the surface of the tuber. The warts are caused by the presence of numerous cells of a chytrid infecting the tuber (Figure 25-1).
2. Now look at Figure 25-2, a photomicrograph of a chytrid similar to that which causes black wart disease.

diseased (infected) portion of tuber

normal (uninfected) portion of tuber

Biodisc/Visuals Unlimited/Corbis

Figure 25-1 Section of potato tuber infected by black wart pathogen.

rhizoids

25 μm

John Taylor/Visuals Unlimited, Inc.

Figure 25-2 Chytrid (71×).

25.2 Phylum Zygomycota: Zygosporangium-Forming Fungi (*About 30 min.*)

Commonly called "zygomycetes," all members of this phylum produce a thick-walled zygote called a **zygosporangium**. Most zygomycetes are saprobes. The common black bread mold, *Rhizopus*, is a representative zygomycete. Before the introduction of chemical preservatives into bread, *Rhizopus* was an almost certain invader, especially in high humidity.

MATERIALS

Per student:
- culture of *Rhizopus*
- prepared slide of *Rhizopus*
- dissecting needle
- glass microscope slide
- coverslip
- compound microscope

Per student pair:
- dH₂O in dropping bottle

Per lab room:
- demonstration culture of *Rhizopus* zygosporangia, on dissecting microscope

PROCEDURE

Examine Figure 25-7, the life cycle of *Rhizopus*, as you study this organism.

1. Obtain a petri dish culture of *Rhizopus*.
2. Observe the culture, noting that the body of the organism consists of many fine strands. These are called **hyphae** (Figure 25-3). All of the hyphae together are called the **mycelium** Biologists use the term *mycelium* instead of saying "the fungal body."
3. Now note that the culture contains numerous black "dots." These are the **sporangia** (singular, *sporangium;* Figures 25-7a and b). Sporangia contain **spores** (Figures 25-7c–d) by which *Rhizopus* reproduces asexually.
4. Using a dissecting needle, remove a small portion of the mycelium and prepare a wet mount. Examine your preparation with the high-dry objective of your compound microscope.
5. It's likely that when you added the coverslip, you crushed the sporangia, liberating the spores. Are there many or few spores within a single sporangium? _____
6. Identify the **rhizoids** (Figure 25-7a) at the base of a sporangium-bearing hypha. Rhizoids anchor the mycelium to whatever the fungus is growing on.
7. Now observe the demonstration culture of sexual reproduction in *Rhizopus* (Figure 25-4). Two different mycelia must grow in close proximity before sexual reproduction can occur. (The difference in the mycelia is genetic rather than structural. Because they are impossible to distinguish, the mycelia are simply referred to as + and – mating types, as indicated in Figure 25-7.)

Figure 25-3 Bread mold culture (0.5×).

Figure 25-4 Sexual reproduction in the bread mold. Black line consists of zygosporangia (0.5×).

8. Note the black "line" running down the center of the culture plate. These are the numerous **zygosporangia**, the products of sexual reproduction. Here's how the zygosporangia are formed:
   (a) As the hyphae from each mating type grow close together, chemical messengers produced within the hyphae signal them to produce protuberances (Figure 25-7f).
   (b) When the protuberances make contact, gametangia (Figures 25-5, 25-7g) are produced at their tips. Each gametangium contains many haploid nuclei of a single mating type.
   (c) The wall between the two gametangia then dissolves, and the cytoplasms of the gametangia mix.
   (d) Eventually the many haploid nuclei from each gametangium fuse (Figure 25-7h). The resulting cell contains many diploid nuclei resulting from the fusion of gamete nuclei of opposite mating types. Each diploid nucleus is considered a *zygote*. This multinucleate cell is called a zygospore.
   (e) Eventually a thick, bumpy wall forms around this zygospore. Because germination of the zygospore results in the production of a sporangium, the thick-walled zygospore-containing structure is called a **zygosporangium**. Meiosis takes place inside the zygopsporangium so that the spores formed are haploid, some of one mating type, some of the opposite type (Figures 25-6, 25-7i).

9. Obtain a prepared slide of *Rhizopus*. Examine it with the medium- and high-power objective of your compound microscope.
10. Find the stages of sexual reproduction in *Rhizopus,* including gametangia, zygospores, and zygosporangia.

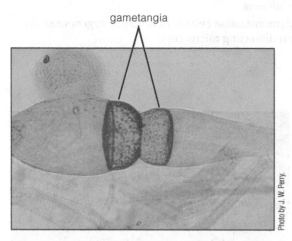

Figure 25-5 Gametangia of a bread mold (230×).

Figure 25-6 Zygospore and zygosporangium of the bread mold (230×).

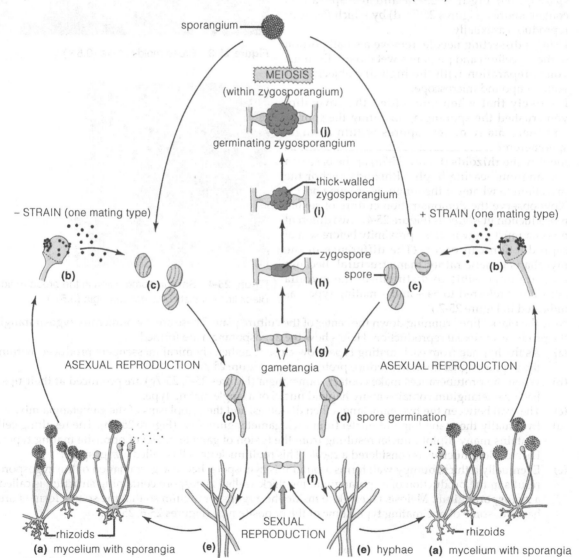

Figure 25-7 Life cycle of *Rhizopus*, black bread mold. (Green structures are 2n.)

Knowing that fungal spores are all around us, why don't we have fungi covering everything we own? Well, given the proper environmental conditions just such a situation can occur. This is particularly true of food products. That's one reason we refrigerate many of our foodstuffs. Producers often incorporate chemicals into some of our foods to retard spoilage, which includes preventing the growth of fungi.

This experiment addresses the hypothesis that *the chemicals placed in bread retard the growth of* Rhizopus. You may wish to review the discussion concerning experimental design in Exercise 1, "The Scientific Method."

MATERIALS

Per student group:

- one slice of bread without preservatives
- one slice of bread with preservatives
- suspension culture of bread mold fungus
- sterile dH$_2$O
- two large culture bowls

- plastic film
- pipet and bulb
- china marker
- metric ruler

PROCEDURE

1. With the china marker, label the side of one culture bowl "NO PRESERVATIVES," the other "WITH PRESERVATIVES." Place the appropriate slice of bread in its respective bowl.
2. Add a small amount of dH$_2$O to the bottom of each culture bowl. This provides humidity during incubation.
3. Add 5 drops of the spore suspension of the bread mold fungus to the center of each slice of bread.
4. Cover the bowls with plastic film and place them in a warm place designated by your instructor.
5. In Table 25-2, list the ingredients of both types of bread.
6. Make a prediction of what you think will be the outcome of the experiment, writing it in Table 25-2.
7. Check your cultures over the next three days, looking for evidence of fungal growth. Measure the diameter of the mycelium present in each culture, using a metric ruler.
8. Record your measurements and conclusion in Table 25-2, accepting or rejecting the hypothesis.

Design an experiment that would allow you to identify the substance that has the effect you observed.

_____

_____

_____

TABLE 25-2	**Growth of Bread Mold**		
Ingredients			
Bread without preservatives:			
Bread with preservatives:			
Prediction:			
		Mycelial Diameter (cm)	
Culture	Day 1	Day 2	Day 3
With preservatives			
No preservatives			
Conclusion:			

Members of the "ascomycetes" produce spores in a sac, the **ascus** (plural, *asci*), which develops as a result of sexual reproduction. Asexual reproduction takes place when the fungus produces asexual spores called **conidia** (singular, *conidium*). The phylum includes organisms of considerable importance, such as the yeasts crucial to the baking and brewing industries, as well as numerous plant pathogens. A few are highly prized as food, including morels and truffles. Truffles cost in excess of $400 per pound!

MATERIALS

Per student:

- glass microscope slide
- coverslip
- dissecting needle
- prepared slide of *Peziza*
- compound microscope

Per student pair:

- culture of *Eurotium*
- dH$_2$O in dropping bottle
- large preserved specimen of *Peziza* or another cup fungus

A. *Eurotium:* A Blue Mold

The blue mold *Eurotium* gets its common name from the production of blue-walled asexual conidia.

PROCEDURE

1. Use a dissecting needle to scrape some **conidia** from the agar surface of the culture provided, then prepare a wet mount. (Try to avoid the yellow bodies—more about them in a bit.)
2. Refer to Figure 25-8 as you observe your preparation with the high-dry objective of your compound microscope.
3. Note that the conidia are produced at the end of a specialized hypha that has a swollen tip.

This arrangement has been named *Aspergillus.* This structure, the *conidiophore,* somewhat resembles an aspergillum used in the Roman Catholic Church to sprinkle holy water, from which its name is derived.

(You may be confused about why we italicize *Aspergillus.* The reason is that this is a scientific name. Fungi other than *Eurotium* produce the same type of asexual structure; hence the asexual structure itself is given a scientific name.)

These tiny conidia are carried by air currents to new environments, where they germinate to form new mycelia.

4. Note the yellow bodies on the culture medium. These are the *fruiting bodies,* known as **ascocarps**, which are the products of sexual reproduction (Figure 25-9).
5. With your dissecting needle, remove an ascocarp from the culture and prepare a wet mount.
6. Using your thumb, carefully press down on the coverslip to rupture the ascocarp.

conidiophore without conidia   conidia

Photo courtesy Biodisc/Visuals Unlimited.

Figure 25-8   Conidiophore and conidia of the blue mold, *Eurotium* (138×).

ascus containing ascospores   ascocarp

Photo by J. W. Perry.

Figure 25-9   Crushed asocarp of *Eurotium* (287×).

7. Observe your preparation with the medium-power and high-dry objectives of your compound microscope. Identify the **asci**, which contain dark-colored, spherical **ascospores** (Figure 25-9).

The sexual cycle of the sac fungi is somewhat complex and is summarized in Figure 25-10.

The female gametangium, the **ascogonium** (Figure 25-10a; plural, *ascogonia*) is fertilized by male nuclei from antheridia (Figure 25-10a).

The male nuclei (darkened circles in Figure 25-10a) pair with the female nuclei (open circles) but do not fuse immediately.

Papillae grow from the ascogonium, and the paired nuclei flow into these papillae (Figure 25-10b).

Now cell walls form between each pair of sexually compatible nuclei (Figure 25-10c).

Subsequently, the two nuclei fuse; the resultant cell is the diploid ascus (Figure 25-10d). (Consequently, the ascus is a zygote.)

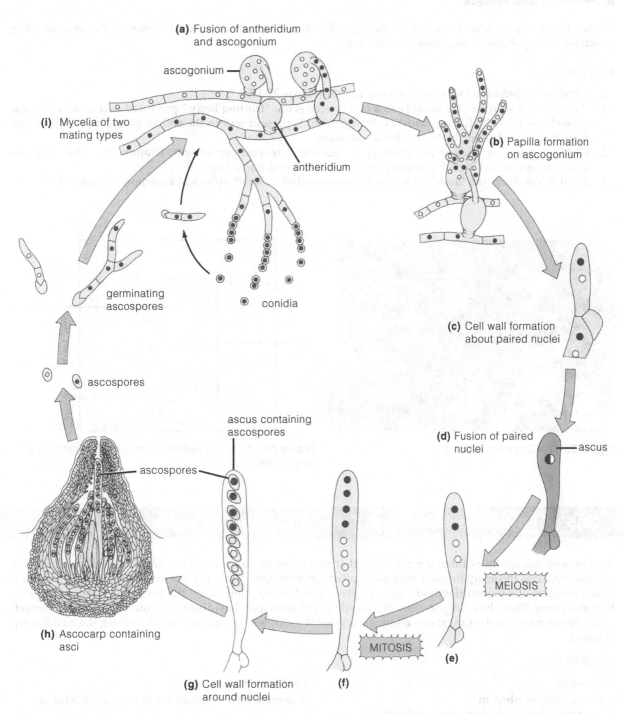

(a) Fusion of antheridium and ascogonium

ascogonium

(i) Mycelia of two mating types

antheridium

(b) Papilla formation on ascogonium

germinating ascospores

conidia

(c) Cell wall formation about paired nuclei

ascospores

ascus containing ascospores

ascospores

(d) Fusion of paired nuclei

ascus

MEIOSIS

MITOSIS

(h) Ascocarp containing asci

(g) Cell wall formation around nuclei

(f)

(e)

Figure 25-10 Life cycle of a sac fungus, such as *Eurotium* or *Peziza*. (Green structure is 2n.)

The nucleus of the ascus undergoes meiosis to form four nuclei (Figure 25-10e).

Mitosis then produces eight nuclei from these four (Figure 25-10f). (Notice that cytokinesis—cytoplasmic division—does not follow meiosis.)

Next, a cell wall forms about each nucleus, some of the cytoplasm of the ascus being included within the cell wall (Figure 25-10g).

Thus, eight haploid uninucleate ascospores (Figure 25-10g) have been formed.

While asci and ascospores are forming, surrounding hyphae proliferate to form the ascocarp (Figure 25-10h) around the asci.

As you see, two different types of ascospores are produced during meiosis. Each ascospore gives rise to a mycelium having only one mating type (Figure 25-10i).

B. *Peziza:* A Cup Fungus

The cup fungi are commonly found on soil during cool early spring and fall weather. Their sexual spore-containing structures are cup shaped, hence their common name.

PROCEDURE

1. Observe the preserved specimen of a cup fungus (Figure 25-11).
2. Actually, the structure we identify as a cup fungus is the "fruiting body," produced as a result of sexual reproduction by the fungus. Most of the organism is present within the soil as an extensive mycelium. Specifically, the fruiting body is called an **ascocarp**.
3. Obtain a prepared slide of the ascocarp of *Peziza* or a related cup fungus. Examine the slide with the medium-power and high-dry objectives of your compound microscope.
4. Identify the elongated fingerlike **asci**, which contain dark-colored, spherical **ascospores** (Figure 25-12).

Figure 25-11 Cup fungi (0.25×).

Figure 25-12 Cross section of an ascocarp from a cup fungus (186×).

25.5 Phylum Basidiomycota: Club Fungi *(About 30 min.)*

Members of this group of fungi are probably that first come to mind when we think of fungi, because this phylum contains those organisms commonly called "mushrooms." Actually the mushroom is only a portion of the fungus—it's the fruiting body, specifically a **basidiocarp**, containing the sexually produced haploid **basidiospores**. These basidiospores are produced by a club-shaped **basidium** for which the group is named. Much (if not most) of the fungal mycelium grows out of sight, within the substrate on which the basidiocarp is found.

MATERIALS

Per student:

- commercial mushroom
- prepared slide of mushroom pileus (cap), c.s. (*Coprinus*)
- compound microscope

Per lab room:

- demonstration specimens of various club fungi

A. Gill Fungi: The Mushrooms

Mushrooms called "gill fungi" have their sexual spores produced on sheets of hyphae that look like the gills of fish.

PROCEDURE

1. Obtain a fresh fruiting body, more properly called a **basidiocarp** (Figure 25-13). Identify the **stalk** and **cap**.
2. Look at the bottom surface of the cap, noting the numerous **gills**. It is on the surface of these gills that the haploid basidiospores are produced. Remember that all the structures you are examining are composed of aggregations of fungal hyphae.
3. Obtain a prepared slide of a cross section of the cap of a mushroom (Figure 25-14). Observe the slide first with the low-power objective of your compound microscope.
4. In the center of the cap, identify the **stalk**. The **gills** radiate from the stalk to the edge of the cap, much as spokes of a bicycle wheel radiate from the hub to the rim.
5. Switch to the high-dry objective to study a single gill (Figure 25-15). Note that the component hyphae produce club-shaped structures at the edge. These are the **basidia** (singular, *basidium*).
6. Each basidium produces four haploid **basidiospores**. Find them. (All four may not be in the same plane of section.)

Each basidiospore is attached to the basidium by a tiny hornlike projection. As the basidiospore matures, it is shot off the projection due to a buildup of turgor pressure within the basidium.

The life cycle of a typical mushroom is shown in Figure 25-16.

Because of genetic differences, basidiospores are of two different types. Mycelia produced by the two types of basidiospores are of two mating strains. Figure 25-16 shows these two different nuclei as open and closed (darkened) circles.

When a haploid basidiospore (Figure 25-16a) germinates, it produces a haploid *primary mycelium* (Figure 25-16b). The primary mycelium is incapable of producing a fruiting body.

Fusion between two sexually compatible mycelia (Figure 25-16b) must occur to continue the life cycle.

Surprisingly, the nuclei of the two mycelia don't fuse immediately; thus, each cell of this so-called *secondary mycelium* (Figure 25-16c) contains two genetically *different* nuclei. This condition is called "dikaryotic."

The secondary mycelium forms an extensive network within the substrate. An environmental or genetic trigger eventually stimulates the formation of the aerial basidiocarp (Figure 25-16d).

Each cell of the basidiocarp has two genetically different nuclei, including the basidia (Figure 25-16e) on the gills.

Within the basidia, the two nuclei fuse; the basidia are now diploid (Figure 25-16f).

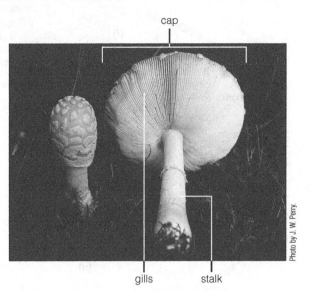

Figure 25-13 Mushroom basidiocarps. The one on the left is younger than that on the right (0.25×).

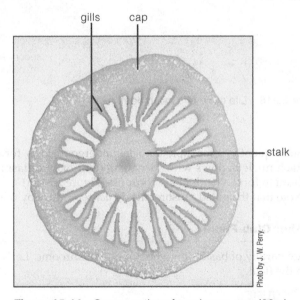

Figure 25-14 Cross section of mushroom cap (23×).

Figure 25-15 High magnification of a mushroom gill (287×).

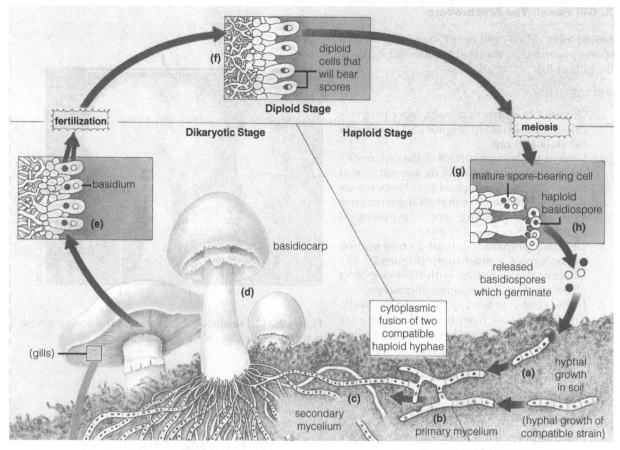

Figure 25-16 Life cycle of a mushroom.

Subsequently, these diploid nuclei undergo meiosis, forming genetically distinct nuclei (Figure 25-16g).

Each nucleus flows with a small amount of cytoplasm through the hornlike projections at the tip of the basidium to form a haploid basidiospore (Figure 25-16h).

Note that the gilled mushrooms do *not* reproduce by means of asexual conidia.

B. Other Club Fungi

A wide variety of basidiomycetes are not mushrooms. Let's examine a few representatives that you're likely to see in the field.

PROCEDURE

1. Examine the representatives of fruiting bodies of other members of the club fungi available in the laboratory.
2. Observe "puffballs" (Figure 25-17).The basidiospores of puffballs are contained within a spherical basidiocarp that develops a pore at the apex. Basidiospores are released when the puffball is crushed or hit by driving rain.
3. Examine "shelf fungi" (Figure 25-18). What you are looking at is actually the basidiocarp of the fungus that has been removed from the surface of a tree.

The presence of a basidiocarp of the familiar shelf fungi indicates that an extensive network of fungal hyphae is growing within a tree, digesting the cells of the wood. As a forester assesses a woodlot to determine the potential yield of usable wood, one of the things noted is the presence of shelf fungi, which indicates low-value (diseased) trees.

The most common shelf fungi are called polypores because of the numerous holes ("pores") on the lower surface of the fruiting body. These pores are lined with basidia bearing basidiospores.

4. Observe the undersurface of the basidiocarp that is on demonstration at a dissecting microscope and note the pores.

Figure 25-17 Puffballs. Note pore for spore escape (0.31×).

Photo by J. W. Perry.

Figure 25-18 Shelf fungus growing around a fence post (0.12×).

Photo by J. W. Perry.

25.6 "Imperfect Fungi" *(About 15 min.)*

This group consists of fungi for which no sexual stage is known. Someone once decided that in order for a life to be complete—to be "perfect"—sex was necessary. Thus, these fungi are "imperfect." Reproduction takes place primarily by means of asexual conidia.

These fungi are among the most economically important, producing antibiotics (for example, one species of *Penicillium* produces penicillin). Others produce the citric acid used in the soft-drink industry; still others are used in the manufacture of cheese. Some are important pathogens of both plants and animals.

MATERIALS

Per student:

- dissecting needle
- glass microscope slide
- coverslip
- prepared slide of *Penicillium* conidia (optional)
- compound microscope

Per student pair:

- dH$_2$O in dropping bottle
- culture of *Alternaria*

Per lab room:

- demonstration of *Penicillium*-covered food *and/or* plate cultures

A. Penicillium*

The genus *Penicillium* has numerous species. The common feature of all species in this genus is the distinctive shape of the hypha that produce the conidia (Figure 25-19).

PROCEDURE

1. Examine demonstration specimens of moldy oranges or other foods. The blue color is attributable to a pigment in the numerous conidia produced by this fungus, *Penicillium*.
2. With a dissecting needle, scrape some of the conidia from the surface of the moldy specimen (or from a petri dish culture plate containing *Penicillium*) and

---

*Some species of *Penicillium* reproduce sexually, forming ascocarps. These species are classified in the phylum Ascomycota. However, not *all* fungi producing the conidiophore form called *Penicillium* reproduce sexually. Those that reproduce only by asexual means are considered "imperfect fungi."

conidia

conidiophore

Photo courtesy G. L. Barron, University of Guelph.

Figure 25-19 *Penicillium* (300×).

prepare a wet mount. Observe your preparation using the high-dry objective. (Prepared slides may also be available.)

3. Identify the **conidiophore** and the numerous tiny, spherical **conidia** (Figure 25-19). The name *Penicillium* comes from the Latin word *penicillus,* meaning "a brush." (Appropriate, isn't it?)

B. *Alternaria*

Perhaps no other fungus causes more widespread human irritation than *Alternaria,* an allergy-causing organism. During the summer, many weather programs announce the daily pollen (from flowering plants, Exercise 24) and *Alternaria* spore counts as an index of air quality for allergy sufferers.

PROCEDURE

1. From the petri dish culture plate provided, remove a small portion of the mycelium and prepare a wet mount.

2. Examine with the high-dry objective of your compound microscope to find the **conidia** (Figure 25-20). Produced in chains, *Alternaria* conidia are multicellular, unlike those of *Penicillium* or *Aspergillus.* This makes identification very easy, since the conidia are quite distinct from all others produced by the fungi.

Figure 25-20   Conidia of *Alternaria* (332×).

25.7   Mutualistic Fungi *(About 20 min.)*

Fungi team up with plants or members of the bacterial or protist kingdoms to produce some remarkable mutualistic relationships. The best way to envision such relationships is to think of them as good interpersonal relationships, in which both members benefit and are made richer than would be possible for each individual on its own.

MATERIALS

Per lab room:

- demonstration specimens of crustose, foliose, and fruticose lichens
- demonstration slide of lichen, c.s. on compound microscope
- demonstration slide of mycorrhizal root, c.s. on compound microscope

A. Lichens

Lichens are organisms made up of fungi and either green algae (kingdom Protista) or cyanobacteria (kingdom Eubacteria). The algal or cyanobacterial cells photosynthesize, and the fungus absorbs a portion of the carbohydrates produced. The fungal mycelium provides a protective, moist shelter for the photosynthesizing cells. Hence, both partners benefit from the relationship.

PROCEDURE

1. Examine the demonstration specimen of a **crustose lichen** (Figure 25-21).

2. What is it growing on? _____

_____

_____

3. Write a sentence describing the crustose lichen.

_____

_____

granite (rock) substrate

crustose lichen

Figure 25-21   Crustose lichen (0.5×).

4. Observe the demonstration specimen of a **foliose lichen** (Figure 25-22).

5. What is it growing on? _____

6. Write a sentence describing the foliose lichen.

   _____

   _____

   _____

   _____

7. Examine the demonstration specimen of a **fruticose lichen** (Figure 25-23).

8. What is it growing on?

   _____

   _____

   _____

Figure 25-22 Foliose lichen (0.5×).

9. Write a sentence describing the fruticose lichen.

   _____

   _____

   _____

apothecia (spore containers)

moss

Figure 25-23 Fruticose lichen (1×).

10. Observe the cross section of a lichen at the demonstration microscope. This particular lichen is composed of fungal and green algae cells (Figure 25-24).
11. Locate the **fungal mycelium** and then the **algae cells**.
12. It's likely that this slide has a cup-shaped fruiting body. To which fungal phylum does this fungus belong?

Figure 25-24   Section of lichen (84×).

B. Mycorrhizae

Mycorrhiza literally means "fungus root." A mycorrhiza is a mutualistic association between plant roots and certain species of fungi. In fact, many of the mushroom species (see Section 25.5.A.) you find in forests (especially those that appear to grow right from the ground) are part of a mycorrhizal association.

The fungus absorbs carbohydrates from the plant roots. The fungal hyphae penetrate much farther into the soil than plant root hairs can reach, absorbing water and dissolved mineral ions that are then released to the plant. Again, both partners benefit. In fact, many plants don't grow well in the absence of mycorrhizal associations.

There are two different types of mycorrhizal roots, **ectomycorrhizae** and **endomycorrhizae.** "Ectos" produce a fungal sheath around the root, and the hyphae penetrate between the cell walls of the root's cortex, but not into the root cells themselves. By contrast, "endos" do not form a covering sheath, and the fungi are found within the cells. We'll look at both types.

MATERIALS

Per student:

- ectomyccorhizal pine root, prep. slide, c.s.
- endomyccorhizal root, prep. slide, c.s.
- compound microscope

PROCEDURE

1. Obtain a prepared slide of an ectomycorrhizal pine root. Examine it with the medium- and high-power objective of your compound microscope.
2. Identify the sheath of fungal hyphae that surround the root.
3. Now look for hyphae between the cell walls within the cortex of the root.
4. Draw what you see in Figure 25-25.
5. Obtain a prepared slide of an endomycorrhizal root (Figure 25-26) and examine it as you did above.
6. Identify the hyphae within the plant root cells.

Figure 25-25 Drawing of ectomycorrhizal pine root (_____×).

highly branched hypha in root cell

hyphae in root cell

Photo by J. W. Perry.

Figure 25-26 Cross section of endomycorrhizal root (110×).

25.8 Experiment: Environmental Factors and Fungal Growth
(About 45 min. to set up)

Like all living organisms, environmental cues are instrumental in causing growth responses in fungi. Intuitively, we know that light is important for plant growth. Light also affects animals in a myriad of ways, from triggering reproductive events in deer to affecting the complex psyche of humans. What effect might light have on fungi? These experiments enable you to determine whether this environmental factor has any effect on fungal growth.

A. Light and Darkness

This experiment addresses the hypothesis that _light triggers spore production of certain fungi._

MATERIALS

Per experimental group (student pair):

- transfer loop
- bunsen burner (or alcohol lamp)
- matches or striker
- three petri plates containing potato dextrose agar (PDA)
- grease pencil or other marker

Per lab bench:

- test tubes with spore suspensions of _Trichoderma viride_, _Penicillium claviforme_, and _Aspergillus ornatus_

PROCEDURE

Work in pairs, and refer to Figure 25-27, which shows how to inoculate the cultures.

1. Receive instructions from your lab instructor as to which fungal culture you should use.

    Note: Do not open the petri plates until step 3.

2. Use a grease pencil or other lab marker to label each cover with your name and the name of the fungus you have been assigned. Write "CONTINUOUS LIGHT" on one petri plate, "CONTINUOUS DARKNESS" on a second plate, and "ALTERNATING LIGHT AND DARKNESS" on the third one.
3. Following the directions in Figure 25-27, inoculate each plate by touching the loop gently on the agar surface approximately in the middle of the plate.

(a) Sterilize the loop by holding the wire in a flame until it is red hot. Allow it to cool before proceeding.

(b) While holding the sterile loop and the bacterial culture, remove the cap as shown.

(c) Briefly heat the mouth of the tube in a burner flame before inserting the loop for an inoculum.

(d) Get a loopful of culture, withdraw the loop, heat the mouth of the tube, and replace the cap.

(e) To inoculate a solid medium in a petri plate, place the plate on a table and lift one edge of the cover.

After Case and Johnson, 1984.

Figure 25-27 Procedure for inoculating a culture plate.

4. Place one plate in each condition:
   - continuous light
   - continuous darkness
   - alternating light and dark
5. In Table 25-3, write your prediction of what will occur in the different environmental conditions.
6. Check the results after 5–7 days and make conclusions concerning the effect of light on the growth of the cultures. Record your results in Table 25-3. Draw what you observe in Figure 25-28.
7. Compare the results you obtained with the results of other experimenters who used different species. Record your conclusions in Table 25-3.

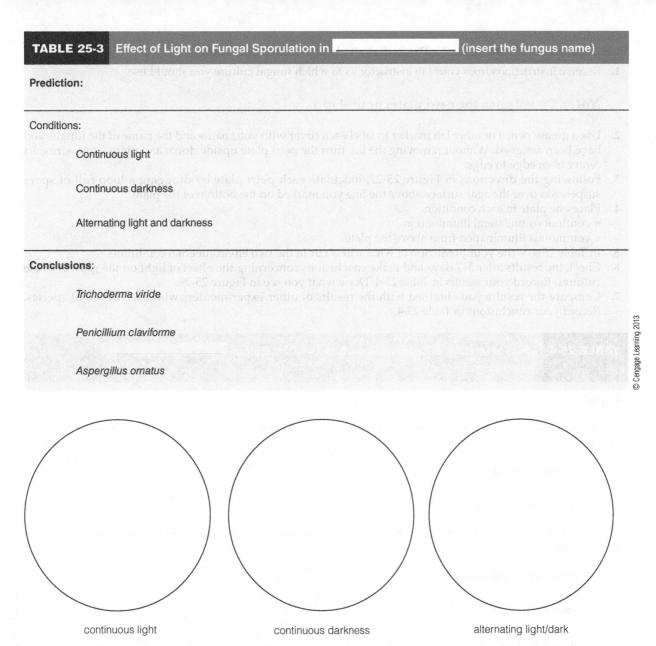

| TABLE 25-3 | Effect of Light on Fungal Sporulation in _____ (insert the fungus name) |

Prediction:

_____

Conditions:

    Continuous light

    Continuous darkness

    Alternating light and darkness

Conclusions:

    Trichoderma viride

    Penicillium claviforme

    Aspergillus ornatus

© Cengage Learning 2013

      continuous light   continuous darkness   alternating light/dark

Figure 25-28 Drawing of effect of alternating light and darkness on sporulation of _____ (insert name of fungus).

B. Directional Illumination

This experiment addresses the hypothesis that *light from one direction causes the spore-bearing hyphae of certain fungi to grow in the direction of the light.*

MATERIALS

Per experimental group (student pair):

- transfer loop
- bunsen burner (or alcohol lamp)
- matches or striker
- two petri plates containing either potato dextrose agar (PDA) or cornmeal (CM) agar
- grease pencil or other marker

Per lab bench:

- test tubes with spore suspensions of
  Phycomyces blakesleeanus (inoculate onto PDA)
  Penicillium isariforme (inoculate onto PDA)
  Aspergillus giganteus (inoculate onto CM)

PROCEDURE

Work in pairs and refer to Figure 25-27, which shows how to inoculate cultures.

1. Receive instructions from your lab instructor as to which fungal culture you should use.

   Note: Do not open the petri plates until step 3.

2. Use a grease pencil or other lab marker to label each cover with your name and the name of the fungus you have been assigned. Without removing the lid, turn the petri plate upside down and place a line across its center from edge to edge.
3. Following the directions in Figure 25-27, inoculate each petri plate by dragging a loop full of spore suspension over the agar surface above the line you marked on the bottom of the plate.
4. Place one plate in each condition:
   - continuous unilateral illumination
   - continuous illumination from above the plate
5. In Table 25-4, write your prediction of what will occur in the two environmental conditions.
6. Check the results after 5–7 days and make conclusions concerning the effect of light on the growth of the cultures. Record your results in Table 25-4. Draw what you see in Figure 25-29.
7. Compare the results you obtained with the results of other experimenters who used different species. Record your conclusions in Table 25-4.

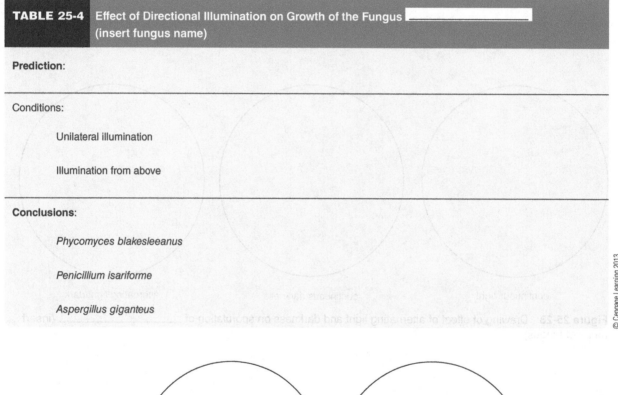

TABLE 25-4	Effect of Directional Illumination on Growth of the Fungus _____ (insert fungus name)

Prediction:

Conditions:

    Unilateral illumination

    Illumination from above

Conclusions:

    Phycomyces blakesleeanus

    Penicillium isariforme

    Aspergillus giganteus

© Cengage Learning 2013

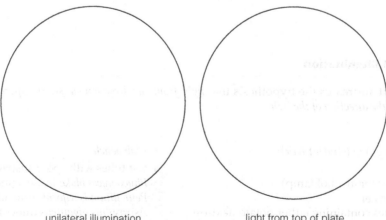

unilateral illumination   light from top of plate

Figure 25-29 Drawing of effect of unilateral illumination on growth of _____ (insert name of fungus).

_____ 1. An organism that grows specifically on nonliving organic material is called
(a) an autotroph.
(b) a heterotroph.
(c) a parasite.
(d) a saprophyte.

_____ 2. Taxonomic separation into fungal phyla is based on
(a) sexual reproduction, or lack thereof.
(b) whether the fungus is a parasite or saprophyte.
(c) the production of certain metabolites, like citric acid.
(d) the edibility of the fungus.

_____ 3. Fungi is to fungus as _____ is to _____.
(a) mycelium/mycelia
(b) hypha/hyphae
(c) sporangia/sporangium
(d) ascus/asci

_____ 4. Which statement is not true of the zygospore-forming fungi?
(a) They are in the phylum Zygomycota.
(b) Ascospores are found in an ascus.
(c) *Rhizopus* is a representative genus.
(d) A zygospore is formed after fertilization.

_____ 5. Which structures would you find in a sac fungus?
(a) ascogonium, antheridium, zygospores
(b) ascospores, oogonia, asci, ascocarps
(c) basidia, basidiospores, basidiocarps
(d) ascogonia, asci, ascocarps, ascospores

_____ 6. The club fungi are placed in the phylum Basidiomycota
(a) because of their social nature.
(b) because they form basidia.
(c) because of the presence of an ascocarp.
(d) because they are dikaryotic.

_____ 7. Which statement is not true of the imperfect fungi?
(a) They reproduce sexually by means of conidia.
(b) They form an ascocarp.
(c) Sex organs are present in the form of oogonia and antheridia.
(d) All of the above are false.

_____ 8. A relationship between two organisms in which both members benefit is said to be
(a) parasitic.
(b) saprotrophic.
(c) mutualistic.
(d) heterotrophic.

_____ 9. An organism that is made up of a fungus and an associated green alga or cyanobacterium is known as a
(a) sac fungus.
(b) lichen.
(c) mycorrhizal root.
(d) club fungus.

_____ 10. A mutualistic association between a plant root and a fungus is known as a
(a) sac fungus.
(b) lichen.
(c) mycorrhizal root.
(d) club fungus.

EXERCISE **25**

Fungi

Post-Lab Questions

25.2 Phylum Zygomycota: Zygosporangium-Forming Fungi

1. Observe this photo at the right of a portion of a fungus you examined in lab.
   (a) What is structure A?

   (b) Are the contents of structure A haploid or diploid?

2. Distinguish between a *hypha* and a *mycelium*.

3. Examine the below photomicrographs of a fungal structure you studied in lab. Is this structure labeled B in the photomicrograph below the product of sexual or asexual reproduction?

(130×)

(120×)

25.4 Phylum Ascomycota: Sac Fungi

4. Distinguish among an *ascus*, an *ascospore*, and an *ascocarp*.

5. Walking in the woods, you find a cup-shaped fungus. Back in the lab, you remove a small portion from what appears to be its fertile surface and crush it on a microscope slide, preparing the wet mount that appears at the right. Identify the fingerlike structures present on the slide.

(287×)

25.5 Phylum Basidiomycota: Club Fungi

6. What type of spores are produced by the fungus pictured at the right?

7. The photo below shows a fungus growing on a dead hemlock tree. What is the common name of a fungus of this sort? Be specific.

(0.5×)

(0.1×)

25.6 "Imperfect Fungi"

8. Explain the name "imperfect fungi."

Food for Thought

9. Give the correct singular or plural form of the following words in the blanks provided.

	Singular	Plural
(a)	hypha	
(b)		mycelia
(c)	zygospore	
(d)		asci
(e)	basidium	
(f)		conidia

10. Lichens are frequently the first colonizers of hostile growing sites, including sunbaked or frozen rock, recently hardened lava, and even gravestones. How can lichens survive in habitats so seemingly devoid of nutrients and under such harsh physical conditions?

Sponges and Cnidarians

After completing this exercise, you will be able to

1. define *larva, asymmetry, radial symmetry, bilateral symmetry, cephalization, coelom, pseudocoelom, monoecious, dioecious, invertebrates, spongocoel, osculum, spicules, choanocyte (collar cell), budding, spongin, polyp, tentacles, medusa, nematocyst, gastrovascular cavity, epidermis, gastrodermis, mesoglea;*

2. list the characteristics of animals;

3. describe how the phyla Porifera and Cnidaria respectively show the cell-specialization and tissue levels of organization;

4. explain the basic body plan of members of the phyla Porifera and Cnidaria;

5. describe the natural history of the phyla Porifera and Cnidaria;

6. identify representatives of the classes Calcarea and Demospongiae of the phylum Porifera and classes Hydrozoa, Scyphozoa, and Anthozoa of the phylum Cnidaria;

7. identify structures (and indicate associated functions) of representatives of these classes.

Introduction

Animals are multicellular, oxygen-consuming, heterotrophic (heterotrophs feed on other organisms or on organic waste) *organisms that exhibit considerable motility* (spontaneous movement). Most animals are *diploid* and *reproduce sexually,* although asexual reproduction is also common. The animal life cycle includes a *period of embryonic development, often with a* **larva**—sexually immature, free-living form that grows and transforms into an adult— or equivalent stage. During the embryonic development of most animals, *three primary germ layers—ectoderm, mesoderm,* and *endoderm*—form and give rise to the adult organs and tissues. Evidence accumulated from centuries of study supports the notion that animals evolved from a group of protistan-like ancestors distinct from those that gave rise to the plants and fungi.

Animal diversity is usually studied in the approximate order of a group's first appearance on Earth. Table 26-1 summarizes the trends evident in this sequence for the phyla considered in this and subsequent diversity exercises:

- In terms of habitat, marine animals precede freshwater and terrestrial forms.
- The organization of animal bodies is initially **asymmetrical**—cannot cut the body into two like halves—but rapidly becomes symmetrical, exhibiting first **radial symmetry**—any cut from the oral (mouth) to the other end through the center of the animal yields two like halves (Figure 26-1a) —and then bilateral symmetry. In **bilateral symmetry**, a cut in only one plane parallel to the main axis yields like right and left halves (Figure 26-1b).

    Bilateral symmetry accompanies the movement of sensory structures and the mouth to the front end of the body to form a head, a process called **cephalization**.

    Spaces within the body are first "baskets" used to filter seawater, then incomplete guts (no anus) appear, and finally complete guts (with an anus) are suspended in an entirely

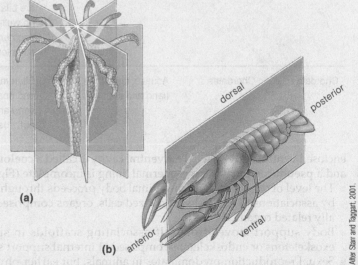

Figure 26-1 Examples of body symmetry. (a) Radial symmetry in a cnidarian polyp. (b) Bilateral symmetry in a crayfish, an arthropod.

After Starr and Taggart, 2001.

Phylum	Common Name	Habitat	Body Organization	Level of Organization
Porifera	Sponges	Aquatic, mostly marine	None or crude radial symmetry	Cell specialization
Cnidaria	Cnidarians	Aquatic, mostly marine	Radial symmetry, incomplete gut	Tissue (ectoderm and endoderm only)
Platyhelminthes	Flatworms	Aquatic, moist terrestrial, or parasitic	Bilateral symmetry, head, incomplete gut	Organ system (all three primary germ layers)
Rotifera	Rotifers	Aquatic (mostly freshwater) or moist terrestrial	Bilateral symmetry, head, complete gut, pseudocoelom	Organ system
Annelida	Annelids some parasitic	Aquatic or moist terrestrial, bilateral symmetry, some parasitic	Bilateral symmetry, head, segmented, complete gut, coelom	Organ system
Mollusca	Molluscans	Aquatic or terrestrial, mostly marine	Unique body plan, complete gut, coelom	Organ system
Nematoda	Roundworms	Aquatic, moist terrestrial, or parasitic	Bilateral symmetry, head, complete gut, pseudocoelom	Organ system
Arthropod	Arthropods	Aquatic, terrestrial (land and air), some parasitic	Bilateral symmetry, head, complete gut, segmented, coelom	Organ system
Echinodermata	Echinoderms	Aquatic, marine	Radial symmetry (larvae are bilaterally symmetrical), no well-defined head, no segmentation, usually complete gut, coelom	Organ system
Chordata	Chordates	Aquatic, terrestrial (land and air)	Bilateral symmetry, head and postanal tail, segmentation, complete gut, coelom	Organ system

TABLE 26-1 Trends in the Evolution of Animals

enclosed ventral body space. This ventral cavity is called a **coelom** if it is lined by tissue derived from mesoderm, and a **pseudocoelom** if the mesodermal lining is incomplete (Figure 26-2).

- The level of organization of the animal body proceeds through aggregates of specialized cells, tissues formed by associations of similarly specialized cells, organs comprised of different tissues, and systems of functionally related organs.

- Body support moves from self-associating scaffolds in sponges to hydrostatic bodies to shells and exoskeletons or endoskeletons comprised of internal support structures.

- Sexual reproduction predominates in animals, but earlier phyla are asexual as well. Earlier forms are often **monoecious** or *hermaphroditic*—individuals have both male and female reproductive structures. Later forms are **dioecious** with male and female reproductive structures in separate sexes. Fertilization of the egg by sperm is usually external in *sessile* (immobile and attached to a surface such as the sea bottom) animals and internal in most mobile forms, and *parthenogenesis* (the egg develops without fertilization) occurs sporadically.

Body Support	Life Cycle	Special Characteristics
Spicules, spongin	Sexual reproduction (mostly monoecious), larva (amphiblastula), asexual reproduction (budding)	Spongocoel, osculum, gemmules, choanocytes (collar cells)
Hydrostatic gut	Sexual reproduction (monoecious or dioecious), larva (planula), asexual reproduction (budding and fragmentation)	Nerve net, nematocysts, two adult body forms—polyp (sessile) and medusa (free swimming)
Muscular	Sexual reproduction (mostly monoecious with internal fertilization); parasites have very complicated life cycles; some asexual reproduction (mostly transverse fission)	Brain, flame cells
Hydrostatic pseudocoelom	Sexual (dioecious with internal fertilization), some parthenogenesis, males much smaller than females or absent	Brain, flame cells, wheel organ, mastax, microscopic animals
Hydrostatic coelom	Sexual reproduction (monoecious or dioecious with mostly internal fertilization), larvae in some, asexual reproduction (mostly transverse fission)	Brain, nephridia, gills in some
Shells, floats (aquatic)	Sexual (monoecious or dioecious with external or internal fertilization), larvae in some	Brain, nephridium or nephridia, most have gills or lungs, external body divided into head, mantle, and foot
Hydrostatic pseudocoelom	Sexual reproduction (mostly dioecious with internal fertilization)	Brain, molt to grow
Exoskeleton of chitin	Sexual reproduction (mostly dioecious with internal fertilization), larvae, metamorphosis, some parthenogenesis	Brain, green glands or Malphigian tubules, gills, tracheae or book lungs, body regions (head, thorax, and abdomen), specialized segments form mouthparts and jointed appendages, molt to grow
Dermal endoskeleton of calcium carbonate (mesoderm)	Sexual reproduction (mostly dioecious with external fertilization), larvae, metamorphosis, high regenerative potential	Radial symmetry, water-vascular system
Most have an endoskeleton of cartilage or bone	Sexual reproduction (mostly dioecious with internal or external fertilization), some larvae, some metamorphosis	Brain, ventral heart, notochord, gill slits, and dorsal hollow nerve cord at some stage of life cycle

---

CAUTION

Specimens are kept in preservative solutions. Use lab gloves and safety goggles, especially if you wear contact lenses, whenever you or your lab mates handle a specimen. If safety goggles do not fit, your glasses should suffice. Wash any part of your body exposed to preservative with copious amounts of water. If preservative solution is splashed into your eyes, wash them with the safety eyewash bottle or eye irrigation apparatus for 15 minutes.

(a) No coelom (*acoelomate* animals)

(b) Pseudocoel (*pseudocoelomate* animals)

(c) Coelom (coelomate animals)

Figure 26-2 Development of ventral body cavity in animals.

| **26.1** | Sponges (Phylum Porifera) *(45 min.)* |

Habitat	aquatic, mostly marine
Body Arrangement	asymmetrical or crude radial symmetry
Level of Organization	cell specialization
Body Support	spicules and/or spongin
Life Cycle	sexual reproduction (mostly monoecious), larva (amphiblastula), asexual reproduction (budding and fragmentation)
Special Characteristics	spongocoel, osculum, gemmules, choanocytes (collar cells)

Aristotle in his *Scala Naturae* said of sponges, "In the sea there are things which it is hard to label as either animal or vegetable." This was a reference to their sensitivity to stimulation and their relative lack of motility.

Sponges arose early from the main line of animal evolution (Figure 26-3). Most sponges are marine, and all forms are *aquatic*. As adults, sponges are *sessile*, but many disperse as free-swimming larvae. Although sponges possess a variety of different types of cells, they are atypical animals in their lack of definite tissues. They exhibit the *cell-specialization level of organization*, as there is a division of labor among the different cell types. Cells are organized into layers, but these associations of cells do not show all the characteristics of tissues. Sponges have a *crude radial symmetry or are asymmetrical*. Sponges along with the animals of most phyla are **invertebrates**—animals that do not posses a backbone or vertebral column.

Three body plans exist in sponges (Figure 26-4). They are referred to as *asconoid, syconoid,* and *leuconoid* and increase in the complexity of their structure in this order.

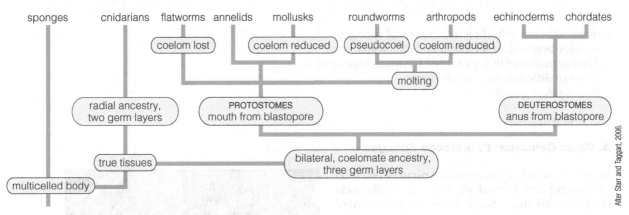

Figure 26-3 Presumed family tree for animals.

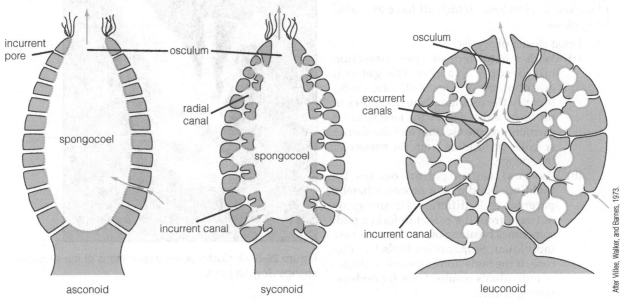

Figure 26-4 Three body plans of sponges. The blue arrows indicate the direction of water flow. Pink areas are lined by collar cells.

Water enters a vase-shaped asconoid sponge through *incurrent pores*; flows directly to a large central internal cavity, the **spongocoel**; and exits through a larger opening, the **osculum**. A syconoid sponge is similar, except that the inner side of the body wall pockets in to form *radial canals* into which branches of the *incurrent canals* drain. In a leuconoid sponge, the radial canals are internalized as chambers within the wall of the sponge. These chambers empty into *excurrent canals* that in turn lead to the osculum. Concurrent with the development of increasingly complex patterns of water flow, the area lined with *collar cells*, which in asconoid sponges is the inner wall of the spongocoel, also becomes internalized, first lining the radial canals of syconoid sponges and then the chambers of leuconoid sponges.

MATERIALS

Per student:

- dissection microscope
- hand lens
- compound microscope, lens paper, a bottle of lens-cleaning solution (optional), a lint-free cloth (optional)
- clean microscope slide and coverslip (optional)

Per student pair:

- preserved specimen of *Scypha (Grantia)*
- prepared slides of
   Scypha spicules (optional)
   a longitudinal section of *Scypha*
   a whole mount of *Leucosolenia*

a whole mount of teased commercial sponge fibers
a whole mount of *Spongilla* spicules freshwater sponge gemmules

Per student group (4):

- 100-mL beaker of heatproof glass (optional)
- bottle of 5% sodium hydroxide (NaOH) or potassium hydroxide (KOH) (optional)
- waste container for 5% hydroxide solution (optional)
- hot plate (optional)
- squeeze bottle of dH₂O (optional)

Per lab room:

- demonstration collection of commercial sponges
- squeeze bottle of 50% vinegar and 50% water
- demonstration of living or dried freshwater sponges
- boxes of different sizes of lab gloves
- box of safety goggles

PROCEDURE

A. Class Calcarea: Calcareous Sponges

Members of this class contain **spicules** (skeletal elements) composed of calcium carbonate ($CaCO_3$). All three body plans are represented in this group. You will study members of the genera *Scypha*, which all have the syconoid body plan, and *Leukosolenia*, which all have asconoid body plans.

1. Dried cluster of *Scypha*.
   (a) With a hand lens or your dissection microscope, examine the general morphology of *Scypha* (Figure 26-5). Identify the osculum. Note the pores in the body wall. Observe the long spicules surrounding the osculum and the shorter spicules protruding from the surface of the sponge.
   (b) Asexual reproduction occurs by **budding**. Budding is a process whereby parental cells differentiate and grow outward from the parent to form a bud, sometimes breaking off to become a new individual. *Scypha* often buds from its base. If the buds don't separate, a cluster of individuals results. Look for buds on your specimen.

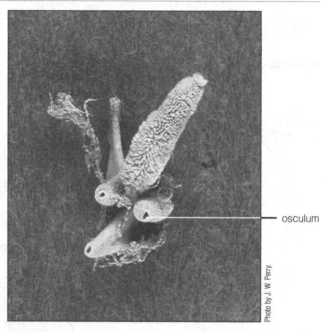
osculum

Photo by J. W. Perry.

Figure 26-5 A cluster of dried specimens of the syconoid sponge *Scypha* (3×).

CAUTION

Hot 5% hydroxide solutions are corrosive. Handle with extreme care. Wear lab gloves and safety goggles. If splashed, wash exposed surface for 15 minutes in running tap water; then flood the area with a 50% vinegar-and-water solution.

---

2. Examine a wet mount (w.m.) or a prepared slide of *Scypha* spicules with your compound microscope, using the medium-power objective. Draw what you observe in Figure 26-6. Follow these instructions to prepare the wet mount:
   (a) Place a small piece of a specimen of *Scypha* in a 100-mL heatproof beaker.
   (b) Carefully add enough 5% sodium hydroxide or potassium hydroxide solution to the beaker to cover the piece and bring this to a boil on the hot plate. Allow the beaker to cool.
   (c) Allow the remains of the sponge to settle to the bottom of the beaker and carefully pour off the liquid into the waste container while retaining the residue.
   (d) Wash the residue by adding distilled water. After the remains of the sponge settle, carefully pour off the water into the waste container.
   (e) Make a wet mount of the residue and draw a few of them in Figure 26-6.
3. Longitudinal section of *Scypha*.
   (a) Orient yourself to the general body plan and other features of *Scypha* (Figure 26-7). Examine a longitudinal section of this sponge with a compound microscope. In your section, trace the path of water as it flowed into and through the sponge in nature (Figure 26-8a). Identify the following structures and place them in the correct order for the water's circulation through the sponge by writing a 1st, 2nd, and 3rd, and so on in the second column of Table 26-2.

Figure 26-6 Calcium carbonate spicules of *Scypha*, w.m. (_____×).

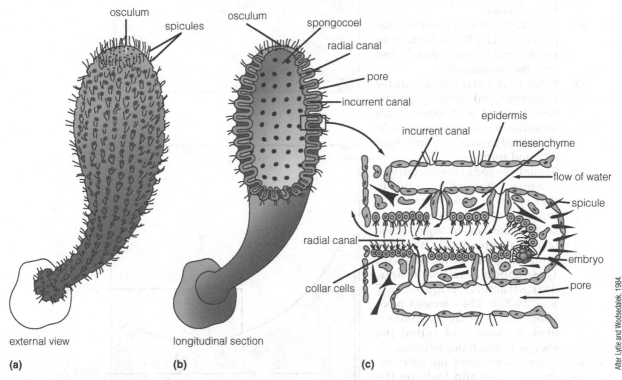

Figure 26-7 *Scypha.* (**a**) External view. (**b**) Longitudinal section. (**c**) Magnified to show detail.

After Lytle and Wodsedalek, 1984.

TABLE 26-2	Circulation of Water through the Syconoid Sponge *Scypha*
Structure	**Order for Water Circulation**
Spongocoel	
Incurrent canals	
Radial canals	
Incurrent pores	
Osculum	

© Cengage Learning 2013

(b) Examine the **collar cells**, which appear as numerous small, dark bodies lining the radial canals (Figure 26-8b). Each bears a flagellum that projects into the radial canal, but it is unlikely that you will be able to see the flagella, even with the high-dry objective. Examine the structure of a collar cell in Figure 26-9. The beating of the flagella of collar cells likely creates currents that help move water through the sponge. The microvilli—fingerlike projections that comprise their collars—play a major role in filtering fine food particles out of the water. Collar cells and perhaps other cells engulf and digest food fragments carried into the sponge by the flow of water.

(c) Identify the *epidermis* with its flat protective cells. It covers the outer surface and incurrent canals, and lines the spongocoel.

(d) Note that between the outer epidermis and inner epidermis lies a region of gelatinous material sometimes called the *mesohyle,* embedded in which are amoeboid cells and spicules.

(e) Sexual reproduction occurs in sponges. Although it's unlikely that you will observe gametes, look for early developmental stages (embryos) of *amphiblastula larvae* in the wall, perhaps protruding into the radial canals. These appear as relatively large, dark structures (Figures 26-7 and 26-8a). They would have soon finished development, broken loose, and exited the sponge through the osculum.

4. With your compound microscope, look for spicules and buds on the prepared slide of a whole mount of the asconoid sponge *Leucosolenia* (Figure 26-10).

spongocoel
amphiblastula larvae
incurrent canal
radial canal
incurrent pore

(a)

collar cells
mesohyle
epidermal cells

Photos by J. W. Perry.

(b)

Figure 26-8 Longitudinal sections of *Scypha*. (**a**) The arrow indicates the path of water flow (96×). (**b**) Radial canals lined with collar cells (384×).

The skeletons of these sponges... supported by spongin fibers...

flagellum   microvilli   nucleus

Collar cell

After Starr and Taggart, 2001.

Figure 26-9   Choanocyte (collar cell).

osculum

bud

Photo by J. W. Perry.

Figure 26-10   Whole mount of *Leucosolenia* (34×).

B. Class Demospongiae: Commercial and Freshwater Sponges

This class contains the majority of sponge species. Most sponges in this class are supported by **spongin** (Figure 26-11b, a flexible substance chemically similar to human hair), by spicules of silica, or both. Silica is silicon dioxide, a major component of sand and of many rocks, such as flint and quartz. All sponges in this class are leuconoid and are able to hold and pass large volumes of water in and through their bodies because of their complex canal systems. Some sponges with skeletons composed only of spongin fibers were once commercially valuable as bath sponges, but synthetic sponges have largely replaced them in today's marketplace.

1. Look over the demonstration specimens of commercial sponges available in your lab room (Figure 26-11a).

(a)

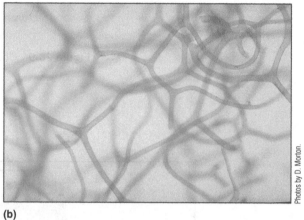
(b)

Photos by D. Morton.

Figure 26-11 (a) Bath sponge. (b) Spongin (74×).

2. With your compound microscope, examine a prepared slide of teased commercial sponge fibers and draw them in Figure 26-12.
3. Examine a prepared slide of silica spicules obtained from a common freshwater sponge of the genus *Spongilla* and draw several of them in Figure 26-13.

Figure 26-12 Teased spongin fibers of a commercial sponge, w.m. (_____×).

Figure 26-13 Silica spicules of *Spongilla*, w.m. (_____×).

4. Freshwater and some marine sponges in this class reproduce asexually by forming *gemmules*, resistant internal buds. In the freshwater varieties, a shell of silica and spicules surrounds groups of cells. During the unfavorable conditions of winter, disintegration of the sponge releases the gemmules. Under the favorable conditions of spring, cells emerge from the gemmules and develop into new individuals. Find and examine a gemmule on the prepared slide of freshwater sponge gemmules (Figure 26-14).

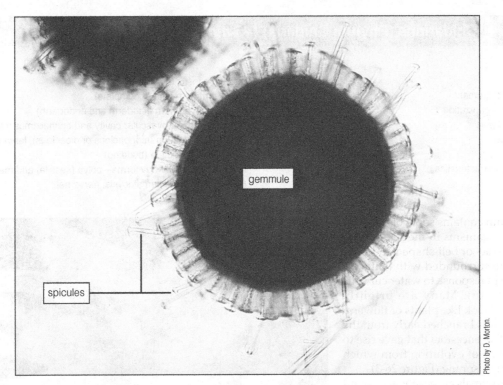

Figure 26-14 Freshwater sponge gemmule, w.m. (150×).

5. Observe the demonstration of living freshwater sponges available in your lab room (Figure 26-15). They look like yellowish-brown, wrinkled scum with perforations and sometimes have a greenish tint due to the presence of symbiotic algae. They are fairly easy to find in nature; search for them in clear, well-oxygenated water, encrusting submerged plant stems and debris such as a waterlogged twig. Slow streams and the edges of ponds where there is some wave action are good places to find freshwater sponges.

Figure 26-15 Dried freshwater sponges, *Sporilla fragilis* with gemmules (0.5×).

Habitat	aquatic, mostly marine
Body Arrangement	radial symmetry, gut (incomplete)
Level of Organization	tissue (derived from ectoderm and endoderm)
Body Support	hydrostatic (gastrovascular cavity and epitheliomuscular cells)
Life Cycle	sexual reproduction (monoecious or dioecious), larva (planula), asexual reproduction (budding)
Special Characteristics	tissues, two adult body forms—polyp (sessile) and medusa (free swimming)—nematocysts, nerve net

This phylum contains some of the most beautiful organisms in the seas. Adult bodies are sac- or bell-shaped and their mouths are surrounded with **tentacles** that move in response to water currents (Figure 26-16). Many are brightly colored and look like plants or flowers.

Cnidarians branched early from the protistan-like ancestors that gave rise to the main line of evolution from which other animals sprang (Figure 26-3).

These animals are *aquatic* and found mostly in shallow marine environments, with the notable exception of the freshwater hydras. Cnidarians have definite tissues and thus show a *tissue level of organization.* They are mostly *radially symmetrical.* Members of this phylum have *guts* and definite *nerve nets.*

Two main body forms exist in cnidarians (Figure 26-17): a **polyp** that is cylindrical in shape, with the oral end and **tentacles** directed upward and the aboral (away from the mouth) surface attached to the sea floor or freshwater bed and a free-swimming **medusa** (jellyfish) that is bell or umbrella shaped, with the oral end and **tentacles** directed downward. Either or both body forms may be present in the Cnidarian life cycle. Also found throughout the group is a larval form called a *planula.*

Cnidarians are efficient predators. All are carnivores that use their tentacles to capture unwary invertebrate and vertebrate prey. Food is captured with the aid of stinging elements called **nematocysts** (Figure 26-18). The nematocysts are discharged by a combination of mechanical and chemical stimuli. The prey is either pierced by the nematocyst or entangled in its filament and pulled toward the mouth by the tentacles. In some species, nematocysts discharge a toxin that paralyzes the prey. The mouth opens to receive the food, which is deposited in the gut. Digestion is started in the gut cavity by enzymes secreted by its lining. It is completed inside the lining cells after they engulf the partially digested food.

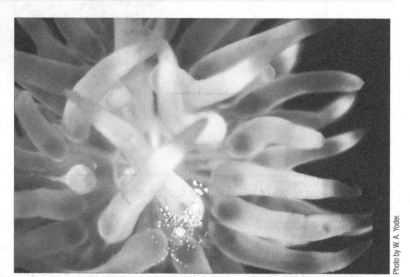

Photo by W. A. Yoder.

Figure 26-16 Pink-tipped sea anemone with mutualistic spotted cleaning shrimp (1×).

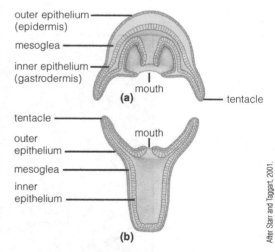

After Starr and Taggart, 2001.

Figure 26-17 Two body forms of Cnidarians. (a) Medusa. (b) Polyp.

MATERIALS

Per student:

- dissection microscope
- compound microscope, lens paper, a bottle of lens cleaning solution (optional), a lint-free cloth (optional)
- clean microscope slide and coverslip

Per student pair:

- prepared slides of
  whole mounts of *Hydra* (showing testes, ovaries, buds, and embryos)
  cross section of *Hydra*
- whole mounts of *Obelia* (showing colonial polyps and medusa)

Per student group (4):

■ small finger bowl
■ scalpel or razor blade
■ preserved specimen of *Gonionemus*
■ prepared slides of
    a whole mount of the medusa (*ephyra*) of
        Aurelia
    a whole mount of planula larvae of *Aurelia*
    a whole mount of scyphistoma of *Aurelia*
    a whole mount of the strobila of *Aurelia*

Per lab room:

■ demonstration specimens of *Physalia* and *Metridium*
■ demonstration collection of corals
■ boxes of different sizes of lab gloves
■ box of safety goggles

Per lab section:

■ culture of live *Hydra*
■ container of fresh or artificial stream water
■ dropper bottle of glutathione
■ culture of live copepods or cladocerans
■ dropper bottle of vinegar

PROCEDURE

A. Class Hydrozoa: Hydrozoans

This is mostly a marine group, except for the hydras, which live in freshwater. A polyp, medusa, or both may be present in the life cycle of a hydrozoan. Marine polyps tend to be colonial.

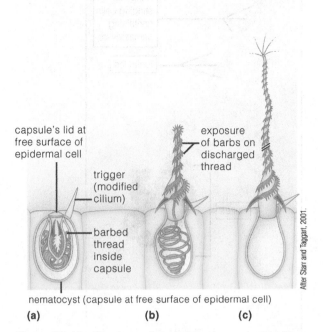

capsule's lid at free surface of epidermal cell

exposure of barbs on discharged thread

trigger (modified cilium)

barbed thread inside capsule

nematocyst (capsule at free surface of epidermal cell)

(a)   (b)   (c)

After Starr and Taggart, 2001.

Figure 26-18 One type of nematocyst, a capsule with an inverted thread inside. This one has a bristlelike trigger (**a**). When prey (or predators) touch the trigger, the capsule becomes more "leaky" to water. As water diffuses inward, pressure inside the capsule increases and the thread is forced to turn inside out (**b**). The thread's tip extends to penetrate the prey, releasing a toxin as it does this (**c**).

1. *Hydra* is a solitary polyp, and it does not have a medusae stage in its life cycle.

    (a) Place a live specimen of *Hydra* in a finger bowl of fresh stream water. Examine the live *Hydra* with a dissection microscope, along with prepared slides of whole mounts with the compound microscope, noting its polyp body form and other structural details (Figure 26-19).

    (b) Observe the tentacles at the oral end (Figure 26-19a). Find the elevation of the body at the base of the tentacles, in the center of which lies a mouth (Figure 26-19b). Note the swellings on the tentacles (Figure 26-19a); each is a stinging cell (*cnidocytes*) that contains a nematocyst. The clear area in the center of the body represents the gut or gastrovascular cavity (Figure 26-19d).

    (c) Look for evidence of sexual reproduction: one to several *testes* or an *ovary* on the body, both of which may occur on the same individual. Testes (Figure 26-19a) are conical and located more orally than the broad, flattened ovary (Figure 26-19b). You may be able to see a zygote or embryo marginally attached to or detached from the body of the *Hydra* (Figure 26-19c). Is *Hydra* monoecious or dioecious?

    (d) *Hydra* also reproduces asexually by budding (Figure 26-19d). Look for buds on your specimens.

    (e) Examine a cross section of *Hydra* (Figure 26-20) and locate the epidermis. The epidermis is derived from ectoderm, one of the primary germ layers. The **epidermis** contains *epitheliomuscular cells, interstitial cells,* and a few stinging cells. Locate the lining of the gastrovascular cavity, or **gastrodermis**, which is derived from the endoderm and composed of epitheliomuscular cells (sometimes called *nutritive muscular cells*), gland cells, and interstitial cells. Between these two layers is a thin gelatinous membrane called the **mesoglea**. In *Hydra*, the mesoglea is without cells.

The two layers of epitheliomuscular cells contract in opposite directions, although in the *Hydra* epidermis the longitudinally arranged contractile filaments are more developed than the circular filaments of the gastrodermis. How might two layers of epitheliomuscular cells function to maintain and change the body shape of a Cnidarian?

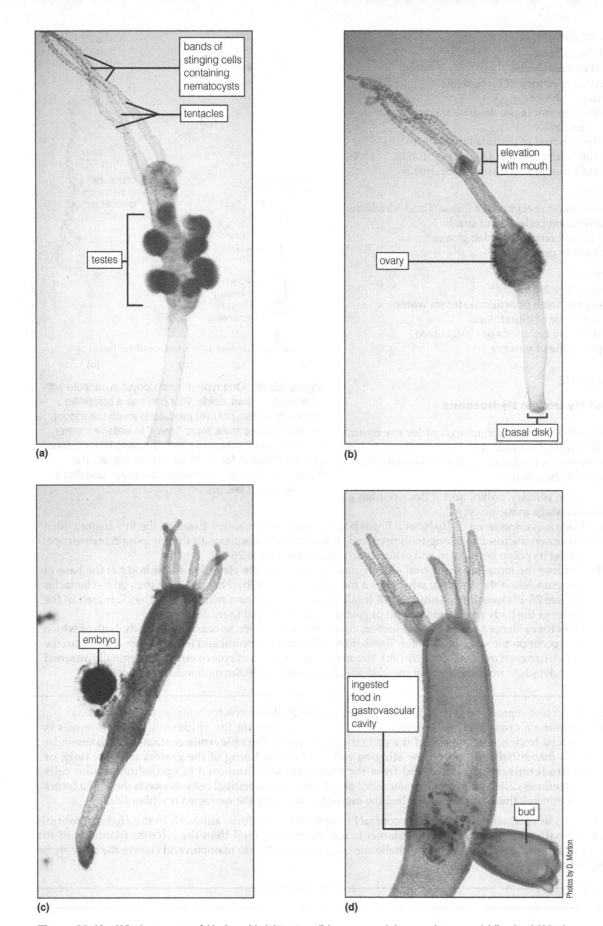

(a)

(b)

(c)

(d)

Figure 26-19 Whole mounts of *Hydra* with (**a**) testes, (**b**) an ovary, (**c**) an embryo, and (**d**) a bud (30×).

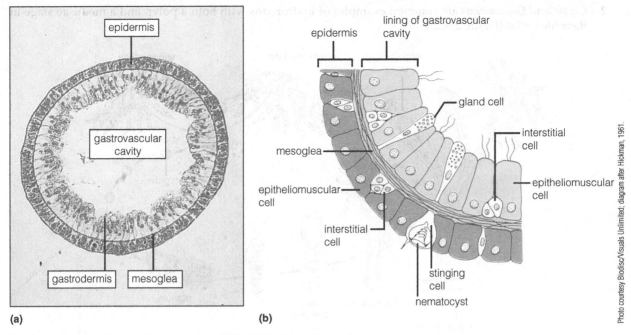

(a)

(b)

Figure 26-20 *Hydra.* **(a)** Cross section (100×). **(b)** Part of the wall.

What additional function can you suggest for the epitheliomuscular cells of the gastrodermis? (*Hint:* What happens to partially digested food?)

_____

_____

_____

_____

Interstitial cells can give rise to sperm, eggs, and any other type of cell in the body.

(f) If it is not already there, place the live *Hydra* in a small finger bowl to the dissection microscope. Add a drop of glutathione and a number of live copepodan or cladoceran crustaceans under the water. The glutathione stimulates the feeding response of *Hydra*. Look for feeding behavior by the *Hydra*. Note the action of the tentacles and the nematocysts. If you do not observe the discharge of nematocysts (Figure 26-21), place a drop of vinegar in the finger bowl and observe carefully. Describe what you observe.

_____

_____

_____

(g) Are any of your *Hydra* green? If so, use a scalpel or razor blade to remove a tentacle. Make a wet mount of the tentacle, being certain to crush it with the coverslip. What do you observe with your compound microscope? Can you explain the green color of your *Hydra*?

_____

_____

_____

Figure 26-21 Portion of a tentacle of *Hydra* with fired and unfired nematocysts, w.m. (800×).

2. *Obelia* and *Gonionemus* are common examples of hydrozoans with both a polyp and a medusae stage in their life cycles (Figure 26-22).

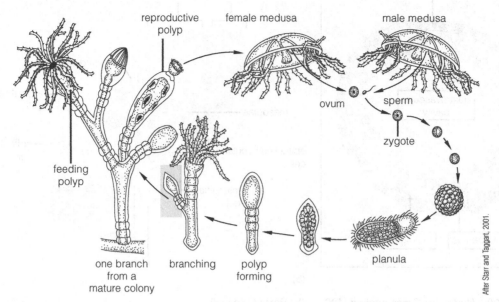

Figure 26-22 Life cycle of the marine hydrozoan *Obelia* that includes medusa and polyp stages. The medusa stage, produced asexually by a reproductive polyp, is free swimming. Fusion of gametes from male and female medusae leads to a zygote, which develops into a planula. The swimming or crawling planula develops into a polyp, which branches to start a new colony. As growth continues, new polyps are formed.

(a) With your compound microscope, examine a prepared slide of a whole mount of a colony of *Obelia* polyps (Figure 26-23a). Identify *feeding* and *reproductive polyps*. The reproductive polyps contain developing medusae.

Figure 26-23 Whole mounts of *Obelia*.
(a) Colonial polyps (15×). **(b)** Side view of a medusa (92×). **(c)** Top view of a medusa (86×).

(b) Similarly observe a whole mount of a medusa and identify the *mouth,* the umbrella-like *bell,* and *tentacles* bearing bands of stinging cells (Figure 26-23b and c).

(c) Switch to a slide of a whole mount of a *Gonionemus* medusa. Compare your preserved specimen to the live medusa seen in Figure 26-24. In addition to the structures listed in Figure 26-23c, identify the muscular *velum* and the *adhesive pads* on the tentacles. Between the bases of the tentacles are balancing organs called *statocysts.* Medusa move by "jet propulsion." Contractions of the body bring about a pulsing motion that alternately fills and empties the cavity of the bell.

3. Look at the demonstration specimen of a preserved Portuguese man-of-war (*Physalia*) (Figure 26-25).

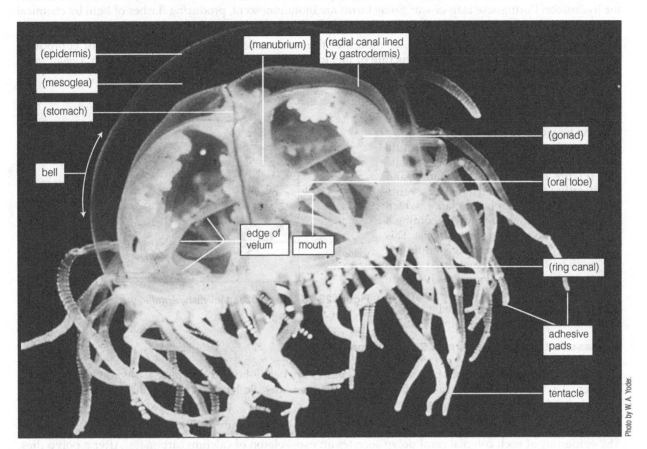

Figure 26-24 Live hydrozoan medusa, *Gonionemus* (4×).

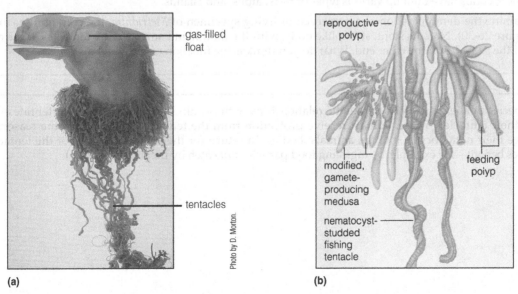

(a)

(b)

Figure 26-25 The Portuguese man-of-war. (**a**) Preserved specimen. (**b**) The tentacles contain several types of modified polyps and medusae.

This organism is really a colonial hydrozoan composed of several types of modified polyps and medusae. Note the conspicuous gas-filled *float*. Its sting is very painful to humans, and a possibly fatal neurotoxin is associated with the nematocysts of the tentacles.

B. Class Scyphozoa: True Jellyfish

This marine class contains the true jellyfish. The medusa is the predominant stage of the life cycle and is generally larger than hydrozoan medusae. The nematocysts in the tentacles and oral arms of jellyfish such as the sea nettle can produce painful stings. A tropical group called the sea wasps is more dangerous to humans than the hydrozoan Portuguese man-of-war. Some forms are bioluminescent, producing flashes of light by chemical reactions. Bioluminescence may lure prey toward the jellyfish or scare potential predators.

1. Look at a prepared slide of a whole mount of the medusa (ephyra) of *Aurelia* with your compound microscope (Figure 26-26). The structure of this medusa is similar to that of the hydrozoan, *Gonionemus*. However, note that the *tentacles* are short and that four *oral arms* surround the square mouth. In this case, prey is captured with the oral arms instead of the tentacles. Also, a velum is absent.

2. Examine prepared slides of planula larvae, a scyphistoma, and a strobila (Figure 26-27). Sexes are separate, and fertilization is internal. The zygote develops into a planula larva, which swims for a while before becoming a sessile polyp called a *scyphistoma*. This is an active, feeding stage, equipped with tentacles and a mouth. At certain times of the year, young medusae are produced asexually by transverse budding. This stage is called a *strobila*, and the process is called strobilization.

Figure 26-26 Scyphozoan jellyfish, *Aurelia*, w.m. (5×).

Labels: (gonad), four oral arms surrounding mouth, (radial canals), (ring canal), (sense organ), gastrovascular cavity, tentacles

Photo courtesy Biodisc/Visuals Unlimited.

C. Class Anthozoa: Corals and Sea Anemones

Class Anthozoa is a marine group in which all members are heavy-bodied polyps that feed on small fish and invertebrates. The largest organisms in this class are the anemones. Both corals (Figure 26-28) and sea anemones attach to hard surfaces or burrow in the sand or mud.

1. Examine the demonstration exoskeletons of a variety of corals (Figure 26-29).

The epidermis of each colonial coral polyp secretes an exoskeleton of calcium carbonate. After a polyp dies, another polyp uses the remaining skeleton of the dead polyp as a foundation and secretes its own skeleton. In this fashion, corals have built up various types of reefs, atolls, and islands.

2. Examine the demonstration of a preserved or living specimen of *Metridium*, the common sea anemone (Figure 26-30). Note its stout, stumplike body, with the mouth and surrounding tentacles at the oral end and the *pedal disk* at the other end. What do you think is the function of the pedal disk?

_____

_____

Some species of anemones form symbiotic relationships with certain small fishes and invertebrates that live among their tentacles. These animals receive protection from the tentacles, which for some reason do not discharge their nematocysts into the animals' bodies. In return for the protective cover of the tentacles, the anemones benefit—for example, by ingesting food particles not eaten by the predatory fish.

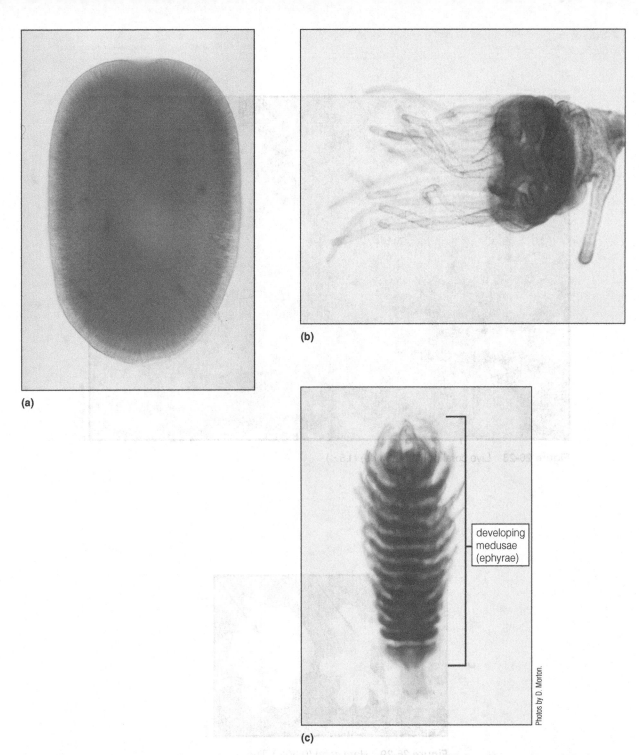

(a)

(b)

developing
medusae
(ephyrae)

Photos by D. Morton.

(c)

Figure 26-27 Stages in the life cycle of *Aurelia*. (**a**) Planular larvae, w.m. (400×). (**b**) Scyphistoma, w.m. (50×).
(**c**) Strobila, w.m. (30×).

Photo by W. A. Yoder.

Figure 26-28 Live coral polyps (arrows) (1.5×).

Photo by D. Morton.

Figure 26-29 Hard coral (0.30×). The arrows indicate sites that were occupied by individual polyps.

(a)

oral disk

mouth

column

pedal disk

tentacles

Photo by D. Morton.

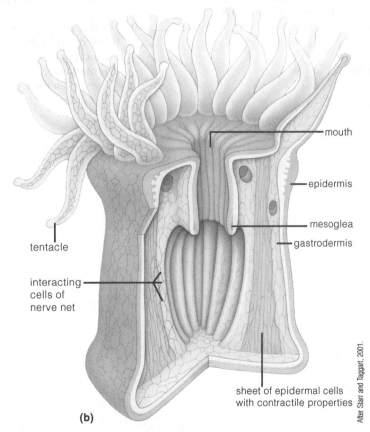

mouth

epidermis

mesoglea

gastrodermis

tentacle

interacting cells of nerve net

sheet of epidermal cells with contractile properties

After Starr and Taggart, 2001.

(b)

Figure 26-30 (a) Top and side views of preserved specimens of the common sea anemone, *Metridium* (1.5×). (b) Organization of a sea anemone.

_____ **1.** Which of the following is characteristic of animals?
(a) heterotrophy
(b) autotrophy
(c) photosynthesis
(d) both b and c

_____ **2.** Sponges are atypical animals because they
(a) reproduce sexually.
(b) are heterotrophic.
(c) lack definite tissues.
(d) are multicellular.

_____ **3.** The "skeleton" of a typical sponge is composed of
(a) bones.
(b) cartilages.
(c) spicules.
(d) scales.

_____ **4.** Many sponges produce both eggs and sperm and thus are
(a) monoecious.
(b) dioecious.
(c) hermaphroditic.
(d) both a and c

_____ **5.** Freshwater sponges reproduce asexually by forming resistant internal buds called
(a) spicules.
(b) larvae.
(c) ovaries.
(d) gemmules.

_____ **6.** Cnidarians evolved from an ancestral group of
(a) sponges.
(b) protests.
(c) fungi.
(d) plants.

_____ **7.** A free-swimming jellyfish has a body form known as a
(a) polyp.
(b) strobila.
(c) medusa.
(d) hydra.

_____ **8.** Cnidarians capture their prey with the use of
(a) poison claws.
(b) nematocysts.
(c) oral teeth.
(d) pedal disks.

_____ **9.** Which statement is true for scyphozoan medusae?
(a) They are the dominant body form.
(b) They are generally smaller than hydrozoan medusae.
(c) Most live in freshwater.
(d) They are scavengers.

_____ **10.** Coral reefs, atolls, and islands are the result of the buildup of coral
(a) polyps.
(b) medusae.
(c) exoskeletons.
(d) wastes.

EXERCISE **26**

Sponges and Cnidarians

Post-Lab Questions

Introduction

1. List six characteristics of the animal kingdom.

2. Define *asymmetry* and *radial symmetry*.

3. Identify the symmetry (asymmetry, radial symmetry, or bilateral symmetry) of the following objects.
   (a) fork

   (b) jagged piece of rock

   (c) rubber ball

26.1 Sponges (Phylum Porifera)

4. Define *cell specialization* and indicate how sponges exhibit this phenomenon.

5. Describe three ways that sponges reproduce.

6. Identify this photo; it is magnified 186×.

_____

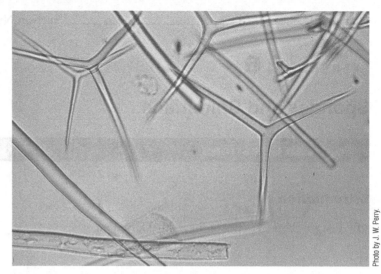

Photo by J. W. Perry.

26.2 Cnidarians (Phylum Cnidaria)

7. Define the tissue level of organization and indicate how cnidarians exhibit this phenomenon.

8. Name and draw the two body forms of cnidarians.

9. Describe the means by which the cnidarians seize and eat faster organisms.

Food for Thought

10. What adaptations of sponges and cnidarians have helped them to endure for so long on Earth?

Flatworms and Rotifers

OBJECTIVES

After completing this exercise, you will be able to

1. define *acoelomate, regeneration, host, intermediate host, cuticle, scolex, proglottid, pseudocoelomate, cloaca, bladder worm*;

2. describe the tissue and organ-system levels of organization;

3. explain the basic body plan of members of the phyla Platyhelminthes and Rotifera;

4. describe the natural history of members of the phyla Platyhelminthes and Rotifera;

5. identify representatives of the classes Turbellaria, Trematoda, and Cestoda of the phylum Platyhelminthes; and representatives of phylum Rotifera;

6. identify structures (and indicate associated functions) of representatives of these groups;

7. outline the life cycles of a human liver fluke;

8. outline the life cycle of *Ascaris*;

9. compare and contrast the anatomy and life cycles of free-living and parasitic flatworms.

Introduction

If you've ever turned over rocks and leaves in a clear, cool, shallow stream or roadside ditch, you may have observed representatives of phylum Platyhelminthes without realizing it. Do you recall any dark, smooth, soft-bodied, flattened or ovoid masses approximately 1 cm or less in length attached to the bottom of the rocks or leaves? This description fits that of a free-living flatworm or planarian. Parasitic flukes and tapeworms also belong to this phylum.

Rotifers are microscopic, the smallest animals. They are mostly bottom-dwelling, freshwater forms, and they are an important prey of larger animals in aquatic food chains.

CAUTION

Specimens are kept in preservative solutions. Use lab gloves and safety goggles, especially if you wear contact lenses, whenever you or your lab mates handle a specimen or other fluids. If safety goggles do not fit, your glasses should suffice. Wash any part of your body exposed to preservative with copious amounts of water. If preservative solution or other fluids are splashed into your eyes, wash them with the safety eyewash bottle or eye irrigation apparatus for 15 minutes.

27.1 Flatworms (Phylum Platyhelminthes) *(About 75 min.)*

Habitat	aquatic, moist terrestrial, or parasitic
Body Arrangement	bilateral symmetry, acoelomate, head (cephalization), gut (incomplete)
Level of Organization	organ system (tissues derived from all three primary germ layers); nervous system with brain; excretory system with flame cells; no circulatory respiratory, or skeletal systems
Body Support	muscles
Life Cycle	sexual reproduction (mostly monoecious with internal fertilization); parasites have very complicated life cycles; some asexual reproduction (mostly transverse fission)
Special Characteristics	bilateral symmetry, head, organ systems

Flatworms have soft, flat, wormlike bodies with *bilateral symmetry* (Figure 26-1). This is the same type of symmetry we exhibit. Flatworms are **acoelomates** in that they lack a body cavity between the gut and body wall (Figure 26-2). The *tissues* of flatworms are *derived from all three primary germ layers:* ectoderm, mesoderm, and endoderm.

Organizationally, these animals represent an important evolutionary transition because they are the simplest forms to exhibit an organ-system level of organization (Figure 27-1) and *cephalization* (a definite head with sense organs). In an evolutionary sense, cephalization goes hand in hand with bilateral symmetry. When an animal with bilateral symmetry moves, the head generally leads, its sensors quickly detecting environmental stimuli that indicate the presence of food or danger ahead. Although there are definite organs, the *digestive system* is still of the *gastrovascular type, incomplete with a mouth and no anus.*

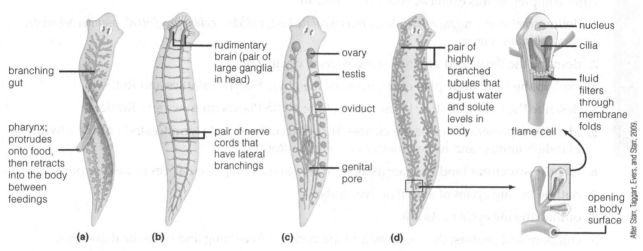

Figure 27-1 Organ systems of one type of flatworm: (a) digestive, (b) nervous, (c) reproductive, (d) water-regulating (excretory).

MATERIALS

Per student:

- dissection microscope
- compound microscope, lens paper, a bottle of lens-cleaning solution (optional), a lint-free cloth (optional)
- scalpel
- blunt probe

Per student pair:

- prepared slides of
  whole mount of *Dugesia* (planaria)
  whole mount of planaria with the digestive system stained
  cross section of planaria (pharyngeal region)
  whole mount of *Fasciola hepatica*
  whole mount of *Clonorchis sinensis* (if available)

- whole mount(s) of *Taenia pisiformis*, with scolex and different types of proglottids
- a whole mount of a bladder worm (cysticercus) of *Taenia solium*

Per student group (4):

- penlight
- glass petri dish (2)

Per lab room:

- chunk of beef liver
- container of fresh stream water
- container of live planarians
- demonstration collection of preserved tapeworms
- boxes of different sizes of latex gloves
- box of safety goggles

PROCEDURE

A. Class Turbellaria: Planarians

Most species in this class are free-living flatworms, although a few species are parasitic or symbiotic with other organisms. Free-living flatworms are found in marine and fresh waters on the underside of submerged rocks, leaves, and sticks. They are especially abundant in cool freshwater streams and along the ocean shoreline. Some live in wet or moist terrestrial habitats.

Planarians of the genus *Dugesia* are the representatives of this class typically studied in biology courses. They are relatively small flatworms, usually 2 cm or less in length. Planarians are monoecious—an individual has both male and female reproductive structures—but apparently do not self-fertilize but rather copulate with each other. Planarians exhibit a high degree of **regeneration**, in which lost body parts are gradually replaced.

1. Microscopically examine a whole mount of a planarian. Refer to Figure 27-2 and locate the **head**, **eyespots**, and **auricles**, lateral projections of the head that are organs sensitive to touch and to molecules dissolved in the water. The **eyespots** are photoreceptors. They are sensitive to light but do not form images.

2. Obtain and similarly examine a whole mount of a planarian with an injected digestive system. Identify the muscular **pharynx** within the **pharyngeal pouch**. The *mouth* is located at the free end of the pharynx. The mouth opens into the pharyngeal cavity, which in turn is continuous with the cavity of the **intestine**. To feed, a free planarian protrudes the pharynx from its ventral (belly) side and sucks up organic morsels (insect larvae, small crustaceans, and other small living and dead animals). The intestine is elaborately branched and occupies much of the animal's body. What function does the extensive branching of the intestine facilitate?

   _____

   _____

   _____

   _____

   _____

3. To observe feeding behavior, place a small piece of beef liver in a clean glass petri dish containing fresh stream water and add several live planarians. Describe what you see with the aid of a dissection microscope.

   _____

   _____

   _____

   _____

You may observe the elimination of waste from the gastrovascular cavity. If you do, describe what you see; if not, state the route by which this must occur.

   _____

   _____

   _____

Figure 27-2 Whole mount of planaria, with injected digestive system (45×).

Set the dish aside and examine it later, especially if you did not observe feeding behavior.

4. Examine a cross section through the pharynx of a planarian with your compound microscope (Figure 27-3). Find the following structures: *pharynx, pharyngeal pouch*, **nerve cords, epidermis, portions of the intestine**, and the several layers of muscles in the body wall. Note that the bottom epidermis is lined by **cilia**. What is the function of these cilia?

   _____

   _____

   _____

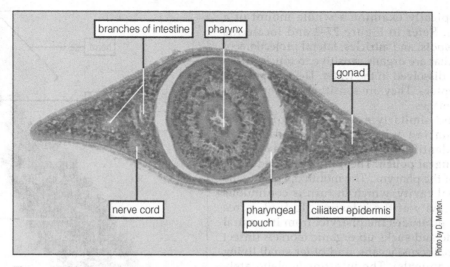

branches of intestine
pharynx
gonad
nerve cord
pharyngeal pouch
ciliated epidermis

Photo by D. Morton.

Figure 27-3 Cross section of planaria (150×).

Much of the rest of the body wall contains three layers of muscle: an outer circular layer, a middle diagonal layer, and an inner longitudinal layer. It is often difficult to distinguish all three layers.

5. Working in groups of four, use a dissection microscope to observe a living planarian in a clean glass petri dish filled with fresh stream water. Note its general size and shape. Touch the animal with a probe. What is its reaction? How does its shape change? Which muscle layers likely contract to produce this shape change?

_____

_____

_____

B. Class Trematoda: Flukes

Flukes are small, leaf-shaped, parasitic flatworms with complex life cycles. They are generally internal parasites of vertebrates, including humans. A protoplasmic but noncellular cuticle covers the surface of their bodies. What is a likely explanation for the presence of this tough, resistant cuticle?

_____

_____

_____

1. Examine a whole mount of a sheep liver fluke, *Fasciola hepatica*, noting its general morphology. Identify the structures indicated in Figure 27-4.
2. Examine a whole mount of an adult *Clonorchis sinensis*, a human liver fluke, if available, or Figure 27-5. This animal is a common parasite in Asia, and humans are the final **host**.

mouth
oral sucker
(cirrus everted through genital pore)
pharynx
esophagus
intestinal ceca
edge of genital pore
(cirrus pouch)
ventral sucker
uterus with eggs
yolk glands
(shell gland)
yolk duct
ovary

Photo by D. Morton.

Figure 27-4 Anterior portion of *Fasciola hepatica*, the sheep liver fluke, w.m. (20×).

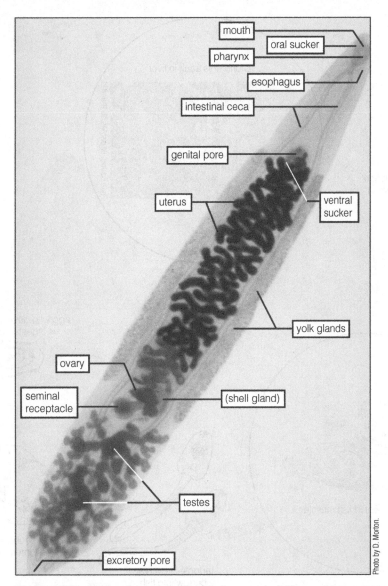

Figure 27-5 Photomicrograph of a whole mount of *Clonorchis sinensis*, a human liver fluke (20×).

Photo by D. Morton.

(a) Identify the structures labeled in Figure 27-5. *Clonorchis* has two suckers for attachment to its host: an **oral sucker** surrounding the mouth and a **ventral sucker**. The digestive tract begins with the **mouth** and continues with a muscular **pharynx**, a short **esophagus**, and two blind pouches or **intestinal ceca**. Nitrogenous wastes are excreted at the tip of the back end through the **excretory pore**.

(b) *Clonorchis* is monoecious. Find the following female reproductive structures: **ovary, yolk glands, seminal receptacle,** and **uterus**. Find the following male reproductive structures: **testes** and **seminal vesicle**, which may be visible in your specimen. During copulation, sperm is conveyed from the testes to the *genital pore* by paired vasa efferentia, which fuse to form the vas deferens. These ducts are difficult to see in most specimens. Copulating individuals exchange sperm at the genital pore, and the sperm is stored temporarily in the seminal receptacle. The yolk glands provide yolk for nourishment of the developing eggs. *Eggs* can be seen as black dots in the uterus, where they mature.

(c) The life cycle of *Clonorchis sinensis* (Figure 27-6) involves two **intermediate hosts**, a snail and the golden carp. Intermediate hosts harbor sexually immature stages of a parasite. Fertilized eggs are expelled from the adult fluke into the human host's bile duct and are eventually voided with the feces of the host. If the eggs are shed in the appropriate moist or aquatic environment, they may be ingested by snails (the first intermediate host).

A larva emerges from the egg inside the snail. The larva passes through several developmental stages and gives rise to a number of tadpole-like larvae. These free-swimming larvae leave the snail,

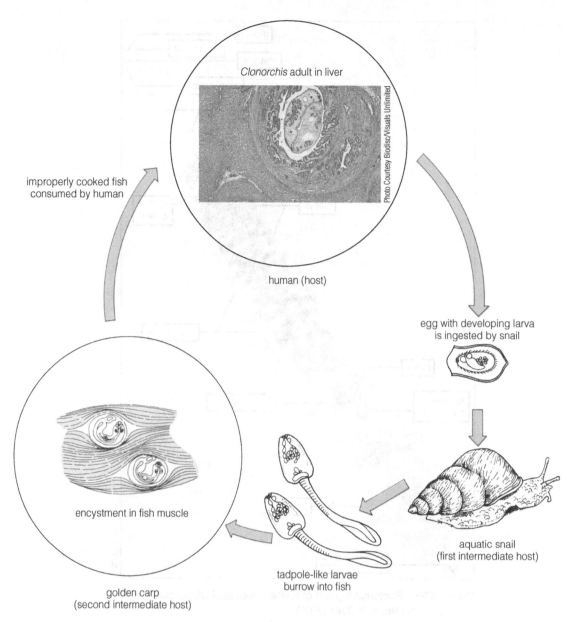

Clonorchis adult in liver

Photo Courtesy Biodisc/Visuals Unlimited

improperly cooked fish
consumed by human

human (host)

egg with developing larva
is ingested by snail

encystment in fish muscle

tadpole-like larvae
burrow into fish

aquatic snail
(first intermediate host)

golden carp
(second intermediate host)

Figure 27-6 Life cycle of a human liver fluke, *Clonorchis sinensis*.

encounter a golden carp (the second intermediate host), and burrow into this fish to encyst in muscle tissue. If raw or improperly cooked fish is eaten by humans, cats, dogs, or some other mammal, the larvae emerge from the cysts and make their way up the host's bile duct into the liver, where they mature into adult flukes. The cycle is then repeated. What is the infectious stage (for humans) of this parasite?

_____

What two main precautions can humans take to reduce exposure to this parasite?

_____

_____

_____

_____

_____

C. Class Cestoda: Tapeworms

Tapeworms are internal parasites that inhabit the intestine of vertebrates. Their flattened, multiunit bodies have no digestive system; instead, they absorb across their body walls predigested nutrients provided by the host. Their bodies are essentially reproductive machines, with extensive, well-developed reproductive organs occupying much of each mature body unit. A thick cuticle covers the body.

1. Look over the demonstration collection of preserved tapeworms taken from a variety of vertebrate hosts.
2. Examine a preserved specimen of *Taenia pisiformis,* a tapeworm of dogs and cats (Figure 27-7). Note that it is divided into three general regions: specialized head or **scolex**, **neck**, and **body**. The body is composed of successive units, the **proglottids**. New immature proglottids are added at the neck. As they move farther from the scolex, proglottids mature. The oldest, hindmost segments are full of eggs and ready to burst and release their zygotes (gravid).
3. Look at a prepared slide of a whole mount of a *Taenia pisiformis* scolex (Figure 27-8). Observe that the scolex is covered with hooks and suckers. For what task does the tapeworm use these **hooks** and **suckers**?

_____

_____

_____

Note the neck and the new proglottids forming at its base.

Figure 27-7   Preserved *Taenia* tapeworm (0.67×).

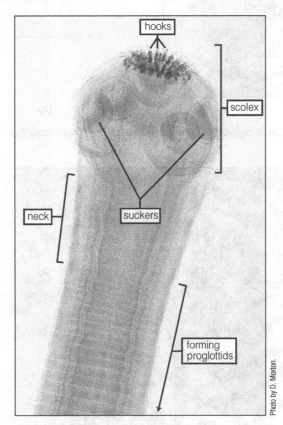

Figure 27-8   Tapeworm scolex (*Taenia pisiformis*), w.m. (40×).

4. Find a whole mount of mature proglottids of *Taenia pisiformis* and examine them with a dissection microscope. Identify the structures indicated in Figure 27-9. The lateral **genital pore** opens into the **vagina** and receives sperm from the **vas deferens**. The *uterus* is usually visible as a line running top to bottom in the middle of the proglottid. The *ovaries* are represented by dark, diffuse masses of tissue lateral to the uterus at the vaginal end of the proglottid. The **testes** are paler, more diffuse masses of tissue lateral to the uterus at the other end. Tapeworms are monoecious. They are one of the few animals that can self-fertilize, perhaps a result of their isolation from each other. Flanking most of the reproductive organs are the **excretory canals**.

5. Locate a gravid proglottid of *Taenia pisiformis* (Figure 27-10). Gravid proglottids are almost completely filled with zygotes in an expanded uterus ready for release as eggs.

Figure 27-9 Tapeworm mature proglottids (*Taenia pisiformis*). (**a**) Whole mount (30×). (**b**) Diagram.

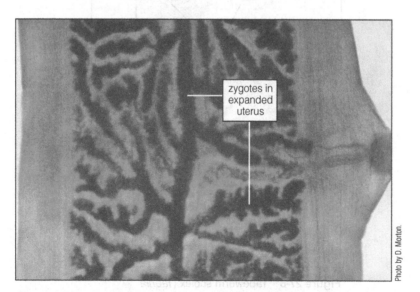

Figure 27-10 Tapeworm gravid proglottid (*Taenia pisiformis*), w.m. (30×).

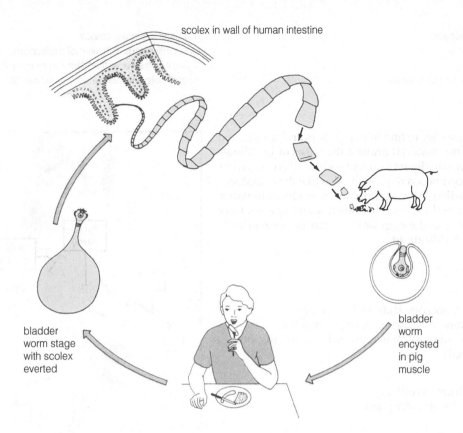

scolex in wall of human intestine

bladder
worm stage
with scolex
everted

bladder
worm
encysted
in pig
muscle

Figure 27-11 Life cycle of the pork tapeworm, *Taenia solium*.

6. The life cycle of the pork tapeworm, *Taenia solium*, involves
two host organisms, the pig and a human (Figure 27-11).
Gravid proglottids containing embryos are voided with the
feces of a human. If a pig ingests a proglottid, the embryos
escape from the proglottid and bore into the intestinal wall
and enter a blood or lymphatic vessel. From there they make
their way to muscle, where they encyst as larvae known as
bladder worms. If a human ingests improperly cooked pork,
a bladder worm "pops" out of its encasement (bladder) and
attaches its scolex to the intestinal wall. Here it matures and
adds proglottids to complete the life cycle.

Which mammal is the host?

_____

Which mammal is the intermediate host?

_____

Examine the bladder worm stage of *Taenia solium* with the
dissection microscope. Draw what you see in Figure 27-12.

Figure 27-12 Drawing of the bladder
worm of *Taenia solium* (_____×).

27.2   Rotifers (Phylum Rotifera) *(About 15 min.)*

Habitat	aquatic or moist terrestrial, mostly fresh water
Body Arrangement	bilateral symmetry, pseudocoelomate, head, gut (complete)
Level of Organization	organ system (tissues derived from all three primary germ layers); nervous system with brain; excretory system with flame cells; no circulatory, respiratory, or skeletal systems

Body Support	hydrostatic (pseudocoelom)
Life Cycle	sexual (dioecious with internal fertilization), some parthenogenesis, males much smaller than females or absent
Special Characteristics	microscopic animals, wheel organ, mastax

Rotifers are easy to find in rain gutters and spouts, and in the slimy material around the bases of buildings. Their thin, usually transparent body wall is covered by a cuticle composed of protein. Also like the nematodes to be studied later, rotifers are pseudocoelomates. Rotifers are dioecious; however, many species have no males, and the eggs develop parthenogenetically (without fertilization).

MATERIALS

Per student:

- clean microscope slide and coverslip
- compound microscope, lens paper, a bottle of lens-cleaning solution (optional), a lint-free cloth (optional)

Per lab room:

- live culture of rotifers
- disposable transfer pipet

PROCEDURE

1. With a disposable transfer pipet, place a drop from the rotifer culture on a clean slide and make a wet mount.
2. Observe the microscopic rotifers with the compound microscope. The elongate, cylindrical body is divisible into the **trunk** and the **foot** (Figure 27-13).

The foot bears two to several "sticky" *toes* for adhering to objects. The upper end of the trunk bears a **corona** of cilia. These cilia beat in such a fashion as to give the appearance of a wheel (or two) turning, hence the common references to this structure as the wheel organ and to these animals as wheel animals. The cilia create currents that sweep organic food particles into the mouth at the center of the wheel organ. The cilia also enable the organism to move. Inside the trunk, below the wheel organ, look for the movement of a grinding organ, the **mastax**. This structure is equipped with jaws made hard by a substance called chitin. Considering its location, what is the likely function of the mastax?

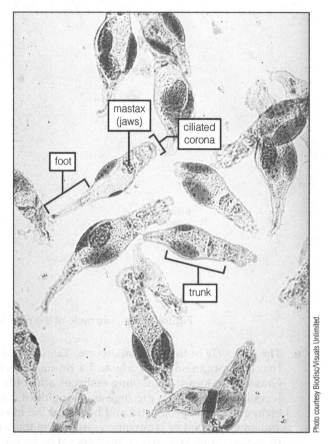

Figure 27-13 Prepared whole mount of rotifers (130×).

_____

_____

_____

_____ 1. Cephalization is
   (a) the division of the trunk into a scolex, neck, and body.
   (b) the presence of a head with sense organs.
   (c) sexual reproduction involving self-fertilization.
   (d) the ability to replace lost body parts.

_____ 2. Flatworms
   (a) are radially symmetrical.
   (b) possess a body cavity.
   (c) reproduce by parthenogenesis.
   (d) have tissues derived from all three primary germ layers.

_____ 3. Free-living flatworms (planaria) move by using
   (a) cilia.
   (b) flagella.
   (c) pseudopodia.
   (d) a muscular foot.

_____ 4. The flukes and tapeworms are covered by a protective
   (a) cuticle.
   (b) shell.
   (c) scales.
   (d) slime layer.

_____ 5. The life cycle of the human liver fluke has _____ intermediate hosts.
   (a) one
   (b) two
   (c) three
   (d) four

_____ 6. Tapeworms do not have a
   (a) reproductive system.
   (b) head.
   (c) excretory system.
   (d) digestive system.

_____ 7. The oldest proglottid of a tapeworm is
   (a) the scolex.
   (b) the one nearest its neck.
   (c) the one in its middle.
   (d) the one at its end.

_____ 8. Bladder worms are found in
   (a) proglottids in human feces.
   (b) proglottids in the human intestine.
   (c) improperly cooked pork.
   (d) none of the above

_____ 9. Nematodes and rotifers have a body cavity that is
   (a) called a coelom.
   (b) called a pseudocoelom.
   (c) completely lined by tissues derived from mesoderm.
   (d) both a and c

_____ 10. Rotifers obtain their food by the action of
   (a) tentacles.
   (b) cilia on the wheel organ.
   (c) a muscular pharynx.
   (d) pseudopodia.

EXERCISE **27**

Flatworms and Rotifers

Post-Lab Questions

27.1 Flatworms (Phylum Platyhelminthes)

1. How is bilateral symmetry different from radial symmetry?

2. List the characteristics of flatworms.

3. Distinguish between a host and an intermediate host.

4. Identify and label this illustration. It is magnified 9×.

A _____

B _____

C _____

D _____

E _____

Photo courtesy Biodisc Visuals Unlimited.

5. Describe several adaptations of parasitic flatworms to their external environment.

27.2 Rotifers (Phylum Rotifera)

6. Pseudocoel means "false body cavity." Why is this term applied to the body cavity of rotifers?

Food for Thought

7. Contrast the digestive systems of free-living and parasitic flatworms.

8. Explain the relationship between the tremendous numbers of eggs produced by flukes and tapeworms and the complexity of their life cycles.

9. The relatively simple animals *Hydra* and *Dugesia* can regenerate lost body parts, but humans generally cannot. Discuss this in terms of tissue differentiation and the comparative levels of structural complexity of these organisms.

10. Search the Internet for sites that include references to flatworms or rotifers. List two addresses and briefly describe their contents.

    http:// _____

    _____

    _____

    _____

    http:// _____

    _____

    _____

    _____

Segmented Worms and Mollusks

OBJECTIVES

After completing this exercise, you will be able to

1. define *coelom, coelomate, protostome, deuterostome, segmentation, peritoneum, setae, clitellum, cocoon, foot, mantle;*

2. differentiate between protostomes and deuterostomes;

3. describe the natural history of members of the phyla Annelida and Mollusca;

4. identify representatives of the classes Oligochaeta, Polychaeta, and Hirudinea of the phylum Annelida;

5. outline the life cycle of an earthworm;

6. identify representatives of the classes Bivalvia, Gastropoda, and Cephalopoda of the phylum Mollusca;

7. outline the life cycle of a freshwater clam;

8. identify structures (and indicate their associated functions) of the representatives of these phyla and classes.

Introduction

Some time after the origin of bilateral symmetry, the animals that subsequently evolved developed a true ventral body cavity or **coelom**. A true body cavity is lined by tissue derived entirely from mesoderm (Figure 26-2). The appearance of the coelom has great evolutionary significance, for it accommodates, cushions, and protects organs; allows an increase in overall body size and flexibility; and contributes to the development of systems primarily derived from mesoderm.

   Coelomates, animals possessing a coelom (Figure 26-3), took two divergent evolutionary paths based on whether the *blastopore*—the first opening in a developing embryo—became the mouth (**protostomes**) or anus (**deuterostomes**) (Table 28-1). During subsequent evolutionary change, the coelom was reduced (mollusks and joint legged animals), lost (flatworms), or modified to a pseudocoel (rotifers and roundworms).

TABLE 28-1	Evolution of Coelomates	
Path	**Blastopore Becomes**	**Phyla**
Protostomes	Mouth	Mollusca, Annelida, and Arthropoda
Deuterostomes	Anus	Echinodermata, Hemichordata, and Chordata

© Cengage Learning 2013

CAUTION

Specimens are kept in preservative solutions. Use lab gloves and safety goggles, especially if you wear contact lenses, whenever you or your lab mates handle a specimen or other fluids. If safety goggles do not fit, your glasses should suffice. Wash any part of your body exposed to preservative with copious amounts of water. If preservative solution or other fluids are splashed into your eyes, wash them with the safety eyewash bottle or eye irrigation apparatus for 15 minutes.

Habitat	aquatic or moist terrestrial, some parasitic
Body Arrangement	bilateral symmetry, coelomate, head, body segmented, gut (complete)
Level of Organization	organ system (tissues derived from all three primary germ layers), nervous system with brain, circulatory system (closed), excretory system (nephridia), respiratory system (gills in some), no skeletal system
Body Support	hydrostatic (coelom)
Life Cycle	sexual reproduction (monoecious or dioecious with mostly internal fertilization), larvae in some, asexual reproduction (mostly transverse fission)
Special Characteristics	segmented, closed circulatory system

The most striking annelid characteristic is the division of the cylindrical trunk into a series of similar segments. *Annelids* were the first animals to evolve the condition of **segmentation**. Segmentation is internal as well as external, with segmentally arranged components of various organ systems and the body cavity. The coelom is more or less divided by *septa* into compartments within each segment, each lined by **peritoneum**. Unlike the proglottids of the cestodes, segments cannot function independently of each other. The *circulatory system* is *closed*, with the blood entirely contained in vessels. There is a well-developed *nervous system* with a central nervous system composed of two fused dorsal ganglia (brain) and ventral nerve cords. The circulatory system is not segmented. Segmentation is significant in evolutionary history because each segment or group of segments can become specialized. Although this is an important characteristic of most of the phyla we have yet to study, it is barely evident in the earthworm.

MATERIALS

Per student:

- pins
- blunt probe or dissecting needle

Per student pair:

- preserved earthworm
- dissection microscope
- dissection pan
- fine dissecting scissors
- *Eisenia foetida* cocoons

Per lab room:

- labeled demonstration dissection of the internal anatomy of the earthworm (optional)
- demonstration collection of living and preserved earthworms and polychaetes
- several preserved leeches
- live freshwater leeches in an aquarium
- large plastic bag for disposal of dissected specimens
- boxes of different sizes of lab gloves
- box of safety goggles

A. Oligochaetes (Class Oligochaeta)

PROCEDURE

1. Refer to Figure 28-1 as you examine the living earthworms on demonstration in the lab. You probably already know several characteristics of oligochaetes because of past observations with the earthworm (*Lumbricus terrestris*), especially if you fish. Recalling past experiences with this organism, list as many features of the earthworm as you can.

   _____

   _____

   _____

   _____

2. Let's see how you did! Obtain a preserved earthworm and have a dissection microscope handy. Is its body bilaterally or radially symmetrical?_____

   _____

circular muscles | longitudinal muscles | dorsal blood vessel | coelom | cuticle

bladderlike storage region of nephridium | nephridium's thin loop reabsorbs some solutes, relinquishes them to blood

blood vessels | body wall

seta (retracted) | ventral blood vessel | nerve cord | nephridium

(a)

funnel (coelomic fluid with waste enters here) | external pore (fluid containing wastes discharged here)

(b)

(c) hearts blood vessels

pharynx | coelomic chambers | mouth

esophagus | crop (storage) | gizzard (mashing)

(d)

brain | nerve cord

(e)

After Starr and Taggart, 2001.

Figure 28-1 Earthworm body plan. (**a**) Midbody, transverse section. (**b**) A nephridium, one of many functional units that help maintain the volume and the composition of body fluids. (**c**) Portion of the closed circulatory system. The system is linked in its functioning with nephridia. (**d**) Part of the digestive system, near the worm's head end. (**e**) Part of the nervous system.

3. Examine the external anatomy (Figure 28-2). Note the segments. Count them and record the number:_____

   (a) Very few segments are added after hatching. Note the **prostomium**, a fleshy lobe that hangs over the **mouth**; both structures are part of the first segment.

   (b) Look for **setae**, tiny bristle-like structures on the ventral surface, with the dissection microscope. Take the specimen between your fingers and feel for them. What is their likely function?

   _____

   _____

   _____

   _____

   (c) Use the dissection microscope to help you find the following. A pair of small **excretory pores** is found on the lateral or ventral surfaces of each segment, except the first few and the last. On the sides of segment 14, the openings (*female pores*) of the oviducts can be seen. The openings (*male pores*) of the sperm ducts, with their swollen lips, can be found on segment 15. The **clitellum** is the enlarged ring beginning at segment 31 or 32 and ending with 37. This glandular structure secretes a slimy band around two copulating individuals. The **anus** is the vertical slit in the terminal segment.

4. *Dissection of earthworm internal anatomy.*

   (a) Place your worm in a dissection pan and stick a pin through each end of the specimen. With fine scissors, make an incision just to the right of the dorsal black line (blood vessel), 10 segments anterior to the anus, and cut superficially to the mouth. (You can use the prostomium as an indicator of the dorsal side of the animal if the black line cannot be seen.) Gently pull the incision apart and note that the coelom is divided into a series of compartments by septa. Carefully cut the septa free of the body wall with a scalpel and pin both sides to the pan at 5- to 10-segment intervals. Cover the specimen with about 0.5–1.0 cm of tap water and examine the internal anatomy (Figure 28-3).

   (b) Use your blunt probe or dissection needle to find the male reproductive organs, the light-colored **seminal vesicles**. These can be found in segments 9–12. They are composed of three sacs, within which are the *testes*. A sperm duct leads from the *seminal* vesicles to the male pore.

   (c) Find two pairs of female reproductive organs—the white, spherical **seminal receptacles** in segments 9 and 10. There are ovaries in segment 13. An oviduct runs from each ovary to the female pore.

(a)

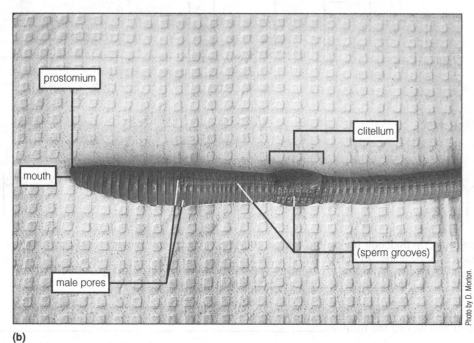

(b)

Figure 28-2 (a) External anatomy of the earthworm (numbers refer to the segment numbers). (b) External view of preserved earthworm.

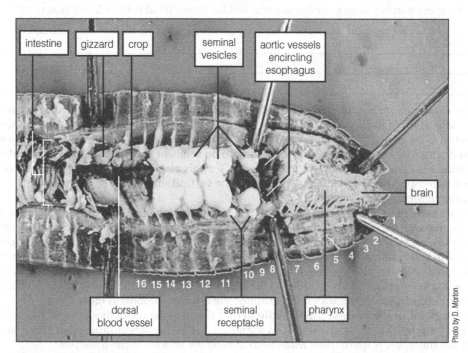

Figure 28-3 Dissection of the anterior end of an earthworm. The first 16 segments are numbered.

(d) Locate the organs of the digestive tract. The *buccal cavity* occupies the first three segments. The muscular **pharynx** is the swelling in the digestive tract just behind the mouth. This organ is responsible for sucking soil particles containing food into the mouth. The *esophagus* extends from the pharynx through segment 14. The *crop* is a large, thin-walled sac in segments 15 and 16 that serves as a temporary storage organ for food. The **gizzard**, a grinding organ, is posterior to the crop. The **intestine**, the site of digestion and absorption, extends from the gizzard to the anus.

(e) Trace the parts of the circulatory system. The **dorsal blood vessel** runs along the dorsal side of the digestive tract and contains blood that flows toward the head. Five pairs of **aortic vessels** ("hearts") encircle the esophagus in segments 7–11, connecting the dorsal blood vessel with the **ventral blood vessel** (Figure 28-4). The ventral vessel runs along the ventral side of the digestive tract, carrying blood backward. The primary pumps of the circulatory system are the dorsal and ventral vessels. The dorsal vessel contains valves to prevent blood from flowing backward.

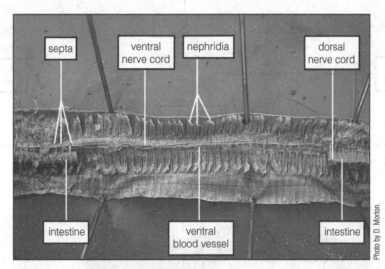

Figure 28-4 Dissection of the posterior end of an earthworm. The intestine has been partially removed to expose the ventral nerve cord.

(f) Find the two-lobed **brain** (cerebral ganglia) on the anterior, dorsal surface of the pharynx in segment 3. The **ventral nerve cord** arises from the brain and extends along the floor of the body cavity to the last segment. Although they are difficult to locate, paired lateral nerves branch from the segmental ganglia along the nerve cord.

(g) Locate a pair of **nephridia**—coiled white tubes—at the base of every segment but the first three and last one. These structures constitute the "kidneys" of the earthworm (Figure 28-4).

(h) Dispose of your dissected specimen in the large plastic bag provided for this purpose.

5. Use a dissection microscope to examine cocoons from *Eisenia foetida*, another species of earthworm. Identify eggs and embryos. Earthworms are monoecious—individuals have both male and female reproductive tracts. Copulation usually takes 2–3 hours with individuals facing belly to belly in opposite directions, joined together at their clitellums. These organs secrete a slimy substance that forms a band around the worms. Sperm are transferred between the participants, and the sperm are stored temporarily in the seminal receptacles.

A few days after the individuals separate, each worm secretes a **cocoon**. The cocoon receives eggs and stored sperm from the seminal receptacles. The eggs are fertilized, and the cocoon moves forward as the worm backs out. The cocoon then slips off the front end of the worm and is deposited in the soil. In *Lumbricus terrestris*, a single young earthworm completes development using the other fertilized eggs as food, eventually breaks free of the cocoon, and becomes an adult in several weeks. As long as the stored sperm lasts, the earthworm continues to form cocoons.

6. Use your dissection microscope to examine a prepared slide of a cross section of the earthworm (Figure 28-5). First look at the body wall. A thin **cuticle** covers the body. The **epidermis**, which lies beneath it, secretes the cuticle, and internal to this are an **outer circular layer** and an **inner longitudinal layer** of muscle. Identify the other labeled structures in Figure 28-5.

B. Polychaetes (Class Polychaeta)

The polychaetes are abundant marine annelids with dorso-ventrally flattened bodies. They are most common at shallow depths in the intertidal zone at the seashore and are prey for a variety of marine invertebrates.

Examine the polychaetes on demonstration in the lab. Although they resemble oligochaetes in many ways, notice that the polychaetes have fleshy, segmental outgrowths called **parapodia** (Figure 28-6). These structures

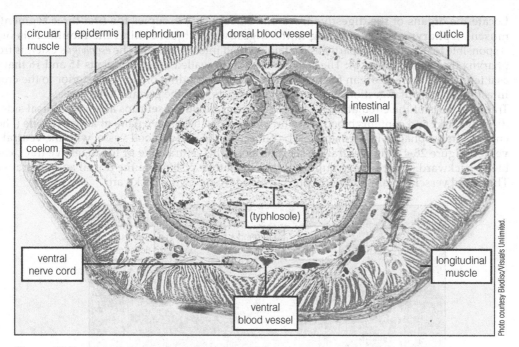

Figure 28-5 Cross section of an earthworm (20×).

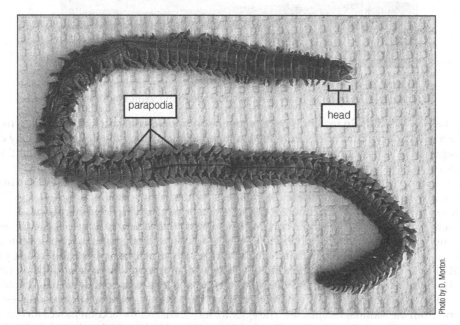

Figure 28-6 External anatomy of the clamworm, *Neanthes.*

are equipped with numerous setae, the characteristic for which they get their class name, *Polychaeta,* meaning "many bristles." Notice also the relatively complex **head**.

C. Leeches (Class Hirudinea)

The leeches are dorso-ventrally flattened annelids that are usually found in freshwater.

1. Examine the preserved specimens of leeches (Figure 28-7a). They lack parapodia and setae. They are predaceous or parasitic; parasitic species suck blood with the aid of a muscular pharynx. The segments surrounding the mouth are modified into a small **anterior sucker**. The mouth is supplied with jaws, made hard with the substance chitin, used to wound the host and supply the leech with blood. Parasitic leeches secrete an anticoagulant into the wound to prevent the blood from clotting. A **posterior sucker** helps the leech attach to the host or prey.

posterior sucker

mouth surrounded by anterior sucker

Photo by D. Morton.

(a)

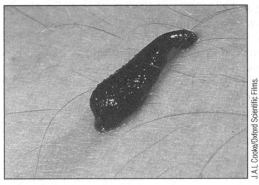

J.A.L. Cooke/Oxford Scientific Films.

(b)

Figure 28-7 Leeches. **(a)** Preserved specimen. **(b)** Live, feeding on a human.

2. Observe the movement of living freshwater leeches (Figure 28-7b) as they swim through the water in an aquarium. Explain their movements in terms of the contraction and relaxation of circular and longitudinal layers of muscle that comprise part of their body wall.

_____

_____

_____

_____

28.2   Mollusks (Phylum Mollusca) *(40–60 min.)*

Habitat	aquatic or terrestrial, mostly marine
Body Arrangement	head and unique body plan, gut (complete)
Level of Organization	organ system (tissues derived from all three primary germ layers), nervous system with brain, excretory system (nephridium or nephridia), circulatory system (open), respiratory system (most have gills or lungs), no skeletal system
Body Support	shells, floats (aquatic)
Life Cycle	sexual (monoecious or dioecious with external or internal fertilization), larvae in some
Special Characteristics	coelomate; open circulatory system; respiratory system; external body divided into head, mantle, and foot

This is the second largest animal phylum and includes snails and nudibranchs, slugs, bivalves—clams, mussels, and oysters—octopuses, cuttlefish, and squids. Bodies are typically soft (*molluscus* in Latin means "soft") and often covered by protective shells. Apart from the squids and some octopuses (and the land snails and slugs, which have adopted a terrestrial existence), *mollusks inhabit shallow marine and fresh waters*, where they crawl along or burrow into the soft substrate. Many species are valued foods for humans.

Two characteristics distinguish the mollusks from other animals. They possess a ventral, muscular **foot** for movement and a dorsal integument, the **mantle**, which in different groups of mollusks secretes shells, functions in gaseous exchange, and facilitates movement. Even forms without shells usually have mantles.

MATERIALS

Per student:

- scalpel
- blunt probe or dissecting needle
- compound microscope, lens paper, a bottle of lens-cleaning solution (optional), a lint-free cloth (optional)

Per student pair:

- preserved freshwater clam
- dissection pan
- prepared slide of a cross section of clam gill
- dissection microscope
- glass petri dish
- prepared slide of glochidia

Per lab room:

- labeled demonstration dissection of a freshwater clam (optional) and the internal anatomy of a squid
- demonstration collection of bivalve shells, and living and preserved specimens
- freshwater aquarium with snails (for example, *Physa*)
- demonstration collection of gastropod shells, and living and preserved specimens
- several preserved squids, octopuses, and chambered nautiluses
- large plastic bag for disposal of dissected specimens
- boxes of different sizes of lab gloves
- box of safety goggles

PROCEDURE

A. Bivalves (Class Bivalvia)

Bivalves are so named because they have shells composed of two halves or *valves*. Included in this class are the clams, mussels, oysters, and scallops. They have a hatchet-shaped (laterally flattened) body and a foot used for burrowing in soft substrates.

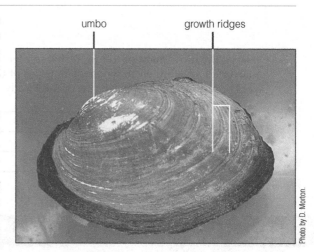
Figure 28-8 External view of a freshwater clam.

1. *Study the external features of a freshwater clam.*
   (a) Obtain and examine a freshwater clam in a dissection pan (Figure 28-8). Each **valve** has a hump on the dorsal surface (back), the **umbo**, which points toward the front of the organism. The umbo is the oldest part of the valve.
   (b) Encircling the umbo are concentric rings of annual growth; the raised portions (*growth ridges*) represent periods of restricted winter growth. Determine the age of your clam by counting the number of ridges formed by the growth rings. Age of clam: _____

2. *Dissect a freshwater clam.*
   (a) Remove the left valve by cutting the *anterior* and *posterior adductor muscles* that hold the valves together. To do this, first identify the anterior adductor muscle in Figure 28-9 and then slip a scalpel between the valves at its approximate location feeling for a firm structure with the scalpel edge. Once you find it, cut back and forth. Repeat this process for the posterior adductor muscle. Once these muscles are severed, slide the scalpel between the valve to be removed and the tissues that line its inner surface. With the flat side of the scalpel, hold the tissues down while you remove the valve.
   (b) The membrane that lines the inner surface of each valve is the **mantle**, which secretes the calcium carbonate shell. Pearls form as a result of irritations (usually grains of sand or small pebbles) in the mantle and sometimes are found embedded in the *pearly layer,* the inner of three layers that comprise the shell. Note that the mantle forms an **incurrent siphon** and an **excurrent siphon** at the rear end.

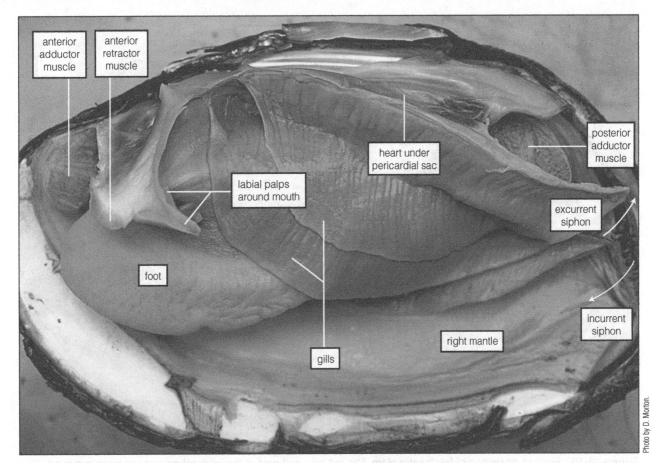

Figure 28-9 Dissection of a freshwater clam. The left valve and mantle have been removed. Arrows indicate the path of water flow into the incurrent siphon and out of the excurrent siphon.

(c) Remove the mantle on the left side by cutting it free with a scalpel. The relatively simple body plan includes a ventral foot and a dorsal visceral mass. Identify the **foot** and two sets of **gills**, one on each side of the *visceral mass*. The gills function in gaseous exchange. Water enters the incurrent siphon and flows over the gills, ultimately leaving through the excurrent siphon. Gills also trap food particles contained in incoming water; these are transported to the mouth by the cilia on the gills. Find the **labial palps**, which are situated around the mouth.

(d) The circulatory system is *open*, so the blood passes from arteries leading from the heart through body spaces called sinuses. Blood is returned to the heart by veins draining the mantle and gills. Find the **heart** in the pericardial sac between the visceral mass and the hinge between the valves.

(e) Dispose of your dissected specimen in the large plastic bag provided for this purpose.

(f) Examine the labeled dissection prepared by your instructor. Identify the **mouth, esophagus, stomach, intestine, digestive gland** (liver), **anus, nephridium** (kidney), and **gonad** (Figure 28-10).

3. Examine the demonstration slide of a transverse section of the gill with your compound microscope. Identify the structures labeled in Figure 28-11.

4. Fertilization is internal in bivalves. Sperm taken in through the female's incurrent siphon fertilize eggs in the gills. In many bivalves, *glochidia* larvae develop from the fertilized eggs and after several months leave the gill area via the excurrent siphons to parasitize fish by clamping onto the gills or fins with their jaw-like valves. The fish grows tissue over the parasite, which remains attached for 2–3 months. The glochidium then breaks out of the fish to develop into an adult on the lake or river bottom. Microscopically look at glochidia in a prepared slide (Figure 28-12).

5. *Study bilvalve diversity.* Examine the assortment of bivalve shells and preserved specimens on demonstration. List the features they have in common.

_____

_____

_____

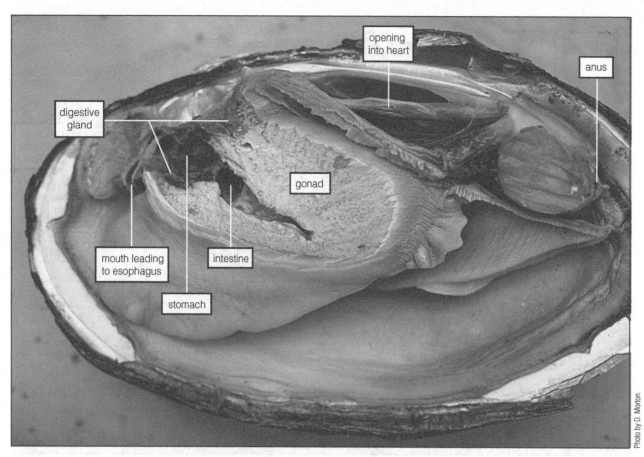

Figure 28-10 Further dissection of freshwater clam. The left gills and part of the visceral mass have been removed.

List some of the differences.

_____

_____

_____

How can you tell which live on sandy bottoms?

_____

B. Snails, Slugs, and Nudibranchs (Class Gastropoda)

Slugs and nudribranchs (Figure 28-13) have no shell; the former two are terrestrial, the latter marine. Nudibranchs are very ornate gastropods, often brightly colored, and frequently adorned with numerous fleshy projections.

1. Place a live freshwater snail (for example, *Physa*) in a glass petri dish. Once the snail has attached itself to the glass, invert the petri dish and use the dissection microscope to observe it moving along a slimy path.
   A *slime gland* in the front of the foot secretes mucus. Briefly describe the muscular contractions of the foot that allow the animal to glide over this mucus. _____

   _____

   Looking at the foot through the glass, you can see the **mouth**. Describe its location. _____

   _____

2. In snails with spirally coiled shells, the shell either spirals to the snail's right or left as it grows. Which way does your snail's shell spiral? _____

   _____

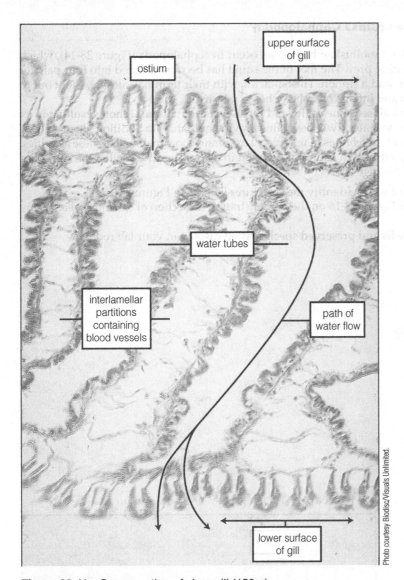

Figure 28-11   Cross section of clam gill (150×).

Labels in figure: ostium, upper surface of gill, water tubes, path of water flow, interlamellar partitions containing blood vessels, lower surface of gill

Photo courtesy Biodisc/Visuals Unlimited.

Figure 28-12   Whole mount of glochidia (250×).

Photo by D. Morton.

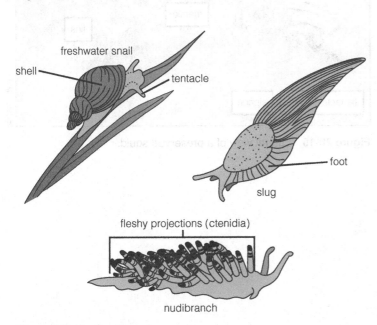

Labels in figure: freshwater snail, shell, tentacle, foot, slug, fleshy projections (ctenidia), nudibranch

Figure 28-13   Gastropods.

C. Squids, Octopuses, and Nautiluses (Class Cephalopoda)

Several significant modifications of the basic molluskan body plan occur in cephalopods (Figure 28-14), which are adapted for rapid swimming and catching prey. The foot of the squid has become divided into four pairs of arms and two tentacles, each with suckers, and a siphon. The tentacles, with their terminal suckers, shoot out to grasp prey. The muscular mantle draws water into its chamber when it relaxes.

Subsequent contraction of the mantle wall seals the cavity and forces water out of the siphon, resulting in jet propulsion propelling the animal through the water. Two lateral fins provide guidance. In addition, there are two large eyes that superficially resemble those of vertebrates. A relatively large brain coordinates all of these activities.

Nautiluses have shells, but shells are reduced in squids and absent in octopuses. The shell of the squid lies dorsally beneath the mantle and is called the pen.

1. Examine the external morphology of a squid. Identify the structures labeled in Figure 28-15.
2. Identify those structures indicated in Figure 28-16 on the demonstration dissection of the internal anatomy of the squid.
3. Look at the variety of cephalopod shells and preserved specimens on display in your lab room.

octopus

chambered nautilus

Figure 28-14   Cephalopods.

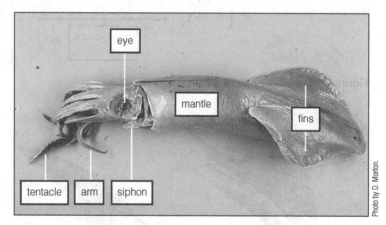

Figure 28-15   Lateral view of a preserved squid.

Figure 28-16 Internal anatomy of female squid. Nidamental glands and the ovary are absent in male specimens, and a penis occupies the same location as the oviduct.

_____ **1.** The protostomes are animals whose
  (a) stomach is in front of the crop.
  (b) mouth is covered by a fleshy lip.
  (c) blastopore becomes a mouth.
  (d) digestive tract is lined by mesoderm.

_____ **2.** The deuterostomes are animals whose
  (a) stomach is in front of the crop.
  (b) mouth is covered by a fleshy lip.
  (c) blastopore becomes the anus.
  (d) digestive tract is lined by mesoderm.

_____ **3.** Further evolution of the protostomes changed the coelom by
  (a) losing it.
  (b) reducing it.
  (c) it becoming a pseudocoel.
  (d) all of the above

_____ **4.** Earthworms exhibit segmentation, defined as the
  (a) division of the body into a series of similar segments.
  (b) presence of a true coelom.
  (c) difference in size of the male and female.
  (d) presence of a "head" equipped with sensory organs.

_____ **5.** The copulatory organ of the earthworm is the
  (a) penis.
  (b) clitellum.
  (c) gonopodium.
  (d) vestibule.

_____ **6.** Leeches belong to the phylum
  (a) Arthropoda.
  (b) Mollusca.
  (c) Annelida.
  (d) Cnidaria.

_____ **7.** One of the two major distinguishing characteristics of mollusks is
  (a) the presence of three body regions.
  (b) the mantle.
  (c) segmentation of the body.
  (d) jointed appendages.

_____ **8.** Functions of the mantle in clams include
  (a) secreting the shell.
  (b) forming pearls around irritating grains of sand.
  (c) forming the incurrent and excurrent siphons.
  (d) all of the above

_____ **9.** Which of the following is a gastropod?
  (a) clam
  (b) snail
  (c) squid
  (d) octopus

_____ **10.** Which of the following is a cephalopod?
  (a) clam
  (b) snail
  (c) slug
  (d) octopus

Name _____ Section Number _____

EXERCISE **28**

Segmented Worms and Mollusks

Post-Lab Questions

Introduction

1. Indicate the differences between protostomes and deuterostomes.

2. List the animal phyla that are protostomes and those that are deuterostomes.

3. What happens to the coelom as each phyla of protostomes evolve?

28.1 Annelids (Phylum Annelida)

4. Briefly describe the life cycle of an earthworm.

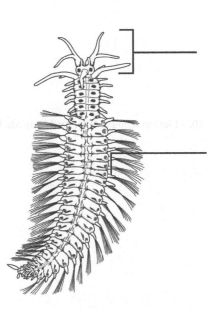

5. Label this diagram of an annelid and circle its class (Oligochaeta, Polychaeta, or Hirudinea).

6. Explain what causes the growth ridges found on the shells of bivalves.

7. List some structures that distinguish bivalves from the other molluskan classes.

8. What characteristics distinguish slugs from nudibranchs?

Food for Thought

9. Is it possible that some of the monsters reported by ancient mariners were giant squid or octopi? Search the Internet before giving and explaining your answer.

10. Define *segmentation* and indicate how the annelids and your body exhibit this phenomenon.

Roundworms and Joint-Legged Animals

After completing this exercise, you will be able to

1. define *pseudocoelomate, cloaca, bladder worm exoskeleton, hemolymph, chitin, carapace, sexual dimorphism, gills, tracheae;*

2. explain the term *ecdysis;*

3. identify representatives of the phylum Nematoda;

4. outline the life cycle of *Ascaris;*

5. identify representatives of the subphyla Crustacea, Hexapoda, Myriapoda, and Chelicerata of the phylum Arthropoda;

6. identify structures (and indicate their associated functions) of the representatives of these phyla and classes.

Introduction

Although joint-legged animals and roundworms at first appear quite different from each other (e.g., segmentation compared to none, legs compared to a legless wormlike body, and a reduced coelom compared to a pseudocoel), these two groups of animals share one characteristic: they molt. Molting or **ecdysis** is the periodic loss of the outer covering of the integument during growth. Unlike our epidermis, which in two to three weeks renews itself one cell at a time, the exoskeleton of joint-legged animals and the cuticle of roundworms are shed all at once. Actually, our hairs, which are grown in follicles derived from the epidermis, are likewise shed as a whole.

CAUTION

Specimens are kept in preservative solutions. Use lab gloves and safety goggles, especially if you wear contact lenses, whenever you or your lab mates handle a specimen or other fluids. If safety goggles do not fit, your glasses should suffice. Wash any part of your body exposed to preservative with copious amounts of water. If preservative solution or other fluids are splashed into your eyes, wash them with the safety eyewash bottle or eye irrigation apparatus for 15 minutes.

29.1 Roundworms (Phylum Nematoda) *(About 50 min.)*

Habitat	aquatic, moist terrestrial, or parasitic
Body Arrangement	bilateral symmetry, pseudocoelomate, head, gut (complete)
Level of Organization	organ system (tissues derived from all three primary germ layers); nervous system with brain; no circulatory, respiratory, or skeletal systems
Body Support	hydrostatic (pseudocoelom)
Life Cycle	sexual reproduction (mostly dioecious with internal fertilization)
Special Characteristics	pseudocoelomate, complete gut

Nematodes also called *roundworms*, like rotifers, are **pseudocoelomates**, which literally means they have a false body cavity or *pseudocoel* (Figure 26-2). This term is somewhat unfortunate, because there *is* a body cavity. It is not considered a true body cavity because tissues derived from mesoderm incompletely line it. Also, in an evolutionary sense it is likely derived from the body cavity of ancestral coelomates. Unlike flatworms, roundworms have a complete gut with both a mouth and an anus. Together, the pseudocoel and the complete digestive system comprise a tube-within-a-tube arrangement, a body plan that is seen in most of the phyla yet to be studied. Roundworms have slender, cylindrical bodies that taper at both ends. A tough, nonliving cuticle of protein covers them.

Parasitic roundworms of vertebrates, including humans, are ascarids, hookworms, *Trichinella* (Figure 29-1), pinworms, and the filarial worms of humans that cause elephantiasis by obstructing lymphatic vessels. Deworming of puppies often results in the expulsion of dog ascarids from the digestive tract. The most studied ascarid is *Ascaris lumbricoides*, which parasitizes humans.

MATERIALS

Per student:

- dissection microscope
- dissecting needle

Per student pair:

- finger bowl

Per lab room:

- collection of free-living roundworms
- tray of moist soil
- container of fresh stream water
- demonstration dissections of
    a male *Ascaris* and
    a female *Ascaris*
- demonstration microscope of a cross section of
    a male *Ascaris* and
    a female *Ascaris*
- boxes of different sizes of lab gloves
- box of safety goggles

A. Free-Living Roundworms

PROCEDURE

1. Examine the demonstration collection of free-living roundworms.
2. Place some moist soil in a finger bowl with some fresh stream water. Using a dissection microscope, look for translucent roundworms in the soil sample (Figure 29-2).

    Describe the behavior of any roundworms you find and make a note of any visible anatomical features they possess.

    _____
    _____
    _____
    _____
    _____
    _____
    _____
    _____
    _____
    _____
    _____

Figure 29-1 *Trichinella spiralis* larvae encysted in muscle (46×). This organism causes the disease trichinosis, which is usually contracted by eating undercooked pork or wild game.

Figure 29-2 Free-living nematodes, *Rhabditella* females, w.m. (350×).

B. *Ascaris*

Ascaris is a common parasite of humans, pigs, horses, and other mammals. Adults range from 15 to 40 cm in length, with males being smaller and having a hook shape to the posterior part of the body.

> **CAUTION**
>
> With your lab gloves on, wash your hands and instruments thoroughly after examining *Ascaris* roundworms; although unlikely, some eggs may still be alive, even though the specimen has been preserved.

1. Examine a female *Ascaris* (Figure 29-3a). At the front end, the triangular *mouth* is surrounded by three lips. The opening on the ventral surface near the other end of the body is the *anus*. A *genital pore* is located about one-third the distance from the mouth.
2. Look at the demonstration dissection and demonstration cross section of a female *Ascaris* and identify the structures labeled in Figure 29-4a and b. The paired **lateral lines** each contain an *excretory tube*. These tubes open to the outside through a single **excretory pore** located near the mouth on the ventral surface. The **ovaries** are the threadlike ends of a Y-shaped reproductive tract. The ovary leads to a larger **oviduct** and a still larger **uterus**. The two uteri converge to form a short, muscular **vagina** that opens to the outside through the **genital pore**.
3. Examine a male *Ascaris* (Figure 29-3b). The lips and mouth are the same as that of the female. However, the male has a *cloaca*—an exit for both the reproductive and digestive systems—instead of an anus. A pair of *penial spicules* protrudes from this opening.

Figure 29-3 *Ascaris.* (a) Female. (b) Male.

(a)

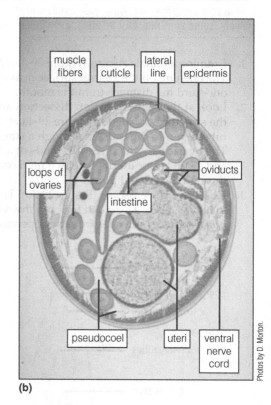

(b)

Photos by D. Morton.

Figure 29-4 (a) Dissection of female *Ascaris*. (b) Cross section of female *Ascaris* (26×).

4. Look at the demonstration dissection and demonstration cross section of a male *Ascaris* and identify the structures labeled in Figure 29-5a and b. The reproductive system superficially resembles that of the female. It consists of a single tubular structure that includes a threadlike **testis** joined to a larger **vas deferens**, an even larger **seminal vesicle**, and terminally a short, muscular ejaculatory duct that empties into the cloaca.

5. After copulation, the eggs are fertilized in the female oviduct. The eggs, surrounded by a thick shell, are expelled through the genital pore to the outside; as many as 200,000 may be shed into the host's intestinal tract per day. Examine a prepared slide with whole *Ascaris* eggs, and draw what you see in Figure 29-6.

The eggs are eliminated in the host's feces. They are very resistant and can live for years under adverse conditions. Infection with *Ascaris* results from ingesting eggs in food or water contaminated by feces or soil. The eggs pass through the stomach and hatch in the small intestine. The small larvae migrate through the bloodstream, exit the circulatory system into the respiratory system, and crawl up the respiratory tubes and out the trachea into the throat. There they are swallowed to reinfect the intestinal tract and mature. Sometimes larvae exit the nasal passages rather than being swallowed. The entire journey of the larva from intestine back to intestine takes about 10 days.

(a)

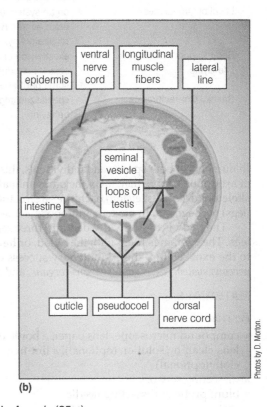

Photos by D. Morton.

(b)

Figure 29-5 (a) Dissection of male *Ascaris.* (b) Cross section of male *Ascaris* (35×).

Figure 29-6 Drawing of the *Ascaris* eggs
(_____×).

Habitat	aquatic, terrestrial (land and air), some parasitic
Body Arrangement	bilateral symmetry, coelomate, body regions (head, thorax, and abdomen), segmented (specialized segments form mouthparts and jointed appendages), gut (complete)
Level of Organization	organ system (tissues derived from all three primary germ layers), nervous system with brain, excretory system (green glands or Malphigian tubules), circulatory system (open), respiratory system (gills, trachae, or book lungs)
Body Support	exoskeleton of chitin
Life Cycle	sexual reproduction (mostly dioecious with internal fertilization), larvae, metamorphosis, some parthenogenesis
Special Characteristics	specialized segments, exoskeleton of chitin, metamorphosis, flight in some, complex behavior

In numbers of both species and individuals, this is the largest animal phylum. There are more than 1 million species of arthropods, more than all of the other animal phyla combined. Arthropods have both segmentation and an **exoskeleton** (external skeleton) of **chitin**—a structural polysaccharide. Arthropod ancestors had one pair of appendages (legs) per segment. In modern arthropods, some of these appendages evolved into other useful structures.

The body is typically divided into three regions: the *head, thorax,* and *abdomen.* The mouthparts are modified legs. The coelom is filled with the blood, or **hemolymph,** and connected to an *open circulatory system.* In addition to the exoskeleton, the evolutionary success of arthropods is due in large part to their *highly developed central nervous system, well-developed sense organs,* and *complex behavior.*

MATERIALS

Per student:

- compound microscope, lens paper, a bottle of lens-cleaning solution (optional), a lint-free cloth (optional)
- dissecting scissors
- blunt probe or dissecting needle
- scalpel

Per student pair:

- dissection microscope
- preserved crayfish
- dissection pan
- grasshopper (*Romalea*)

- prepared slide of a whole mount of grasshopper mouthparts

Per lab room:

- demonstration collections of
  living and preserved and mounted crustaceans
  living and preserved and mounted insects
  living and preserved centipedes
  living and preserved millipedes
  living and preserved and mounted spiders, horseshoe crabs, scorpions, ticks, and mites
- large plastic bag for disposal of dissected specimens
- boxes of different sizes of lab gloves
- box of safety goggles

PROCEDURE

A. Crustaceans (Subphylum Crustacea)

Some of our most prized seafoods are crustaceans. This group contains shrimps, lobsters, crabs, and crayfish—and animals of considerably less culinary interest, including water fleas, sand fleas, isopods (sow or pill bugs), ostracods, copepods, and barnacles. Most species are marine, but some live in freshwater. Most isopods occupy moist areas on land. For the most part, crustaceans are carnivorous, scavenging, or parasitic.

Crustaceans have two pairs of antennae on the head, and their exoskeleton is hardened on top and sometimes on the sides to form a protective **carapace.**

1. Examine the demonstration specimens of crustaceans on display in the lab.
2. Check out the external features of a crayfish.
   (a) Obtain a crayfish, a fairly typical crustacean, and rinse it in water at the sink. Place the rinsed crayfish in a dissection pan.
   (b) Recognize the two major body regions (Figure 29-7): an anterior **cephalothorax**, composed of a fused head and thorax, and a posterior *abdomen.* Note the **carapace.** The portion of the carapace that extends between the eyes is the **rostrum.**

(c) Identify the pair of large, image-forming **compound eyes** (comprised of many closely packed photosensory units) each one atop a movable stalk, a pair of **antennae**, and two pairs of smaller and shorter **antennules**. The first pair of antennules are considered short antennae.

(d) Find the **mouth**, which is comprised of three pairs of mouthparts—one pair of **mandibles** and two pairs of **maxillae**. Three pairs of **maxillapeds** (Figure 29-8) surround the mouthparts.

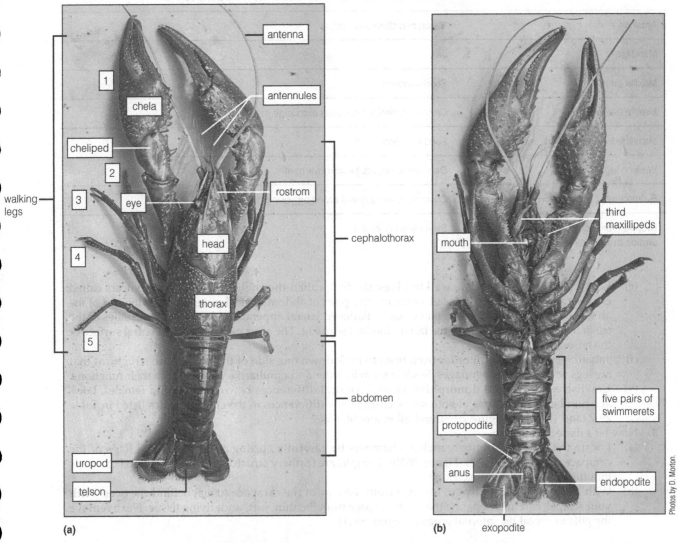

Figure 29-7 (a) Dorsal and (b) ventral views of the external anatomy of the crayfish. The five walking legs are numbered in (a).

Figure 29-8 Crayfish mouthparts.

TABLE 29-1   Function of Crayfish Legs and Modified Appendages

Structure	Function
Antennule	Contains a statocyst, an organ of balance, in the basal segment
Antenna	Vision and chemoreception
Mandible	Jaw
Maxilla (first)	Food handling
Maxilla (second)	Creates current for gaseous exchange in the gills
Maxillipeds (first, second, and third)	Food handling
Walking legs (1–5)	Defense (chelipeds) and movement
Swimmerets (1–5)	Copulation (males) and brooding young (female)
Uropod (combines with telson and other uropod to form tail fan)	Swimming backward

© Cengage Learning 2013

(e) Locate the five pairs of large **walking legs**; the first, called the **chelipeds**, bear large pincers called **chelae**. Continuing toward the tail, count the five pairs of abdominal **swimmerets**. Near the end of the abdomen, locate the **uropods**, a pair of large, flattened lateral appendages located on both sides of the *telson*, which is an extension of the last abdominal segment. The **anus** opens onto the ventral surface of the telson.

(f) Table 29-1 summarizes in order from front to back down one side of the body those structures that are legs or modified appendages. Review them in order and familiarize yourself with their functions.

(g) Crayfish exhibit **sexual dimorphism** (morphological differences between male and female). Look at a number of specimens of both sexes, observe any differences in the characteristics listed in Table 29-2 (and shown in Figure 29-9), and fill in any blanks.

3. Now let's dissect a crayfish.

(a) Locate the **gills** within the branchial chambers by carefully cutting away the lateral flaps of the carapace with your scissors (Figure 29-10). The gills are feathery structures containing blood channels that function in gaseous exchange.

(b) With scissors, superficially cut forward from the rear of the carapace to just behind the eyes. With your scalpel, carefully separate the hard carapace from the thin, soft, underlying tissue. Next, remove the gills to reveal the internal organs (Figure 29-11).

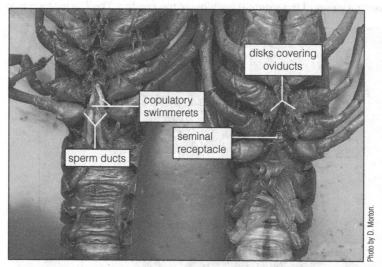

Figure 29-9   Ventral views of (left) a male, (right) a female crayfish.

TABLE 29-2	Sexual Dimorphisms in Crayfish (Figure 29-9)	
Characteristic	**Male**	**Female**
Swimmerets	Front two pairs of swimmerets enlarged for copulation and transferring sperm to the female	No modifications
Walking legs	Openings of the *sperm ducts* at the bases of 5th pair	*Seminal receptacle* in the middle between the bases of the 4th and 5th pairs and discs covering the oviducts at the bases of 3rd pair
Width of abdomen	Narrow	Broad

© Cengage Learning 2013

gills

Photo by D. Morton.

Figure 29-10 Internal anatomy of the crayfish with side of carapace removed.

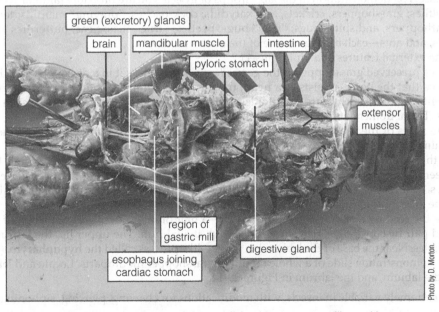

green (excretory) glands

brain

mandibular muscle

intestine

pyloric stomach

extensor muscles

region of gastric mill

digestive gland

esophagus joining cardiac stomach

Photo by D. Morton.

Figure 29-11 Internal anatomy of the crayfish with carapace, gills, and heart removed.

(c) Note the two longitudinal bands of *extensor muscles* that run dorsally through the thorax and abdomen. In the abdomen, find the large *flexor muscles* lying ventrally below the extensor muscles and intestine. What is the function of these two sets of muscles?

_____

_____

_____

(d) Locate the small, membranous heart or its location just posterior to the stomach. Blood flows from the heart into arteries, which open into *sinuses* (open spaces). Blood returns to the heart through holes in its wall.

(e) Identify the organs of the upper digestive tract. The mouth leads to the tubular **esophagus**, which empties into the **cardiac stomach**. At the border between the cardiac stomach and the **pyloric stomach** is the **gastric mill**, a grinding apparatus composed of three chitinous teeth. What role in digestion do you think this structure plays?

_____

_____

_____

(f) Note the large **digestive gland**. This organ secretes digestive enzymes into the cardiac stomach and takes up nutrients from the pyloric stomach. Absorption of nutrients from the tract continues in the intestine, which runs from the abdomen to the *anus*.

(g) Locate the **green glands**, the excretory organs situated ventrally in the head region near the base of the antennae. A duct leads to the outside from each green gland.

(h) The gonads lie beneath the heart. They will be obvious if your specimen was obtained during the reproductive season. If not, they will be small and difficult to locate. In a female, try to find the *ovaries* just beneath the heart. In the male, two white *testes* will occupy a similar location.

(i) Remove the organs in the cephalothorax to expose the *ventral nerve cord*. Observe the segmental ganglia and their paired lateral nerves. Trace the nerve cord forward to locate the **brain**. Note the nerves leading from the brain to the eyes, antennules, antennae, and mouthparts.

(j) Dispose of your dissected specimen in the large plastic bag provided for this purpose.

B. Insects (Subphylum Hexapoda)

Of the more than 1 million species of arthropods, more than 850,000 of them are insects. These animals occupy virtually every kind of terrestrial and freshwater habitat. This extraordinary proliferation of species is almost certainly due to the evolution of wings. Insects were the first organisms to fly and thus were able to exploit a variety of opportunities not available to other animals.

1. Examine insects on demonstration in the lab. Groups of insects you are probably familiar with—dragonflies and damselflies; grasshoppers, crickets, and katydids; cockroaches; "praying" mantids; termites; cicadas, aphids, leafhoppers, and spittlebugs; "true" bugs; beetles; "true" flies; fleas; butterflies and moths; and wasps, bees, and ants—each belongs to one of the orders of insects.

2. Examine the external features of a typical insect.
   (a) Obtain a preserved grasshopper of the genus *Romalea* and place it in a dissection pan (Figure 29-12).
   (b) Observe that the body consists of a **head**, **thorax**, and **abdomen**. The thorax is composed of three segments, each of which bears a pair of legs. The middle and back segments also each bear a pair of wings. The abdomen, unlike the situation in crustaceans, has no appendages.
   (c) On the sides of the thorax and abdomen find the **spiracles**, tiny openings into the **tracheae** (or breathing tubes), which course through the body and function in gaseous exchange.
   (d) Note that the **head** of the grasshopper contains a pair of **compound eyes**, which form images. Between these eyes, find three simple eyes, the **ocelli**, which although light sensitive, do not form images. A single pair of antennae characterizes the insects from the crustaceans (which have two) and the arachnids (which have none).
   (e) Locate the feeding appendages (Figure 29-13)—a pair of **mandibles** and two pairs of **maxillae**, the second pair fused together to form the lower lip, the **labium**. The upper lip, the **labrum**, covers the mandibles. Near the base of the labium is a tongue-like process called the **hypopharynx** (Figure 29-14).

3. Look at the demonstration slide of a whole mount of grasshopper mouthparts. Locate and label a mandible, a maxilla, the labium, and the labrum in Figure 29-14.

Mouthparts are extremely variable in insects, with modifications for chewing, piercing, siphoning, and sponging (Figure 29-15).

(a)

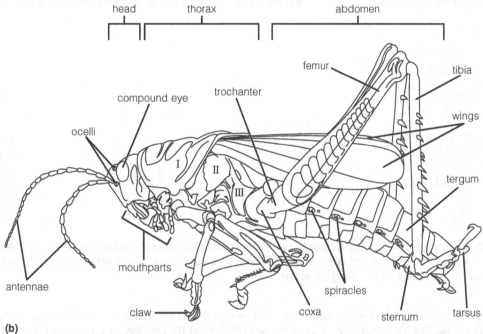

(b)

Figure 29-12 Photograph (**a**) and diagram (**b**) of the external anatomy and body form of a grasshopper, a typical insect.

C. Centipedes and Millipedes (Subphylum Myriapoda)

Centipedes are swift, predaceous arthropods adapted for running. The body is flattened with one pair of legs per segment, except for the head and the rear two segments (Figure 29-16a). The first segment of the body bears a pair of legs modified as *poison claws* for seizing and killing prey. In some tropical species (which can get as long as 20 cm), the poison can be dangerous to humans. Centipedes live under stones or the bark of logs. Their prey consists of other arthropods, worms, and mollusks. The common house centipede eats roaches, bedbugs, and other insects.

Figure 29-13 Grasshopper mouthparts.

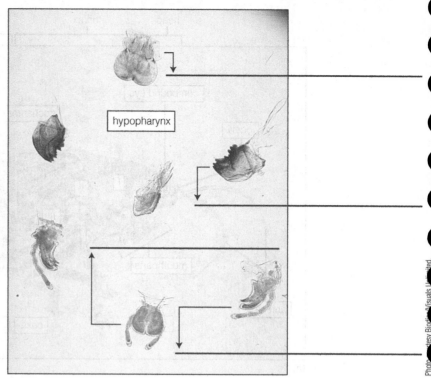

hypopharynx

Figure 29-14 Isolated grasshopper mouthparts, w.m. (7×).

antenna labrum
compound eye
mandible
maxilla
palps
labium

(a)

labium

(b)

maxilla

(c)

(d)

Figure 29-15 Examples of insect appendages. Headparts of (**a**) grasshoppers, a chewing insect; (**b**) flies, which sponge up nutrients with a specialized labium; (**c**) butterflies, which siphon up nectar with a specialized maxilla; and (**d**) mosquitoes, with piercing and sucking appendages.

Although superficially similar, the millipedes and centipedes differ in many ways. The millipedes typically have cylindrical bodies. All segments, except those of the short thorax, bear two pairs of legs. There are no poison claws (Figure 29-16b). Millipedes are very slow arthropods that live in dark, moist places. They scavenge on decaying organic matter. When handled or disturbed, they often curl up into a ball and secrete a noxious fluid from their scent glands as a means of defense.

1. Examine the centipedes on demonstration in the lab.
2. Similarly observe the millipedes on display in the lab.

D. Subphylum Chelicerata: Spiders, Horseshoe Crabs, Scorpions, Ticks, and Mites

Today most species are terrestrial, but the early chelicerates were marine. Horseshoe crabs represent these ancient marine forms. Their bodies and five pairs of walking legs are concealed under a tough carapace (Figure 29-17a).

The body of spiders and scorpions consists of a *cephalothorax* and *abdomen*. In ticks and mites, these parts are fused. The cephalothorax bears six pairs of appendages, the rear four of which are walking legs (Figure 29-17b).

How many pairs of walking legs do insects have? _____

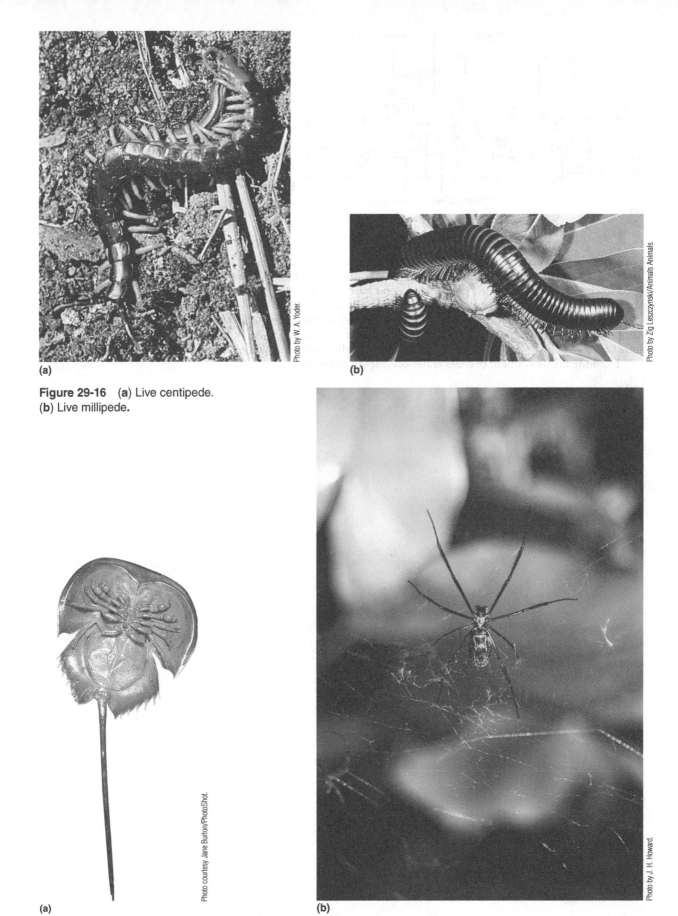

Figure 29-16 (a) Live centipede. (b) Live millipede.

Figure 29-17 (a) Ventral view of a horseshoe crab. (b) Live spider. *Continues*

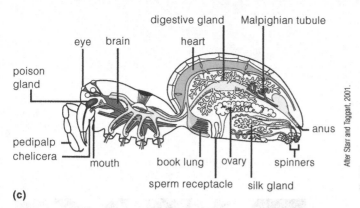

Figure 29-17 (c) Internal anatomy of a spider. *Continued*

(c)

After Starr and Taggart, 2001.

Chelicerates have no true mandibles or antennae, and their eyes are simple. In spiders, the first pair of appendages bear fangs. Each fang has a duct that connects to a poison gland. The second pair of appendages is used to chew and squeeze their prey. This second pair is also sensory, and males use them to store and transfer sperm to females. Most, but not all, spiders spin webs to catch their prey. They secrete digestive enzymes into the prey's (usually an insect's) body, and the liquefied remains are sucked up. Other chelicerates have front appendages specialized to their particular method of feeding. Ticks suck the blood of vertebrates and most mites are scavengers—for example, dust mites eat the shed skin cells that are a major component of house dust.

Examine the assortment of chelicerates on display in the lab.

_____ 1. Structures that are shed in one piece include
   (a) the cuticle of roundworms.
   (b) the exoskeleton of arthropods.
   (c) human hair.
   (d) all of the above

_____ 2. Nematodes and rotifers have a body cavity that is
   (a) called a coelom.
   (b) called a pseudocoelom.
   (c) completely lined by tissues derived from mesoderm.
   (d) both a and c

_____ 3. Filarial roundworms cause elephantiasis by
   (a) encysting in muscle tissue.
   (b) promoting the growth of fatty tumors.
   (c) obstructing lymphatic vessels.
   (d) laying numerous eggs in the joints of their hosts.

_____ 4. Digestive wastes of the male _Ascaris_ roundworm exit the body through the
   (a) anus.
   (b) cloaca.
   (c) mouth.
   (d) excretory pore.

_____ 5. The animal phylum with the most species is
   (a) Mollusca.
   (b) Annelida.
   (c) Arthropoda.
   (d) Platyhelminthes.

_____ 6. The body of arthropods includes
   (a) a head.
   (b) a thorax.
   (c) an abdomen.
   (d) all of the above

_____ 7. Sexual dimorphism, as seen in the crayfish, is
   (a) the presence of male and female individuals.
   (b) the production of eggs and sperm by the same individual.
   (c) another term for copulation.
   (d) the presence of observable differences between males and females.

_____ 8. The grinding apparatus of the digestive system of the crayfish is/are the
   (a) oral teeth.
   (b) gizzard.
   (c) pharyngeal jaw.
   (d) gastric mill.

_____ 9. The insects were the first organisms to
   (a) show bilateral symmetry.
   (b) exhibit segmentation.
   (c) fly.
   (d) develop lungs.

_____ 10. Like the insects, the arachnids (spiders and so on) have
   (a) three pairs of walking legs.
   (b) one pair of antennae.
   (c) true mandibles.
   (d) an abdomen.

EXERCISE **29**

Roundworms and Joint-Legged Animals

Post-Lab Questions

Introduction

1. Indicate the differences between protostomes and deuterostomes, and list the phyla of animals in each group.

2. Describe ecdysis in roundworms and joint-legged animals.

29.1 Roundworms (Phylum Nematoda)

3. *Pseudocoel* means "false body cavity." Why is this term applied to the body cavity of roundworms?

29.2 Joint-Legged Animals (Phylum Arthropoda)

4. Define *sexual dimorphism*, describe it in the crayfish, and list two other animals that exhibit this phenomenon.

5. Identify and label the structures noted in this diagram.

A. _____   E. _____   H. _____
B. _____   F. _____   I. _____
C. _____   G. _____   J. _____
D. _____

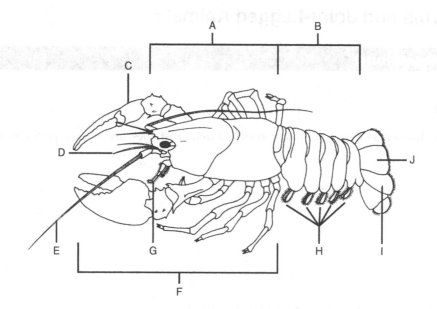

6. How has flight been at least partly responsible for the success of the insects?

7. List several differences between insects and spiders.

Food for Thought

8. List the roundworm parasites and use the Internet to learn how they gain entry into the body. Describe that process here.

9. Write the phylum and choose the appropriate description for each animal (or group of animals) listed in the following table.

Animal	Phylum	Symmetry (none, radial, or bilateral)	Level of Organization (cell, tissue, organ system)	Body Cavity (none, pseudocoelomate, or coelomate)	Gut (none, incomplete, or complete)
Sponge					
Hydra and Jellyfish					
Flatworm					
Rotifer					
Segmented worm					
Clam, snail, and octopus					
Roundworm					
Crayfish, insect, and spider					

10. Define *segmentation* and indicate how the annelids, arthropods, and your body exhibit this phenomenon.

Echinoderms and Invertebrate Chordates

After completing this exercise, you will be able to

1. define *dermal endoskeleton, water-vascular system, notochord, pharyngeal gill slits, dorsal hollow nerve cord, post-anal tail, invertebrate*;

2. describe the natural history of members of phylum Echinodermata and the invertebrate members of phylum Chordata;

3. identify some representatives of the echinoderm classes (sea stars, brittle stars, sea urchins, and sea cucumbers);

4. compare and contrast the invertebrate chordates (subphyla Urochordata and Cephalochordata);

5. identify structures (and indicate associated functions) of the representatives of these phyla and subphyla.

Introduction

The ancestors of echinoderms and chordates, the phylum to which we belong, had a coelom (body cavity) and were deuterostomes (first embryonic opening becomes anus). Although the adult forms of these two phyla look quite different, chordates are thought to have evolved from the bilaterally symmetrical larvae of ancestral echinoderms some 600 million years ago.

There is an additional small phylum, the Hemichordata, whose members (acorn worms) have both echinoderm and chordate characteristics. Acorn worms are *long, slender, wormlike* animals (Figure 30-1a). Most *live in shallow seawater.* They *obtain food by burrowing in mud and sand or filter feeding.* Evidence of their former activity can be seen on exposed tidal flats where mud or sand that has passed through their bodies is left in numerous coiled, ropelike piles (Figure 30-1b).

(a)

(b)

Figure 30-1 (a) Preserved acorn worm. (b) Ropelike piles of sand formed by burrowing acorn worms.

30.1 Echinoderms (Phylum Echinodermata) *(60 min.)*

Habitat	aquatic, marine
Body Arrangement	radial symmetry (larvae are bilaterally symmetrical), coelomate, no well-defined head, no segmentation, gut (usually complete)

Level of Organization	organ system (tissues derived from all three primary germ layers), circular nervous system with radial nerves, reduced circulatory system, no respiratory and excretory system, dermal endoskeleton (mesoderm)
Body Support	endoskeleton of calcium carbonate
Life Cycle	sexual reproduction (mostly dioecious with external fertilization), larvae, metamorphosis, high regenerative potential
Special Characteristics	radial symmetry, no segmentation, water-vascular system, dermal endoskeleton

CAUTION

Specimens are kept in preservative solutions. Use lab gloves and safety goggles, especially if you wear contact lenses, whenever you or your lab mates handle a specimen or other fluids. If safety goggles do not fit, your glasses should suffice. Wash any part of your body exposed to preservative with copious amounts of water. If preservative solution or other fluids are splashed into your eyes, wash them with the safety eyewash bottle or eye irrigation apparatus for 15 minutes.

Echinoderm means "spiny skin." These are marine animals; they live on the bottom of both shallow and deep seas. Their feeding methods range from trapping organic particles and plankton (e.g., sea lilies and feather stars) to scavenging (sea urchins) and predatory behavior (sea stars).

The echinoderms exhibit five-part *radial symmetry* and a calcareous (contains calcium carbonate) **dermal endoskeleton** (internal skeleton) composed of many small plates. Much of the *coelom* is taken up by a unique *water-vascular system*, which functions in movement, attachment, respiration, excretion, food handling, and sensory perception.

MATERIALS

Per student:

- dissecting scissors
- blunt probe or dissecting needle

Per student pair:

- dissection microscope
- preserved sea star
- dissection pan
- dissection pins
- prepared slide of
    a cross section of a sea star arm (ray)
    a whole mount of bipinnaria larvae
- compound microscope, lens paper, a bottle of lens-cleaning solution (optional), and a lint-free cloth (optional)

Per lab room:

- collections of
    preserved or mounted brittle stars, sea urchins, sea biscuits, and sand dollars (preserved specimens and skeletons), preserved sea cucumbers
- live specimens (optional)
- collection of preserved or mounted feather stars and sea lilies
- large plastic bag for disposal of dissected specimens
- boxes of different sizes of lab gloves
- box of safety goggles

A. Sea Stars (Class Asteroidea)

The sea stars are familiar occupants of the sea along shores and coral reefs. They are slow-moving animals that sometimes gather in large numbers on bare areas of rock. Many are brightly colored. Some sea stars are more than 1 m in diameter.

PROCEDURE

1. Obtain a preserved specimen of a sea star and keep your specimen moist with water in a dissection pan. Note the **central disk** on the *aboral* side—the side without the mouth and the **five arms** attached to it. Find the **sieve plate** (madreporite), a light-colored calcareous roundish structure near the edge of the disk between two arms (Figure 30-2a). The pores in the sieve plate open into the water-vascular system.
2. With a dissection microscope, note the many protective **spines** scattered over the surface of the body. Near the base of the spines are many small pincerlike structures, the **pedicellariae** (Figure 30-2b). The *valves* of these structures grasp objects that land on the surface of the body, such as potential parasites. Also among the spines are many soft, hollow **skin gills** (dermal branchiae) that communicate directly with the coelom and function in the exchange of gases and excretion of ammonia (a nitrogen-containing metabolic waste).
3. Locate the **mouth** on the oral side (Figure 30-3a). Note that an **ambulacral groove** extends from the mouth down the middle of the oral side of each arm. Numerous **tube feet** extend from the water-vascular system

(a)

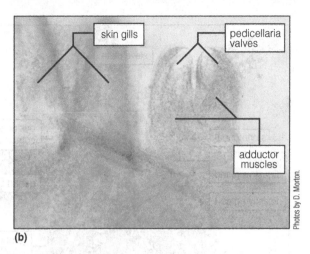

Photos by D. Morton.

(b)

Figure 30-2 (a) Aboral view of sea star. (b) Pedicellaria and skin gills, w.m. (205×).

and occupy this groove. Each tube foot consists of a bulblike structure attached to a **sucker** (Figure 30-3b). The animal moves by alternating the suction and release mechanisms of the tube feet. Tube feet are also used to adhere to the shells of bivalves and to pry them open to get at their soft insides. The tube feet, along with the skin gills, also function in the exchange of gases and excretion of ammonia.

4. With your dissecting scissors, cut across the top of an arm about 1 cm from the tip. Next, cut out a rectangle of spiny skin by carefully cutting along each side of the arm to the central disk and then across the top of the arm at the edge of the disk. Observe the hard, calcareous plates of the dermal endoskeleton as you cut. Remove the rectangle of skin to uncover the large *coelom*, which contains the internal organs (Figure 30-4).

5. Cut around the *sieve plate* to remove the upper portion of the body wall of the *central disk*. The *mouth* connects via an extremely short esophagus to the clearly visible pouchlike **cardiac stomach**. The cardiac stomach opens into the upper *pyloric stomach*. A slender, short *intestine* leads from the upper side of the stomach to the *anus*. Find the two green, fingerlike **digestive glands** in each arm, which produce digestive enzymes and deliver them to the pyloric stomach.

6. Identify the dark-colored **gonads** that are located near the base of each arm. The sexes are separate but difficult to distinguish, except by microscopic examination. In nature, sperm and eggs are released into the seawater, and the fertilized eggs develop into bipinnaria larvae.

7. The water-vascular system is unique to echinoderms (Figure 30-5). Note that the *sieve plate* leads to a short **stone canal**, which in turn leads to the *circular canal* surrounding the mouth. Five *radial canals* lead from the circular canal into the ambulacral grooves. Each radial canal connects by short side branches with many pairs of tube feet.

8. The nervous system (not shown in Figure 30-3) is simple. A circular *nerve ring* surrounds the mouth, and a *radial nerve* extends from this into each arm, ending at a light-sensitive eyespot. There are no specific excretory organs. Dispose of your dissected specimen in the large plastic bag provided for this purpose.

(a)

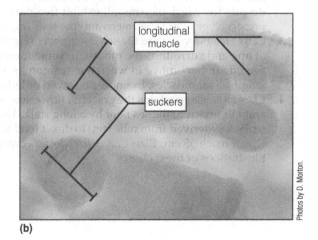

Photos by D. Morton.

(b)

Figure 30-3 (a) Oral view of sea star. (b) Close-up of tube feet, w.m. (78×).

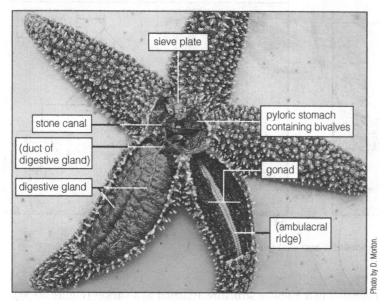

Figure 30-4 Internal anatomy of a sea star.

water-vascular system

Figure 30-5 The water-vascular system of a five-armed sea star. The ring canal is located in the central disk, and each radial canal extends into one of the arms.

9. Examine a prepared slide of a cross section of an arm with your compound microscope. Identify the structures labeled in Figure 30-6.

10. Examine a prepared slide of a whole mount of bipinnaria larvae. The digestive tract, including the *mouth, esophagus, stomach, intestine,* and *anus,* is clearly visible (Figure 30-7).

11. Observe any available preserved, plastic-mounted, or living specimens of other sea stars.

B. Other Echinoderms

PROCEDURE

1. *Class Ophiuroidea* includes the brittle stars (Figure 30-8). These echinoderms have slender arms and move relatively rapidly, for echinoderms! In life, the rays are much more flexible than those of the sea stars. Examine preserved, plastic-mounted, or living specimens of brittle stars.

2. *Class Echinoidea* contains the sea urchins, animals that lack arms. They have long, movable spines, which surround the top and sides of a compact skeleton called the **test** (Figure 30-9). Sea urchins ingest food by means of a complex structure, *Aristotle's lantern,* which contains teeth. The sea biscuits and sand dollars are also members of this class. They have flat, disk-shaped bodies. Sea urchins, sea biscuits, and sand dollars, despite their lack of arms, all exhibit five-part radial symmetry and move by means of tube feet. Study preserved or living specimens and the tests (Figure 30-10) of members of this class.

3. *Class Holothuroidea* are the sea cucumbers (Figure 30-11). No spines are present. A collection of tentacles at one end surrounds the mouth. In some forms, the tube feet occur over the entire surface of the body. Sea cucumbers move in wormlike fashion as a result of the contractions of two layers of circular and longitudinal muscles. Examine preserved or living sea cucumbers.

4. *Class Crinoidea* contains the graceful, flowerlike feather stars and sea lilies (Figure 30-12). These stationary animals attach to the sea floor by a long stalk. The arms are featherlike; each contains a ciliated groove and tentacles (derived from tube feet) to direct food to the mouth. There can be from 5 to over 200 arms, some of which reach 35 cm. *Class Concentricycloidea* contains the sea daisies. Examine any available specimens and illustrations of these classes.

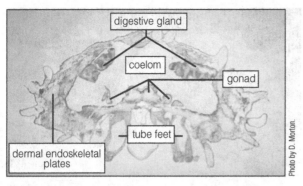

Figure 30-6　Cross section of a sea star arm (23×).

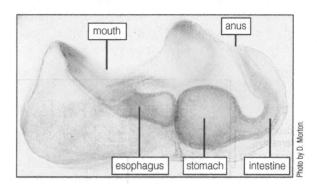

Figure 30-7　Bipinnaria larva (196×).

(a)

(b)

Figure 30-8　(a) Dried and (b) live brittle star.

(a)　　　　　　　(b)

Figure 30-9　(a) Aboral and (b) oral views of a sea urchin.

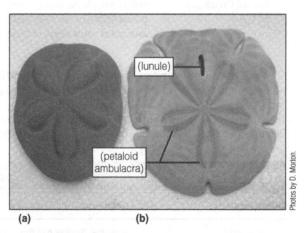

(a)　　　　　　　(b)

Figure 30-10　(a) Sea biscuit and (b) sand dollar tests.

dendritic
tentacles
surrounding
mouth

(ambulacral
rows)

(a)

Photos by D. Morton and W. A. Yoder.

(b)

Figure 30-11 **(a)** Preserved and **(b)** live sea cucumber.

30.2 Chordates (Phylum Chordata) (50 min.)

Habitat	aquatic, terrestrial (land and air)
Body Arrangement	bilateral symmetry, coelomate, head and post-anal tail, segmentation, gut (complete)
Level of Organization	organ system (tissues derived from all three primary germ layers), nervous system with brain, circulatory system (closed with a ventral heart), organ systems highly developed
Body Support	most have a mesoderm-derived endoskeleton of cartilage or bone
Life Cycle	sexual reproduction (mostly dioecious with internal or external fertilization), some larvae, some metamorphosis
Special Characteristics	notochord, pharyngeal gill slits, dorsal hollow nerve cord, and a post-anal tail at some stage of life cycle

JWalker/Jupiter Images

Figure 30-12 Feather star.

The word *chordate* refers to one of the four major diagnostic characteristics shared by all members of this phylum at least some time in their life span: a **notochord, pharyngeal gill slits,** a **dorsal hollow nerve cord,** and a **post-anal tail** (Table 30-1). Most chordates are also vertebrates—animals that possess a backbone or vertebral column—but a few are not. The latter animals belong to the subphyla Urochordata and Cephalochordata. They are **invertebrates** because they lack a vertebral column. All of the animal phyla you have studied so far are also invertebrates.

TABLE 30-1	Chordate Characteristics	
Characteristic	**Definition**	**Developmental Fate in Humans**
Notochord	A dorsal, flexible rod that provides support for most of the length of the body	Center of intervertebral disks
Pharyngeal gill slits	Paired, lateral outpockets of pharynx that perforate through its wall	Auditory tubes and endocrine glands of neck
Dorsal hollow nerve cord	A tube of nervous tissue dorsal to notochord	Brain and spinal cord
Post-anal tail	Posterior tail that extends past the anus	Present in embryo

© Cengage Learning 2013

MATERIALS

Per student:

- blunt probe

Per student pair:

- dissection microscope
- compound microscope, lens paper, a bottle of lens-cleaning solution (optional), and a lint-free cloth (optional)
- dissection pan

- preserved or mounted sea tunicates (sea squirts)
- preserved and plastic mounted lancelet specimens
- prepared slide of a whole mount of a lancelet
- prepared slide of a cross section of a lancelet in the region of the pharynx
- boxes of different sizes of lab gloves
- box of safety goggles

A. Tunicates (Subphylum Urochordata)

Tunicates are also called sea squirts. Both common names are descriptive of obvious features of these animals. A leather-like "tunic" covers the adult, and water is squirted out of an excurrent siphon (Figure 30-13).

Sea squirt larvae resemble tadpoles in general body form and have a notochord confined to the post-anal tail. The notochord and tail degenerate when the larva becomes an adult tunicate. The larva also has a primitive brain and sense organs. These structures undergo reorganization into a nerve ganglion and nerve net in the adult. The number of pharyngeal gill slits increases in the adult.

1. Examine a preserved or plastic mounted specimen of a sea squirt with a dissection microscope. These animals are small, inactive, and very common marine organisms that inhabit coastal areas of all oceans. The adult is a filter feeder, capturing organic particles into an incurrent siphon by ciliary action. Individuals either float freely in the water (singly or in groups) or are sessile, attached to the bottom as branching individuals or colonies.

2. Water enters a sea squirt through the *incurrent siphon*. It travels into the *pharynx*, where it seeps through *gill slits* to reach a chamber, the *atrium*. The water eventually exits through the *excurrent siphon*. Back in the pharynx, food particles are trapped in sticky mucus and then passed to the digestive tract. Undigested materials are discharged from the anus into the atrium. Identify as many of these structures as possible.

(b) Body plan of the tadpole-like larva, shown midsagittal section.

(c) A new larva swims about for a brief period. Metamorphosis begins when its head attaches to a substrate. The notochord, tail, and most of the nervous system are resorbed (recycled to form new tissues). Slits in the pharynx wall multiply. Organs rotate until the openings through which water enters and leaves the pharynx are directed away from the substrate.

(a)

Figure 30-13   **(a)** Adult form of a sea squirt. **(b)** A sea squirt larva. **(c)** Metamorphosis of a larva into the adult.

B. Lancelets (Subphylum Cephalochordata)

The lancelets are distributed worldwide and are especially abundant in coastal areas with *warm, shallow waters*. *Amphioxus* (Figure 30-14) is the commonly studied representative of this subphylum. The word *Amphioxus* means "sharp at both ends," and this certainly describes its *elongate, fishlike body*. Lancelets reach 50–75 mm in length as adults. Despite their streamlined appearance, these organisms are not very active. They spend most of their time buried in the sand with their heads projecting while they filter organic particles from the water.

1. Examine a preserved lancelet with the dissection microscope (Figure 30-15). Note that the body is translucent, with a low, continuous dorsal and caudal (tail) **fin**. Find the mouth surrounded by tentacles and the

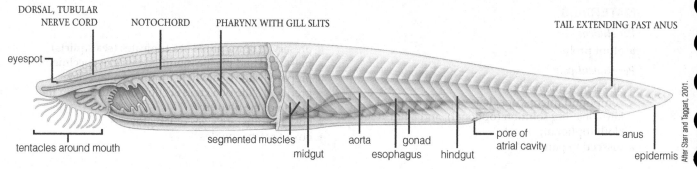

Figure 30-14 Cutaway view of a lancelet. The four Chordate characteristics are capitalized.

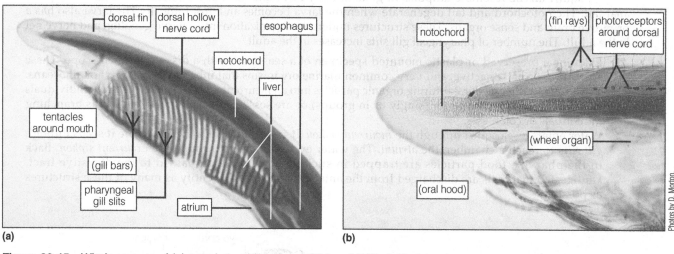

(a)

(b)

Figure 30-15 Whole mounts of (**a**) anterior end (30×) and (**b**) head (100×) of a lancelet.

roughly 150 **pharyngeal gill slits**. Trace below the flow of water from the **mouth** to the pore of the atrial cavity.

_____

_____

_____

2. Describe the capture of food and the path it takes through the digestive system. Unlike the tunicates, the *anus* in a lancelet opens externally.

_____

_____

_____

3. Find the flexible **notochord** extending nearly the full length of the individual; this structure persists into the adult stage. There is a small brain, with a **dorsal hollow nerve cord** that bears light-sensitive cells (the *eyespot*) at its anterior end.

4. Examine a cross section of a lancelet with a compound microscope and identify the structures indicated in Figure 30-16.

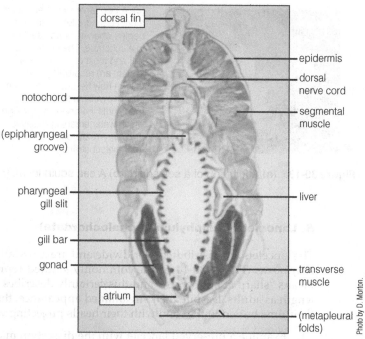

Figure 30-16 Cross section of lancelet in region of pharynx (20×).

_____ 1. Echinoderms and chordates are
   (a) deuterostomes.
   (b) protostomes.
   (c) animals whose blastopore becomes a mouth.
   (d) both b and c

_____ 2. The skin gills of sea stars are structures
   (a) for the exchange of gases and excretion of ammonia.
   (b) of defense.
   (c) for movement.
   (d) that produce the skeletal elements.

_____ 3. The tube feet of a sea star
   (a) bear tiny toes.
   (b) are located only at the tips of the arms.
   (c) function in movement.
   (d) protect the organism from predatory fish.

_____ 4. Aristotle's lantern is a tooth-bearing structure of the
   (a) sea stars.
   (b) tunicates.
   (c) acorn worms.
   (d) sea urchins.

_____ 5. The sieve plate, stone canal, circular canal, and radial canals of a sea star are structures of the
   (a) nervous system.
   (b) water-vascular system.
   (c) digestive system.
   (d) excretory system.

_____ 6. The dermal endoskeleton of echinoderms is made of
   (a) cartilage.
   (b) bone.
   (c) calcium carbonate.
   (d) chitin.

_____ 7. Which structure is **not** a major diagnostic feature of the chordates?
   (a) dorsal hollow nerve cord
   (b) notochord
   (c) pharyngeal gill slits
   (d) vertebral column

_____ 8. The sea squirts and lancelets have an inner chamber that expels water. This chamber is called the
   (a) intestine.
   (b) bladder.
   (c) atrium.
   (d) nephridium.

_____ 9. Invertebrates
   (a) do not have a vertebral column.
   (b) have a vertebral column.
   (c) are all members of the phylum Chordata.
   (d) do not include animals that are members of the phylum Chordata.

_____ 10. Which animal is a chordate?
   (a) sea star
   (b) sea cucumber
   (c) acorn worm
   (d) lancelet

EXERCISE **30**

Echinoderms and Invertebrate Chordates

Post-Lab Questions

30.1 Echinoderms (Phylum Echinodermata)

1. Describe the various structures on the aboral "spiny skin" of a sea star and discuss their functions.

2. Describe the various functions of tube feet.

3. Identify the following structures on this aboral view of the tip of a sea star arm.

A _____

B _____

C _____

Photo by J. W. Perry.

(78×)

4. Describe reproduction in the sea star.

5. List in order the structures in the water-vascular system of a sea star.

6. List the four major characteristics of chordates.

7. Why are sea squirts and lancelets referred to as invertebrate chordates?

8. Compare the presence or absence of the four chordate characteristics in adult sea squirts and lancelets.

9. Compare arthropods, echinoderms, and chordates in terms of their similarities and differences.

Food for Thought

10. Hypothesize an evolutionary relationship among the bipinnaria larva of echinoderms, larval and adult tunicates, and lancelets.

Vertebrates

After completing this exercise, you will be able to

1. define *vertebrate, vertebral column, cranium, vertebrae, cloaca, lateral line, placoid scale, operculum, atrium, ventricle, artery, vein, amniotic egg, ectothermic, endothermic, viviparous;*

2. describe the basic characteristics of members of the subphylum Vertebrata;

3. identify representatives of the vertebrate classes, Cephalaspidomorphi, Chondrichthyes, Osteichthyes, Amphibia, Reptilia, Aves, and Mammalia;

4. identify structures (and indicate associated functions) of representatives of the vertebrate classes;

5. construct a dichotomous key to the animals (optional).

Introduction

In terms of the numbers of individuals and species, chordates do not constitute a large phylum; however, chordates known as vertebrates have had a disproportionately large ecological impact. The **vertebrates** have the *four basic characteristics of chordates* listed in the previous exercise, plus a cranium and a **vertebral column**. The dorsal hollow nerve cord has differentiated into a *brain* and a *spinal cord*. Bones protect both of these structures, the brain by the bones of the **cranium** (braincase) and the spinal cord by the **vertebrae**, the bones that make up the vertebral column.

Like echinoderm larvae and sea squirt larvae and lancelets, vertebrates are *cephalized, bilaterally symmetrical,* and *segmented*. In adults, segmentation is most easily seen in the musculature, vertebrae, and ribs. The body is typically divided into a *head, neck, trunk,* and *tail*. If appendages are present, they are paired, lateral *thoracic appendages* (pectoral fins, forelimbs, wings, and arms) and *pelvic appendages* (pelvic fins, hindlimbs, and legs), which are linked to the vertebral column and function to support and to help move the body. Seven classes of vertebrates have representatives alive today (lampreys, cartilaginous fishes, bony fishes, amphibians, reptiles, birds, and mammals), and one class is completely extinct (armored fishes).

CAUTION

Specimens are kept in preservative solutions. Use lab gloves and safety goggles, especially if you wear contact lenses, whenever you or your lab mates handle a specimen or other fluids. If safety goggles do not fit, your glasses should suffice. Wash any part of your body exposed to preservative with copious amounts of water. If preservative solution or other fluids are splashed into your eyes, wash them with the safety eyewash bottle or eye irrigation apparatus for 15 minutes.

31.1 Lampreys (Class Cephalaspidomorphi) *(12 min.)*

The ancestors of lampreys were the first vertebrates to evolve. Lampreys have a cartilaginous (made of cartilage), primitive skeleton.

Lampreys are represented by both marine and freshwater species and by some species that use seawater and fresh water at some point in their lives. Most lampreys feed on the blood and tissue of fishes by rasping wounds in their sides. A landlocked population of the sea lamprey is infamous for having nearly decimated the commercial fish industry in the Great Lakes. Only a vigorous control program that targeted lamprey larvae restored this industry.

MATERIALS

Per student:
- scalpel
- blunt probe or dissecting needle

Per student pair:
- dissection microscope
- dissection pan

Per student group:
- prepared slide of a whole mount of a lamprey larva or ammocoete
- preserved specimen of sea lamprey

Per lab room:
- boxes of different sizes of lab gloves
- box of safety goggles

PROCEDURE

1. With a dissection microscope, observe a prepared slide of a whole mount of a lamprey larva or ammocoete. Sea lampreys spawn in freshwater streams. Ammocoetes hatch from their eggs and, after a period of development, burrow into the sand and mud. They are long-lived, metamorphosing into adults after as long as 7 years. Because of their longevity and dissimilar appearance, adult lampreys and ammocoetes were long thought to be separate species.

The ammocoete is considered by many to be the closest living form to ancestral chordates. Unlike a lancelet, it has an eye (actually two median eyes), internal ears (otic vesicles), and a heart, as well as several other typical vertebrate organs. Identify the structures labeled in Figure 31-1.

2. Examine a preserved sea lamprey (Figure 31-2). Note its slender, rounded body. The skin of the lamprey is soft and lacks scales. Look at the round, suckerlike **mouth,** inside of which are circular rows of horny, rasping **teeth** and a deep, rasping **tongue.** Although there are no lateral, paired appendages, there are two **dorsal fins** and a **caudal fin** (tail fin). Count and record below the number of pairs of external **gill slits.**

_____

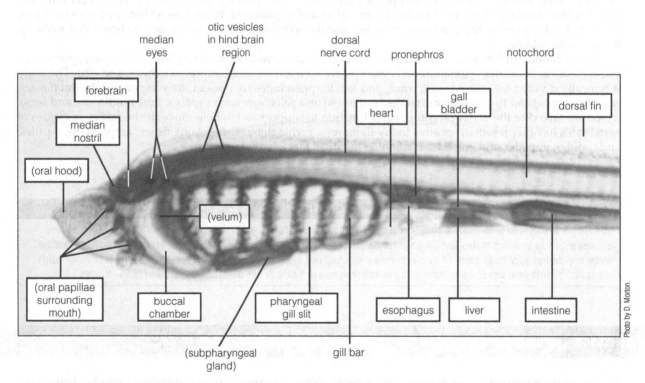

Figure 31-1   Whole mount of ammocoete (40×).

(a)

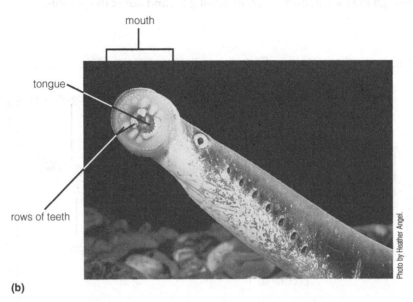

(b)

Figure 31-2 (a) Side view and (b) oral disk of a sea lamprey.

31.2   Cartilaginous Fishes (Class Chondrichthyes) *(12 min.)*

The first vertebrate fossils to show jaws and paired appendages were the heavily armored *placoderms* (class Placodermi). These fishes arose about 425 million years ago. Current hypotheses suggest that the ancestors of placoderms relatively quickly gave rise to the cartilaginous fishes.

Members of the class Chondrichthyes are *jawed fishes* with *cartilaginous skeletons* and *paired appendages*. The evolution of jaws and paired appendages and the evolution of more efficient respiration and a better developed nervous system, including sensory structures, were critical events in the history of vertebrate evolution. Together these adaptations allowed cartilaginous fishes to chase, catch, and eat larger and more active prey. This mostly marine group includes the carnivorous skates, rays, and sharks.

MATERIALS

Per student:

- scalpel
- forceps
- dissecting scissors

Per student pair:

- dissection microscope
- dissection pan

Per student group:

- preserved specimen of
  dog fish (shark)

Per lab room:

- collection of
  preserved cartilaginous fishes
  shark jaws with teeth
- boxes of different sizes of lab gloves
- box of safety goggles

PROCEDURE

1. Look at the assortment of cartilaginous fishes on display.
2. Refer to Figure 31-3a as you examine the external anatomy of a preserved dog fish (shark).
   (a) How many dorsal fins are there? _____
   (b) Notice the front pair of lateral appendages, the **pectoral fins,** and the back pair, the **pelvic fins**. The **tail fin** has a *dorsal lobe* larger than the *ventral* one. In the male, the pelvic fins bear **claspers,** thin processes for transferring sperm to the oviducts of the female. Examine the pelvic fins of a female and a male.
   (c) Identify the opening of the **cloaca** just in front of the pelvic fins. The cloaca is the terminal organ that receives the products of the digestive, excretory, and reproductive systems.
   (d) There are five to seven pairs of gill slits in cartilaginous fishes, six in the dog fish. Observe the most anterior gill slit, which is called the *spiracle*, located just behind the eye. Trace the flow of seawater in nature through the mouth, over the pharyngeal gills, and out of the gill slits.

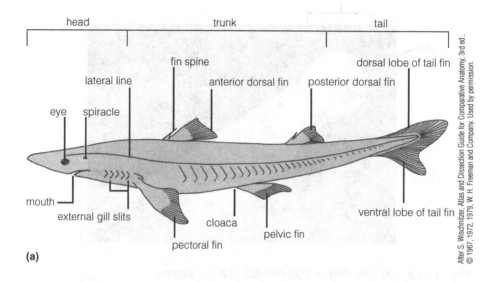

(a)

After S. Wischnitzer, Atlas and Dissection Guide for Comparative Anatomy, 3rd ed., © 1967, 1972, 1979, W. H. Freeman and Company. Used by permission.

(b)

Figure 31-3 (a) External appearance of the dogfish (shark), *Squalus acanthias*. (b) Shark jaw.

(e) Locate the **nostrils,** which open into blind olfactory sacs; in cartilaginous fishes, they don't connect with the pharynx, as your nostrils do. In cartilaginous fishes, they function solely in olfaction (smell). The **eyes** are effective visual organs at short range and in dim light. There are no eyelids.

(f) Find the dashed line that runs along each side of the body. Each is called a **lateral line** and together function to detect vibrations in the water. Lateral lines consist of a series of minute canals perpendicular to the surface that contain sensory hair cells. When the hairs are disturbed, nerve impulses are initiated; their frequency enables the fish to locate the disturbance.

(g) **Placoid scales,** toothlike outgrowths of the skin, cover the body. Run your hand from head to tail along the length of the animal. How does it feel?

_____

Now run your hand in the opposite direction along the animal. How does it feel this time?

_____

Cut out a small piece of skin with your scissors, pick it up with your forceps, and examine its surface with the dissection microscope. Draw what you see in Figure 31-4.

Figure 31-4 Drawing of shark skin (_____×).

3. Examine the demonstration of a shark jaw with its multiple rows of teeth (Figure 31-3b).

31.3 Bony Fishes (Class Osteichthyes) *(12 min.)*

The bony fishes, the fishes with which you are most familiar, inhabit virtually all the waters of the world and are the largest vertebrate group. They are economically important, commercially and as game species. The ancestors of cartilaginous fish gave rise to the first bony fishes about 415 million years ago. As their name suggests, the *skeleton* is at least *partly ossified (bony)*, and the flat *scales* that cover at least some of the surface of most bony fishes are *bony* as well. Gill slits are housed in a common chamber covered by a bony movable flap, the **operculum**.

MATERIALS

Per student:
- scalpel
- compound microscope, lens paper, a bottle of lens-cleaning solution (optional), and a lint-free cloth (optional)
- clean microscope slide and coverslip
- dH₂O in dropping bottle
- forceps
- blunt probe or dissecting needle

Per student pair:
- dissection pan

Per student group:
- preserved specimens of yellow perch

Per lab room:
- collection of preserved bony fishes
- boxes of different sizes of lab gloves
- box of safety goggles

PROCEDURE

1. Examine the assortment of bony fishes on display.
2. Examine a yellow perch as a representative advanced bony fish (Figure 31-5).
   (a) Identify the *spiny* **dorsal fin** located in front of the *soft* **dorsal fin.** Paired **pectoral fins** and **pelvic fins** are also present, and behind the **anus** is an unpaired **anal fin.** The **tail fin** consists of *dorsal* and *ventral lobes* of approximately equal size. The fins, as in the cartilaginous fishes, are used to brake, steer, and maintain an upright position in the water.

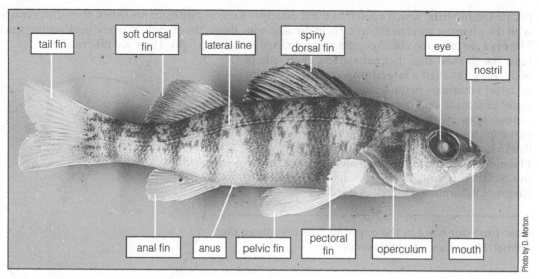

Figure 31-5 Preserved yellow perch.

(b) Note the double **nostrils**, leading into and out of *olfactory sacs*. The eyes resemble those in sharks, with no eyelids. With forceps, pry open the operculum to see the organs of respiration, the **gills.**

(c) Find the **lateral line.** This functions similarly to that of the shark.

(d) Bony scales cover the body. Using forceps, remove a scale, make a wet mount, and examine it with the compound microscope. Locate the *annual rings*, which indicate the approximate age of the fish. How are the annual rings of the fish scale analogous to the annual ridges of the clam shell?

_____

_____

_____

Draw the scale in Figure 31-6.

Figure 31-6 Drawing of yellow perch scale (_____×).

31.4   Amphibians (Class Amphibia) *(30 min.)*

Amphibians include the first vertebrates to partially live on land, having evolved about 370 million years ago from a group of lobe-finned fishes. The paired appendages are modified as legs, which support the individual during movement on land. Respiration by one species or another or by the different developmental stages of one species is by lungs, gills, and the highly vascularized skin and lining of the mouth. There is a *three-chambered heart*, compared to the two-chambered heart of fishes, with two *circuits for the blood circulation*, compared to one circuit in fishes. Reproduction requires water, or at least moist conditions on land. Fertilized eggs hatch in water, and larvae generally live in water. The skeleton is bonier than that of the bony fishes, but a considerable proportion of it remains cartilaginous. The *skin* is usually *smooth and moist*, with mucous glands; scales are usually absent. This group of vertebrates includes the frogs, toads, salamanders, and tropical, limbless, burrowing, mostly blind caecilians.

MATERIALS

Per student:

- forceps
- dissecting scissors
- blunt probe or dissecting needle
- dissection pins

Per student pair:

- preserved farm-raised leopard frog

Per lab room:

- collection of preserved bony fishes
- collection of preserved amphibians
- skeleton of frog
- skeleton of human
- boxes of different sizes of lab gloves
- box of safety glasses

PROCEDURE

1. Examine preserved specimens of a variety of amphibians.
2. The leopard frog illustrates well the general features of the vertebrates and the specific characteristics of the amphibians. Obtain a preserved specimen and after rinsing it in tap water, examine its external anatomy (Figure 31-7).

    (a) Find the two *nostrils* at the tip of the head. These are used for inspiration and expiration of air. Just behind the eye locate a disk-like structure, the *tympanum*, the outer wall of the middle ear. There is no external ear. The tympanum is larger in the male than in the female. Examine the frogs of other students in your lab.

    Is your frog a male or female?

    _____

    (b) At the back end of the body, locate the *cloacal opening.*

    (c) The forelimbs are divided into three main parts: the **upper arm, forearm,** and **hand.** The hand is divided into a **wrist, palm,** and **fingers** (digits). The three divisions of the hindlimbs are the **thigh, shank** (lower leg), and **foot.** The foot is further divided into three parts: the **ankle, sole,** and **toes** (digits).

3. Examine the internal anatomy of the frog.

    (a) With the scissors, cut through the joint at both angles of the jaw. Identify the structures labeled in Figure 31-8. The region containing the opening into the **esophagus** and the **glottis** is the **pharynx** (throat). The esophagus leads to the stomach and the rest of the digestive tract; the glottis leads into the blind respiratory tract.

    (b) Fasten the frog, ventral side up, with pins to the wax or rubbery surface of a dissection pan. Lift the skin with forceps.

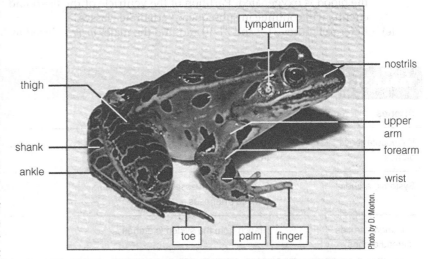

Figure 31-7 External anatomy of the frog.

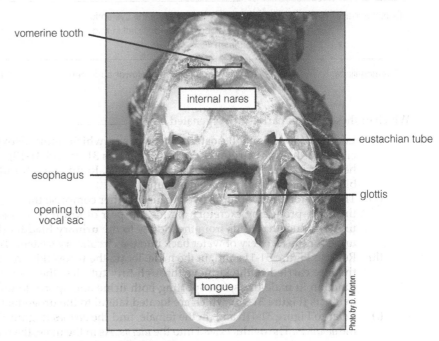

Figure 31-8 Oral cavity of the frog.

Then make a superficial cut with your scissors just left or right of center from the lower abdomen forward to the tip of the lower jaw. Pin back the skin on both sides to expose the large abdominal muscles. Lift these muscles with your forceps, and cut through the body wall with your scissors again from the lower abdomen forward to the tip of the lower jaw, cutting through the sternum (breastbone) but not damaging the internal organs. Pin back the body wall as you did the skin to expose the internal organs (Figure 31-9).

(c) Use Figure 31-9 to locate the *spleen* (Figure 31-9c) and the following organs of the digestive system: **stomach, small intestine, large intestine** (colon), **liver, gall bladder,** and **pancreas.** Trace the esophagus from its opening in the pharynx to the stomach. Find the **bronchi** (the singular is *bronchus*), which lead toward the **lungs.** Are the bronchi dorsal or ventral to the esophagus?

(d) Identify the **heart** with two thin-walled **atria** and the thick-walled **ventricle** and the **conus arteriosus,** along with the right and left branches of the **truncus arteriosus** (Figure 31-9a). The latter structure carries blood to the paired **pulmocutaneous arches** and **systemic arches.** In frogs and other amphibians a *pulmocutaneous circuit* circulates blood to and from the lungs and the skin, and a *systemic circuit* services the rest of the body. Even though there is only one ventricle, because of the structure of the heart and its large arteries, most of the deoxygenated blood returning from the body is pumped into the pulmocutaneous circuit before the oxygenated blood is pumped into the systemic circuit. In comparison, a fish has a two-chambered heart with only one atrium and a one-circuit circulation. A two-circuit system is more efficient because blood pressure drops less after the blood is oxygenated. Partition of the ventricle of the heart and the further separation of the two circuits will continue in subsequent vertebrate classes.

(e) Refer to Figures 31-9 and 31-10 and find the major *arteries* listed in Table 31-1.

TABLE 31-1	Major Arteries of the Frog	
Arteries	**Location**	**Function Is to Convey Blood to**
Pulmocutaneous arches	First pair of vessels branching off truncus arteriosus	Lungs and skin
Systemic arches	Second pair of vessels branching off truncus arteriosus	The rest of the body
Common carotids (carotid arches)	Branch from the systemic arches	Head
Subclavians	Branch from the systemic arches	Arms
Dorsal aorta	Formed by the fusion of the systemic arches along dorsal body wall in mid abdomen	Lower half of the body
Common iliacs	Division of dorsal aorta in lower abdomen	Legs

© Cengage Learning 2013

Which of these arteries carries deoxygenated blood? _____

(f) Locate the **anterior** and **posterior vena cavae,** which return deoxygenated blood from the systemic circuit to the right atrium of the heart (Figures 31-9c and 31-10). Other veins return blood from the head, arms, and legs to one of the vena cavae. Right and left **pulmonary veins** return oxygenated blood from the lungs to the left atrium.

(g) The excretory and reproductive organs together comprise the *urogenital system* (Figure 31-11). Locate the urine-producing excretory organs, the pair of **kidneys** located dorsally in the body cavity. The **ureter,** a duct that leads from the kidney to the **urinary bladder** (Figure 31-9a), an organ that stores urine for the recovery of water back into the circulatory system. The bladder empties into the *cloaca.*

(h) Refer to Figure 31-11a and, in the male, locate the **testes** (Figure 31-9c); these organs produce sperm that are carried to the kidneys through tiny tubules, the *vasa efferentia.* The ureters serve a dual function in male frogs, transporting both urine and sperm to the cloaca. Find the vestigial female oviducts (Figure 31-9b), which are located lateral to the urogenital system.

(i) Refer to Figure 31-11b and, in the female, find the *ovaries* (Figure 31-9d); these organs expel eggs into the *oviducts.* The oviducts lead into the *uterus.* As in the male, the reproductive tract ends in the cloaca.

(j) Locate the *fat bodies* (Figures 31-9c and d), many yellowish, branched structures just above the kidneys. They store food reserves for hibernation and reproduction.

(k) The nervous system of vertebrates is composed of (1) the *central nervous system,* the brain and spinal cord, and (2) the *peripheral nervous system,* nerves extending from the central nervous system. Turn your frog over and remove the skin from the dorsal surface of the head between the eyes and along the vertebral column. With your scalpel, shave thin sections of bone from the skull, noting the shape and size of the *cranium,* until you expose the *brain.* Pick away small pieces of bone with your forceps to expose the entire brain. Use the same procedure to expose the vertebrae and *spinal cord.* Note the *cranial nerves* coming from the brain and the *spinal nerves* coming from the spinal cord. Spinal nerves are also easy to see running along the dorsal wall of the abdomen.

(l) Dispose of your dissected specimen in the large plastic bag provided for this purpose.

4. Compare the frog and human skeleton.

(a) The skeleton of vertebrates consists of the following: (1) the **axial skeleton,** consisting of the bones of the **skull, sternum, hyoid bone, vertebral column,** and rib cage (when present); and (2) the **appendicular skeleton,** with the bones of its **girdles** and their appendages. The **pectoral girdle** consists of the paired **clavicle** and **scapula** bones (**suprascapular** in the bullfrog). The latter articulates forms a joint with the **humerus.** The **pubis, ischium,** and **ilium** bones form the pelvic girdle, which articulates with the femur. Compare the skeleton of the bullfrog and human (Figure 31-12), and identify the axial and appendicular portions of the skeleton.

(b) There are differences in the two skeletons, but their basic plan is remarkably similar. To a large extent, the size and shape of the different parts of the skeleton of a vertebrate correlate with body specializations and behavior. List some reasons for the differences in the girdles, appendages, and cranium of the frog and human skeletons.

_____

_____

_____

31.5   Reptiles (Class Reptilia) *(12 min.)*

Reptiles are the oldest group of vertebrates *adapted to life primarily on land,* although many do live in fresh water or seawater. They arose from the ancestors of amphibians about 300 million years ago. Their *skeleton* is bonier than that of amphibians. The *dry skin* is covered by *epidermal scales* and there are almost no skin glands. Reptiles lay **amniotic eggs** (Figure 31-13). Inside these eggs, embryos are suspended by *fetal membranes* in an internal aquatic environment surrounded by a shell to prevent their drying out.

There is no larval stage. The amniotic egg (characteristic of birds and some mammals as well as reptiles) and lack of larvae are adaptations to living an entire life cycle on land. The *three* or *four-chambered hearts* of reptiles consist of two atria and a partially divided ventricle or in crocodiles, two ventricles. The nervous system, especially the brain, is more highly developed than that of amphibians.

Reptiles, like the fishes and amphibians, are largely **ectothermic**, without the capability to maintain a relatively high core body temperature physiologically and with a greater dependence on gaining or losing heat from or to their external environment. Reptiles and other ectotherms have an adaptive advantage over endothermic mammals in warm and humid areas of Earth because they expend minimal energy on maintaining body temperature, which leaves more energy for reproduction. This advantage is reflected in the greater numbers of individuals and species of reptiles compared to mammals in the tropics. Mammals have the advantage in moderate to cold areas.

MATERIALS

Per student pair:

■ dissection pan

Per lab room:

■ collection of preserved reptiles
■ skeleton of snake

■ turtle skeleton or shell
■ boxes of different sizes of lab gloves
■ box of safety goggles

PROCEDURE

1. Examine an assortment of preserved reptiles and note their diversity as a group. This diverse group of vertebrates includes the turtles, lizards, snakes, crocodiles, and alligators.

Figure 31-9 Abdominal views of dissected frogs. (**a–c**) Male; (**d**) female. *Continues.*

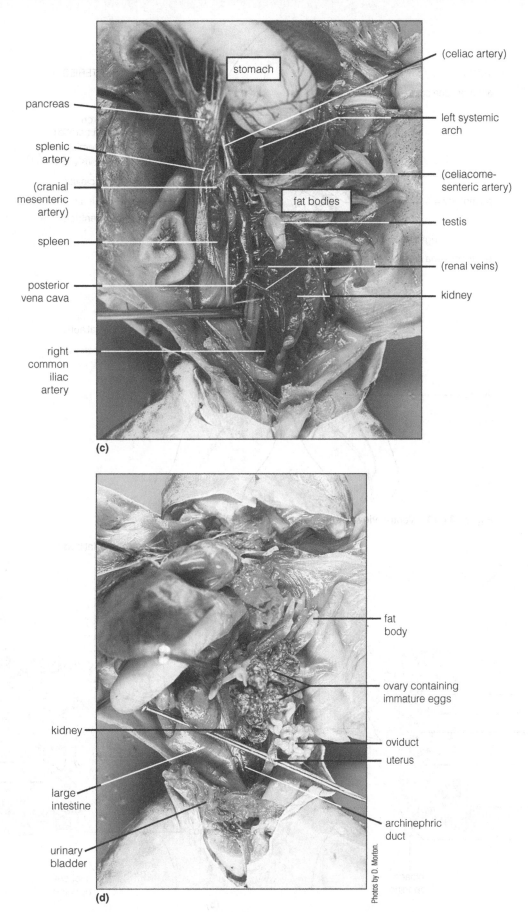

(c)

- pancreas
- splenic artery
- (cranial mesenteric artery)
- spleen
- posterior vena cava
- right common iliac artery
- stomach
- (celiac artery)
- left systemic arch
- (celiacome-senteric artery)
- fat bodies
- testis
- (renal veins)
- kidney

(d)

- kidney
- large intestine
- urinary bladder
- fat body
- ovary containing immature eggs
- oviduct
- uterus
- archinephric duct

Photos by D. Morton.

Figure 31-9 *Continued.*

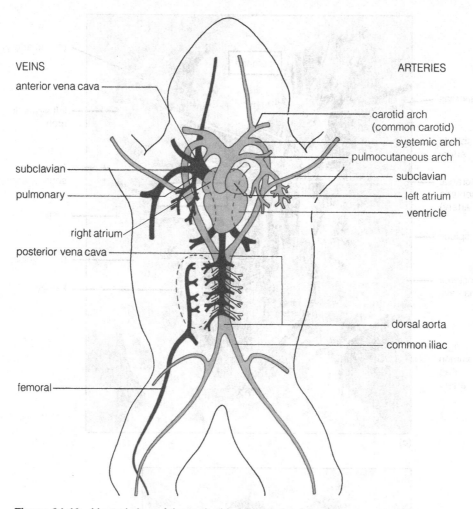

Figure 31-10 Ventral view of the major blood vessels of the frog.

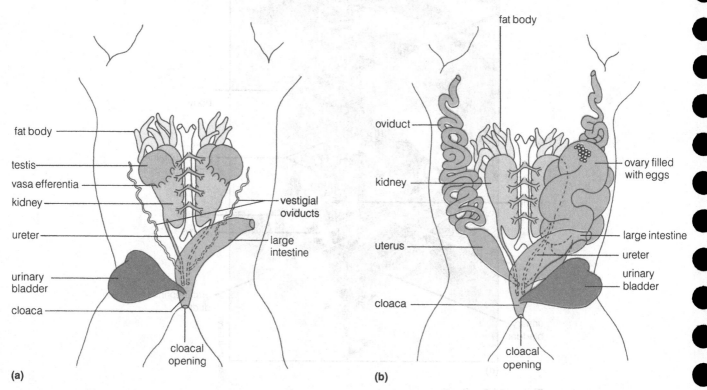

Figure 31-11 Ventral views of the urogenital systems of **(a)** male and **(b)** female frogs.

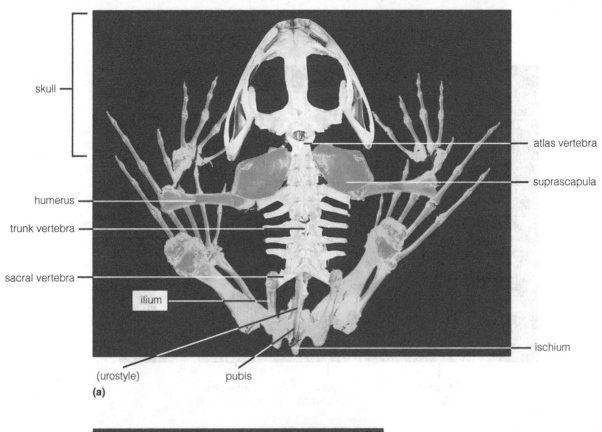

skull

atlas vertebra

suprascapula

humerus

trunk vertebra

sacral vertebra

ilium

ischium

(urostyle)   pubis

(a)

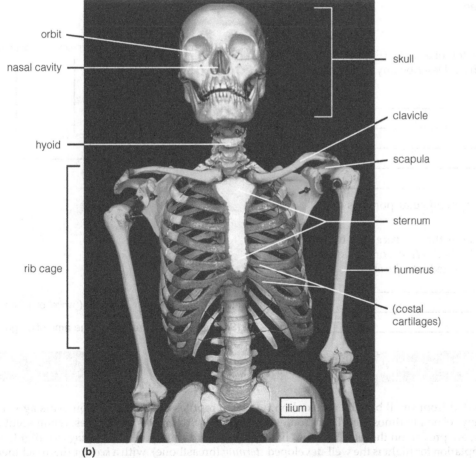

orbit

nasal cavity

skull

hyoid

clavicle

scapula

sternum

rib cage

humerus

(costal cartilages)

ilium

(b)

Figure 31-12 Skeletons of (**a**) a bullfrog and (**b, c**) a human. The appendicular skeleton is colored yellow and the axial skeleton is uncolored. *Continues.*

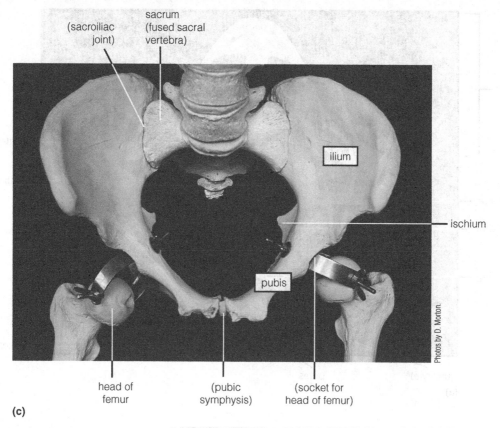

(c)

Figure 31-12 *Continued.*

2. Compare the skeleton of a snake (Figure 31-14) with that of the frog. Describe any differences you see.

_____

_____

_____

_____

_____

Identify the axial and appendicular portions of the snake skeleton.

3. Look at the inside of the *carapace* (the upper portion) of a turtle shell. What portions of the skeleton are incorporated into the shell?

_____

_____

_____

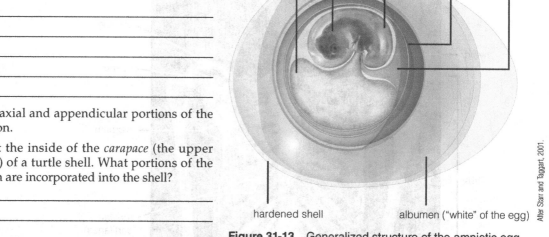

Figure 31-13 Generalized structure of the amniotic egg.

31.6 Birds (Class Aves) *(12 min.)*

Birds are likely descended from small bipedal (walked on two legs) reptiles about 160 million years ago and are thought to be closely related to dinosaurs. Their bodies are covered with *feathers;* and scales, reminiscent of their reptilian heritage, are present on the feet. The front limbs in most birds are modified as *wings* for flight. An additional internal adaptation for flight is the well-developed *sternum* (breastbone), with a *keel* for the attachment of powerful muscles for flight (Figure 31-15). Birds are **endothermic** vertebrates, capable of maintaining high core body temperatures physiologically.

numerous
free ribs
(no sternum)

unfused lower jaw and
other adaptations allow for
a flexible jaw mechanism

Photo by D. Morton.

Figure 31-14 Snake skeleton.

skull (lightened by bone fusion)

large eye orbit

cervical vertebrae

scapula

furcula (fused
clavicles)

coracoid

humerus

vertebral ribs

ilium

sternal ribs

keel of sternum
(attachment of
major flight muscles)

ischium

caudal vertebrae

pubis

femur

hyoid
(detached)

Photo by D. Morton.

Figure 31-15 Bird skeleton.

The major *bones* of birds are *hollow* and contain *air sacs connected to the lungs*. Birds have a *four-chambered heart*, with two atria and two ventricles (Figure 31-16). This permits the complete separation of oxygenated and deoxygenated blood. Why is this circulatory arrangement an advantage for birds, as opposed to that found in amphibians and reptiles? (*Hint:* Recall that birds are endothermic and most can fly.)

_____

_____

_____

The nervous system resembles that of reptiles. However, the *larger brain* permits more muscular coordination, resulting in advanced behavior; the optic lobes are especially well developed in association with a keen sense of sight.

  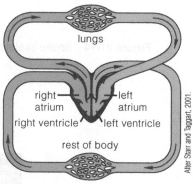

(a) In fishes, a two-chambered heart (atrium, ventricle) pumps blood in one circuit. Blood picks up oxygen in gills and delivers it to rest of body. Oxygen-poor blood flows back to heart.

(b) In amphibians, a heart pumps blood through two partially separate circuits. Blood flows to lungs, picks up oxygen, and returns to heart. It mixes with oxygen-poor blood still in heart, flows to rest of body, and returns to heart.

(c) In birds and mammals, the heart is fully partitioned into two halves. Blood circulates in two circuits: from the heart's right half to lungs and back, then from the heart's left half to oxygen-requiring tissues and back.

Figure 31-16 Circulatory systems of **(a)** fishes, **(b)** amphibians, and **(c)** birds and mammals.

MATERIALS

Per student pair:
- dissection microscope

Per lab room:
- an assortment of feathers, stuffed birds, or bird illustrations
- several field guides to birds

PROCEDURE

1. Examine a feather and identify the **rachis** (shaft) and **vane** (Figure 31-17). Examine the vane with the dissection microscope and note the **barbs** and **barbules.** What else do birds use their feathers for besides flight?

_____

_____

2. Identify the axial and appendicular portions of the skeleton (Figure 31-15). Note the various adaptations for flight, including the elongated wrists and ankles.
3. The upper and lower jaws are modified as variously shaped *beaks* or *bills,* with the shapes reflecting the feeding habits of the species. No teeth are present in adults. Examine the assortment of birds or bird illustrations and speculate on their food preferences by studying the configurations of their bills. Check your conclusions with a field guide or other suitable source that describes the food habits.

31.7 Mammals (Class Mammalia) *(12 min.)*

Mammals arose from an ancient branch of reptiles over 200 million years ago. The term *mammal* stems from the *mammary glands,* which all adult female mammals possess. They produce milk that is fed to mammalian young (Figure 31-18). The *mammalian brain* is the *largest* of all other vertebrates, and its surface area is increased by grooves and folds (Figure 31-19). Behavior is more complex and flexible. *Hair* is present during some portion of the life span. Mammals are equipped with a variety of modifications and outgrowths of the skin in addition to hair, all made of the protein keratin. These include horns, spines, nails, claws, and hoofs. Mammalian dentition is intricate, with teeth specialized for cutting, grooming, wounding, tearing, slicing, and grinding. The teeth in the upper and lower jaws match up.

Like birds, mammals are *endothermic* and the *heart* is *four-chambered*. The ear frequently has a cartilaginous outer portion called the *pinna*, which functions to collect sound waves. In addition to mammary glands, there are three other types of skin glands: *sebaceous, sweat,* and *scent glands.*

MATERIALS

Per lab room:

- stuffed mammals or mammal illustrations
- mammalian placentas and embryos (in utero)

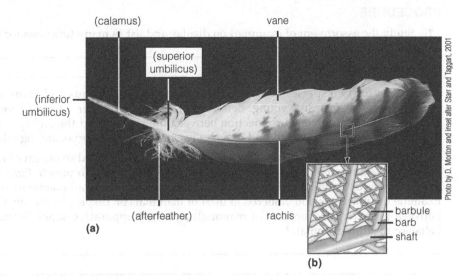

Figure 31-17 (**a**) Feather and (**b**) expanded view of the vane.

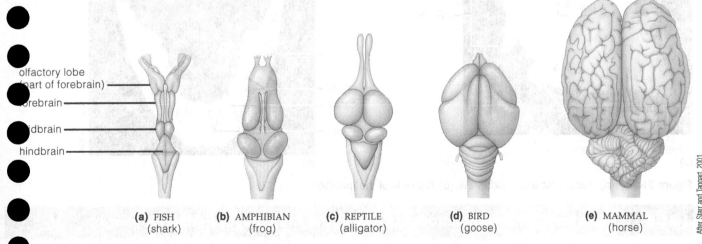

Figure 31-18 Female dog with nursing puppies.

(a) FISH (shark) **(b)** AMPHIBIAN (frog) **(c)** REPTILE (alligator) **(d)** BIRD (goose) **(e)** MAMMAL (horse)

Figure 31-19 Evolutionary trend toward an expanded, more complex brain, as suggested by comparing the brain of existing vertebrates: (**a**) shark; (**b**) frog; (**c**) alligator; (**d**) goose; and (**e**) horse. These dorsal views are not to the same scale.

PROCEDURE

1. Study the assortment of mammals on display and list as many functions for hair as you can.

_____

_____

2. Except for two species of *monotremes* that lay eggs (platypus and spiny anteater), most mammals are **viviparous**—bear live young. Before birth, an embryo (later a fetus) develops in the wall of the uterus along with a *placenta*, a connection between the mother and the embryo. The placenta exchanges gases with, delivers nutrients to, and removes wastes from the embryo, among other functions.

Some viviparous mammals (*marsupials*—kangaroos, opossums, and so on) give birth early, and along with spiny anteater hatchlings, continue development suckling milk in a skin pouch. *Eutherian* mammals—those you are most likely to be familiar with, give birth later, but the young of all mammals receive extended parental care. Examine the placentas and embryos in uteri of mammals on display in the lab. Can you suggest a relationship between the early development of mammals and the comparative sophistication of the nervous system and behavior of adult mammals?

_____

_____

3. Look at Figure 31-20 and identify the teeth present in the skull of the human skeleton. Fill in the numbers of each type in the upper and lower jaws and their functions in Table 31-2.

TABLE 31-2	Human Dentition		
Type of Tooth	**Number in Upper Jaw**	**Number in Lower Jaw**	**Function**
Incisors			
Canines			
Premolars			
Molars			

© Cengage Learning 2013

Figure 31-20 (a) Human maxilla in side view. (b) Top view of the mandible.

Photos by D. Morton.

31.8 Construction of a Dichotomous Key to the Animals (optional) *(50 min.)*

Your instructor will provide you with instructions and perhaps other pertinent materials to use with your textbook and lab manual.

_____ 1. Animals that have the four basic characteristics of chordates plus a vertebral column are
(a) invertebrates.
(b) hemichordates.
(c) cephalochordates.
(d) vertebrates.

_____ 2. The ammocoete is the larva of
(a) lampreys.
(b) sharks.
(c) bony fishes.
(d) amphibians.

_____ 3. Placoid scales are characteristic of class
(a) Cephalaspidomorphi.
(b) Chondrichthyes.
(c) Osteichthyes.
(d) Reptilia.

_____ 4. The bony movable flap that covers the gills and gill slits is called the
(a) operculum.
(b) cranium.
(c) tympanum.
(d) colon.

_____ 5. Which group of animals is endothermic?
(a) fishes
(b) mammals
(c) reptiles
(d) amphibians

_____ 6. The bones that surround and protect the brain are collectively called the
(a) spinal cord.
(b) vertebral column.
(c) pelvic girdle.
(d) cranium.

_____ 7. The lampreys are unusual vertebrates in that they have no
(a) eyes.
(b) jaws.
(c) gill slits.
(d) mouth.

_____ 8. The structure of the cartilaginous and bony fishes that detects vibrations in the water is the
(a) anal fin.
(b) operculum.
(c) nostrils.
(d) lateral line.

_____ 9. Amphibians have
(a) a two-chambered heart.
(b) a three-chambered heart.
(c) a four-chambered heart.
(d) none of the above

_____ 10. The amniotic egg of reptiles, birds, and mammals is an adaptation to
(a) thwart carnivorous predators.
(b) allow life on land.
(c) compensate for the short period of development of the young.
(d) protect the young from the nitrogenous wastes of the mother during embryonic development.

EXERCISE **31**

Vertebrates

Post-Lab Questions

Introduction

1. What characteristic of vertebrates is missing in all invertebrates?

2. List the four basic characteristics of chordates.

31.1 Lampreys (Class Cephalaspidomorphi)

3. What is an ammocoete? What is its possible significance to the evolution of vertebrates?

4. How do lampreys differ from other vertebrates?

31.2 Cartilaginous Fishes (Class Chondrichthyes)

5. Explain how the adaptations of cartilaginous fishes make them better predators.

31.3 Bony Fishes (Class Osteichthyes)

6. Identify this vertebrate structure. What do the rings present?

(24×)

31.5 Reptiles (Class Reptilia)

7. Describe an amniotic egg. What is its evolutionary significance?

31.7 Mammals (Class Mammalia)

8. What are the unique characteristics of mammals?

9. Describe the evolution of the vertebrate heart.

Food for Thought

10. About 65 million years ago, an asteroid impact likely caused a mass extinction, which led to the demise of dinosaurs and created new opportunities for surviving plants and animals. Create a short evolutionary scenario for the next human-made or natural mass extinction event.

Animal Development

OBJECTIVES

After completing this exercise, you will be able to

1. define *sexual reproduction, gametes, ovum, sperm, zygote, fertilization, gonads, ovaries, testes, gametogenesis, oogenesis, spermatogenesis, meiosis, yolk, acrosome, blastodisc, vegetal pole, animal pole, seminiferous tubules, interstitial cells, testosterone, Sertoli cells, follicle, estrogen, progesterone, ovulation, corpus luteum, implantation, uterus, blastomere, morula, blastula, blastocoel, gray crescent, blastocyst, inner cell mass, trophoblast, placenta, archenteron, blastopore, primitive streak, notochord, neural tube, somites, amniotic cavity, embryonic disc;*

2. draw a mammalian sperm and label its segments;

3. describe the structure of chicken and frog ova and how they differ from a typical mammalian ovum;

4. recognize interstitial cells, seminiferous tubules, Sertoli cells, and sperm in a prepared section of a mammalian testis;

5. recognize primary oocytes, primordial and secondary follicles, and a corpus luteum in a prepared slide of a mammalian ovary;

6. describe spermatogenesis and oogenesis in mammals;

7. describe the events and consequences of sperm penetration and fertilization.

8. compare and contrast cleavage in the sea star, frog, chicken, and human;

9. explain differences in cleavage according to (a) the amount and distribution of yolk in the ovum and (b) the evolution of mammals;

10. describe gastrulation, the formation of the primary germ layers (ectoderm, mesoderm, endoderm), and their derivatives.

Introduction

Sexual reproduction typically involves the fusion of the nuclei of two **gametes,** called the **ovum** (plural, *ova*) in females and **sperm** in males, to form the first cell of a new individual, the **zygote.** This fusion is referred to as **fertilization**.

Gametes are produced in reproductive organs called **gonads,** usually in individuals of two separate sexes—**ovaries** in females and **testes** in males. **Gametogenesis,** gamete formation, reduces the number of chromosomes by half. Gametes have 22 *autosomes,* one of each of the 22 pairs found in most other cells of the body plus one *sex chromosome,* an X or Y. Gametes with a half set of chromosomes are referred to as *haploid.* Cells with a full set of chromosomes are *diploid.* Fertilization produces a diploid zygote, whose combination of genes is unlike those of either parent. Other than cases of identical twins, triplets, and so on, it is also very unlikely that the genes of one zygote will be the same as those of any other zygote, even those derived from the same parents. This variation is an advantage to a species in a changing and unpredictable environment. Why?

_____

_____

_____

Note: Depending on the timing of your lab and to prepare for the observation of a live frog zygote, your instructor may demonstrate the fertilization of frog eggs before you start this exercise.

Most sperm have at least one flagellum and are specialized for motility. They contribute little more than their chromosomes to the zygote.

Ova are specialized for storing nutrients, and they contain the molecules and organelles needed to fuel, direct, and maintain the early development of the embryo. Nutrients are stored as **yolk** in the cytoplasm. Consequently, mammalian ova are larger than body cells and in some species reach a diameter of 0.2 mm. In frogs, additional yolk increases the diameter of the ovum to 2 mm, and in chickens, it reaches about 3 cm.

MATERIALS

Per student:

- compound light microscope, lens paper, bottle of lens-cleaning solution (optional)
- lint-free cloth (optional)
- glass microscope slide
- coverslip
- dissecting needle
- one-piece plastic dropping pipet

Per student pair:

- unfertilized hen's egg
- several paper towels
- dissection pan
- Syracuse dish

- two camel-hair brushes
- dissection microscope

Per lab group (table or bench):

- model of a frog ovum (optional)

Per lab section:

- live frog sperm in pond water
- live frog ova in pond water

Per lab room:

- phase-contrast compound light microscope (optional)

PROCEDURE

A. Sperm

1. With the high-dry objective of your compound microscope, study a prepared slide of bull sperm. Draw several sperm in Figure 42-1. Each sperm has three major segments: the *head, midpiece,* and *tail.* Label the major segments of one sperm in your drawing. The tail is typically composed of a single *flagellum.*

2. *Skip this step if your compound microscope does not have an oil-immersion objective.* Switch to the oil-immersion objective. Find the **acrosome** located in the head of a sperm and *mitochondria,* in its midpiece. The acrosome partially covers the front of the nucleus. The function of the acrosome is to release enzymes to aid in the penetration of the egg. Why does a sperm have a lot of mitochondria relative to its cell size?

   _____

   _____

   _____

3. Place one drop of frog sperm suspension on a glass microscope slide and make a wet mount. Observe the movements of sperm flagella using either the phase-contrast compound microscope or your compound microscope with the iris diaphragm partially closed to increase contrast. Describe what you see.

   _____

   _____

   _____

   _____

Figure 42-1 Drawing of bull sperm (_____×).

1. Investigate the egg of a chicken.
   (a) Obtain an unfertilized chicken egg (Figure 42-2). Crack it open as you would in the kitchen and carefully spill the contents into a hollow made from paper towels placed in a dissection pan.
   (b) Only the yolk is the ovum. Look on its surface for the **blastodisc,** a small white spot just under the cell membrane. This area is free of yolk and contains the nucleus. This is where fertilization occurs if sperm are present in the hen's oviducts. The walls of the oviduct secrete the *albumin* (egg white).
   (c) Examine the *shell* and the two *shell membranes.* The shell membranes are fused except in the region of the air space at the blunt end of the egg. Note the two shock absorber–like *chalazae* (singular, *chalaza*), which suspend the ovum between the ends of the egg. They are made of thickened albumin and may help rotate the ovum to keep the blastodisc always on top of the yolk.

2. Compare a frog egg to a chicken egg.
   (a) Gently place a live frog egg in a Syracuse dish half filled with pond water and examine it with a dissection microscope. Use two clean camel-hair brushes to transfer the egg. *Do not let the egg dry out.* The ovum is enclosed in a protective jelly membrane. Which surface (light side or dark side) of the ovum floats up in the pond water?

   _____

   (b) Look at a model of a frog ovum. Ova from different species of animals vary in the amount and distribution of yolk. Frog ova have a moderate amount of yolk that is concentrated in the lower half of the ovum (Figure 42-3). This half of the ovum is called the **vegetal pole**. The nucleus is located in the upper, yolk-free half, the **animal pole**. Note that the animal pole is black. This is because it contains pigment granules. Why does a frog ovum have less yolk than a bird ovum?

   _____

   _____

Suggest one or more possible functions for the black pigment in the animal pole. (*Hint:* one function is the same as that for the pigment in your skin that increases when exposed to sunlight.)

_____

_____

_____

3. See Figure 42-8 for a diagram of a human egg as it would appear in the upper oviduct. The egg is surrounded by a membrane, the *zona pellucida*, and a layer of follicle cells. Why do most mammalian ova have very little yolk?

   _____

   _____

Figure 42-2 Unfertilized chicken egg.

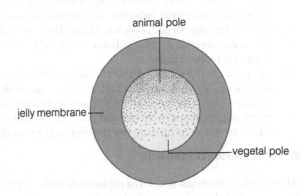

Figure 42-3 Frog egg.

Gamete formation (**gametogenesis**) is called **oogenesis** in females and **spermatogenesis** in males. The general scheme and terminology of gametogenesis are summarized in Table 42-1. **Meiosis** is a process by which events in the nucleus of a diploid cell use two cytoplasmic divisions to form haploid gametes or cells that will mature into gametes. The nuclear events associated with the first division are referred to as meiosis I, and those of the second division are called meiosis II.

TABLE 42-1	Gametogenesis	
	Type of Cell	
Condition of Cell	**Male**	**Female**
Mitotically active	Spermatogonium	Oogonium
Before meiosis I	Primary spermatocyte	Primary oocyte
Before meiosis II	Secondary spermatocyte	Secondary oocyte and first polar body
After meiosis II	Spermatid	Ovum and three polar bodies
After differentiation	Sperm	—

© Cengage Learning 2013

MATERIALS

Per student:

- compound light microscope, lens paper, bottle of lens-cleaning solution (optional), lint-free cloth (optional)
- prepared slides of a section of
  adult mammalian testis stained with iron hematoxylin
  adult mammalian ovary with follicles
  adult mammalian ovary with a corpus luteum

PROCEDURE

A. Mammalian Spermatogenesis

1. With your compound microscope, look at a prepared slide of the testis (Figure 42-4). Most of the interior of a testis is filled with coiled **seminiferous tubules**. Transverse and oblique sections are present in your slide. Look for glandular **interstitial cells** between the seminiferous tubules. Interstitial cells secrete the male sex hormone **testosterone.**
2. Center a cross section of a seminiferous tubule in the field of view and increase the magnification until you see only a portion of the tubule's wall. In the wall of the seminiferous tubule, identify as many stages of spermatogenesis as possible, as well as **Sertoli cells**, which function to nurture the developing sperm (Figure 42-5).

B. Mammalian Oogenesis

After birth, in humans and most other mammals, oogonia are not present because all of them have started oogenesis. There is an excess supply of primary oocytes present at birth (~2 million in a newborn girl).

In the ovaries, primary oocytes are located within cellular balls called **follicles**. In addition to supporting the developing oocytes, follicle cells also secrete the female sex hormones, **estrogen** and **progesterone**. A typical mammalian ovary contains a number of stages of follicular development (Figure 42-6).

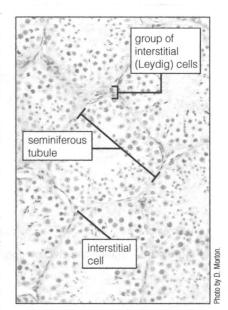

Figure 42-4 Transverse section of the testis (200×).

Photo by D. Morton.

A primordial follicle whose thin walls are one cell thick initially surrounds each primary oocyte. Most follicles degenerate, and in humans, only about 300,000 primary oocytes remain at puberty. The majority of these oocytes also degenerate. With each turn of the female cycle, several follicles begin to mature, and one (rarely two or more) of each batch of oocytes finally bursts from the surface of the ovary and is swept into the oviduct. The release of oocytes from the ovary is called **ovulation** (Figure 42-7).

Around the time of ovulation, the primary oocyte divides to form a secondary oocyte and the first polar body. The zona pellucida and a capsule of follicle cells (Figure 42-8) surround an ovulated secondary oocyte. A sperm must first pass through this barrier before penetration of the egg membrane and fertilization can occur. Upon fertilization, the secondary oocyte divides again to form an ovum and another polar body. The first polar body may also divide, resulting in a total of four polar bodies.

Follicle cells left behind in the ovary after ovulation develop collectively into a large roundish structure called the **corpus luteum** (the name means "yellow body" and refers to its color in a fresh ovary). The corpus luteum continues to secrete female sex hormones, especially progesterone.

Figure 42-5 Spermatogenesis (800×).

Figure 42-6 Mammalian ovary (25×).

1. With the compound microscope, examine the prepared slide of an ovary. Look for primordial follicles (Figure 42-9a).

Both the follicles and their primary oocytes are small compared with maturing follicles and their primary oocytes. Groups of primordial follicles tend to occur between maturing follicles or between maturing follicles and the ovarian wall. Note that a single layer of smaller cells compose the wall of the primordial follicle.

2. Now look for maturing follicles. In maturing follicles, the size of the cells in the follicle wall and of the primary oocyte itself increases. Also, the follicle cells divide, causing the wall to become first two cells thick and then multilayered. Then a space appears between the follicle cells (Figure 42-9b). This fluid-filled space increases in size until the primary oocyte and the follicle cells immediately around the primary oocyte are suspended in it (Figure 42-9c). The mass of cells is connected to the rest of the wall by a narrow stalk of follicle cells. Just before ovulation, the follicle reaches its maximum size and bulges from the surface of the ovary.

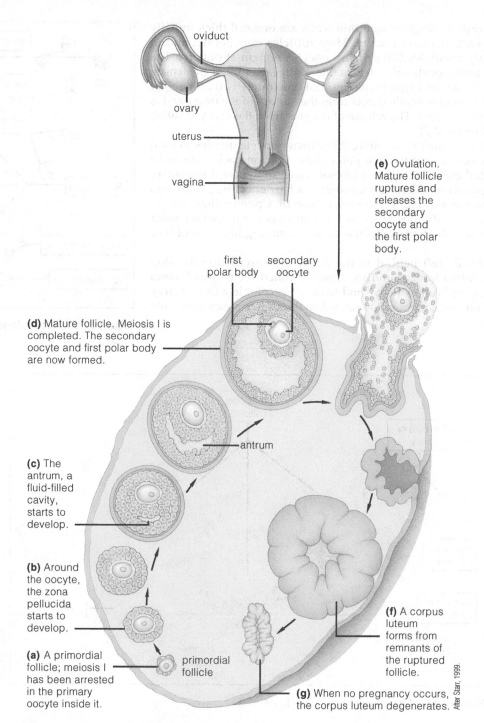

Figure 42-7 Cyclic events in a human ovary, drawn as if sliced lengthwise through its midsection. Events in the ovarian cycle proceed from the growth and maturation of follicles, through ovulation (rupturing of a mature follicle with a concurrent release of a secondary oocyte). For illustrative purposes, the formation of these structures is drawn as if they move clockwise around the ovary. In reality, their maturation occurs at the same site.

Labels within figure:

oviduct

ovary

uterus

vagina

(e) Ovulation. Mature follicle ruptures and releases the secondary oocyte and the first polar body.

first polar body

secondary oocyte

(d) Mature follicle. Meiosis I is completed. The secondary oocyte and first polar body are now formed.

antrum

(c) The antrum, a fluid-filled cavity, starts to develop.

(b) Around the oocyte, the zona pellucida starts to develop.

(a) A primordial follicle; meiosis I has been arrested in the primary oocyte inside it.

primordial follicle

(f) A corpus luteum forms from remnants of the ruptured follicle.

(g) When no pregnancy occurs, the corpus luteum degenerates.

After Starr, 1999.

3. Replace the slide on the microscope with one of a mammalian ovary with a corpus luteum. Locate a corpus luteum (Figure 42-10).

4. If an embryo does not successfully implant in the **uterus**, the corpus luteum degenerates and is replaced by scar tissue. This scar is now called the *corpus albicans* (Figure 42-11).

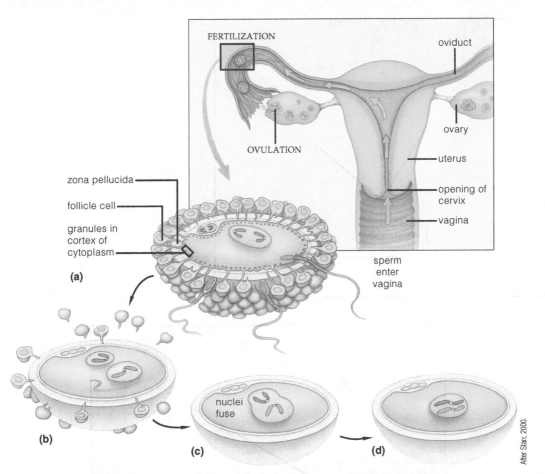

Figure 42-8 Fertilization. (**a**) Many sperm surround a secondary oocyte. Acrosomal enzymes clear a path through the zona pellucida. (**b**) When a sperm does penetrate the secondary oocyte, granules in the egg cortex release substances that make the zona pellucida impenetrable to other sperm. Penetration also stimulates meiosis II of the oocyte's nucleus. (**c**) The sperm's tail degenerates and its nucleus enlarges and fuses with the oocyte nucleus. (**d**) With fusion, fertilization is over. The zygote has formed.

42.3 Sperm Penetration and Fertilization in the Frog *(10 min.)*

In humans and most other mammals, both fertilization (in the upper oviduct) and **implantation** and subsequent development to a late stage (in the uterine wall) take place in the mother. Other animals, such as frogs, have external fertilization and development. At the beginning of the lab, or just before, your instructor induced ovulation in a female frog. Sperm obtained from the shredded testes of a male frog were then added to fertilize these ova.

MATERIALS

Per student pair:
- Syracuse dish
- two camel-hair brushes
- dissection microscope

Per lab group (table or bench):
- model of a frog zygote (optional)

Per lab section:
- live frog zygotes in pond water
- pond water
- video or link(s) to Internet site(s) with video of frog development (optional)

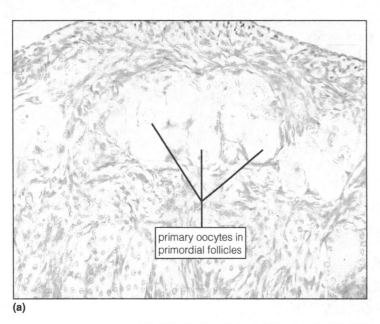

(a)

primary oocytes in primordial follicles

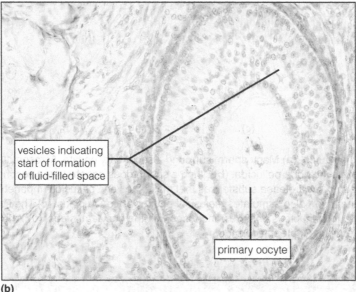

vesicles indicating start of formation of fluid-filled space

primary oocyte

(b)

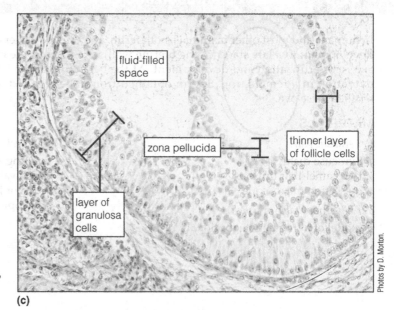

fluid-filled space

zona pellucida

thinner layer of follicle cells

layer of granulosa cells

(c)

Photos by D. Morton.

Figure 42-9 (**a**) Group of primordial follicles (450×), (**b**) maturing follicles (450×), and (**c**) portion of a mature secondary follicle (40×).

Figure 42-10 Corpus luteum (100×).

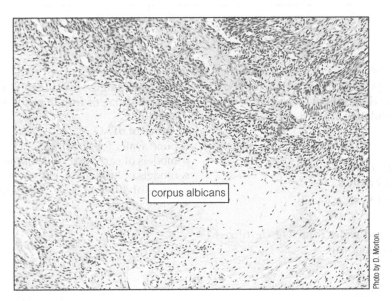

Figure 42-11 Corpus albicans (100×).

PROCEDURE

1. Using two clean camel-hair brushes, gently transfer to a Syracuse dish half-filled with pond water a live frog zygote that has not yet begun to cleave and examine it with a dissecting microscope. *Do not let the zygote dry out.*

Which surface of the zygote (light or dark side) floats up in the pond water? _____

Compared with ova, do frog zygotes show a change in their pattern of coloration after fertilization? (*Hint:* look between the darkly pigmented and unpigmented areas.) _____ (yes, no)

If so, describe what you observe.

_____

_____

2. If you cannot observe fertilization directly, study a model of a frog zygote, watch a video, or follow links provided by your instructor on early frog development.

Cleavage is a special type of cell division that occurs first in the zygote and then in the cells formed by successive cleavages, the **blastomeres**. Unlike typical cell division, there is no period of cytoplasmic growth between the cleavage divisions, causing the blastomeres to become smaller and smaller. After a number of cleavages, the blastomeres form a solid cluster of cells called the **morula**. Cleavage continues until a hollow ball of cells, called the **blastula**, is formed. This stage marks the end of cleavage. Because of the smaller blastomeres, the size of the blastula is only slightly larger than that of the zygote.

In many organisms whose ova have little yolk (e.g., sea stars and humans), cleavage is *complete* and nearly *equal*, resulting in separate blastomeres that are all about the same size. In frogs and other animals with moderate amounts of yolk, cleavage is complete but unequal with the larger yolk-laden cells at the vegetal pole and the smaller cells with little yolk at the animal pole. There is so much yolk in the ova of many animals (e.g., most fish, reptiles, birds, and the two mammals that lay eggs—platypuses and spiny anteaters) that complete cleavage of the entire zygote is impossible, so it forms a disclike embryo that sits on the surface of the yolk. This type of cleavage is incomplete and is called *discoidal*.

CAUTION

Preserved specimens are kept in preservative solutions. Use lab gloves whenever you handle a specimen. Wash any part of your body exposed to this solution with lots of water. If preservative solution is splashed into your eyes, wash them with the safety eyewash for 15 minutes. Even if you wear contact lenses, you should wear safety goggles during a procedure and when observing a procedure. Eyeglasses should suffice when goggles do not fit over them.

MATERIALS

Per student:

- compound light microscope, lens paper, bottle of lens-cleaning solution (optional), lint-free cloth (optional)
- prepared slide of a whole mount of sea star development through gastrulation

Per student pair:

- two Syracuse dishes
- two blue camel-hair brushes (optional)
- two red camel-hair brushes
- dissection microscope

Per lab section:

- frog embryos in pond water from eggs fertilized 1 hour before the lab (optional)

Per lab room:

- preserved specimens of two-, four-, and eight-cell cleavage stages; morulae (32-cell cleavage stage) and blastulae of frog in easily accessible screw-top containers
- source of dH_2O
- pond water (optional)
- models of early frog development
- models of human development
- boxes of different sizes of lab gloves
- safety goggles

PROCEDURE

A. Cleavage in Sea Stars

1. With your compound microscope, observe a prepared slide with whole mounts of early sea star embryos. Find a zygote; two-, four-, and eight-cell cleavage stages; a morula; and a blastula and draw them in Figure 42-12. Be sure to adjust the fine-focus knob to see the three-dimensional aspects of these stages. The blastula is a hollow ball of flagellated blastomeres surrounding a cavity called the **blastocoel**. Label the blastomeres and blastocoel in your drawing of the sea star blastula.
2. What is the orientation (parallel or perpendicular) relative to each other of the first two cleavage planes?

_____

What is the orientation (parallel or perpendicular) of the third cleavage plane compared with the first cleavage plane?

_____

B. Cleavage in Frogs

1. *Optional.* If your instructor prepared fertilized frog eggs 1 hour before the lab, you will be able to watch the first two cleavage divisions during this laboratory. At room temperature about 1 hour after addition of the sperm to the eggs, a region of less pigmented cytoplasm, the **gray crescent**, appears opposite the site

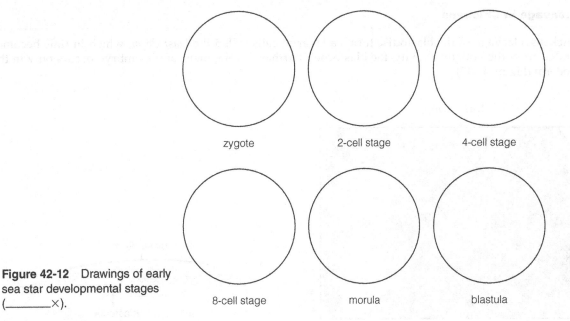

Figure 42-12 Drawings of early sea star developmental stages (_____×).

zygote   2-cell stage   4-cell stage

8-cell stage   morula   blastula

of sperm penetration (Figure 42-13). The first cleavage division occurs about 2 hours after fertilization, the second a half hour later, and the third after another 2 hours. Gently place several live frog zygotes in a Syracuse dish half filled with pond water and examine them with a dissection microscope. Use two blue camel-hair brushes to transfer the zygote. *Do not let the zygote dry out.*

pigmented cortex — gray crescent —
yolk-rich cytoplasm — sperm penetrating frog egg

After Starr and Taggart, 2001.

Figure 42-13 Formation of the gray crescent.

2. Wear lab gloves and safety goggles. If living embryos are unavailable, look at preserved specimens under the dissecting microscope. Use two red camel-hair brushes to transfer each stage in turn to a Syracuse dish half filled with distilled water. When you are done, return the specimen to its container. *The embryo specimens are in a preservative solution, so make sure you do not use the red brushes to manipulate the live embryos because the residual preservative will harm them.*
3. Examine preserved specimens of eight-cell, morula, and blastula stages.
4. Study the models of the early stages of frog development.
5. Draw the stages of frog development in Figure 42-14.
6. Note that cleavage in the vegetal pole lags behind that of the animal pole. Why? (*Hint*: what is present in the vegetal pole that would hinder cleavage?)

_____

_____

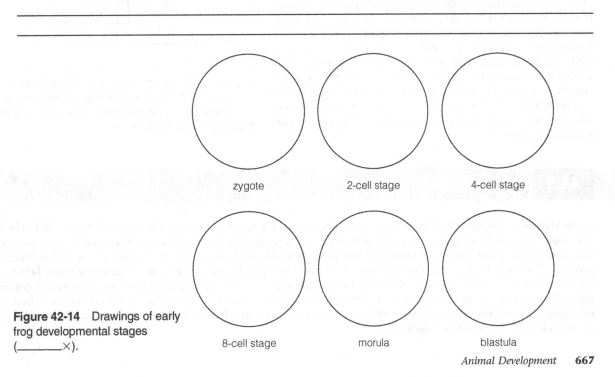

zygote   2-cell stage   4-cell stage

Figure 42-14 Drawings of early frog developmental stages (_____×).

8-cell stage   morula   blastula

C. Cleavage in Chickens

In chickens, cleavage of the blastodisc forms a layer of cells called the *blastoderm*, which in time becomes separated from the yolk by a cavity, the blastocoel. Further development of the embryo occurs only in the blastoderm (Figure 42-15).

Figure 42-15 Cleavage in the chicken. (**a**) Surface view (42×). (**b**) Transverse section along diameter indicated in (**a**).

D. Cleavage in Humans

Examine models of the early stages of human development. Because the ovum has little yolk, cleavage is complete and nearly equal. At the end of cleavage, a hollow ball of cells is formed. However, this **blastocyst** differs from a blastula in that a group of cells aggregate at one pole of the inner surface of the blastocoel (Figure 42-16). These cells are called the **inner cell mass**, and similar to the blastoderm of chickens, further development of the embryo proceeds there only. The remaining cells that surround the blastocoel are called the **trophoblast**. The blastula stage coincides with implantation of the embryo in the uterus.

Current evolutionary thought is that modern reptiles, birds, and mammals evolved from earlier reptilian ancestors that had external development and ova rich in yolk. Internal development in mammals linked nourishment of the embryo directly to the mother and removed the need for large, yolky eggs. The cost of producing excessive yolk would have been a biological liability; in this case, natural selection (an evolutionary process) resulted in mammalian ova with little yolk. However, gastrulation and subsequent developmental events in reptiles, birds, and mammals are remarkably similar.

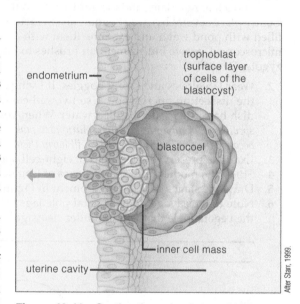

Figure 42-16 Section through a human blastocyst as it attaches to the inner lining (endometrium) of the uterus and starts implantation by burrowing into it (day 6–7 after fertilization).

42.5 Gastrulation *(15 min.)*

Gastrulation is the first time embryonic cells undergo typical cell division with periods of growth between divisions. These cells start the process of specialization and undertake migrations from one embryonic location to another. Groups of some cells even undergo programmed cell death (*apoptosis*) as part of the developmental process. The basic body plan is established. This body is typically made up of three **primary germ layers** or tissues and a front and back end, which can be divided along its longitudinal axis into near identical right and left sides. In animals having at least the organ level of organization, the primary germ layers are called the **ectoderm**, **mesoderm**, and **endoderm** and give rise to organs and, after continued cell specializations, subtypes of the four adult basic tissues (Table 42-2).

TABLE 42-2 Tissue Derivatives of the Primary Germ Layers

Layer	Derivatives
Ectoderm	Nervous tissues, epidermis (keratinized stratified squamous epithelium) and the structures it forms
Mesoderm	Muscle tissues, connective tissues, and epithelia of the urinary and reproductive systems
Endoderm	Epithelial lining of most of the digestive tract and respiratory tract, and associated glands (e.g., the liver)

© Cengage Learning 2013

As development proceeds, four extraembryonic membranes (also called *fetal membranes* in mammals) form in support of further embryonic development both in the shells of birds (Figure 42-17) and in the uterine walls of mammals. In mammals, the exchange of gasses, nutrients, wastes, and so on takes place across the **placenta** (Figure 42-18), which is partly maternal and partly embryonic in origin.

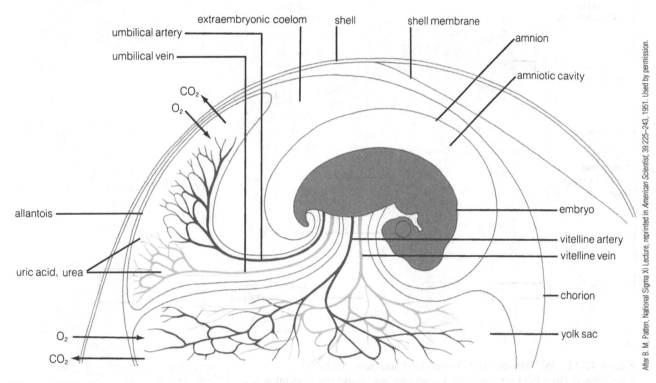

Figure 42-17 Extraembryonic membranes of the chicken.

After B. M. Patten, National Sigma Xi Lecture, reprinted in *American Scientist*, 39:225–243, 1951. Used by permission.

MATERIALS

Per student:

- compound light microscope
- lens paper
- bottle of lens-cleaning solution (optional)
- lint-free cloth (optional)
- prepared slide of a whole mount of sea star development through gastrulation
- prepared slides with whole mounts of chicken embryos at 18 and 24 hours of incubation

Per student pair:

- two Syracuse dishes
- two blue camel-hair brushes (optional)
- two red camel-hair brushes
- dissection microscope
- fertile hen's eggs incubated for 18 and 24 hours (optional)

Per student group (bench or table):

- models of human gastrulation

Per lab section:

- frog embryos (early gastrulae) in pond water from eggs fertilized 21 hours before the lab (optional)
- frog embryos (late gastrulae) in pond water from eggs fertilized 36 hours before the lab (optional)
- pond water

Per lab room:

- preserved specimens of early and late gastrulae of frog in easily accessible screw-top containers
- a source of dH_2O
- pond water (optional)
- models of early and late gastrulae of frog
- boxes of different sizes of lab gloves
- safety goggles

Figure 42-18 (a) Relationship between fetal and maternal blood circulation in (b) a full-term placenta. Blood vessels extend from the fetus, through the umbilical cord, and into chorionic villi. Maternal blood spurts into spaces between the villi, but the two bloodstreams do not intermingle. Oxygen, carbon dioxide, and other small solutes diffuse across the placental membrane surface.

After Starr, 2000.

PROCEDURE

A. Gastrulation in Sea Stars

1. Reexamine with the compound microscope the prepared slide bearing whole mounts of the early stages of sea star development. Using the low- and medium-power objectives, find a blastula (Figure 42-19a).
2. Locate an early gastrula (Figure 42-19b). As gastrulation starts, the vegetal pole flattens and folds in like a pocket to create a new cavity, the **archenteron** ("ancient gut").
3. Find a late gastrula (Figure 42-19c). The hole connecting the archenteron to the outside is called the **blastopore**. Gastrulation initially forms two layers of cells—the ectoderm covering the outside of the gastrula and the endoderm lining the archenteron. Then the mesoderm buds off from the inner tip of the archenteron, and its cells migrate to form a third layer of cells between the ectoderm and endoderm.

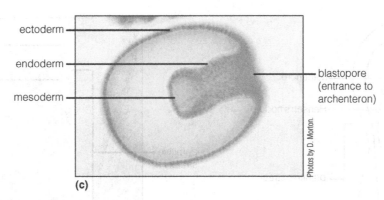

Figure 42-19 Gastrulation in the sea star (320×). (**a**) Late blastula, (**b**) early gastrula, and (**c**) late gastrula.

B. Gastrulation in Frogs

1. Gastrulation in frogs is affected by the large amount of yolk in the vegetal hemisphere. Because the pigmented cells of the animal pole divide faster, they partially overgrow the yolk-laden cells of the vegetal pole. Examine a living or preserved gastrula using the same protocol previously described for earlier developmental stages.
2. Examine models of an early and a late gastrula. Note that gastrulation does not occur simultaneously over the surface of the vegetal pole. Rather, it starts at a point just under what will be the anus of the adult frog and continues, forming a crescent (Figure 42-20a) that will close to form a circle around a plug of yolk-laden cells, the *yolk plug* (Figure 42-20b). The initial point of the folding-in is referred to as the *dorsal lip of the blastopore*.

Figure 42-20 (**a**) Early and (**b**) late gastrulation in the frog.

1. Obtain a prepared slide bearing a whole mount of a chicken gastrula (18 hours of incubation) and one of an embryo incubated for 24 hours.

2. Observe the gastrula using only the low- and medium-power objectives. Similar to cleavage, gastrulation in chickens is influenced by the large amount of yolk. The gastrula does not fold in like a pocket through a blastopore; rather, cells move or migrate into a groove on the blastoderm called the **primitive streak** (Figure 42-21a). At one end of the primitive streak, the migrating cells pile up to form *Hensen's node*. This is thought to be equivalent to the dorsal lip of the blastopore.

3. Examine the slide of the embryo at 24 hours of incubation. The three-layered embryo forms in the same axis as the primitive streak but in front of Hensen's node (Figure 42-21b). The three layers from the top of the

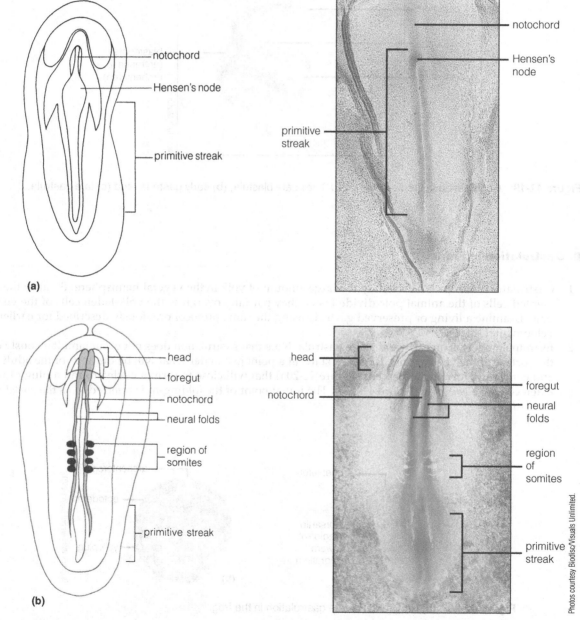

Figure 42-21 Gastrulation in the chicken. (**a**) Gastrulation (18 hours of incubation) (28×); (**b**) early embryo (24 hours of incubation) (16×). The embryos have been removed from the surface of the yolk.

embryo toward the yolk are the ectoderm, mesoderm, and endoderm. One of the first recognizable structures in the embryo is the mesodermal **notochord.** The notochord induces the formation of the embryo's nervous system from the ectoderm. Find *neural folds* on either side of the notochord. With time, the neural folds will fuse like a zipper, anterior to posterior, and in so doing will form the **neural tube** (Figure 42-22). Likewise, the head of the embryo has lifted off the surface of the yolk and has thereby formed the anterior portion of the digestive tract, the *foregut.*

4. Note the two rows of **somites** on either side of the neural folds (Figure 42-21b). These are segmental condensations of mesoderm that will later develop into the skeleton, the skeletal muscles of the trunk, and the dermis of the skin. Count the number of pairs of somites present in this embryo and record this number:

_____

5. *Optional.* If your instructor has fertile hen's eggs incubated for 18 and 24 hours, examine them under the dissection microscope.

D. Gastrulation in Humans

Examine the models of human gastrulation. Human gastrulation follows much the same scenario as that of chickens. However, before gastrulation occurs, a cavity forms between the inner cell mass and the trophoblast. This is the **amniotic cavity** of one of the fetal membranes, the *amnion* (Figure 42-23). Also, cells from the inner cell mass grow downward along the inner surface of the trophoblast, fuse, and form the **yolk sac cavity.** Between the amniotic and yolk sac cavities is the embryonic disc. The **embryonic disc** in mammals is the equivalent of the blastoderm in chickens. Thus, gastrulation commences in the embryonic disc with the formation of a primitive streak.

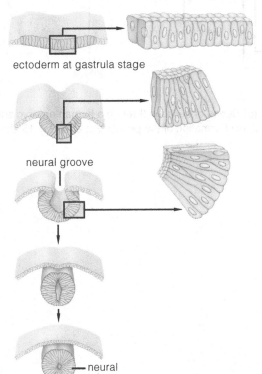

ectoderm at gastrula stage

neural groove

neural tube

After Starr and Taggart, 2001.

Figure 42-22   Formation of the neural tube.

(a)

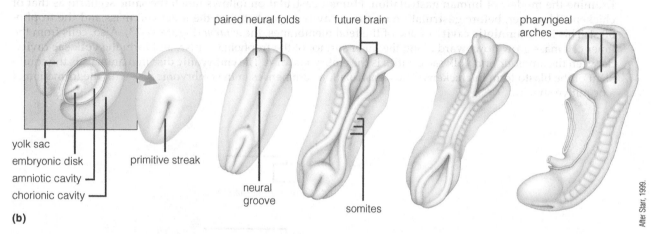

(b)

After Starr, 1999.

Figure 42-23 (**a**) Series of sections through a human embryo showing development just after implantation (days 10–14 after fertilization). (**b**) Formation of the primitive streak (day 15 after fertilization).

_____ 1. Sperm
 (a) are male gametes.
 (b) are female gametes.
 (c) contain yolk.
 (d) are produced in the ovaries.

_____ 2. Ova are
 (a) male gametes.
 (b) female gametes.
 (c) specialized for motility.
 (d) both a and c

_____ 3. The formation of gametes in the gonads
can best be called
 (a) gametogenesis.
 (b) spermatogenesis.
 (c) oogenesis.
 (d) none of the above

_____ 4. Which structure is found in a section of
the testis?
 (a) secondary spermatocytes
 (b) sperm
 (c) Sertoli cells
 (d) all of the above

_____ 5. Oocytes are found in an ovary in
 (a) seminiferous tubules.
 (b) follicles.
 (c) corpora lutea.
 (d) none of the above

_____ 6. One primary oocyte will form
 (a) one ovum.
 (b) four ova.
 (c) up to three polar bodies.
 (d) both a and c

_____ 7. Which process results in a zygote?
 (a) meiosis
 (b) mitosis
 (c) fertilization
 (d) none of the above

_____ 8. The entrance into the cavity formed
during gastrulation in sea stars and frogs
is called the
 (a) archenteron.
 (b) blastocoel.
 (c) blastocyst.
 (d) blastopore.

_____ 9. The three primary germ layers are formed
during
 (a) fertilization.
 (b) cleavage.
 (c) organ formation.
 (d) gastrulation.

_____ 10. Muscle tissues, connective tissues, and
the epithelia lining the urinary and
reproductive systems arise from
 (a) mesoderm.
 (b) endoderm.
 (c) ectoderm.
 (d) two of the above.

EXERCISE **4 2**

Animal Development

Post-Lab Questions

42.1 Gametes

1. Define and characterize the following:
   (a) gametes

   (b) gonads

   (c) gametogenesis

2. Describe the similarities and differences between sperm and ova.

3. Compare chicken, frog, and mammalian ova as to the size and amount of yolk present.

42.2 Gametogenesis

4. Why do you think four sperm cells are produced as a result of gametogenesis but only one ovum is produced?

5. Are oogonia present in adult women? _____ (yes or no) Explain your answer.

42.3 Sperm Penetration and Fertilization in the Frog

6. Read about the gray crescent in your textbook. How does its location relate to the site of sperm penetration and the cytoplasmic events following it?

7. Identify the following sea star developmental stages (185×).

A. _____

B. _____

C. _____

D. _____

8. How do the amount and distribution of yolk in animal zygotes affect cleavage?

42.5 Gastrulation

9. List the primary germ layers formed by gastrulation. What tissues will they form in the adult?

Food for Thought

10. As various newspaper articles, books, and movies suggest, the cloning of human beings—producing new individuals from activated somatic cells, perhaps followed by uterine implant—is now possible. Can you suggest any biological advantages or disadvantages to having the Earth populated with clones of a few of the best examples of our species?

The Natural Arsenal: An Experimental Study of the Relationships Between Plants and Animals

After completing this exercise, you will be able to

1. define *herbivore, plant secondary compound, allelochemical, toxin, bioactive, cytotoxic, bioassay;*

2. explain the ecological role of many plant toxins and their potential effects on herbivores, pathogens, or competitors;

3. describe the nature of the chemical "arms race" between plants and herbivores;

4. state scientific hypotheses and predictions, design a simple experiment with proper controls and replication, evaluate the results, and reach conclusions based on the data provided by the experiment.

Introduction

"NO! Don't touch that leaf!" ... "Don't eat that berry!" Sound like something grownups said to you when you were young? Why shouldn't you eat the berries of American yew bushes, or any part of the foxglove plant? Why is one nightshade species called "deadly"? Why have so many of us learned to identify poison ivy ("leaves of three, let it be")? Because they're "poisonous," right?

So why do plants produce chemicals that are harmful to people or other animals? Recall that plants occupy the producer trophic level. They use solar energy to build organic molecules from water and carbon dioxide in the process of photosynthesis, and also incorporate into their tissues mineral nutrients absorbed via their roots. Plants compete with each other for crucial resources and occupy the base of most food webs, with animals and other **herbivore** consumers (herbivores are organisms that eat plants) eating them in order to acquire the nutrients and energy stored in the plant body.

Plants would seem to be at a distinct disadvantage in the predation and competition relationships we just described. The vast majority are rooted in the earth; certainly plants aren't able to evade predators by moving away. Nor can they physically move to more advantageous locations for gathering sunshine or minerals. Nonetheless, they are not defenseless against the vast array of herbivores and competitors. In addition to various physical defenses like thorns and tough tissues, most plants have highly effective chemical weapons.

All higher plants have **secondary compounds**. These are chemicals that do NOT fall into the major chemical groupings of carbohydrates, proteins, fats, or nucleic acids. They occur irregularly, with most secondary compounds occurring in a few kinds of plants but not in others. More importantly, most secondary substances have no known role in the metabolism of the plants in which they occur. Rather, they seem to perform a variety of functions, including that of chemical defense agent.

The secondary chemical compound signals that are active between different species are called **allelochemicals**. Caffeine, nicotine, strychnine, organic cyanide compounds, and curare are just a few of the "weapons" in the chemical arsenal that plants have evolved to defend themselves against animal consumers, plant competitors, and pathogenic (disease-causing) microbes. For example, tannins in the leaves of oaks and other plants combine with leaf proteins and digestive enzymes in an insect's gut and inhibit protein digestion by the insect. Thus tannins considerably slow the growth of most caterpillars and other herbivores.

Of course, herbivores may counter such toxic effects through the evolutionary modification of their own biochemistry or physiology. (**Toxins** react with specific cellular components to kill cells or alter growth or development in harmful ways.) Herbivore species that coevolve detoxification mechanisms of secondary chemicals may be able to specialize on plant hosts that are poisonous to most other species.

One familiar example is the Monarch butterfly, *Danaus plexippus*. The adult female lays eggs on milkweed (*Asclepias*) plants. The eggs hatch into an immature stage called a *larva*, which we know as the "caterpillar." The larvae eat the milkweed leaves and eventually complete their developmental cycle. What makes the Monarch/milkweed relationship so intriguing is that milkweed plants contain potent heart poisons that deter nearly all herbivore feeding. Monarch butterflies have evolved metabolic pathways, however, to detoxify the milkweed poison. In fact, Monarch larvae store the milkweed toxin in their tissues and thereby protect themselves from predators such as birds!

Not all allelochemicals act as toxins that reduce herbivore survival. Some alter the development of insects by interfering with the production of crucial hormones, while others act as repellants that prevent feeding. Still others have antibiotic effects that inhibit infections by pathogens.

In this exercise, you will investigate the harmful effects of some plant compounds on animals and other plants, focusing especially on those bioactive compounds that may be **cytotoxic**, or poisonous to specific cell types. You'll work with a group to design and conduct bioassays to identify potentially **bioactive** compounds, that is, molecules that have a targeted biological effect on survival, growth, or reproduction. A **bioassay** is a method of screening for potentially active substances by exposing a test population of living organisms to the substance in a controlled environment. A bioassay provides an evaluation by measuring the quantity of a substance that causes a defined effective dose.

Bioassays are used for a variety of purposes. They enable researchers to find plant chemicals that show biological activity on selected research organisms. For example, botanists and biochemists use bioassays to screen unstudied plants for potentially useful, naturally occurring drugs. The National Institutes of Health, the National Cancer Institute, and several major U.S. pharmaceutical companies have launched intensive bioassay "chemical prospecting" efforts in tropical rainforests to find new sources of drugs in the fights against cancer, AIDS, heart disease, and many other health problems.

Bioassays are also used by the pharmaceutical industry in other ways. Some pharmaceuticals are cytotoxic agents; chemotherapy agents, for example, are toxic to cancer cells. Certain side effects of chemotherapy are due to the chemical's cytotoxic effect on other body cells as well. Cytotoxic effects are due to interactions with specific biochemical pathways. Therefore, these chemicals are toxic to cells that utilize that specific pathway, but have little to no effect on other cells that don't use the pathway.

While it's unlikely that you will discover an unidentified cancer-fighting chemical or natural herbicide in the plants in your lab, you might very well find cytotoxic agents. It's important to keep in mind that the reason those chemicals exist in the first place is the result of coevolution between plants and their herbivores, competitors, and pathogens. The more we know about what organisms make these chemicals, why they are made, how they are made, and the consequences of the secondary compounds to the parties involved, the more we will know about the evolutionary process and about potential practical uses of such chemicals for our own benefit.

You will use two test organisms in your bioassays. The first, *Artemia*, or brine shrimp, is a small crustacean inhabitant of salty lakes like the Great Salt Lake. *Artemia* are filter feeders that sweep algae and other tiny food particles into their mouths as they swim. They therefore usually occupy a primary consumer (herbivore) position in aquatic ecosystems. One bioassay will look for effects on *Artemia* cells as a general indication of the presence of cytotoxic compounds in a plant extract.

You may have used the second bioassay organism, Wisconsin Fast Plants (*Brassica rapa*), in a previous bioassay (see Exercise 1). Fast Plants are small, very fast-growing plants of the cabbage family. A bioassay with Fast Plants serves to identify potential herbicides (plant-killing compounds) or plant-growth stimulants by looking at the effect of a plant extract on seed germination and plant growth over a single day.

43.1   Experimental Design

Work in groups of four to explore the effects of plant secondary compounds on cell survival of *Artemia*, and/or the effects on seed germination and growth of Fast Plants. Your instructor will direct you to the plant materials that are available for testing.

Develop a hypothesis that you will test. Your hypothesis might relate to differences between extracts of different plant species with respect to effects on *Artemia* cell survival. Or you might wish to test the effect that a single plant extract has on *Artemia* cell survival versus its effect on Fast Plant germination and growth.

Remember, there is no *single* correct hypothesis.
The hypothesis we will test is:

_____

_____

_____

Design an experiment using the materials available in the lab and the following bioassay procedures to test your hypothesis.
Our experimental design is:

_____

_____

_____

_____

What will be your control treatment(s)? What is the purpose of the control treatment?

_____

_____

_____

How will you provide replication to improve the reliability of your results?

_____

_____

Write a prediction for your experiment.

_____

_____

_____

List the possible general outcomes of your experiment. For each, indicate if that outcome would support *or* falsify your prediction and hypothesis.

_____

_____

_____

_____

Develop a work plan to carry out your experiment so that each group member has specific tasks to accomplish and contribute to the overall group effort. For example, if your experiment will test the differences between extracts of two plant species with respect to their ability to harm *Artemia*, two group members might prepare the bioassay for one species, and the other two might run the bioassay for the second plant species. You also might divide up the work of collecting data for the duration of the bioassay.

43.2 Bioassay Procedures

A. Preparation of Plant Extract (About 20 min.)

MATERIALS

Per student group:
- 25-mL graduated cylinder
- two 20-mL beakers
- 50-mL beaker
- small mortar and pestle
- spatula
- plant material of your choice
- glass stirring rod

Per lab room:
- several electronic balances able to weigh in 0.1-g increments
- weighing papers or boats
- liquid nitrogen (optional)

PROCEDURE

1. Grind about 1 g of the plant tissue to a fine paste with the mortar and pestle. (If liquid nitrogen is available, carefully pour a small amount over the plant material to instantly freeze it.)

CAUTION
Liquid nitrogen is extremely cold and will cause cryogenic burns. DO NOT touch the liquid or allow any to splash onto your skin.

If using leaf tissue, try not to include large veins; if using root tissue, wash off all soil very well. Grind the tissue *for at least 5 minutes.* The goal is to rupture virtually all the plant cells to mix their contents in the bioassay liquid. When you think you've ground the tissue adequately, continue grinding for two more minutes.

2. Use the balance to measure out two 0.1-g samples of the paste onto two pieces of weighing paper or two weighing boats.

3. Measure 10 mL of prepared brine into one labeled 20-mL beaker, and 10 mL of distilled water into a second labeled 20-mL beaker. Mix a 0.1-g sample of plant paste into each beaker, being careful to scrape off ALL plant material, and stir to create uniform suspensions. This extract has a concentration of 0.1 g plant material/10 mL, or 10 mg/mL. (Recall that 1000 mg = 1 g.) You will use the brine mixture for brine shrimp bioassays, and the dH$_2$O mixture for Fast Plant bioassays.

B. *Artemia* Bioassay (About 1 hour)

MATERIALS

Per student group:

- glass microscope slides
- coverslips
- fine-pointed, water-resistant marker (Sharpie or similar) or wax pencil
- wide-mouth plastic graduated transfer pipets
- razor blade or scalpel
- trypan blue stain in dropping bottle
- acetic acid in dropping bottle
- dissecting needle
- compound microscope
- plant extract(s) prepared in brine in part A

Per lab room:

- live *Artemia* in aquarium or beaker
- plant extracts
- paper towels

PROCEDURE

1. Label one microscope slide "Negative control" and a second microscope slide "Positive control."
2. Obtain a number of brine shrimp and brine in the 50-mL beaker.
3. Place a brine shrimp onto each slide, transferring only a few drops of brine with the animal. Blot excess brine with a paper towel. The brine shrimp should be surrounded in a small brine droplet.
4. Swirl the trypan blue stain bottle to suspend the stain mixture evenly. Place a couple drops of stain atop the brine shrimp on each slide. The brine shrimp should not be able to swim, but should be covered by the liquid. Blot excess stain with a paper towel.
5. Place the negative control slide on the microscope stage and focus on the brine shrimp at low magnification. Observe the structure of the animal, locating the point where the "tail" emerges behind the main body. (See Figure 43-1.)
6. Using a sharp scalpel, cut about ¹/₂ to ²/₃ of the tail off the brine shrimp.
7. Put a coverslip over the severed tail sections. Observe the cut ends of the tail. Amoebocytes, the small roundish cells that ooze out of the tail cavity, are excellent bioassay subjects. They respond to cytotoxic agents in much the same way that human cells do. Healthy cells exclude trypan blue stain and appear colorless, but damaged and dead cells will take up the stain and appear blue (Figure 43-2). Do not confuse clumps of dye crystals with the very round cells.
8. Find a field of view where the amoebocytes aren't being moved by liquid movements. Count the number of cells that are colorless in appearance, and the number that are blue for a total of about 25 cells total. Calculate the percentage of dead cells. This number represents the "background" rate for dead cells. Record your data in Table 43-1.
9. Repeat steps 4–5 for the positive control brine shrimp.
10. Add a drop of acetic acid to the severed tail section for the positive control treatment and mix with a dissecting needle. (Acetic acid is a potent cytotoxin.) Add a coverslip and wait a couple minutes before observing with the microscope.
11. Count unstained and stained cells (about 25 total), and calculate the percentage of dead cells. This number illustrates the effects of a strong cytotoxin on *Artemia* amoebocytes. If you see no stained cells, wait up to 30 minutes for a cytotoxic effect to become visible. Record your data in Table 43-1.
12. Test your plant extract(s) similarly by cutting off a brine shrimp tail in a drop of trypan blue stain on a clean slide, then adding 1–2 drops of plant extract. Add a coverslip, wait a few minutes, then count stained (dead) and unstained (living) cells (about 25 total). Record your data in Table 43-1.

Figure 43-1 *Artemia*, brine shrimp.

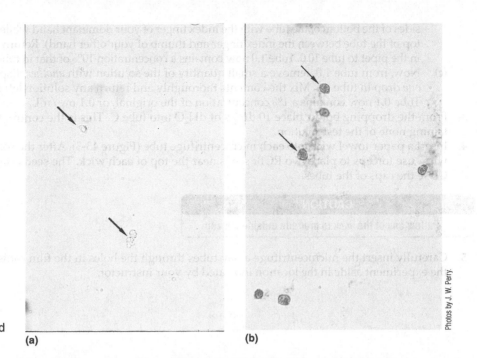

Figure 43-2 (a) Healthy (unstained) cells, (b) dead (stained) cells (500×).

(a)

(b)

Photos by J. W. Perry.

TABLE 43-1	Effect of Plant Extracts on *Artemia* Amoebocytes			
Treatment	Droplet Order on Slide	Number Unstained (Live) Cells	Number Stained (Dead) Cells	Percentage Dead Cells
Negative control	Brine + trypan blue			
Positive control	Brine + trypan blue + acetic acid			
Plant extract: _____	Brine + trypan blue + plant extract 1			
Plant extract: _____	Brine + trypan blue + plant extract 2			
Plant extract: _____	Brine + trypan blue + plant extract 3			

© Cengage Learning 2013

C. Fast Plant Bioassay (About 30 min.)

MATERIALS

Per student group:

- fine-pointed, water-resistant marker (Sharpie or similar)
- 35-mm film canister with lid prepunched with four holes
- four microcentrifuge tubes with caps
- four paper-towel wicks

- disposable pipets and bulb
- forceps
- eight Wisconsin Fast Plants seeds
- 15-cm plastic ruler
- dH₂O in dropping bottle
- plant extract(s) prepared in dH₂O in Part A

PROCEDURE

1. Using a fine-pointed, water-resistant marker, label the caps and/or sides of the four microcentrifuge tubes 10.0, 1.0, 0.1, and C (for Control).
2. Place 10 drops of the previously prepared plant extract into the tube labeled 10.0. This tube now contains 10 mg/mL of the test extract. You will now make *serial dilutions* of the solution, producing concentrations of 1.0 mg/mL and 0.1 mg/mL of the test substance:
   (a) Add 9 drops of dH₂O to tubes 1.0 and 0.1.
   (b) From tube 10.0, remove a small quantity of the solution with the disposable pipet and place *one* drop into tube 1.0. Mix the contents thoroughly by "thipping" the side of the microcentrifuge tube (flicking the

The Natural Arsenal: An Experimental Study of the Relationships Between Plants and Animals **683** sides of the bottom of the tube with the index finger of your dominant hand while holding the sides of the top of the tube between the index finger and thumb of your other hand). Return any solution remaining in the pipet to tube 10.0. Tube 1.0 now contains a concentration 10% of that in tube 10.0, or 1.0 mg/mL.

(c) Now, from tube 1.0, remove a small quantity of the solution with *another* disposable pipet and place *one* drop in tube 0.1. Mix the contents thoroughly and return any solution left in the pipet to tube 1.0. Tube 0.1 now contains a 1% concentration of the original, or 0.1 mg/mL.

3. From the dropping bottle, place 10 drops of dH₂O into tube C. This is the control for the experiment, containing none of the test solution.

4. Insert a paper-towel wick into each microcentrifuge tube (Figure 43-3). After the solution has moistened the wick, use forceps to place two RCBr seeds near the top of each wick. The seeds should adhere to the wick. Close the caps of the tubes.

CAUTION
Do not allow any of the wick to protrude outside the cap.

5. Carefully insert the microcentrifuge assay tubes through the holes in the film canister lid (Figure 43-4). Set the experiment aside in the location indicated by your instructor.

Figure 43-3   A labeled bioassay tube with paper wick.

Figure 43-4   Experimental apparatus for Fast Plant bioassay.

6. How can you provide replication for your experiment? Why would this be a good idea? Explain.

_____

_____

_____

7. After 24 hours or more, examine your bioassay to see how many, and which, seeds germinated. Record your results in Table 43-2. In addition to recording the response as "germinated" (G) or "did not germinate" (DNG), also indicate the extent of any germination by measuring and recording the length in millimeters (mm) of the roots and shoots of seed 1 (S1) and seed 2 (S2) for each treatment. If you are testing a second plant extract, record those results in Table 43-3.

TABLE 43-2 Effect of ▬▬▬▬▬ Extract on Germination of Fast Plant Seeds						
	Germination		Length of Roots (mm)		Length of Shoots (mm)	
Tube	Seed 1	Seed 2	Seed 1	Seed 2	Seed 1	Seed 2
Control (dH₂O)						
0.1 mg/mL extract						
1.0 mg/mL extract						
10.0 mg/mL extract						

© Cengage Learning 2013

TABLE 43-3	Effect of _____ Extract on Germination of Fast Plant Seeds					
	Germination		Length of Roots (mm)		Length of Shoots (mm)	
Tube	Seed 1	Seed 2	Seed 1	Seed 2	Seed 1	Seed 2
Control (dH₂O)						
0.1 mg/mL extract						
1.0 mg/mL extract						
10.0 mg/mL extract						

43.3 Analysis of Results

Do your bioassay results indicate any cytotoxicity of the plant extract(s) you tested? _____

If yes, do your results indicate cytotoxicity toward plant cells, animal cells, or both? _____

Using your experimental results, write a conclusion regarding the effect of the plant extract(s) on your test organism(s).

_____

_____

Does your conclusion support your prediction *or* prove it unsound? Is your hypothesis supported or falsified by your conclusion? Explain.

_____

_____

_____

List possible sources of error in your experiment and explain why or how they might decrease the reliability of your results.

_____

_____

_____

_____ **1.** Plant secondary compounds are chemicals that
(a) have no known metabolic function in the plant.
(b) are required for enzyme function.
(c) are generally carbohydrates or proteins.
(d) are important in cell division.

_____ **2.** Allelochemicals are active in preventing
(a) herbivore feeding.
(b) germination of plant competitors.
(c) infection by pathogens.
(d) all of the above

_____ **3.** Chemicals that are poisonous to specific cell types are said to be
(a) hazardous.
(b) cytotoxic.
(c) allelochemicals.
(d) bioactive.

_____ **4.** Bioassays
(a) are performed in a test tube using killed cells.
(b) expose a population of living organisms to a test substance.
(c) are used for chemotherapy.
(d) are none of the above.

_____ **5.** *Artemia*, brine shrimp,
(a) are aquatic organisms.
(b) live in salty ecosystems.
(c) are filter-feeding primary consumers.
(d) are all of the above.

_____ **6.** Plant defenses against herbivore grazing include
(a) thorns.
(b) plant secondary compounds.
(c) mobility.
(d) both a and b

_____ **7.** Trypan blue is
(a) taken up by living cells.
(b) taken up by dead cells.
(c) taken up by both living and dead cells.
(d) used to identify plant cells.

_____ **8.** Dead *Artemia* cells that have been treated with trypan blue appear
(a) colorless.
(b) blue.
(c) red.
(d) indistinguishable from living treated cells.

_____ **9.** The dH$_2$O-only treatment in the Fast Plant bioassay provides
(a) a control.
(b) moisture for seed germination.
(c) dilution of potential cytotoxins.
(d) none of the above

_____ **10.** *Artemia* and Fast Plant bioassays can be used to identify
(a) cytotoxins.
(b) herbicides.
(c) plant growth stimulators.
(d) all of the above

EXERCISE 43

The Natural Arsenal: An Experimental Study of the Relationships Between Plants and Animals

Post-Lab Questions

Introduction

1. Why have plants evolved secondary compounds?

2. Describe how a pharmaceutical company might use a bioassay to identify potential drugs in rainforest plants.

3. Would a chemical that is cytotoxic to brine shrimp cells necessarily have the same effect on Fast Plant cells? Explain.

43.1 Experimental Design

4. How can replication be increased in the *Artemia* bioassay to improve reliability of results?

43.2.B. Artemia *Bioassay*

5. What was the purpose of the *Artemia* slide prepared with droplets of
   (a) brine and trypan blue only?

   (b) brine, trypan blue, and acetic acid?

6. If seed germination took place in 100% of plants at the 1.0 mg/mL concentration, and no germination was observed at the 0.1 mg/mL concentration, how would you modify a second experiment to determine the actual effective concentration?

Food for Thought

7. If you found no cytotoxic effects with your plant extract, does this prove the extract is not cytotoxic? Explain.

8. If you found no cytotoxic effects with your plant extract, does this prove that the plant species from which the extract was made has no cytotoxic allelochemicals? Explain.

9. How might you alter the two bioassay procedures to provide more information? Describe and explain.
   (a) *Artemia* bioassay:

   (b) Fast Plant bioassay:

10. What other kinds of tests could you perform to provide more information about possible cytotoxicity of a plant extract?

Human Impact on the Environment

OBJECTIVES

After completing this exercise, you will be able to

1. define *runoff, evapotranspiration, fossil fuels, habitat loss, stream, pool, riffle, abiotic, biotic, watershed, point source pollution, nonpoint source pollution, pH, dissolved oxygen, nitrates, phosphates, chloride, fecal coliform bacteria, macroinvertebrate, larvae, Stream Monitoring Biotic Index;*

2. explain how human alterations of land may affect water resources, temperature, atmospheric composition, pollution, and maintenance of species;

3. describe the impacts of inorganic and nutrient pollution on stream organisms;

4. explain the importance of dissolved oxygen in stream water;

5. describe how the aquatic macroinvertebrates present in a stream can indicate water quality;

6. discuss limitations and strengths of standard chemical water tests and the Stream Quality Index;

7. discuss some of the ways in which human activity in a watershed can affect stream water quality.

Introduction

Global warming, extinction of species, damage to the stratospheric ozone layer, toxic chemical spills, ground water contamination, and deforestation. This partial list of environmental effects linked to our expanding human population is diverse and alarming. Each of these issues is a complex problem with scientific, economic, philosophical, sociological, and political aspects, and no single exercise (or entire course!) can fully address any of these issues. However, this exercise, which focuses on some of the ways humans alter terrestrial (land) habitats and affect water quality, will give you an idea of how scientists build the data base they use to assess environmental problems.

45.1   Impact of Land Use Changes

We depend completely on a healthy environment to provide clean air, water, and food; maintain the balance of the atmosphere and climate; decompose wastes; maintain wildlife and other organisms; and provide us with pharmaceuticals, building materials, and much more. Our economies and cultures rely on intact, healthy, functioning environments.

While every organism impacts the environment, our human numbers and technologies make us the most significant force of landscape alteration as we convert natural landscapes to human uses. In this activity you will analyze several locales typical in the United States to gauge some ways that human-caused changes affect their abilities to provide essential environmental services.

PROCEDURE

Study Figure 45-1, photos of a (a) suburban shopping area, (b) residential development, and (c) protected natural area, all located within two miles of each other in east-central Wisconsin. The mall and residential development occupy land that was similar to the natural area before their construction. (Alternatively, your instructor may provide information about three local areas.) As you read the questions and explanations below, fill in Table 45-1. Indicate briefly for each numbered statement how the characteristics of each site affect that feature.

(a)

(b)

(c)

Photos by Joy B. Perry

Figure 45-1 East-central Wisconsin (**a**) strip mall, (**b**) residential development, (**c**) protected natural area.

We rely on adequate fresh water from groundwater and surface sources (rivers and lakes) for irrigation water to grow crops, for industrial processes, and for personal and home usage.

1. Compacted, impenetrable or steeply sloped ground surfaces cause most rainwater and snow melt to run off, flowing over the ground surface by gravity toward low points. Most **runoff** eventually reaches streams, carrying with it any pollutants picked up along the way. In contrast, level, porous ground surfaces with many plant roots allow rainfall to soak into the soil and eventually replenish groundwater supplies. To what extent does each site affect runoff, and how?

2. Wetlands and soils with good water infiltration are able to release water to support plant growth during dry periods. Plants are the base of food chains, with all animals (including humans) depending directly or indirectly on plants for their nutrition. To what extent does each site affect water availability during a drought, and how?

   The ground surface and vegetation on a site can modify daily and annual temperature changes.

3. Plants release water from pores in their leaves in a process called **evapotranspiration**. The evaporation creates a local cooling effect. To what extent does each site have a cooling effect due to evapotranspiration?

4. Dark-colored solid surfaces such as building roofs, roads, and parking lots absorb solar radiation and release that energy as heat. These surfaces have a heating effect on their surroundings, in contrast to vegetated or light-colored surfaces. To what extent does each site have a heating effect on the surrounding area?

Fossil fuels (petroleum, natural gas, and coal) provide most of the energy needed for transportation and electricity production in the United States. The energy is released when the fuels are burned; combustion

TABLE 45-1 Impact of Land Use Changes			
Feature	Site _____	Site _____	Site _____
Impact on water quantity:			
1. Runoff during rainfall			
2. Water availability during drought			
Impact on temperature fluctuations:			
3. Cooling by evapotranspiration			
4. More heat produced than absorbed from sun			
Impact on pollution and climate:			
5. Increases air pollutants from fossil fuel combustion			
6. Net producer *or* consumer of carbon dioxide			
7. Pollutants added to soil and/or water			
Impact on species diversity:			
8. Number of species greater than, similar to, *or* less than 150 years ago			
9. Changes in predominance of native species from 150 years ago			

products include carbon dioxide, carbon monoxide, soot, ozone, and other substances that damage the human respiratory system.

In addition, rising carbon dioxide levels in the atmosphere accelerate global warming. Plants remove carbon dioxide from the atmosphere in the process of photosynthesis; as all organisms undergo cellular respiration and when microbes decompose dead organic matter, the carbon dioxide is returned to the atmosphere.

Additional human contributions to pollution include trash and waste production and disposal, pesticide use, and overfertilization of lawns and agricultural areas that may pollute water resources.

5. To what extent does each site degrade air quality by causing increased fossil fuel combustion?
6. Is each site a net producer *or* consumer of carbon dioxide?
7. What kinds of pollutants does each area release into the soil and/or water?

Habitat loss is the single greatest cause for extinction today, followed closely by the impact of invasive species. Every species has specific requirements for the range of physical and chemical properties of its habitat, as well as for interactions with many other species. Some species have very narrow requirements; even small environmental disturbances can overstress these organisms and cause their local or global extinction. Conversely, other species are adaptable to a broad range of conditions and have become widely distributed geographically. Some of these species, such as English sparrows, Norway rats, German cockroaches, and fire ants, spread aggressively and become invasive, reducing native species.

8. Do you estimate the number of species living on each site to be greater than, similar to, or less than the number present 150 years ago? _____
9. What changes, if any, do you think there have there been in the types of species present over the past 150 years? _____

Which human activities or types of changes did you observe to have the greatest impact on the environment? Explain. _____
_____
_____

Which environmental services seem to have been least impacted by commercial and housing development? Which have been most impacted? Explain. _____

_____

_____

Which of the sites has the greatest ability to provide essential environmental services? _____

Which of the sites has the least ability to provide essential environmental services? _____

We will always need energy sources and homes, as well as other resources from the environment. Suggest three changes that would lessen the environmental impact of commercial and residential developments.

1. _____

2. _____

3. _____

45.2   Evaluation of Water Quality of a Stream

A **stream** is a body of running water flowing on the earth. Streams range from shallow, narrow brooks tumbling down mountainsides to broad, deep rivers like the Mississippi. Regardless of its size, every stream has distinct major habitat types that influence the types of organisms living there. Relatively slow-moving, deep waters are called **pools**, while **riffles** are shallow areas with fast-moving current bubbling over rocks (Figure 45-2).

Riffles are places where stream water tumbling over rocks and gravel bottom recharges the water with oxygen. Because of the higher dissolved oxygen levels and the rocks and gravel that provide habitat, most stream inhabitants live in riffles. The rapid current brings oxygen for cellular respiration as well as a steady supply of food from upstream. Pools, on the other hand, are still areas with lower oxygen content. Pools tend to have muddy beds, catch organic matter from upstream, and are areas of decomposition and nutrient recycling.

Gaseous, liquid, and solid substances enter the stream and either dissolve in the water or are carried along as suspended particles. The current thus transports these substances to where they may affect organisms downstream. The current speed, type of bottom structure, temperature, and dissolved substances are the **abiotic** components of the stream ecosystem. These abiotic components influence the life and habits of the organisms inhabiting the flowing water, the **biotic**, or living, components of the stream ecosystem.

The single most important factor influencing the abiotic and biotic components is the character of the **watershed**, all the surrounding land area that serves as drainage for a stream. A watershed may cover a few acres of land surrounding a very small stream, or include tens of thousands of square kilometers for a large river. You can think of a watershed as a bowl, with the stream flowing across the bottom. Water that falls on the higher elevations (the sides of the bowl) of a watershed eventually flows into the stream. Your instructor will provide you with information about the boundaries and terrain of the watershed of the stream you will study.

(a)   (b)

Figure 45-2   Stream habitats. **(a)** Pool leading into a riffle. **(b)** Closer look at a riffle.

The quality of a stream depends on its watershed and the human activities that occur there. In general, a stream is of the highest quality when the watershed and streamside vegetation remain in a natural state, while most human influences tend to be detrimental to stream quality. These human-induced effects can be lumped under the general term *pollution*. The most common types of water pollutants are:

- *Human pathogens*, disease-causing agents, such as bacteria, viruses, and protists.
- *Toxic chemicals*, both organic (carbon-containing) and inorganic. Toxic chemicals can harm humans, and fish and other aquatic life. They include acids, heavy metals, petroleum products, pesticides, and detergents.
- *Organic wastes*, such as sewage, food-processing and paper-making wastes, and animal wastes. Organic wastes can be decomposed by bacteria, but the process uses up oxygen dissolved in the water. The decomposition of large quantities of organic wastes can deplete the water of oxygen, causing fish, insects, and other aquatic oxygen-requiring organisms to die.
- *Plant nutrients*, such as nitrates and phosphates, can cause too much growth of algae and aquatic plants. When the masses of algae and plants die, the decay process can again deplete the critical dissolved oxygen (DO) in the water.
- *Sediments*, or suspended matter, the particles of soil or other solids that become suspended in the water. Sediment originates where soil has been exposed to rainfall, most often from construction sites, forestry operations, and agriculture. This is the biggest pollutant by weight, and it can reduce photosynthesis by clouding the water and can carry pesticides and other harmful substances with the soil particles. When sediment settles, it can destroy fish feeding and spawning areas and clog and fill stream channels, lakes, and harbors.
- *Heat*, or thermal pollution. Heated water holds less dissolved oxygen than colder water, so the addition of heated water by industries must be closely monitored to ensure that dissolved oxygen isn't driven to too low levels.

All these substances enter water as either "point" or "nonpoint" pollution. **Point source pollution** occurs at a specific location where the pollutants are released from a pipe, ditch, or sewer. Examples of point sources include sewage treatment plants, storm drains, and factory discharges. Point sources are relatively easy to identify, regulate, and monitor. Federal and state governments regulate the type and quantity of some types of pollutants for each point source discharge.

Nonpoint source pollution enters streams from a vast number of sources, with no specific point of entry contributing a large amount of pollutants. Most nonpoint source pollution results when rainfall and runoff carry pollutants from large, poorly defined areas into a stream. Examples of nonpoint source pollution include the washing of fertilizers and pesticides from lawns and agricultural fields, and soil erosion from construction sites. Because sources of nonpoint pollution are difficult to identify and define, it is much more difficult to regulate.

What human activities can you name that might be affecting your study stream? _____

_____

_____

45.2.A. Evaluation and Sampling at the Stream

In this section, you will take several measurements in the water and collect water samples for analysis. Your class will divide into groups, with each group performing different tasks. As a class you will measure the temperature and pH of the water, plus determine several nutrient/pollutant levels. Additionally, you will collect macroinvertebrates for classification and sample the water for the presence of potentially pathogenic (disease-causing) bacteria.

45.2.A.1. Physical and Chemical Sampling

MATERIALS

Per student:
- disposable plastic gloves (optional)

Per student group (4):
- nail clippers or scissors
- plastic beaker
- plastic sample bottles
- watch or clock

Per lab room:
- thermometer
- portable pH meter or pH indicator paper
- Hach or other dissolved oxygen test kit
- Hach or other nitrate test kit
- Hach or other chloride test kit
- Hach or other phosphate test kit
- dH$_2$O
- paper towels

PROCEDURE

(a) Temperature. Stream organisms are typically more sensitive to higher temperatures. In addition to affecting the metabolic rate of the cold-blooded aquatic organisms, cooler water holds more dissolved oxygen than warmer water.

Measure the water temperature holding a thermometer about 10 cm below the water surface if possible. Keep the thermometer in the water for approximately 1 min. so the temperature can equilibrate. Record the temperature measurements from three locations, then total them and calculate the average temperature. Enter the average temperature in Table 45-2.

Temperature: 1 _____ ; 2 _____ ; 3 _____ ; Average: _____

TABLE 45-2	Stream Measurements and Water Quality Standards			
Physical/Chemical Measurement	**Average Value**	**Water Quality Standards**		**Probable Cause of Degradation**[a]
		General[b]	**Trout Stream**	
Temperature		<32°C	<20°–23°C	Lack of shade
pH		6.0–8.5	6.5–8.5	Acid drainage
Dissolved oxygen (DO)		>5 mg/L	>6 mg/L	Organic and nutrient sources
Nitrate (NO_3^-)		<2 mg/L	<10 mg/L	Organic and nutrient sources; fertilizers
Phosphate (PO_4^-)		<0.1 mg/L		Organic and nutrient sources; fertilizers
Chloride (Cl^-)		<30 mg/L		Road salt, sewage, agricultural chemicals
Total coliform bacteria		200 colonies/100 mL[c]		Sewage, animal wastes

© Cengage Learning 2013

[a] Probable cause(s) of values failing to meet standards.
[b] Standards for swimming and to protect general aquatic life. (*Source*: Wisconsin Department of Natural Resources.)
[c] Standards for safe human contact. (*Source*: Wisconsin Department of Natural Resources.)

(b) pH. pH is a measure of the concentration of hydrogen ions in the water. pH signifies the degree of acidity or alkalinity of water. The pH scale ranges from 0 (most acidic) to 14 (most basic). A solution with a pH of 7 is neutral. A change of only 1 on the scale means a tenfold change in the hydrogen ion concentration of the water.

Most aquatic organisms thrive in water of pH 6–8. pH that is too low can damage fish gills. Low water pH can also cause some minerals, such as aluminum, to become toxic. The higher the pH, the more carbonates, bicarbonates, and salts are dissolved in the water. Streams with moderate concentrations of these substances are nutritionally rich and support abundant life.

Use the pH meter or indicator paper to determine the pH of your stream water. Try to sample both riffle and pool areas. Determine and record the average pH in Table 45-1.

pH: 1 _____ ; 2 _____ ; 3 _____ ; Average: _____

Perform each following chemical analyses on three sites in the stream, average your readings, and record the average concentration in Table 45-2. Follow the instructions provided with each test kit.

(c) Dissolved oxygen (DO). Aquatic animals, like most living organisms, require oxygen for their metabolic processes. This oxygen is present in dissolved form in water. If much organic matter (for example, sewage) is present in water, microorganisms use the dissolved oxygen in the process of decomposing the organic matter. In that case, the level of dissolved oxygen might fall too low to be available for aquatic animals. DO requirements vary by species and physical condition, but many studies suggest that 4–5 parts per million (ppm) is the minimum needed to support a diverse fish population. The DO of good fishing waters generally averages about 9 ppm. When DO levels drop below 3 ppm, even pollution-tolerant fish species may die.

Dissolved oxygen: 1 _____ ; 2 _____ ; 3 _____ ; Average: _____

(d) **Nitrate (NO$_3^-$).** Nitrogen (N) is a nutrient required for plant life. Nitrogen in the form of **nitrates** (NO$_3^-$) is a common component of the synthetic fertilizers used on lawns, golf courses, and farm fields to stimulate plant growth. Leaking sewage tanks, municipal wastewater treatment plants, manure from livestock and other animals, and discharges from car exhausts are all sources of stream nitrates. Excessive nitrates in streams can cause overgrowth of algae and other plant life. This plant growth may decrease the light available to other stream life, but eventually dies and decays. The decay process can deplete water of the vital dissolved oxygen.

Nitrate: 1 _____; 2 _____; 3 _____; Average: _____

(e) **Phosphate (PO$_4^-$).** Phosphorous (P), another element crucial to plant life, is also a common component of commercial fertilizers in the form of **phosphates** (PO$_4^-$). When it rains, varying amounts of phosphates wash from farm fields and other fertilized areas into nearby waterways. Like nitrates, phosphate enrichment also causes nutrient problems in streams. Excessive levels indicate pollution by nutrient sources or organic substances (fertilizers, sewage, detergents, animal wastes).

Phosphate: 1 _____; 2 _____; 3 _____; Average: _____

(f) **Chloride (Cl$^-$).** **Chloride** is one of the major ions in sewage; it also enters waterways when washed from roadways that have been treated with salt (NaCl, sometimes CaCl$_2$) in wintertime to melt ice and snow. Agricultural chemicals are another source of chloride in water. Water with high chloride content is toxic to plant life.

Chloride: 1 _____; 2 _____; 3 _____; Average: _____

45.2.A.2. Biological Sampling

MATERIALS

Per student:
- hip boots or other footwear that can get wet
- forceps or tweezers

Per student group (4):
- sterile water sample collection bottles or containers
- kick-seine or D-net sampler
- white enamel pan
- bottle of alcohol
- sample collecting jars
- waterproof markers

Per lab room:
- one or more Coliscan dish plus Easygel bottle
- 1-mL sterile dropping pipets
- nail clipper

PROCEDURE

(a) **Fecal coliform bacteria.** Fecal coliform bacteria are tiny, rod-shaped bacteria that live in the intestines of humans and all warm-blooded animals and pass out of the body in feces. They can cause human disease if they enter a drinking water supply, and they are also associated with other pathogenic bacteria. You will sample the water of your stream to determine whether any fecal coliform bacteria are present.
   1. Use a marker to label the edge of a Coliscan plate with the date and other identifying information.
   2. Collect a water sample from beneath the surface of the stream.
   3. Use a sterile pipet and transfer 1 mL of the water into the Easygel bottle. Be careful not to touch the inside of the bottle or cap with anything to maintain sterility. Swirl the bottle to mix, then pour into the labeled petri dish. Place lid on dish and gently swirl until the entire dish is covered with liquid. Be careful not to splash over the side or on the lid.
   4. Place dishes right-side-up on a level spot, preferably warm, until solid.
   5. Incubate the sample at 35°–40°C for 24 hours, *or* at room temperature for 48 hours.

(b) **Aquatic macroinvertebrates. Macroinvertebrates**, animals that are large enough to be seen with the naked eye and that lack a backbone, are an important part of the stream ecosystem. Nearly all of the macroinvertebrates present in the water are immature insects, called **larvae**, which mature and then spend their adult lives on land or in the air. Most aquatic larvae feed on decaying organic matter, but some graze on algae or pursue other animals. Other aquatic macroinvertebrates include mollusks (shelled organisms such as snails and clams), arthropods (relatives of shrimp and lobsters such as crayfish and scuds), and various types of worms.

Most aquatic macroinvertebrates, especially those that live on or in the bottom of riffle areas are good indicators of water quality. Aquatic macroinvertebrates can be separated into four general groups on the basis of their tolerance to pollution. Some bottom dwellers like dobsonfly larvae need a high-quality, unpolluted environment and are placed in Group 1 (Figure 45-3). Dominance of Group 1 organisms in a stream signifies good water quality. Group 2 organisms, including caddisfly and dragonfly larvae, also require good water quality, with low levels of pollutants. Group 3 organisms include blackfly larvae and scuds. They can exist in a wide range of

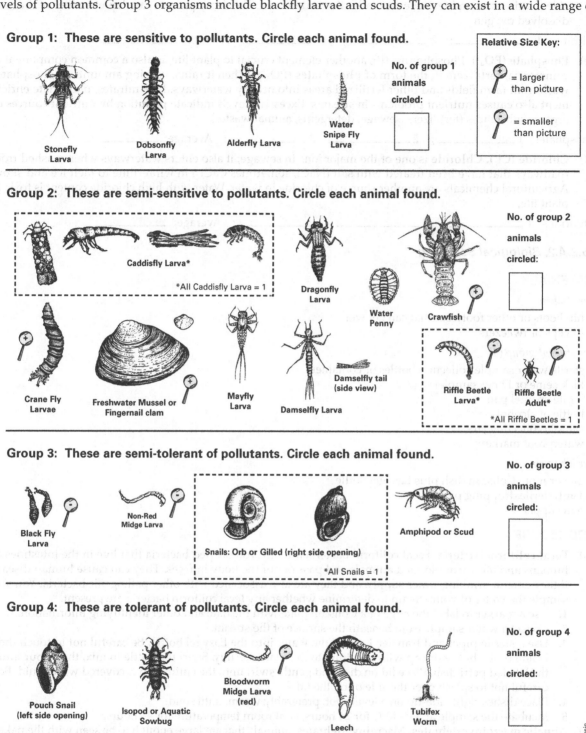

Group 1: These are sensitive to pollutants. Circle each animal found.

Stonefly Larva Dobsonfly Larva Alderfly Larva Water Snipe Fly Larva

No. of group 1 animals circled:

Relative Size Key:
⊕ = larger than picture
⊖ = smaller than picture

Group 2: These are semi-sensitive to pollutants. Circle each animal found.

Caddisfly Larva*
*All Caddisfly Larva = 1

Dragonfly Larva

Water Penny

Crawfish

Crane Fly Larvae Freshwater Mussel or Fingernail clam Mayfly Larva Damselfly Larva Damselfly tail (side view)

Riffle Beetle Larva* Riffle Beetle Adult*
*All Riffle Beetles = 1

No. of group 2 animals circled:

Group 3: These are semi-tolerant of pollutants. Circle each animal found.

Black Fly Larva Non-Red Midge Larva Snails: Orb or Gilled (right side opening) Amphipod or Scud
*All Snails = 1

No. of group 3 animals circled:

Group 4: These are tolerant of pollutants. Circle each animal found.

Pouch Snail (left side opening) Isopod or Aquatic Sowbug Bloodworm Midge Larva (red) Leech Tubifex Worm

No. of group 4 animals circled:

For more information, call (608) 265-3887 or (608) 264-8948.
Download and print data sheets from
http://www.watermonitoring.uwex.edu/wav/monitoring/sheets.html

© 2008 University of Wisconsin. This publication is part of a seven-series set, "Water Action Volunteers – Volunteer Monitoring Factsheet Series." All recording forms are free and available from the WAV coordinator. WAV is a cooperative program between the University of Wisconsin-Extension & the Wisconsin Department of Natural Resources. University of Wisconsin-Extension is an EEO/Affirmative Action employer and provides equal opportunities in employment and programming, including Title IX and ADA requirements.

Water Action Volunteers

© 2008 University of Wisconsin

Figure 45-3   Stream insects and other macroinvertebrates.

water quality conditions and include crayfish and dragonfly larvae. Group 4 organisms are tolerant of pollution and include red midge and aquatic sowbugs and leeches.

By looking at the diversity of macroinvertebrates present, you will be able to get a general idea of the health of a stream. Typically, waters of higher quality support a greater diversity (more kinds) of pollution-intolerant macroinvertebrates. As water becomes more polluted, fewer kinds of organisms thrive. You will collect samples of macroinvertebrates and separate them into general types to determine a Stream Quality Index Value.

Try to use the kick-seine or D-frame net to sample from riffle areas only, since these areas usually have a higher quality environment, with more dissolved oxygen, for macroinvertebrates. Sample from pools only if most of the stream is pool area.

Work in groups for this activity.

1. Select a riffle area with a depth of 7 to 30 cm, and stones that are 5 to 25 cm in diameter or larger if possible. Move into the sample area from the downstream side to minimize disturbance.
2. One student should hold the kick-seine or D-frame net at the downstream edge of the riffle. Be sure that the bottom edge of the screen is held tightly against the stream bottom. Don't allow any water to flow over the top of the seine or you might lose specimens.
3. Other group members should walk in front of the net and begin the collection procedure. Pick up all rocks fist-sized or larger and rub their surfaces thoroughly in front of the net to dislodge all organisms into the seine. Then disturb the streambed for a distance of 1 m upstream of the net. Stir up the bed with hands and feet until the entire 1-m² area has been worked over. Kick the streambed with a sideways motion to allow bottom-dwelling organisms to be carried into the net.
4. Remove the net from the water with a forward-scooping motion so that no specimens are washed from the surface. Carry the seine to a flat area of the stream bank for examination.
5. Rinse the organisms and debris collected to the bottom of the screen. Many aquatic macroinvertebrates are very small, so be certain to remove all of them from the screen. Use forceps to remove any that cling to the screen. Place the collection in a collecting jar; drain off as much water as possible and cover the material with alcohol to kill and preserve the organisms. Label each jar to identify the area sampled.

45.2.B. Laboratory Analysis—Evaluating Biological Tests and Samples

1. Fecal Coliform Bacteria

Inspect the dishes that have been incubated and count the *purple* colonies (*not* light blue, blue-green, white or pink). Multiply that number by 100 to determine the number of fecal coliform bacterial colonies per 100 mL of water. Record in Table 45-2.

Fecal coliform bacteria in excess of 200 colonies per 100 mL (2 colonies per plate) indicate contamination of water with animal or human wastes and are unsafe for human contact.

2. Macroinvertebrates: determining the Stream Monitoring Biotic Index Value

Identification of aquatic organisms can be difficult. However, biological sampling results can be rapidly translated into a water quality assessment without actually identifying each insect specimen, but by determining the number of kinds of certain macroinvertebrates that were collected.

MATERIALS

Per student:

- petri dishes
- forceps or tweezers
- white paper *or* white enamel pan
- dissection microscope *or* magnifying glass

PROCEDURE

(a) Pour a portion of a macroinvertebrate sample into a petri dish. Place a piece of white paper onto the stage of a dissecting microscope to provide an opaque white background, and then observe the specimens in the petri dish. Alternatively, you might pour a sample into a white enamel pan and observe the specimens with a magnifying glass.

(b) Use forceps or tweezers to sort all the organisms into "look-alike" groups, or taxa (Figure 45-3). Look primarily at body shape and number of legs and "tails" to aid in identification. Record each taxonomic group present in your sample under the appropriate group number in Table 45-3.

Group 1 are pollution-intolerant organisms; Group 2 are semi-sensitive to pollutants; Group 3 are semi-tolerant to pollutants; and Group 4 organisms are pollution-tolerant. *For purposes of this lab, disregard organisms you may find but that are not pictured in Figure 45-3.*

c. Determine the Stream Monitoring Biotic Index Value, a measure of stream ecosystem health, as follows (see example below):

1. Each pollution-tolerance group is assigned an importance value as follows:
   Group 1 = importance value 4
   Group 2 = importance value 3
   Group 3 = importance value 2
   Group 4 = importance value 1
2. Count the number of taxa (*types* of organisms) in each group and multiply that number by the importance value. Record the total number of taxa identified for each group, plus the resulting group values in Table 45-3. Also record the total number of taxa identified in Table 45-3.
3. Add the group values for all four groups; record in Table 45-3.
4. Divide the totaled group values by the total number of different taxa identified to yield the Stream Monitoring Biotic Index Value.

Example:

Taxa Identified in Stream Sample

Group 1 (Pollution Intolerant)	Group 2 (Semi-sensitive to Pollutants)	Group 3 (Semi-tolerant to Pollutants)	Group 4 (Pollution Tolerant)
stonefly	caddisfly	scud	pouch snail
	crawfish	gilled snail	aquatic sowbug
			leech
No. taxa **1** × Importance Value **4** = Group Value **4**	No. taxa **2** × Importance Value **3** = Group Value **6**	No. taxa **2** × Importance Value **2** = Group Value **4**	No. taxa **3** × Importance Value **1** = Group Value **3**

A. Total Number Taxa Identified = 1 + 2 + 2 + 3 = **8**
B. Sum of Group Values = 4 + 6 + 4 + 3 = **17**
C. Stream Monitoring Biotic Index Value = Sum of Group Values (B.) ÷ Total Number Taxa Identified (A.) = 17 ÷ 8 = **2.12**

TABLE 45-3 Stream Monitoring Biotic Index Worksheet for (stream name) _____

Taxa Identified in Stream Samples

Group 1 (Pollution Intolerant)	Group 2 (Semi-sensitive to Pollutants)	Group 3 (Semi-tolerant to Pollutants)	Group 4 (Pollution Tolerant)
No. taxa _____ × Importance Value 4 = Group Value _____	No. taxa _____ × Importance Value 3 = Group Value _____	No. taxa _____ × Importance Value 2 = Group Value _____	No. taxa _____ × Importance Value 1 = Group Value _____

A. Total Number Taxa Identified = _____
B. Sum of Group Values = _____ + _____ + _____ + _____ = _____
C. Stream Monitoring Biotic Index Value = Sum of Group Values (B.) ÷ Total Number Taxa Identified (A.) = _____

© Cengage Learning 2013

TABLE 45-4	Interpreting the Stream Monitoring Biotic Index Value
Stream Monitoring Biotic Index Value	**Water Quality**
3.6 and above	Excellent
2.6–3.5	Good
2.1–2.5	Fair
2.0 or less	Poor

© Cengage Learning 2013

What does this index number mean? Table 45-4 provides guidance in interpreting the Stream Monitoring Biotic Index Value.

In addition to indicating general water quality, the aquatic macroinvertebrate survey can provide you with information regarding the types of pollutants that may be affecting the stream. If you identified few taxa of pollution-tolerant invertebrates, but observed great numbers of individuals of these taxa, the stream water may be overly enriched with organic matter, or have severe organic pollution. Conversely, if you found relatively few taxa and only a few individuals of each kind (or if you found *no* macroinvertebrates but the stream appears clean), you might suspect the presence of toxic chemicals. A diversity of taxa, with an abundance of individuals for many of the taxa, indicates a healthy stream with good to excellent water quality.

45.2.C. Analysis of Results

Table 45-2 lists acceptable levels of a few chemicals in water to protect aquatic life, as well as the probable causes of test values that fail to meet those standards. Compare your test results with those values. Also consider your findings from biological observations.

Are your observations, chemical measurements, and biological observations consistent? (Refer to Tables 45-2 and 45-3.) That is, do they *all* indicate that your stream is healthy, with good water quality? Or conversely, do they *all* point to a stream in trouble, with poor water quality? Or do your results conflict, with some indicators of good quality and some indicators of poor water quality? Explain. _____

_____

If your results aren't clear-cut, speculate on why this might be so.

_____

_____

What might you do to increase the consistency and reliability of your results?

_____

_____

Which of your observed or measured factors indicate(s) higher quality water?

_____

_____

Which of your observed or measured factors indicate(s) lower water quality?

_____

_____

Why might you find a low Stream Monitoring Biotic Index Value, even if the chemical and physical parameters you measured are within limits for "good" water quality?

_____

_____

If you found indications of organic or nutrient pollution, what might be some of the sources for this pollution in your stream's watershed?

_____

_____

_____

(Continues on p. 714.)

Do you think most of the pollutants in your stream result from point source or nonpoint source pollutants? Why?

_____

_____

Briefly describe three ways that the negative impacts on your stream could be reduced or eliminated.

_____

_____

_____

_____ 1. Runoff of rainwater is minimized on
(a) hard surfaces like parking lots.
(b) compacted ground.
(c) level, spongy ground.
(d) steep slopes.

_____ 2. Dark-colored solid surfaces
(a) have a heating effect on their surroundings.
(b) have a cooling effect on their surroundings.
(c) release carbon dioxide.
(d) increase evapotranspiration.

_____ 3. The greatest cause of extinction of species is
(a) runoff.
(b) habitat loss.
(c) invasive species.
(d) evapotranspiration.

_____ 4. Which of these is **not** a type of water pollutant?
(a) dissolved oxygen
(b) toxic chemicals
(c) organic wastes
(d) sediment

_____ 5. pH is
(a) a measure of phosphorous concentration.
(b) a measure of hydrogen ion concentration.
(c) measured by counting the number of different kinds of aquatic insects.
(d) measured on a scale from 1 to 100.

_____ 6. Dissolved oxygen content in stream water is affected by
(a) organic matter in the water.
(b) overgrowth of algae.
(c) water nutrient levels.
(d) all of the above

_____ 7. Which pollutant would most likely be the source of coliform bacteria in a stream?
(a) fertilizers from a golf course
(b) discharge from a factory
(c) forestry activities
(d) sewage or animal wastes

_____ 8. Most of the aquatic macroinvertebrates in a stream are
(a) clams.
(b) insect larvae.
(c) worms.
(d) arthropods such as crayfish.

_____ 9. Group 1 aquatic macroinvertebrates
(a) require high-quality, unpolluted water.
(b) require polluted water.
(c) are tolerant of a wide range of water quality conditions.
(d) include leeches.

_____ 10. Nonpoint source pollutants include
(a) fertilizers from lawns.
(b) pesticides from farm fields.
(c) soil erosion from construction sites.
(d) all of the above

EXERCISE **45**

Human Impact on the Environment

Post-Lab Questions

45.1 Impact of Land Use Changes

1. A wooded area is converted to a housing development and strip mall. Predict and briefly describe three ways this change in land use could affect atmospheric carbon dioxide levels.

2. How can plants reduce the temperature of their surroundings? Would this effect be as great during winter in northern temperature regions as during the summer?

3. Describe how changing the ways that land surfaces are used by humans cause changes in water resources.

45.2 Evaluation of Water Quality of a Stream

4. Why is it important for sewage treatment plants to remove nitrates and phosphates from sewage before discharging it into a river? Explain.

5. Trout are fish that require relatively low-temperature water. Suppose a shaded trout stream has its overhanging streamside trees removed. Explain the possible effects of this action on the trout population over the course of a summer.

45.2.A. Evaluation and Sampling at the Stream

6. At right are partial results of chemical sampling of one stream. What do these results tell you about the suitability of this stream as fish habitat? What are likely causes for these values?

Parameter	Measurement
Fecal coliform bacteria	1800/100 mL
Nitrate	8.5 mg/L
DO	3 mg/L

45.2.B. Laboratory Analysis—Evaluating Biological Tests and Samples

7. Here are the data from one stream's aquatic macroinvertebrate sample.

Taxa Present:

Group 1 (Pollution Intolerant)	Group 2 (Semi-sensitive to Pollutants)	Group 3 (Semi-tolerant to Pollutants)	Group 4 (Pollution Tolerant)
Stonefly larvae	Crane fly larvae	Non-Red Midge larvae	Sowbug
Dobsonfly larvae	Dragonfly larvae	Scud	
	Crayfish		
	Caddisfly larvae		
	Damselfly larvae		

Calculate the Stream Monitoring Biotic Index Value. What does this sample indicate about the water quality?

8. Referring to the stream in question 7, suppose you also know there are very few individuals of the Group 1 and 2 taxa present while scuds are extremely abundant. Does this information alter your assessment of the water quality of the stream? Why or why not?

Food for Thought

9. Describe two ways that stream water quality that is healthy for trout differs from that in which trout would be unlikely to survive.

10. A stream flows through marshes, farmland, and suburban housing developments before emptying into the ocean. Describe three ways that the water quality of the stream is affected by the different land areas along its course.

Measurement Conversions

Metric to American Standard	American Standard to Metric
Length	**Length**
1 mm = 0.039 inch	1 inch = 2.54 cm
1 cm = 0.394 inch	1 foot = 0.305 m
1 m = 3.28 feet	1 yard = 0.914 m
1 m = 1.09 yards	1 mile = 1.61 km
1 km = 0.622 mile	
Volume	**Volume**
1 mL = 0.0338 fluid ounce	1 fluid ounce = 29.6 mL
1 L = 4.23 cups	1 cup = 237 mL
1 L = 2.11 pints	1 pint = 0.474 L
1 L = 1.06 quarts	1 quart = 0.947 L
1 L = 0.264 gallon	1 gallon = 3.79 L
Mass	**Mass**
1 mg = 0.0000353 ounce	1 ounce = 28.3 g
1 g = 0.0353 ounce	1 pound = 0.454 kg
1 kg = 2.21 pounds	

Genetics Problems

You may find it helpful to draw your own Punnett squares on a separate sheet of paper for the following problems.

Monohybrid Problems with Complete Dominance

1. In mice, black fur (B) is dominant over brown fur (b). Breeding a brown mouse and a homozygous black mouse produces all black offspring.

   (a) What is the genotype of the *gametes* produced by the brown-furred parent? _____

   (b) What genotype is the brown-furred parent? _____

   (c) What genotype is the black-furred parent? _____

   (d) What genotype is the black-furred offspring? _____

   (e) If two F_1 mice are bred with one another, what phenotype will the F_2 offspring be, and in what proportion?

   phenotype _____

   proportion _____

2. The presence of horns on Hereford cattle is controlled by a single gene. The hornless (H) condition is dominant over the horned (h) condition. A hornless cow was crossed repeatedly with the same horned bull. The following results were obtained in the F_1 offspring:

   eight hornless cattle

   seven horned cattle

   What are the parents' genotypes?

   cow _____

   bull _____

3. In fruit flies, red eyes (R) are dominant over purple eyes (r). Two red-eyed fruit flies were crossed, producing the following offspring:

   76 red-eyed flies

   24 purple-eyed flies

   (a) What is the approximate ratio of red-eyed to purple-eyed flies? _____

   (b) Based on your experience with previous problems, what two genotypes give rise to this ratio? _____

   (c) What are the parents' genotypes? _____

   (d) What is the genotypic ratio of the F_1 offspring? _____

   (e) What is the phenotypic ratio of the F_1 offspring? _____

Monohybrid Problems with Incomplete Dominance

4. Petunia flower color is governed by two alleles, but neither allele is truly dominant over the other. Petunias with the genotype R^1R^1 are red-flowered, those that are heterozygous (R^1R^2) are pink, and those with the R^2R^2 genotype are white. This is an example of **incomplete dominance**. (Note that superscripts are used rather than upper- and lowercase letters to describe the alleles.)

   (a) If a white-flowered plant is crossed with a red-flowered petunia, what is the genotypic ratio of the F_1 offspring? _____

   (b) What is the phenotypic ratio of the F_1 offspring? _____

   (c) If two of the F_1 offspring are crossed, what phenotypes will appear in the F_2 generation? _____

   (d) What will be the genotypic ratio in the F_2 generation? _____

Monohybrid Problems Illustrating Codominance

5. Another type of monohybrid inheritance involves the expression of *both* phenotypes in the heterozygous situation. This is called **codominance**.

    One well-known example of codominance occurs in the coat color of Shorthorn cattle. Those with reddish-gray roan coats are heterozygous (RR'), and result from a mating between a red (RR) Shorthorn and one that's white ($R'R'$). Roan cattle don't have roan-colored hairs, as would be expected with incomplete dominance, but rather appear roan as a result of having both red *and* white hairs. Thus, the roan coloration is not a consequence of pigments blending in each hair. Because the R and R' alleles are *both* fully expressed in the heterozygote, they are codominant.

    (a) If a roan Shorthorn cow is mated with a white bull, what will be the genotypic and phenotypic ratios in the F_1 generation?

    genotypic ratio _____

    phenotypic ratio _____

    (b) List the parental genotypes of crosses that could produce at least some

    white offspring _____

    roan offspring _____

Monohybrid, Sex-linked Problems

6. In humans, as well as in many other animals, sex is determined by special sex chromosomes. An individual containing two X chromosomes is a female, while an individual possessing an X and a Y chromosome is a male. (Rare exceptions of XY females and XX males have recently been discovered.)

    I am a male/female (circle one).

    (a) What sex chromosomes do you have? _____

    (b) In terms of sex chromosomes, what type of gametes (ova) does a female produce? _____

    (c) What are the possible sex chromosomes in a male's sperm cells? _____

    (d) Which parent's gametes will determine the sex of the offspring? _____

7. The sex chromosomes bear alleles for traits, just like the other chromosomes in our bodies. Genes that occur on the sex chromosomes are said to be sex-linked. More specifically, the genes present on the X chromosome are said to be X-linked. Many more genes are present on the X chromosome than are found on the Y chromosome. Nonetheless, those genes found on the Y chromosome are said to be Y-linked.

    The Y chromosome is smaller than its homologue, the X chromosome. Consequently, most of the loci present on the X chromosome are absent on the Y chromosome.

    In humans, color vision is X-linked; the gene for color vision is located on the X chromosome but is absent from the Y chromosome.

    Normal color vision (X^N) is dominant over color blindness (X^n). Suppose a color-blind man fathers the children of a woman with the genotype $X^N X^N$.

    (a) What genotype is the father? _____
    (b) What proportion of daughters will be color-blind? _____
    (c) What proportion of sons will be color-blind? _____

8. One daughter from the preceding problem marries a color-blind man.

    (a) What proportion of their sons will be color-blind? (Another way to think of this is to ask: What are the *chances* that their sons will be color-blind?) _____

    (b) Explain how a color-blind daughter might result from this couple.

    _____

    _____

Dihybrid Problems

Recall that pigmented eyes (P) are dominant to nonpigmented (p), and dimpled chins (D) are dominant to nondimpled chins (d).

9. A pigment-eyed, dimple-chinned man marries a blue-eyed woman without a dimpled chin. Their first-born child is blue-eyed and has a dimpled chin.

    (a) What are the possible genotypes of the father? _____

    (b) What genotype is the mother? _____

    (c) What alleles may have been carried by the father's sperm? _____

10. Suppose a dimple-chinned, blue-eyed man whose father lacked a dimple marries a woman who is homozygous recessive for both traits.

    (a) What is the expected genotypic ratio of children produced in this marriage? _____

    (b) What is the expected phenotypic ratio? _____

11. In his original work on the genetics of garden peas, Mendel found that yellow seed color (YY, Yy) is dominant over green seeds (yy) and that round seed shape (RR, Rr) is dominant over shrunken seeds (rr). Mendel crossed pure-breeding (homozygous) yellow, round-seeded plants with green, shrunken-seeded plants.

    (a) What will be the genotype and phenotype of the F_1 produced from such a cross?

        genotype _____

        phenotype _____

    (b) If the F_1 plants are crossed, what will be the expected phenotypic ratio of the F_2 generation?

    _____

Multiple Alleles

12. The major blood groups in humans are determined by **multiple alleles**; that is there are *more than* two possible alleles, any one of which can occupy a locus.

    In this ABO blood group system, a single gene can exist in any of three allelic forms: I^A, I^B, or i. The alleles A and B code for production of antigen A and antigen B (two proteins) on the surface of red blood cells. Alleles A and B are codominant, while allele i is recessive.

    Four blood groups (phenotypes) are possible from combinations of these alleles (Table 1).

TABLE 1	The ABO Blood Groups		
Blood Type	**Antigen Present**	**Antibody Present**	**Genotype**
O	Neither A nor B	A and B	ii
A	A	B	I^AI^A or I^Ai
B	B	A	I^BI^B or I^Bi
AB	AB	Neither A nor B	I^AI^B

    (a) Is it possible for a child with blood type O to be produced by two AB parents? _____ (yes or no) Explain.

    _____

    _____

    _____

    (b) In a case of disputed paternity, the child is type O, the mother type A. Could an individual of the following blood types be the father? _____ Explain each possibility.

        O_____

        A_____

        B_____

        AB_____

Chi-Square Analysis

13. In fruit flies, red eyes (*R*) are dominant over white eyes (*r*). A student performs a cross between a heterozygous red-eyed fly and a white-eyed fly. The student counts the offspring and finds 65 red-eyed flies and 49 white-eyed flies.

    (a) What is the expected phenotypic ratio of this cross? _____

    (b) Using a χ^2 test, determine whether the deviation between the observed and the expected is the result of chance.

        $\chi^2 =$ _____

    (c) Conclusion

    _____

    _____

14. In fruit flies, gray body (*G*) is dominant over ebony body (*g*).

    (a) A red-eyed, gray-bodied fly known to be heterozygous for both traits is mated with a white-eyed fly that is heterozygous for body color.

        What is the expected phenotypic ratio for this mating? _____

    (b) The observed offspring consist of 15 white-eyed, ebony-bodied flies; 31 white-eyed, gray-bodied flies; 12 red-eyed, ebony-bodied flies; and 38 red-eyed, gray-bodied flies.

        What is the χ^2 value for this cross? _____

    (c) Is it likely that the observed results "fit" the expected values? _____

Terms of Orientation in and Around the Animal Body

Body Shapes

Symmetry. The body can be divided into almost identical halves.

Asymmetry. The body cannot be divided into almost identical halves (for example, many sponges).

Radial symmetry. The body is shaped like a cylinder (for example, sea anemone) or wheel (for example, sea star).

Bilateral symmetry. The body is shaped like ours in that it can be divided into halves by only one symmetrical plane (midsagittal).

Directions in the Body

Dorsal. At or toward the back surface of the body.

Ventral. At or toward the belly surface of the body.

Anterior. At or toward the head of the body—ventral surface of humans.

Posterior. At or toward the tail or rear end of the body—dorsal surface of humans.

Medial. At or near the midline of a body. The prefix *mid-* is often used in combination with other terms (for example, midventral).

Lateral. Away from the midline of a body.

Superior. Over or placed above some point of reference—toward the head of humans.

Inferior. Under or placed below some point of reference—away from the head of humans.

Proximal. Close to some point of reference or close to a point of attachment of an appendage to the trunk of the body.

Distal. Away from some point of reference or away from a point of attachment of an appendage to the trunk of the body.

Longitudinal. Parallel to the midline of a body.

Axis. An imaginary line around which a body or structure can rotate. The midline or *longitudinal axis* is the central axis of a symmetrical body or structure.

Axial. Placed at or along an axis.

Radial. Arranged symmetrically around an axis like the spokes of a wheel.

Planes of the Body

Sagittal. Passes vertically to the ground and divides the body into right and left sides. The *midsagittal* or *median plane* passes through the longitudinal axis and divides the body into right and left halves.

Frontal. Passes at right angles to the sagittal plane and divides the body into dorsal and ventral parts.

Transverse. Passes from side to side at right angles to both the sagittal and frontal planes and divides the body into anterior and posterior parts—superior and inferior parts of humans. This plane of section is often referred to as a cross section.